Methods in Neurosciences

Volume 11

Receptors: Model Systems and Specific Receptors

Methods in Neurosciences

Edited by

P. Michael Conn

Department of Pharmacology
The University of Iowa
College of Medicine
Iowa City, Iowa

Volume 11
Receptors: Model Systems and Specific Receptors

ACADEMIC PRESS, INC.
Harcourt Brace Jovanovich, Publishers
San Diego   New York   Boston   London   Sydney   Tokyo   Toronto

Front cover photograph (paperback edition only): Autoradiographic distribution of the thymic β_2-adrenergic receptor. A Loats Image Analysis System (Amersham) was used to analyze differences in receptor localization. Cold colors (including blue, violet, and rose) indicate the absence or low concentration of receptor; green, orange, yellow, and red represent increasing receptor concentrations. In the section shown from a proestrous female rat thymus gland, a high concentration of receptor can be seen distributed over the medullary regions. Courtesy of Drs. Bianca Marchetti and Maria C. Morale, Department of Pharmacology, Medical School, University of Catania, Italy.

Academic Press, Inc.
1250 Sixth Avenue, San Diego, California 92101-4311

United Kingdom Edition published by
Academic Press Limited
24–28 Oval Road, London NW1 7DX

International Standard Serial Number: 1043-9471

International Standard Book Number: 0-12-185271-7 (Hardcover)

International Standard Book Number: 0-12-185272-5 (Paperback)

PRINTED IN THE UNITED STATES OF AMERICA
93 94 95 96 97 98   EB   9 8 7 6 5 4 3 2 1

Table of Contents

Contributors to Volume 11

Article numbers are in parentheses following the names of contributors. Affiliations listed are current.

ALAIN BEAUDET (20), Laboratory of Neuroanatomy, Montreal Neurobiological Institute, McGill University, Montreal, Quebec H3A 2B4, Canada

ANN M. BENZ (15), Department of Psychiatry, Washington University School of Medicine, St. Louis, Missouri 63110

ERIC L. BITTMAN (6), Department of Zoology and Program in Neuroscience and Behavior, University of Massachusetts, Amherst, Massachusetts 01003

STEPHEN R. BLOOM (8), Department of Medicine, Royal Postgraduate Medical School, Hammersmith Hospital, London W12 ONN, England

S. MARC BREEDLOVE (1), Department of Psychology and Graduate Group in Neurobiology, University of California, Berkeley, Berkeley, California 94720

A. CADIEUX (4), Department of Pharmacology, University of Sherbrooke Medical School, Sherbrooke, Quebec J1H 5N4, Canada

ANNICK CAUVIN (24), Laboratoire de Chimie Biologique et de la Nutrition, Université Libre de Bruxelles, B-1070 Brussels, Belgium

JOËLLE CHABRY (20), Institut de Pharmacologie Moléculaire et Cellulaire, Centre National de la Recherche Scientifique, Sophia Antipolis, 06560 Valbonne, France

FRÉDÉRIC CHECLER (20), Institut de Pharmacologie Moléculaire et Cellulaire, Centre National de la Recherche Scientifique, Sophia Antipolis, 06560 Valbonne, France

YI-ZHANG CHEN (2), Laboratory of Neuroscience, Department of Physiology, The Second Military Medical University, Shanghai 200433, People's Republic of China

JEAN CHRISTOPHE (24), Laboratoire de Chimie Biologique et de la Nutrition, Université Libre de Bruxelles, B-1070 Brussels, Belgium

DANIELA CIRILLO (23), Department of Biomedical Science and Oncology, University of Torino Medical School, Torino, Italy 10126

C. S. COCKRAM (12), Department of Medicine, The Chinese University of Hong Kong, Prince of Wales Hospital, Shatin N.T., Hong Kong

P. D'Orléans-Juste (4), Department of Pharmacology, University of Sherbrooke Medical School, Sherbrooke, Quebec J1H 5N4, Canada

Errol B. De Souza (3), CNS Diseases Research, The Du Pont Merck Pharmaceutical Company, Experimental Station, Wilmington, Delaware 19880

M. B. Emerit (22), INSERM U. 288, Neurobiologie Cellulaire et Fonctionnelle, Faculté de Médecine Pitié-Salpêtrière, 75634 Paris, France

Louise M. Freeman (1), Department of Psychology, University of California, Berkeley, Berkeley, California 94720

Hong Fu (2), Laboratory of Neuroscience, Department of Physiology, The Second Military Medical University, Shanghai 200433, People's Republic of China

Paola Gallo (7), Department of Neurology, Second Neurologic Clinic, University of Padova School of Medicine, 35137 Padova, Italy

Steen Gammeltoft (13), Department of Clinical Chemistry, Bispebjerg Hospital, DK-2400 Copenhagen NV, Denmark

J. A. Gingrich (22), INSERM U. 288, Neurobiologie Cellulaire et Fonctionnelle, Faculté de Médecine Pitié-Salpêtrière, 75634 Paris, France

Bruno Giometto (7), Department of Neurology, Second Neurologic Clinic, University of Padova School of Medicine, 35137 Padova, Italy

H. Gozlan (22), INSERM U. 288, Neurobiologie Cellulaire et Fonctionnelle, Faculté de Médecine Pitié-Salpêtrière, 75634 Paris, France

Zuo Guo (2), Laboratory of Neuroscience, Department of Physiology, The Second Military Medical University, Shanghai 200433, People's Republic of China

M. Hamon (22), INSERM U. 288, Neurobiologie Cellulaire et Fonctionnelle, Faculté de Médecine Pitié-Salpêtrière, 75634 Paris, France

Janice M. Hickok (15), Department of Psychiatry, Washington University School of Medicine, St. Louis, Missouri 63110

Robert T. Jensen (17), Digestive Disorders Branch, National Institute of Diabetes and Digestive and Kidney Diseases, National Institutes of Health, Bethesda, Maryland 20892

Richard Kris (23), Department of Pharmacology, New York University Medical Center, New York, New York 10016

ELLEN E. LADENHEIM (17), Department of Psychiatry and Behavioral Sciences, The Johns Hopkins University School of Medicine, Baltimore, Maryland 21205

MANFRED P. LUTZ (10), Center for Basic Research in Digestive Diseases, Mayo Clinic, Rochester, Minnesota 55905

PAUL G. LYSKO (11), Department of Cardiovascular Pharmacology, SmithKline Beecham Pharmaceuticals, King of Prussia, Pennsylvania 19406

JEAN MAZELLA (20), Institut de Pharmacologie Moléculaire et Cellulaire, Centre National de la Recherche Scientifique, Sophia Antipolis, 06560 Valbonne, France

LAURENCE J. MILLER (10), Center for Basic Research in Digestive Diseases, Mayo Medical School, Clinic and Foundation, Rochester, Minnesota 55905

M.-C. MIQUEL (22), INSERM U. 288, Neurobiologie Cellulaire et Fonctionnelle, Faculté de Médecine Pitié-Salpêtrière, 75634 Paris, France

TERRY W. MOODY (23), Department of Biochemistry and Molecular Biology, The George Washington University Medical Center, Washington, D.C. 20037

TIMOTHY H. MORAN (17), Department of Psychiatry and Behavioral Sciences, The Johns Hopkins University School of Medicine, Baltimore, Maryland 21205

LUIGI NALDINI (23), Department of Biomedical Science and Oncology, University of Torino Medical School, Torino, Italy 10126

PONNAL NAMBI (11), Department of Renal Pharmacology, SmithKline Beecham Pharmaceuticals, King of Prussia, Pennsylvania 19406

M. G. NICHOLLS (12), Department of Medicine, Christchurch Hospital, Christchurch 1, New Zealand

D. REGOLI (4), Department of Pharmacology, University of Sherbrooke Medical School, Sherbrooke, Quebec J1H 5N4, Canada

PATRICK ROBBERECHT (24), Laboratoire de Chimie Biologique et de la Nutrition, Université Libre de Bruxelles, B-1070 Brussels, Belgium

STEVEN A. ROSENZWEIG (18), Department of Cell and Molecular Pharmacology and Experimental Therapeutics, Medical University of South Carolina, Charleston, South Carolina 29425

ENRIQUE ROZENGURT (16), Imperial Cancer Research Fund, Laboratory of Growth Regulation, London WC2A 3PX, England

JAMES SINNETT-SMITH (16), Imperial Cancer Research Fund, Laboratory of Growth Regulation, London WC2A 3PX, England

DAVID M. SMITH (8), Department of Medicine, Royal Postgraduate Medical School, Hammersmith Hospital, London W12 ONN, England

BARBARA C. SWARZENSKI (15), Department of Psychiatry, Washington University School of Medicine, St. Louis, Missouri 63110

TOSHIHIRO TAKAO (3), CNS Diseases Research, The Du Pont Merck Pharmaceutical Company, Experimental Station, Wilmington, Delaware 19880

JEFFREY B. TATRO (5), Division of Endocrinology, Diabetes, Metabolism, and Molecular Medicine, New England Medical Center Hospitals; and Department of Medicine, Tufts University School of Medicine, Boston, Massachusetts 02111

BRUNO TAVOLATO (7), Department of Neurology, Second Neurologic Clinic, University of Padova School of Medicine, 35137 Padova, Italy

IAN L. TAYLOR (19), Departments of Medicine and Cell Biology, Division of Gastroenterology, Duke University Medical Center, Durham, North Carolina 27710; and Durham Veterans Administration Medical Center, Durham, North Carolina 27705

RICHARD D. TODD (15), Departments of Psychiatry and Genetics, Washington University School of Medicine, St. Louis, Missouri 63110

ANDRÉ VANDERMEERS (24), Laboratoire de Chimie Biologique et de la Nutrition, Université Libre de Bruxelles, B-1070 Brussels, Belgium

MARIE-CLAIRE VANDERMEERS-PIRET (24), Laboratoire de Chimie Biologique et de la Nutrition, Université Libre de Bruxelles, B-1070 Brussels, Belgium

STEVEN R. VIGNA (19), Departments of Cell Biology and Medicine, Division of Gastroenterology, Duke University Medical Center, Durham, North Carolina 27710; and Durham Veterans Administration Medical Center, Durham, North Carolina 27705

JEAN-PIERRE VINCENT (20), Institut de Pharmacologie Moléculaire et Cellulaire, Centre National de la Recherche Scientifique, Sophia Antipolis, 06560 Valbonne, France

ANDREW A. WELCHER (21), Amgen Inc., Amgen Center, Thousand Oaks, California 91320

PATRICIA M. WHITAKER-AZMITIA (14), Department of Psychiatry, Health Sciences Center, State University of New York at Stony Brook, Stony Brook, New York 11794

DAVID C. WHITCOMB (19), Departments of Medicine and Physiology, Division of Gastroenterology and Hepatology, University of Pittsburgh Medical Center, Pittsburgh, Pennsylvania 15213

ZSUZSANNA WIESENFELD-HALLIN (9), Section of Clinical Neurophysiology, Department of Clinical Physiology, Karolinska Institute, Huddinge University Hospital, S-141 86 Huddinge, Sweden

XIAO-JUN XU (9), Section of Clinical Neurophysiology, Department of Clinical Physiology, Karolinska Institute, Huddinge University Hospital, S-141 86 Huddinge, Sweden

V. T. F. YEUNG (12), Department of Medicine, The Chinese University of Hong Kong, Prince of Wales Hospital, Shatin N.T., Hong Kong

IAN ZACHARY (16), Imperial Cancer Research Fund, Laboratory of Growth Regulation, London WC2A 3PX, England

Preface

Receptors initiate the means by which cellular regulators exert their actions on target cells. Because of the central role of cell–cell communication and signal transduction, receptors are of intrinsic interest to neuroscientists.

Receptor studies utilize both traditional methods of analysis and modern molecular techniques. Volumes 11 and 12 of this series are divided into sections describing, in a pragmatic way, "model" receptor techniques, molecular techniques, and techniques for the determination of receptor subclasses and for localization and consideration in ligand design. The chapters are written in a way that will allow readers to "export" the technology described to the study of other receptor systems in their own areas of interest. Techniques include PCR protocols, methods for the assessment of gene expression, transfection, cloning, autoradiography, *in situ* hybridization, radioligand binding, receptor solubilization and purification, and coupling to effector systems.

The goal of these volumes—and of the others in this series—is to provide in one source a view of the contemporary techniques significant to a particular branch of the neurosciences, information which will prove invaluable not only to the experienced researcher but to the student as well. Of necessity some archival material has been included, but the authors have been encouraged to present information that has not yet been published, to compare (in a way not found in other publications) different approaches to similar problems, and to provide tables that direct the reader, in a systematic fashion, to earlier literature as an efficient means to summarize data. Flow diagrams and summary charts will guide the reader through the processes described.

The nature of this series permits the presentation of methods in fine detail, revealing "tricks" and short cuts that frequently do not appear in the literature owing to space limitations. Lengthy operating instructions for common equipment will not be included except in cases of unusual application. The contributors have been given wide latitude in nomenclature and usage since they are best able to make judgments consistent with current changes.

I wish to express my appreciation to Mrs. Sue Birely for assisting in the organization and maintenance of records, and to the staff of Academic Press for their efficient coordination of production. Appreciation is also expressed to the contributors, particularly for meeting their deadlines for the prompt and timely publication of this volume.

P. MICHAEL CONN

Methods in Neurosciences

[1]   Steroid Receptors in the Central Nervous System

Louise M. Freeman and S. Marc Breedlove

Introduction

Steroid hormones exert powerful influences over the structure and function of both the developing and the mature nervous system. In fact, the proposition that steroid hormones could alter the developing and mature nervous system was first indicated on the basis of behavior. Castrated males of most species will eventually stop copulating and testosterone treatment can reinstate the behavior as long as the regimen is maintained. Similarly, sexual receptivity in females is abolished by ovariectomy and, in rats, for example, sequential treatment with estrogen and progesterone will result, a few hours later, in 6–8 hr of receptivity. Phoenix *et al.* (1) proposed that, in addition to such "activational" effects, steroids could also "organize" the developing nervous system, permanently rendering it masculine or feminine. The eventual discovery of sexual dimorphism in the vertebrate central nervous system (CNS) and the discovery that early exposure to testicular steroids was responsible for the development of masculine morphology amply confirmed this organizational hypothesis (2). Although the organizational–activational distinction has been useful to behavioral endocrinologists, the basic cellular action of steroids, change in gene expression, is similar throughout development (3). This change can often manifest itself as an alteration in the behavior of the organism. As such, steroids provide an opportunity to perturb normal neural processes and monitor the resulting changes in behavior, thereby illuminating the structural and/or physiological bases of neural development and function. We will review the methods of monitoring steroid influence, which center, as we will see, on monitoring the receptors for these hormones.

Steroids are lipophilic molecules consisting of four interconnected carbon rings, the so-called cyclopentanoperhydrophenanthrene rings, also known as sterane (Fig. 1). Cholesterol serves as the primary precursor to steroid synthesis, and the capacity and proclivity with which an organ will produce a particular steroid depend on the activity of various enzymes required for synthesis of the steroid. There are several competing systems of nomenclature for the various steroids, but we will rely on the names most commonly associated with each hormone in the neuroscience literature. Steroids are

Methods in Neurosciences, Volume 11

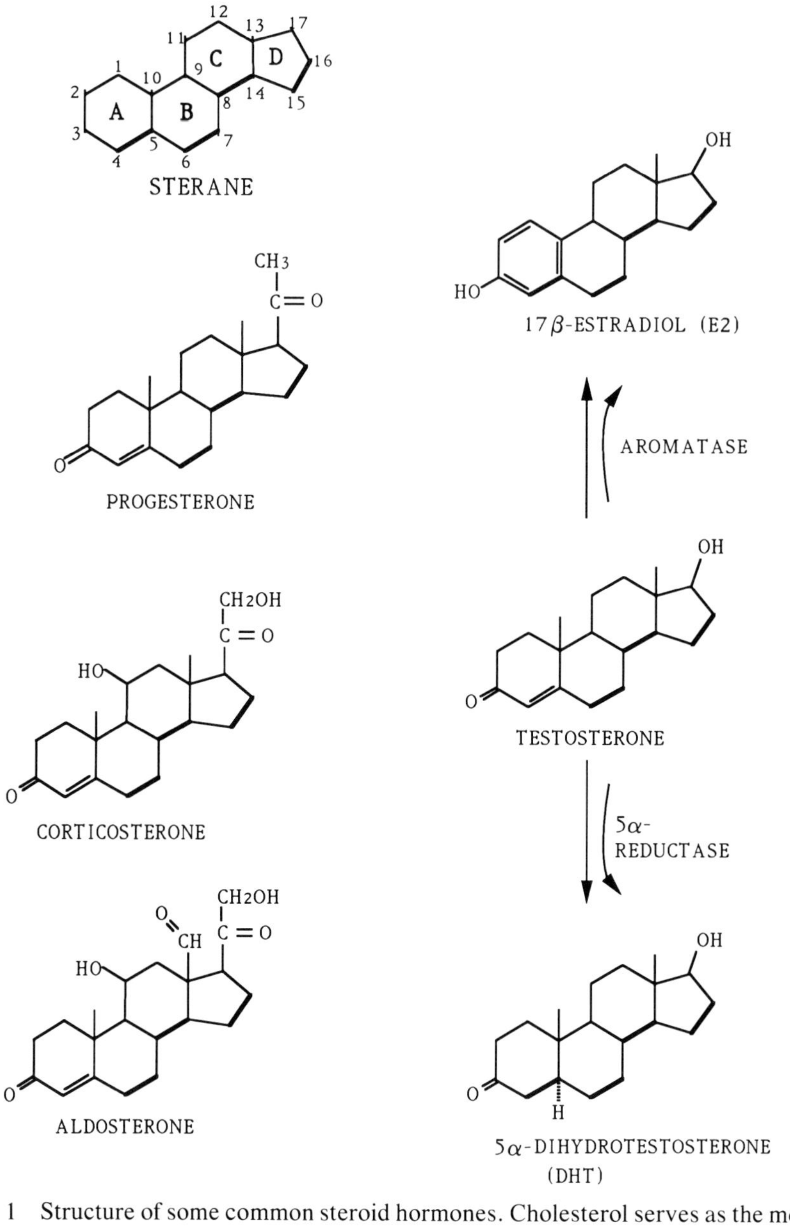

FIG. 1   Structure of some common steroid hormones. Cholesterol serves as the most common source of the basic steroid nucleus of four interconnected carbon rings (sterane). Most of the synthetic steps are facilitated by specific enzymes; thus, production of steroids is controlled by the relative activity of various enzymes and hence particular synthetic pathways. Testosterone can serve as a prohormone to either estradiol or dihydrotestosterone, but the reverse reactions do not occur.

TABLE I   Partial Listing of Steroids Active in the Nervous System

Tissue of origin	Functional classification	Specific examples
Gonads (sex steroids)		
Testicular	Androgens	Testosterone (T)
		Dihydrotestosterone (DHT)
		Androstenedione
Ovarian	Estrogens	Estradiol (E_2)
		Estriol
		Estrone
	Progestins	Progesterone (Pg)
Adrenal cortex	Glucocorticoids	Cortisol
		Corticosterone
	Mineralocorticoids	Aldosterone
Skin (or diet)	Vitamin D_3 metabolites	$1,25(OH)_2D_3$
		$24,25(OH)_2D_3$
Prothoracic glands	Ecdysteroids	Ecdysone
Thyroid[a]	Thyroid hormones	Triiodothyronine (T_3)
		Thyroxine (T_4)

[a] Note that thyroid hormones are not true steroids, but resemble steroids and behave much like steroids; for example, they alter gene expression after binding to a member of the steroid receptor superfamily of proteins.

usually classified either by the organs that primarily secrete them or by the class of action they promote (Table I). Most androgenic steroids are also anabolic, that is, they promote muscle growth.

Steroids act by binding to specific protein receptors that are synthesized by target cells. Different steroids bind to different receptors, which display considerable homology with each other and with other proteins derived from a "superfamily" of genes, all of which have in common the property of altering gene expression (4). These proteins have a highly variable N-terminal region, a highly conserved central region that binds DNA, and a moderately conserved, ligand-binding C terminus. The lipophilic nature of steroids allows them to enter cells freely and bind to receptors that, depending on the receptor, are found in either the cytoplasm or the nucleus. The allosterically conjugated steroid–receptor complex in turn binds to DNA to alter gene transcription. The sequence of nucleotides in the promotor region to which the steroid–receptor complex binds, that is, the "hormone-responsive element," differs somewhat for various steroids, but they are by and large quite similar. This has led to considerable speculation about cofactors, dimerization, and complex interactions that would allow different hormones (e.g., progestins and androgens) to exert such disparate biological effects when their receptors appear to bind the same DNA sites.

Investigation of steroid action can monitor (i) steroids themselves, (ii) the enzymatic machinery that produces them, (iii) the protein receptors that empower them to alter gene expression, (iv) alterations in gene expression, or (v) consequent changes in cell morphology and/or function. At this point it should be noted that there is an increasing number of reports of steroid effects that occur too quickly to reflect changes in gene expression; such effects may be the result of steroid action on the plasma membrane (5, 6). This chapter, however, is concerned with steroids in their traditional gene-regulating role and with the monitoring of classical steroid receptors as an index of steroid action. Because relatively few cells in the CNS produce receptors to a given steroid hormone, once a steroid has been shown to alter behavior or some other index of neural function, the mapping of neural centers that possess the appropriate receptor can quickly focus the search for the mechanisms mediating that change by eliminating many neural candidates. We will point out examples of such deductive reasoning as we describe the various methods for monitoring steroid receptors.

Biochemical Assays

In biochemical assays one dissociates the tissue or cells of interest and exposes suspected receptors to radiolabeled steroid ligands. After allowing sufficient time and appropriate conditions for them to bind each other, steroid–receptor complexes are separated from free steroid by one of a variety of techniques in order to infer both the number and the affinity of the protein molecules for the steroid of interest. This approach is complicated by the fact that many other proteins also have a weak affinity for steroids. Thus one must distinguish between the functionally significant, "specific" binding by the relatively rare receptors from the functionally insignificant, "nonspecific" binding by the other, abundant proteins. Nonspecific binding is assessed by incubating the labeled ligand in the presence of 100- to 1000-fold unlabeled ligand. Such competition should displace labeled ligand from almost all of the relatively rare, high-affinity receptor sites, but prevent little of the label from binding to the low-affinity, nonspecific sites. One simply subtracts the amount of binding to the labeled steroid in the presence of excess unlabeled ligand (nonspecific binding) from the amount of binding when only labeled steroid is available (total binding) to estimate specific binding (Fig. 2). Among the many ways to separate bound from unbound steroid are Sephadex columns (7) or activated charcoal, each of which detain unbound steroid; glass fiber filters that do not bind free steroid but that will nonspecifically bind protein, and therefore the occupied receptor (8, 9); and DNA cellulose filtration, which exploits the affinity of steroid–receptor complexes for nucleotides (10).

As with other allosteric interactions, the steroid–receptor complex has a

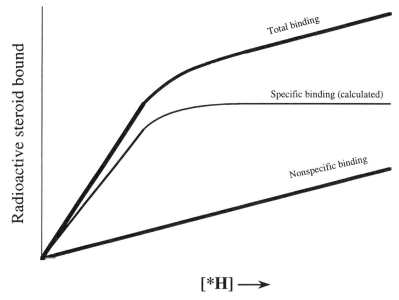

FIG. 2   Schematic depiction of the amount of protein binding to a radiolabeled steroid hormone from a homogenate sample of brain incubated in increasing concentrations of hormone. The upper curve depicts the amount of binding seen when only labeled steroid is added. This binding represents both high-affinity, specific sites (e.g., receptors) and the low-affinity, nonspecific binding of many proteins. The lower curve depicts the amount of labeled steroid bound in the presence of 100-fold "cold," that is, unlabeled steroid, and thus represents nonspecific binding only. Subtracting the values of the bottom curve (nonspecific binding) from those of the top (total binding) estimates the specific binding (middle curve). The asymptote in the middle curve indicates the saturation of receptors at a particular concentration of hormone.

tendency to dissociate, which can be affected by factors such as pH and temperature. Binding is usually measured at low temperatures, which slow chemical interactions and facilitate their detection. The rate at which the steroid and receptor bind together, the association constant K_a, can be understood as the concentration of complexes [S-R] divided by the product of the concentration of free steroid [S] and free receptors [R]:

$$K_a = [S\text{-}R]/[S][R]$$

Similarly, the dissociation constant K_d is equal to the inverse of K_a, that is, the proportion of the product of concentrations of unbound steroid and receptors divided by the concentration of steroid–receptor complexes:

$$K_d = [S][R]/[S\text{-}R]$$

One can estimate both the K_d and the concentration of receptor by the use of Scatchard analyses, in which one counts the specific binding at a variety of concentrations of labeled steroid, including concentrations beyond saturation of the receptors. Plotting the ratio of specifically bound steroid over free steroid on the y axis versus the concentration of bound steroid on the x axis generates a Scatchard plot (Fig. 3). If the total number of receptor sites is n, then the concentration of unoccupied receptor is the total minus those receptors that are occupied:

$$[R] = n - [S\text{-}R]$$

Substituting this value for [R] in the previous equation for K_d and algebraically rearranging the terms into the Scatchard format of [S-R]/[S] for the y term and [S-R] for the x term yields the following formula:

$$[S\text{-}R]/[S] = -1/K_d [S\text{-}R] + n/K_d$$

Thus, the slope of the Scatchard line should be proportional to K_d, while the x intercept estimates the total number of receptors. A nonlinear Scatchard plot indicates a more complicated binding phenomenon, either more than one class of receptor or some type of cooperativity phenomenon; in that case, the K_d and n estimates are more difficult (11) and must be considered with some caution. Biochemical techniques also allow comparisons of cross-competing steroids.

Some of the complicating factors of examining CNS steroid receptors with biochemical assays include the following.

1. Lack of cellular resolution: The specific site of receptor localization is limited by the amount of nervous tissue that can be practically dissected. Microdissection techniques (12) are a common feature in studies that examine steroid receptor levels in specific brain nuclei (13–15).

2. Attempts to separate homogenized tissue into nuclear and cytoplasmic fractions may be incomplete, leading to incorrect conclusions concerning the location of receptors within a cell. Such an artifact may account for the cytosolic estrogen receptor detected by some when other techniques suggest estrogen receptors reside primarily in the nucleus (16–18).

3. The radiolabeled ligand may cross-react with some other protein. For instance, rat α-fetoprotein (AFP) binds estradiol with high affinity and can distort biochemical studies of estrogen receptors; this problem has been

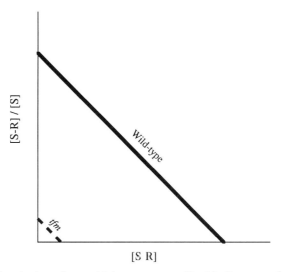

FIG. 3   Scatchard plot of steroid hormone-specific binding as calculated by the method depicted in Fig. 2. The abscissa indicates the concentration of specifically bound ligand, while the ordinate indicates the ratio of specifically bound to unbound hormone. The slope of such a plot is an estimate of the affinity of the receptor for the ligand, while the x intercept estimates the total number of binding sites. In this example, tissue from an androgen-competent animal is compared with tissue from an androgen-incompetent (*tfm*) rat. The affinities of the receptors seem identical, but the *tfm* rats have far fewer functional receptors (35).

overcome by using either a ligand (moxestrol) or a separation method (DNA–cellulose) that does not bind AFP (19).

4. The ligand could be metabolized to something else before binding a protein.

Steroid Autoradiography

In the classic model, the steroid–receptor complex must interact with DNA to affect target cells. Therefore, one can identify such cells by the accumulation of steroid in their nuclei. This monitoring is typically accomplished by injecting a radiolabeled steroid into systemic circulation, allowing sufficient time for nuclear accumulation (1–2 hr) and placing thin slices of the tissue of interest next to film to detect radioactivity within the nuclei of target but not nontarget cells. Because of the need for fairly high spatial resolution to detect silver grains over the nuclei rather than cytoplasm, most steroid autoradiography is done with a low-energy-emitting isotope, tritium, which will affect only those portions of the film quite close to the label. The need for spatial resolution also favors placing the tissue on microscope slides previously dipped in nuclear track emulsion such as NTB-3 (Kodak, Rochester, NY), which, after sufficient exposure (6–100 weeks), can be developed in the manner of standard black-and-white film.

Because of concerns that the steroid might diffuse away from the site of accumulation, early steroid autoradiography used unfixed tissue rapidly removed from decapitated subjects (20). Tissue was quickly frozen, then sectioned in a cryostat in a darkroom and mounted on emulsion-coated slides, which, at room temperature, quickly thaw the sections and cause them to adhere. Optimal safelights, such as Thomas Instruments duplex (Charlottesville, VA) for Kodak NTB-emulsion can greatly facilitate sectioning. This thaw-mount method of steroid autoradiography in the brain was developed simultaneously by Pfaff (21) and Stumpf (22). Several subsequent studies have successfully examined nuclear accumulation in perfused animals (23, 24). It is possible to use fluorescent retrograde markers to identify particular classes of neurons in autoradiograms. Arnold (25) first managed this feat in the fresh-frozen bird brain using primuline as the marker, but the apparent stability of the labeled steroid during perfusion has made flurogold available as an anatomical marker (26, 27). The most common criterion for determining if a cell has accumulated steroid is a density of silver grains over the nucleus three to five times that of the background, but more quantitative criteria, including Poisson models, are also available (28).

Some of the disadvantages of steroid autoradiography are the following.

1. The considerable amount of time that must be allowed for the tissue to expose the film: In some cases a few weeks are sufficient, but in others more than a year of exposure is required before convincing concentration can be seen over nuclei (29). One can obviate this delay by use of high specific activity labels (i.e., six tritium atoms in one molecule) or radiolabels with a shorter half-life. For example, the developing time of estradiol autoradiograms can be reduced from 4 months to 17 days by the use of ^{125}I-tagged estradiol (30). Another estradiol analog, 11β-methoxy-16-iodoestradiol (MIE$_2$), is reported to give comparable resolution in only 16 hr (23). However, one must be concerned about how far from the cell nucleus the particle may travel in order to expose the film when higher energy ligands are used.

2. The considerable expense of injecting sufficient radiolabeled steroid to label all target cells within an animal: This consideration makes experiments with large animals especially prohibitive, but may be circumvented via *in vitro* autoradiography, in which the tissue of interest is removed and exposed to a solution of radiolabeled steroid. This technique has been successful in peripheral tissues with a high concentration of steroid receptors (e.g., the

genital tract) (31), but to our knowledge its only successful demonstration in the CNS is the labeling of estrogen receptors in the rat brain by MIE_2 (32). This method allowed topographical localization of receptors within 2 hr but did not give cell-by-cell resolution.

3. The concern that radioactivity detected in the nucleus of a cell may not be part of the originally injected ligand, but a metabolite. This is, of course, also a concern in biochemical assays.

4. The demands of working with a sharp microtome blade, radioactive material, and delicate tissue in semidarkness.

5. The concern that steroids may have important, nongenomic actions that may not require nuclear accumulation and therefore may not be monitored by autoradiography.

On the other hand, among the advantages of steroid autoradiography are the cell-by-cell resolution of target neurons and, in conjunction with anatomical markers such as histofluorescence (33) or immunocytochemistry (34), the distinction of various classes of neurons. One also gains an indication of whether nuclear accumulation, a prerequisite of function, has taken place. For example, the single-base pair substitution and single-amino acid substitution in the *tfm* rat mutation (35) cannot be detected via any available antisera or probes to the transcript, but can be seen in the failure of *tfm* tissue to accumulate steroid (36). Similarly, autoradiography indicates that some spinal motoneurons in the rat are first able to accumulate androgen between days 7 and 14 of life (37; see Fig. 4), which constrains hypotheses about the sites of androgen action on neuromuscular development. The caveat that the steroid may be metabolized to another hormone has been used to assay such metabolism by intentionally labeling those hydrogen atoms that are cleaved in the conversion of testosterone to estradiol (see Fig. 1) (38).

Immunocytochemistry

The availability of the rat monoclonal antibody H222 to the estrogen receptor provided one of the first indications that even unbound steroid receptors might normally reside in cell nuclei, and that previous detection of unbound receptors in cytoplasmic fractions may have been an artifact of the biochemical process (39, 40). For immunocytochemistry (ICC) in the CNS, tissue is typically fixed, sectioned, and then exposed to reactions either as free-floating sections (41) or mounted on slides for subsequent reactions. Binding of the primary antibody is visualized with standard ICC methods such as peroxidase–anti-peroxidase (42), immunofluorescence (43), or avidin–biotin complexing (44). Signals can be enhanced by a multiple bridging technique (45)

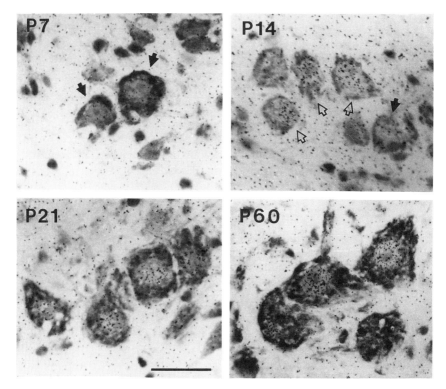

FIG. 4   Steroid autoradiograms showing the ontogeny of androgen accumulation in developing perineal motoneurons in rats. Note that the density of silver grains over the unstained neuropil is comparable across these autoradiograms, but the density of silver grains over motoneuronal nuclei increases with age. Based on the Poisson criterion, only a minority of these motoneurons evidenced accumulation at 7 days of age (P7), whereas by P14, the adult number of labeled motoneurons was achieved (open arrows point to labeled cells and solid arrows point to unlabeled cells). The density of labeling over the nuclei increases at subsequent ages (37). Bar = 40 μm.

or immunogold–silver staining (46). Standard ICC concerns are relevant when localizing steroid receptors in the CNS. For instance, does omitting the primary antibody or preabsorbing with the appropriate proteins or peptides abolish staining? Does another protein, perhaps another steroid receptor, share the epitope and therefore also bind the antisera?

Immunocytochemistry offers the same spatial resolution as autoradiography at greatly reduced costs and delays. Estrogen receptor-like immunoreactivity detected by H222 has generally agreed well with steroid autoradiography in guinea pig brain (47), and in zebra finch and canary brain (41), but H222 has not consistently succeeded in rat brain [but see also Henry *et al.* (48)]. Immunocytochemical techniques can be used to double-label neurons and have indicated that individual neurons can respond to more than one steroid. Gahr (49) has combined H222 immunocytochemistry with dihydrotestosterone autoradiography to show that some neurons of the zebra finch brain express both androgen and estrogen receptors. By sequential ICC using different primary antibodies and the use of different chromogen or fluorescent compounds for visualization, Warembourgh *et al.* (43) have shown that estrogen and progesterone receptors can occupy the same neurons in the guinea pig brain. Another advantage of ICC is that receptors can be studied at the subcellular level in the absence of their natural ligands. For example, in adrenalectomized rats, electron microscopic examination of glucocorticoid receptors visualized by immunogold–silver-enhanced ICC showed them to be located primarily in the cytoplasm, while replacement therapy causes translocation to the nucleus (50). A similar study in ovariectomized rats, however, suggests that most estrogen receptors are located in the nucleus whether occupied or not (51). Available antisera against the rat androgen receptor indicate that this protein normally resides in the nucleus of peripheral tissues (51a, 51b) and of motoneurons, at least in intact males (S. M. Breedlove, unpublished observations).

Monitoring Steroid Receptor Transcripts

Steroid receptors can also be studied in the CNS by examining the RNA message for the receptor with a radiolabeled DNA or RNA probe complementary to the steroid receptor message. Such techniques show that the gene for the steroid receptor protein is being transcribed; it is, of course, possible that translational or posttranslational events prevent the formation of a functional receptor. Nonetheless, studies localizing receptor messages generally show good agreement with studies locating steroid receptors by other means (52–54). One advantage in searching for the receptor message is that mRNA is a relatively stable molecule (55), allowing, for example, the localization of mRNAs from human autopsy tissue (56). Another is that, provided the DNA sequences of the genes are known, probes can be synthesized that distinguish receptor subtypes (57). Two methods by which steroid receptor mRNA can be studied are Northern blots and *in situ* hybridization. The cloning and sequencing of the genes for steroid receptors have made these methods practical and popular for studying changes in expression of steroid receptor genes.

For a Northern blot, mRNA is extracted from homogenized tissue and separated by gel electrophoresis. The RNAs are then transferred to a nitrocellulose sheet and incubated with a radiolabeled strand of oligonucleotides complementary to the mRNA of interest. The Northern blot technique has been used to locate and quantify levels of androgen receptor (AR) mRNA in the brain, and study the changes in AR mRNA following castration and replacement therapy (58). Northern blots can also demonstrate the specificity of synthetic DNA probes for a particular thyroid receptor subtype (57).

For *in situ* hybridization, the same essential strategy is applied, but in slices of tissue, allowing cell-by-cell resolution of brain regions that express steroid receptor genes. Comprehensive reviews of methodological concerns are available elsewhere (59–61). In brief, CNS tissue is thinly sliced, mounted, incubated with the labeled cDNA or RNA probe, rinsed, and developed in a manner similar to autoradiography. Common controls include pretreatment with RNase and incubation with the sense-strand probe that does not hybridize to the mRNA. Of particular concern for both Northern blots and *in situ* hybridization for steroid receptor message is the possibility of the probe hybridizing to transcripts for other members of the steroid receptor family of genes. *In situ* hybridization maps of steroid receptor expression in the rat brain have been made for estrogen (52–54), androgen (52), progesterone (54), glucocorticoids (62), and thyroid hormones (57). Such maps are in close agreement with the findings of autoradiography and ICC. Although it is difficult to measure absolute levels of mRNA with *in situ* hybridization, it is possible to compare levels of gene transcription in different regions and under different conditions (63). The shorter half-life of the nucleotide probe means a shorter developing time than in steroid autoradiography. Finally, because of its applicability to human autopsy tissue, *in situ* hybridization can potentially be used to map steroid receptor sites in the human brain for the first time.

Each of the methods described has its strengths and drawbacks, but they can be used to complement each other. Any comprehensive investigation of steroid action on the CNS should include as many as are practical to gain a complete understanding of the hormone of interest.

References

1. C. Phoenix, R. Goy, A. Gerall, and W. Young, *Endocrinology (Baltimore)* **65,** 369–382 (1959).
2. A. P. Arnold and R. A. Gorski, *Annu. Rev. Neurosci.* **7,** 413–442 (1984).
3. A. P. Arnold and S. M. Breedlove, *Horm. Behav.* **19,** 469–498 (1985).
4. M. Beato, *Cell (Cambridge, Mass.)* **56,** 335–344 (1989).
5. Y. Delville, *Neurosci. Biobehav. Rev.* **15,** 407–414 (1991).
6. M. Schumacher, H. Coirini, D. W. Pfaff, and B. S. McEwen, *Science* **250,** 691–694 (1990).

7. M. Ginsburg, B. D. Greenstein, N. J. MacLusky, I. D. Morris, and P. J. Thomas, *Steroids* **23,** 773–791 (1974).

8. L. Cousens and B. Eskin, *Anal. Biochem.* **121,** 39–48 (1982).

9. R. B. Fishman, L. Chism, G. L. Firestone, and S. M. Breedlove, *J. Neurobiol.* **21,** 694–704 (1990).

10. T. O. Fox, Charalambos, and Savakis, *in* ''Solid Phase Biochemistry: Analytical and Synthetic Aspects'' (W. H. Scouten, ed.), pp. 189–221. Wiley, New York, 1983.

11. K. E. Light, *Science* **223,** 76–77 (1984).

12. M. Palkovits, *Brain Res.* **59,** 449–450 (1973).

13. R. J. Handa, C. E. Roselli, and J. A. Resko, *Brain Res.* **445,** 111–116 (1988).

14. C. E. Roselli, R. J. Handa, and J. A. Resko, *Neuroendocrinology* **49,** 449–453 (1989).

15. T. C. Rainbow, B. Parsons, N. J. MacLusky, and B. S. McEwen, *J. Neurosci.* **2,** 1439–1445 (1982).

16. R. J. B. King, *J. Steroid Biochem.* **25,** 451–454 (1986).

17. J. Gorski, W. Welshons, and D. Sakai, *Mol. Cell. Endocrinol.* **36,** 11–15 (1984).

18. J. Gorski, W. W. Welshons, D. Sakai, J. Hanson, J. Walent, J. Kassis, J. Shull, G. Stack, and C. Campen, *Recent Prog. Horm. Res.* **42,** 297–329 (1986).

19. W. J. Friedman, B. S. McEwen, C. D. Toran-Allerand, and J. L. Gerlach, *Dev. Brain Res.* **11,** 19–27 (1983).

20. W. E. Stumpf and M. Sar, *in* ''Methods in Enzymology'' (B. O'Malley and J. Hardman, eds.), Vol. 36, pp. 135–156. Academic Press, New York, 1975.

21. D. W. Pfaff, *Science* **161,** 1355–1356 (1968).

22. W. E. Stumpf, *Science* **162,** 1001–1003 (1968).

23. T. J. Brown, N. J. MacLusky, C. D. Toran-Allerand, J. E. Zielinski, and R. B. Hochberg, *Endocrinology (Amsterdam)* **124,** 2074–2088 (1989).

24. K. P. Corodimas and J. I. Morrell, *J. Comp. Neurol.* **291,** 609–620 (1990).

25. A. P. Arnold, *Brain Res.* **192,** 210–212 (1980).

26. C. A. Lisciotto and J. I. Morrell, *Brain Res.* **516,** 107–112 (1990).

27. K. P. Corodimas and J. I. Morrell, *Exp. Brain Res.* **80,** 381–386 (1990).

28. A. P. Arnold, *J. Histochem. Cytochem.* **29,** 207–211 (1981).

29. S. M. Breedlove and A. P. Arnold, *J. Comp. Neurol.* **215,** 211–216 (1983).

30. W. E. Stumpf, J. K. Morin, B. W. Ennis, J. E. Zielinski, and R. B. Hochberg, *J. Histochem. Cytochem.* **35,** 87–92 (1987).

31. J. M. Shannon, G. R. Cunha, O. Taguchi, K. D. Vanderslice, and S. F. Gould, *J. Histochem. Cytochem.* **30,** 1059–1065 (1982).

32. M. J. Walters, T. J. Brown, R. Hochberg, and N. J. MacLusky, *Soc. Neurosci. Abstr.* **21,** 561.11 (1991).

33. A. S. Heritage, W. E. Stumpf, M. Sar, and L. D. Grant, *Science* **207,** 1377–1379 (1980).

34. B. D. Shivers, R. E. Harlan, and D. W. Pfaff, *Neuroendocrinology* **49,** 23–27 (1988).

35. W. G. Yarbrough, V. E. Quarmby, J. A. Simental, D. R. Joseph, M. Sart, D. B. Lubahn, K. L. Olsen, F. S. French, and E. M. Wilson, *J. Biol. Chem.* **265,** 8893–8900 (1990).

36. S. M. Breedlove, *J. Neurobiol.* **17**, 157–176 (1986).
37. C. L. Jordan, S. M. Breedlove, and A. P. Arnold, *J. Comp. Neurol.* **313**, 441–448 (1991).
38. P. J. Sheridan, *Dev. Neurosci.* **4**, 46–54 (1981).
39. W. V. Welshons, M. E. Lieberman, and J. Gorski, *Nature (London)* **307**, 747–749 (1984).
40. W. J. King and G. L. Greene, *Nature (London)* **307**, 745–747 (1984).
41. M. Gahr, G. Flügge, and H.-R. Guttinger, *Brain Res.* **402**, 173–177 (1987).
42. L. A. Sternberger and N. H. Sternberger, *J. Histochem. Cytochem.* **34**, 599–605 (1986).
43. M. Warembourg, A. Joivet, and E. Milgrom, *Brain Res.* **480**, 1–15 (1989).
44. M. Sar, *Tech. Immunocytochem.* **3**, 43–54 (1985).
45. L. L. Vacca, S. J. Abrahams, and N. E. Naftchi, *J. Histochem. Cytochem.* **28**, 297–307 (1980).
46. C. S. Holgate, P. Jackson, P. N. Cowen, and C. C. Bird, *J. Histochem. Cytochem.* **31**, 938–944 (1983).
47. J. D. Blaustein and J. C. Turcotte, *Brain Res.* **495**, 75–82 (1989).
48. W. W. Henry, K. L. Medlock, D. M. Sheehan, and A. C. Scallet, *Histochemistry* **96**, 157–162 (1991).
49. M. Gahr, *Proc. Natl. Acad. Sci. U.S.A.* **87**, 9445–9448 (1990).
50. Z. Liposits, R. M. Uht, R. W. Harrison, F. P. Gibbs, W. K. Paull, and M. C. Bohn, *Histochemistry* **87**, 407–412 (1987).
51. Z. Liposits, I. Kalló, C. W. Coen, W. K. Paull, and B. Flerkó, *Histochemistry* **93**, 233–239 (1990).
51a. G. S. Prins, L. Birch, and G. L. Greene, *Endocrinol.* **129**, 3187–3199 (1991).
51b. M. Sar, D. B. Lubahn, F. S. French, and E. M. Wilson, *Endocrinol.* **127**, 3180–3186 (1990).
52. R. B. Simerly, C. Chang, M. Muramatsu, and L. W. Swanson, *J. Comp. Neurol.* **294**, 76–95 (1990).
53. G. Pelletier, N. Liao, and M. V. Govindan, *Neurosci. Lett.* **94**, 23–28 (1988).
54. A. H. Lauber, G. J. Romano, and D. W. Pfaff, *J. Steroid Biochem. Mol. Biol.* **40**, 53–62 (1991).
55. G. R. Uhl, B. Cwickel, C. Pagonis, and J. Habener, *Ann. Neurol.* **18**, 149 (1985).
56. M. Brahic, E. Cash, R. A. Smith, C. J. Gibbs, R. M. Garruto, and W. W. Tourtellotte, *Ann. Neurol.* **18**, 337–343 (1985).
57. D. J. Bradley, W. S. Young, and C. Weinberger, *Proc. Natl. Acad. Sci. U.S.A.* **86**, 7250–7254 (1989).
58. V. E. Quarmby, W. G. Yarbrough, D. B. Lubahn, F. S. French, and E. M. Wilson, *Mol. Endocrinol.* **4**, 22–28 (1990).
59. L. M. Angerer, M. H. Stoler, and R. C. Angerer, *in* "*In situ* Hybridization: Applications to Neurobiology" (K. L. Valentino, J. H. Eberwune, and J. D. Barchas, eds.), pp. 42–70. Oxford Univ. Press, New York, 1987.
60. H. Takeda, G. Chodak, S. Mutchnik, T. Nakamoto, and C. Chang, *J. Endocrinol.* **126**, 17–25 (1990).

61. G. R. Uhl, ed., "*In situ* Hybridization in Brain." Plenum, New York, 1986.
62. M. Aronsson, K. Fuxe, Y. Dong, L. F. Agnati, S. Okret, and J. A. Gustofsson, *Proc. Natl. Acad. Sci. U.S.A.* **85,** 9331–9335 (1988).
63. W. S. Young, III and M. J. Kuhar, *in* "*In situ* Hybridization in Brain" (G. R. Uhl, ed.), pp. 243–248. Plenum, New York, 1986.

[2] Membrane Receptor for Glucocorticoids in Mammalian Neurons

Yi-Zhang Chen, Hong Fu, and Zuo Guo

Introduction

It is widely accepted that steroid hormones act by means of a genomic mechanism. The steroid molecule first binds to the DNA molecule within the cell nucleus, and then initiates a series of transcriptional and translational events (1–4). However, a genomic mechanism may not represent the sole mechanism for steroid action; a membrane mechanism may also be invoked. It has been suspected for more than 20 years that there might be a plasma membrane mechanism responsible for nongenomic effects of steroids (4, 5). Membrane binding sites for different steroids in different tissues and organelles have been reported (5, 6). Efforts have been made to characterize the properties of a putative membrane receptor for hormonal steroids, especially estrogens and progestins (5, 6).

Binding sites for hormonal steroids, including glucocorticoid (GC), on the synaptic plasma membrane of neural tissues were first reported by Towle and Sze in 1983 (7). The existence of a membrane receptor for steroids was considered to be elusive at that time. In recent years the interest in searching for a membrane receptor for GC has been renewed (8–11).

The search for a steroid membrane receptor is still in the "infantile" stage. Generally speaking, all methods of receptor research are applicable to the study of the glucocorticoid membrane receptor (GCMR). But some special points, which will be emphasized and exemplified in the following discussion, should be borne in mind. First, because the neuron is an excitable cell and the locus of action is on the plasma membrane, activation of the GCMR would usually lead to rapid excitability or membrane potential changes. Second, because the ligand is a steroid usually thought to be freely permeable to the plasma membrane, the problem of membrane permeation must be carefully scrutinized. Third, because steroids bind with the cytosolic and/or nuclear receptor, in biochemical studies one must be cautious about the contamination of membrane preparations by cytosolic and/or nuclear contents.

Methods in Neurosciences, Volume 11

Binding Characteristics of Glucocorticoid Membrane Receptor

Preparation of Synaptic Plasma Membrane without Contamination by Cytosolic Fractions

A prerequisite for the biochemical study of the GCMR is the preparation of pure synaptic plasma membrane (SPM) from the brain. Contamination by cytosolic fractions should be carefully avoided. This can be achieved by modification of the commonly used method. A pure preparation formed a beneficial starting point for our further biochemical and binding studies (12).

The preparation of SPM was performed using a method described in the literature with modifications. Briefly, the procedures are as follows. The animal is anesthetized intraperitoneally with isoamylethylbarbiturate and the blood is washed out by extensive perfusion with ice-cold 0.9% (w/v) saline, which is administered into the left ventricle of the heart and drained out from holes cut into the left and right auricles. After the perfusate is clear of blood, the brain is removed and cut into pieces, and then homogenized in 5 vol of an ice-cold solution of 0.32 M sucrose. The homogenate is further processed using the following procedures at 0–4°C, as illustrated in Fig. 1.

Marker Enzyme Assay

5'-Nucleotidase (5'-NT) (13), lactate dehydrogenase (LDH) (14), and acetylcholinesterase (AchE) (15) activities are determined to evaluate contamination. If the enzyme activities in the homogenate are assumed to be 100%, in the SPM preparation 5'-NT (marker for plasma membrane) and AchE (marker for neuronal synaptic plasma membrane) activities are increased to 342.6 ± 36.0% ($n = 3$) and 270.5 ± 65.1% ($n = 6$) ($X ± SD$), respectively, and LDH (marker for cytosol) activities decrease to zero, indicating that the plasma membrane fraction has been concentrated during the fractionation process and the SPM preparation obtained is completely devoid of cytosolic contamination.

Radioligand-Binding Assay of Glucocorticoid Membrane Receptor

An SPM preparation is incubated with [^{3}H]corticosterone ([^{3}H]B) at 0–4°C for 3 hr. Nonspecific binding is determined by incubating identical aliquots with both labeled and a 1000-fold excess of unlabeled corticosterone. Free

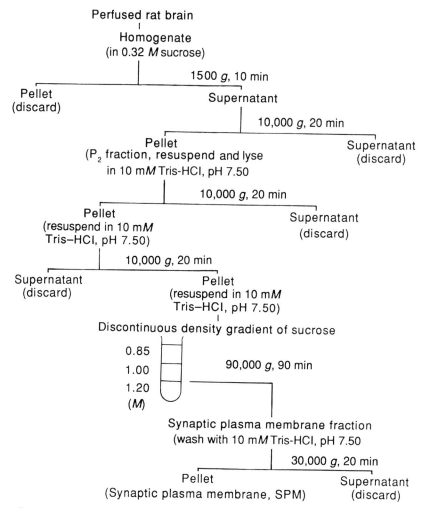

FIG. 1   Scheme for the preparation of synaptic plasma membrane (SPM).

[³H]B is separated by vacuum filtration. The SPM bound with [³H]B is kept on an S6.9 glass fiber filter membrane (Shanghai Yuguang Purification Materials Corporation), and, after drying, counted in 1.5 ml of scintillation counting liquid. The difference between the counts measured in the presence and absence of unlabeled steroid represents the specific binding of SPM.

As revealed by the radioligand-binding assay [³H]B could bind specifically to SPM in a rapid and reversible manner, indicating the existence of specific

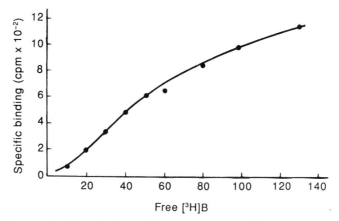

FIG. 2   Specific binding of [³H]corticosterone ([³H]B) with SPM.

membrane-binding sites for GC (GCMR) in SPM. The saturation binding curve presented in Fig. 2 is S shaped, and a convex curve can be seen in the Scatchard plot of the data (Fig. 3). After curve fitting (by the least-squares method) and mathematical treatment of the convex curve with the aid of a computer, the maximal binding capacity (B_{max}) was calculated to be 46.67 ± 4.62 fmol/mg protein, the apparent equilibrium dissociation constant (K_d), 97.48 ± 18.85 nM, and the Hill coefficient, 1.633 ± 0.082 ($n = 8$) (X ± SD).

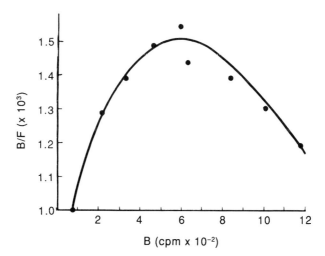

FIG. 3   Scatchard plot of binding of [³H]B with SPM.

Steroid Specificity of Glucocorticoid Membrane Receptor

Competition experiments were carried out using a one-point binding assay in which identical aliquots of SPM were incubated with both labeled and a 1000-fold excess of unlabeled steroids [B, aldosterone (Ald), dexamethasone (Dex), cortisol (F), estradiol (E$_2$), progesterone (P), R5020, RU26988, RU38486, testosterone (T), and triamcinolone acetonide (TA)] and the radioactivity measured after separating free from bound [^{3}H]B. The competitive rate, which is proportional to the binding affinity of each steroid, was calculated by assuming the ability of B to compete with [^{3}H]B is 100%.

As can be seen in Fig. 4, GCMR exhibited significant steroid binding specificity, with the highest binding to mineralocorticoids (Ald), glucocorticoids (B, F, TA, and RU26988), and progestins (R5020 and P), medium to sex hormones (E$_2$ and T), and lowest to RU38486 and Dex.

The steroid-binding specificity of the GCMR conforms with the basic criteria for receptors. It is reported that there are two types of intracellular glucocorticoid receptor (GR) in the rat brain, that is, type I and type II GR (16). The GCMR, similar to the type I GR, showed the best binding with Ald, B, and F and the poorest with Dex and RU38486. On the other hand, GCMR differed from type I GR in its satisfactory binding with TA and RU26988, and in its much lower steroid-binding affinity, which was even lower than that of type II GR. The GCMR seems to possess no similarity to type II GR, when their specificities and affinities of steroid binding are compared.

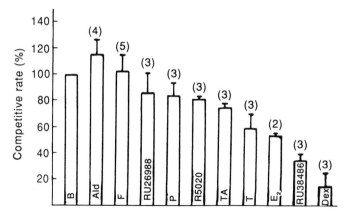

FIG. 4   Steroid binding specificity of GCMR as revealed by the competitive rates of different steroids. Ald, Aldosterone; Dex, dexamethasone; E$_2$, estradiol; F, cortisol; P, progesterone; T, testosterone; TA, triamcinolone acetonide.

Rapid Electrophysiological Effects of Glucocorticoid

In our laboratory, both *in vivo* and *in vitro* electrophysiological techniques are used to study the effect of GCMR response to steroid hormones on nerve cells (17–23).

Microiontophoresis

Unit discharges of central neurons are recorded extracellularly from the center barrel of a glass multibarreled micropipette. The outer barrels contain the following: 0.15 M sodium cortisol-hemisuccinate (pH 7.0); 0.2 M sodium dexamethasone phosphate (pH 6.8); 0.01 M RU38486 chloride (pH 6.2); 0.001 M sodium 17β-estradiol hemisuccinate (E$_2$) (pH 6.0); 2 M NaCl. A retaining current of 5–10 nA with the polarity opposite to that of the microelectrophoretic current is applied to the drug barrels when they are not in use. An iontophoretic current of 40–50 nA is used. The polarity of microphoretic currents for F, Dex, and E$_2$ is negative, and for RU38486 it is positive. The barrel containing 2 M sodium chloride is used for current control studies.

The effectiveness of microiontophoresis is evaluated by radioreceptor assay. For this purpose, Dex or RU38486 is microphoretically ejected from the pipette into normal saline solution in a small glass container, and the solution is collected for assay. The results show that microiontophoresis can effectively release steroids from the micropipette and that the released quantities of steroids are roughly proportional to the time duration of microiontophoresis.

Microiontophoretic experiments confirmed the results of earlier studies in that the primary effect of GC on the neuron is the inhibition of spontaneous discharge. We further showed that this effect was steroid specific and could be antagonized by RU38486.

Radioreceptor Assay

Preparation of Glucocorticoid Receptor

Rat thymocytes are used as the donor of glucocorticoid receptor (GR). Rat thymus is scissored into small pieces, and ground gently in 10 ml Hanks' solution. The solution is filtered through a 200-mesh metal net, the filtrate is then centrifuged at 1500 rpm for 10 min, and the precipitate is resuspended in Hanks' solution (about 1×10^{-6} cells/ml).

Assay of Sample RU38486

All reactions were performed in duplicate. The standard curve is obtained by first incubating 0.5 ml of thymocyte suspension with [³H]Dex (23 mM) and 0–20 ng RU38486 at 37°C for 30 min, and then determining the [³H]Dex specific binding. By determining the [³H]Dex specific binding after incubation with sample solution instead of RU38486, the RU38486 concentration in the sample is obtained from the standard curve (24).

Superfusion of Isolated Neural Tissues

Preparation of Celiac Ganglion

An adult guinea pig is decapitated. The celiac ganglia together with the splanchnic nerve are rapidly excised, transferred to a bathing chamber, and fixed with pins on a plastic plate. The ganglion is perfused with a Kreb's solution of the following composition (millimolar concentrations): NaCl, 117; KCl, 4.7; CaCl₂, 2.5; MgCl₂, 1.2; NaHCO₃, 25; NaH₂PO₄, 1.2; and glucose, 11.5. The solution is equilibrated with 95% O₂ and 5% CO₂, and warmed to 34 ± 1°C.

Intracellular recordings are made from neurons of the isolated ganglion by means of a glass microelectrode filled with potassium acetate with a tip resistance of 30–60 mΩ. Potential changes are amplified with a microamplifier (MEZ-8201; Nikon Kohden, Tokyo, Japan) and recorded on a pen recorder. Using a bridge circuit, hyperpolarizing pulses of 0.1–0.4 nA (100 msec) are passed regularly through the recording microelectrode to monitor the input resistance of the neuron, and the electrode resistance is compensated for by adjusting the bridge circuit.

Cortisol hemisuccinate (F) and cortisol-21–bovine serum albumin (F-BSA) are prepared according to a conventional method (25). One molecule of albumin contains about four or five molecules of steroid molecules. Cortisol, F-BSA, and RU38486 are added to the superfusion fluids. The solutions are introduced by a pump or by gravity into the bathing chamber in which the excised ganglion is fixed. The desired solution is selected using a series of stopcocks.

The experimental results showed that the primary effect of GC on neurons was a hyperpolarization of the membrane, which persisted when F was conjugated to bovine serum albumin, indicating that the locus of action of steroid is on the exterior surface of the neuronal membrane and that the response could be specifically antagonized by RU38486 (Fig. 5).

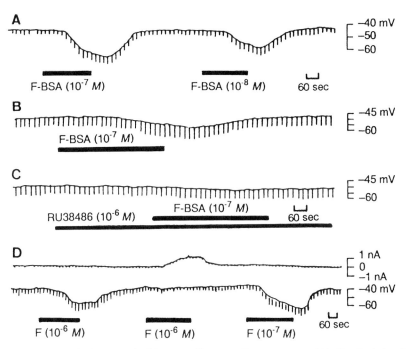

FIG. 5   Effects of glucocorticoids on celiac ganglion neurons. (A) Cortisol–bovine serum albumin (F-BSA) hyperpolarized a celiac ganglion cell in a dose–response manner. (B and C) The effect of F-BSA could be antagonized by RU38486. (D) F-BSA apparently increased the membrane resistance during its hyperpolarizing effect, but when the membrane potential was manually clamped, it decreased the input resistance. [From Hua and Chen (19) with permission.]

Preparation of Brain Slices

Hypothalamus slices, including the paraventricular nucleus of the hypothalamus (PVN), of 300–400 μm thickness, are prepared, using a vibratome, from the freshly excised brains of Wistar rats weighing about 100 g, and are fixed with nylon meshes in a superfusion chamber. The artificial cerebrospinal fluid (ACSF) has the following composition (millimolar concentration): NaCl, 124; KCl, 5; $CaCl_2$, 2.5; KH_2PO_4, 1.2; $MgSO_4$, 1.3; $NaHCO_3$, 26; and glucose, 10. The perfusion and aeration conditions are similar to those for isolated celiac ganglion. Extracellular unit discharges of the PVN neurons were monitored and recorded. The results showed that the effects of GC on PVN neurons were in accordance with those observed in microiontophoretic experiments.

Purification of Glucocorticoid Membrane Receptor by Immunoaffinity Chromatography (26)

We obtained a monoclonal antibody (MAb) to cytosolic glucocorticoid receptor (MAb250) (27) from Dr. S. Okret (Karolinska Institute, Stockholm, Sweden) and found that MAb250 can also bind (react) with GCMR. We first prepared MAb250-Sepharose 4B, and then purified GCMR to about 1000-fold using the following procedures.

Preparation of MAb250-Sepharose 4B

CNBr-activated Sepharose (5 g) is swollen and washed in 1 M HCl and then washed with a coupling buffer (0.5 M NaCl, 0.1 M NaHCO$_3$, pH 9.0). Fifteen milligrams of MAb250 in 8 ml of coupling buffer is mixed with the activated Sepharose and the suspension is rotated end over end for 12 hr at 0–4°C. The unbound protein is removed by washing with the coupling buffer, and the remaining active groups are allowed to react with a 0.2 M glycine solution. The gel is equilibrated in 20 mM sodium phosphate and packed into a column (1.0-cm i.d.) with a bed volume of 3 ml.

Immunoaffinity Chromatography

Synaptic plasma membrane labeled with 80 nM [^{3}H]B is applied to the column by gravity flow. The column is then washed with 50 ml of 0.5 M NaCl in 20 mM sodium phosphate (pH 7.50). The GCMR–[^{3}H]B complex is eluted with 20 ml of 0.1 M acetic acid. Each fraction (2.0 ml) is counted for radioactivity in a liquid scintillation counter (Fig. 6). The protein concentration in each fraction is determined with the protein dye binding method.

Visualization of Glucocorticoid Membrane Receptor with the Immunogold Technique under the Electron Microscope (26)

Preparation of 10-nm Colloidal Gold Particles

Solution A: 1 ml HAuCl$_4$, 79 ml distilled water
Solution B: 4 ml of 1% (w/v) trisodium citrate, 0.1 ml of tannic acid, 0.025 ml of 0.1 M K$_2$CO$_3$, 15.9 ml of distilled water

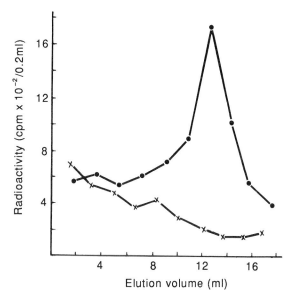

FIG. 6   MAb250-Sepharose 4B chromatography of [^{3}H]B–GCMR complex in SPM isolated from rat brain (with Triton X-100). (●) With [^{3}H]B (80 nM); (×) with [^{3}H]B (80 nM) and B (80 μM).

Both solution A and B are brought to 60°C on a hot plate. Then solution B is quickly added to solution A while stirring. Solution A is reacted with B for about 15 min.

Preparation of Streptavidin–Gold

Streptavidin (340 μg) is added to 20 ml of 10-nm colloidal sols while stirring. Five milliliters of 5% (w/v) BSA is added 5 min later, and reacted for 5 min at room temperature. The streptavidin–gold (SAG) complexes are concentrated and purified using Sephacryl S-400 chromatography.

Preparation of Modified P$_2$ Fractions

The method used for the preparation of modified P$_2$ fractions is the same as that for preparation of SPM, except for omitting the last step of discontinuous sucrose density–gradient ultracentrifugation.

Labeling of Glucocorticoid Membrane Receptor

1. Fix modified P_2 fractions in 4% (w/v) paraformaldehyde at room temperature for 1 hr.
2. Incubate with 0.8% BSA–PBS [0.8% (w/v) BSA in 0.01 M PBS, pH 7.40] for 30 min at room temperature.
3. Incubate with MAb250 (1 : 100) at room temperature for 1.5 hr.
4. Wash with 0.1% BSA-PBS by centrifugation at 10,000 g for 20 min.
5. Incubate with biotinylated horse-anti-mouse IgG (1 : 200) at room temperature for 1 hr.
6. Wash with 0.1% BSA-PBS by centrifugation at 10,000 g for 20 min, three times.
7. Incubate with 0.8% BSA-PBS at room temperature for 30 min.
8. Incubate with SAG (1 : 20) at room temperature for 1.5 hr.
9. Wash with 0.1% BSA-PBS by centrifugation at 10,000 g for 20 min, three times.
10. Fix in 2% (w/v) glutaraldehyde at 4°C overnight.
11. Wash with PBS for 5 min, three times.
12. Process the labeled P_2 fractions using routine electron microscopy (EM) technique, and embed in Epon 812 after postfixation in 1% (w/v) OsO_4 at room temperature for 1 hr. The ultrathin sections are viewed under a JEM-2000 EX electron microscope (JEOL, Tokyo, Japan) after counterstaining with uranyl acetate and lead citrate.

Control Labeling Experiment

The substitution test, that is, replacement of MAb250 with normal mouse IgG, was done without changing any of the other labeling conditions.

Labeling Results

Under the electron microscope, many synaptosomes and a small number of mitochondria were visualized. Gold particles were observed only on the membrane surface of a few nerve terminals (Fig. 7). No labeling was found in the control group.

Conclusions

The study of the membrane receptor of the steroid hormone is still in the early stage. Because GC manifested its effect on neurons at or close to its physiological concentration, it might finally be proved to be a new class

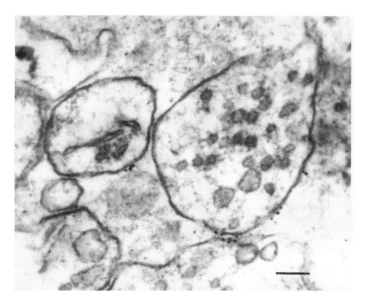

FIG. 7   Immunoelectron microscopic localization of GCMR-like antigenicity on neuronal plasma membrane from rat brain. Streptavidin–gold staining shows the gold particles over the surface of nerve terminals. Bar = 100 nm.

of neuromodulators in addition to amines, peptides, and other bioactive molecules. The detailed characteristics of GC action on the GCMR remain to be elucidated. The most important approach might be to combine the study of GC effects on the membrane potentials of the neuron with its binding characteristics with GCMR.

Acknowledgments

This work was supported by Natural Science Foundation of China (NSFC) Grants 3870210, 39070327, and 39170280. We thank Dr. Sam Okret for the gift of the monoclonal antibody (MAb250). We also thank the Centre de Recherches, Roussel-UCLAF for their generous supply of RU38486 and RU26988.

References

1. L. Gorski and F. Ganon, *Annu. Rev. Physiol.* **38,** 425 (1976).
2. B. W. O'Malley, T. C. Spelsberg, W. T. Schrader, and A. W. Steggles, *Nature (London)* **235,** 141 (1972).

3. B. S. McEwen, E. R. de Kloet, and W. Rostens, *Physiol. Rev.* **66,** 1121 (1986).
4. S. E. Sadler and J. L. Maller, *in* "The Receptors" (P. M. Conn, ed.), Vol. 1, p. 431. Academic Press, Orlando, FL, 1986.
5. C. M. Szego and R. J. Peitras, *in* "Biochemical Actions of Hormones" (G. Litwack, ed.), Vol. 8, p. 307. Academic Press, New York, 1981.
6. E. E. Baulieu, *Mol. Cell. Endocrinol.* **12,** 247 (1978).
7. A. C. Towle and P. Y. Sze, *J. Steroid Biochem.* **18,** 135 (1983).
8. B. Gametchu, *Science* **236,** 456 (1987).
9. Y. Z. Chen and S. Y. Hua, *Neuroscience, Suppl.* **22,** 1008p (1987).
10. M. Schumacher, *Trends Neurosci.* **13,** 359 (1989).
11. M. Orchinik, T. F. Murray, and F. L. Moore, *Science* **252,** 1848 (1991).
12. Z. Guo, Ph.D. Dissertation, Second Military Medical University, Shanghai (1991).
13. Q. Y. Li, Z. M. Vu, and X. Y. Kong, eds., "Practical Laboratory Examination for Clinical Medicine," p. 346. Hubei People's Publisher, Wuhan, 1980.
14. E. Amdor, L. E. Dorfamn, and W. E. C. Waker, *Clin. Chem.* (*Winston-Salem, N.C.*) **9,** 391 (1963).
15. G. L. Ellman, K. D. Courtney, V. Andres, Jr., and R. W. Featherstone, *Biochem. Pharmacol.* **7,** 88 (1961).
16. J. W. Funder, *in* "Adrenal Cortex" (D. C. Anderson and J. S. D. Winter, eds.), p. 86. Butterworth, London, 1985.
17. S. Y. Hua and Y. Z. Chen, *Chin. J. Physiol. Sci.* **3,** 211 (1987).
18. L. G. Wu and Y. Z. Chen, *Acta Pharmacol Sin.* **10,** 306 (1989).
19. S. Y. Hua and Y. Z. Chen, *Endocrinology* (*Baltimore*) **124,** 687 (1989).
20. S. Y. Hua, L. G. Wu, and Y. Z. Chen, *Chin. J. Physiol. Sci.* **5,** 241 (1989).
21. Y. Z. Chen, S. Y. Hua, C. A. Wang, L. G. Wu, Q. Gu, and B. R. Xing, *Neuroendocrinology* **53,** Suppl. 1, 25 (1991).
22. Q. Gu, B. R. Xing, J. H. Xia, and Y. Z. Chen, *Acta Physiol. Sin.* **42,** 472 (1990).
23. T. Z. Li, C. A. Wang, and Y. Z. Chen, *Acta Physiol. Sin.* **43,** 280 (1991).
24. J. Fan, J. X. Tan, and R. B. Xu, *Chin. J. Nucl. Med.* **10,** 39 (1990).
25. Shanghai Research Institute of Endocrinology, *Chin. J. Med. Lab. Technol.* **1,** 25 (1978).
26. H. Fu, Ph.D. Dissertation, Second Military Medical University, Shanghai (1991).
27. S. Okret, A. C. Wikström, and O. Wrange, *Proc. Natl. Acad. Sci. U.S.A.* **81,** 1609 (1984).

[3] Interleukin 1 Receptors in the Brain–Endocrine–Immune Axis

Toshihiro Takao and Errol B. De Souza

Introduction

The cytokine interleukin 1 (IL-1) is one of the key mediators of immunological and pathological responses to stress, infection, and antigenic challenge (1–3). In addition to its immune effects, a role has been postulated for IL-1 as a neurotransmitter/neuromodulator/growth factor in the central nervous system (CNS). Interleukin production has been reported in cultured brain astrocytes and microglia (4–6) and IL-1 has been detected in the brain following cerebral trauma (7, 8) and endotoxin treatment (9). Interleukin-1-like activity is also present in the cerebrospinal fluid (CSF) (10, 11), IL-1 mRNA is present in normal brain (12, 13), and immunohistochemical studies have identified neurons positive for IL-1β-like immunoreactivity in both hypothalamic (14, 15) and extrahypothalamic (15) sites in human brain. Administration of IL-1 in brain produces a variety of effects, including induction of fever (1–3), alteration of slow-wave sleep (16, 17), reduction of food intake (18), induction of analgesia (19), induction of acute-phase glycoprotein synthesis (20, 21), stimulation of thermogenesis (22, 23), and reduction of peripheral cellular immune responses (24). Central as well as peripheral administration of IL-1 has potent neuroendocrine actions, including stimulation of the hypothalamic–pituitary–adrenocortical axis (25–27) and inhibition of the hypothalamic–pituitary–gonadal axis (28). In addition to inducing pituitary proopiomelanocortin (POMC)-derived peptide secretion indirectly via stimulation of hypothalamic corticotropin-releasing factor (CRF) release (29), a number of studies have demonstrated that IL-1 directly induces POMC-derived peptide secretion from dissociated pituitary cells (30, 31) and from AtT-20 mouse pituitary tumor cells (32–34). Furthermore, direct effects of IL-1 at the gonadal level have been reported, including its effects to inhibit sex steroid production by cultured Leydig cells (35) and by primary neonatal testicular cultures (36). These effects of IL-1 in brain and endocrine tissues are presumably mediated through actions of IL-1 at specific high-affinity receptors for the cytokine. In this chapter, we summarize some of the data of our studies and elaborate on methods using ^{125}I-labeled recombinant human IL-1 to identify and characterize IL-1 receptors in the mouse brain–endocrine–

immune axis. In addition, we describe the *in vitro* and *in vivo* modulation of IL-1 receptors.

Methodology

Tissue Preparation

C57BL/6 mice (7–8 weeks) are sacrificed by cervical dislocation and brain and other tissues of interest are dissected (37), weighed, and placed in ice-cold buffer [RPMI 1640, 50 μg/ml gentamicin, 20 mM N-2-hydroxyethylpi-perazine-N'-2-ethanesulfonic acid (HEPES), 1 mg/ml sodium azide, 100 KIU/ml aprotonin, and 10^{-4} M bacitracin; pH 7.4]. Routine characterization assays in tissue homogenates are performed using freshly dissected tissue. Tissues are disrupted in buffer using a Polytron tissue homogenizer (Brink-mann Instruments, Westbury, NY) at setting 6 for 20 sec. The homogenate is centrifuged at 40,000 g for 12 min at 4°C and washed by resuspending in the same buffer and recentrifuging. After the wash, the tissues are resuspended in the same buffer, using a Polytron, to a final protein concentration of 50–80 mg original wet weight per milliliter. The protein concentration of tissues is determined by a modification of the Lowry method (38), using bovine serum albumin (BSA) as the standard.

Interleukin 1 Receptor-Binding Assay

One hundred microliters of the membrane suspension is added to a 1.5-ml polypropylene microtube containing 100 μl of an ^{125}I-labeled IL-1 solution (final concentration range of approximately 50 to 100 pM in competition studies and 10 to 500 pM in saturation studies) and 100 μl of the incubation buffer [tissue preparation buffer with 0.15% (w/v) BSA] or an appropriate concentration of unlabeled IL-1β or other competing peptide. Nonspecific binding is determined in the presence of 300 nM IL-1β. The reaction is allowed to proceed for 2 hr at room temperature (22°C), conditions found to be at equilibrium, that is, at the plateau of the association kinetics curve. The tissue is separated from the incubation medium by centrifugation in a Beckman (Fullerton, CA) microfuge for 5 min at 12,000 g at room temperature. The resulting pellet is washed with 1 ml of Dulbecco's phosphate-buffered saline (PBS) (GIBCO, Grand Island, NY) containing 0.01% (v/v) Triton X-100, pH 7.2. The contents are recentrifuged for 5 min at 12,000 g. The supernatent is aspirated and the microtubes are cut just above the pellet. The radioactivity of the pellet is measured in an LKB (Gaithersburg, MD) γ

counter at 80% efficiency. Unlabeled recombinant human interleukin 1α (IL-1α), recombinant human interleukin 1β (IL-1β), an analog of IL-1β with three amino acids added to the carboxy terminal (IL-$1\beta^+$), and human recombinant tumor necrosis factor α (TNF) are cloned, expressed, and purified at The Upjohn Company (Kalamazoo, MI) (39). Unlabeled rat/human corticotropin-releasing factor (CRF) is purchased from Peninsula Laboratories (Belmont, CA).

Data Analysis

Data from saturation curves are analyzed using the nonlinear curve-fitting program LIGAND of Munson and Rodbard (40). The parameters for the equilibrium dissociation constant (K_D) and maximum number of binding site (B_{max}) values are provided along with statistics on the general fit of the estimated parameters to the raw data. Data from competition curves are also analyzed by the program LIGAND. For each competition curve, estimates of the affinity of radiolabeled ligand for IL-1 receptor are obtained in independent saturation experiments (as above), and these estimates are constrained during the analysis of the apparent inhibitory constant (K_i) values for the various related and unrelated peptides tested. For IL-1-related peptides, all data fit significantly to a single-site model.

Choice of Radioligand

Two biochemically distinct forms of this cytokine, IL-1α and IL-1β, have been isolated (1–3). These polypeptides have been radioiodinated and used as radioligands to label the receptors in a variety of *in vitro* studies, including membrane homogenate and autoradiographic assays. Presently, we routinely use the commercially available preparations of ^{125}I-labeled recombinant human interleukin 1α (specific activity, approximately 1500–2000 Ci/mmol) and interleukin 1β (specific activity, approximately 2500–3000 Ci/mmol) from Du Pont New England Nuclear (Boston, MA). Although it has been reported that IL-1α and IL-1β bind equally to IL-1 receptors (41), ^{125}I-labeled IL-1α showed approximately 20- to 30-fold higher specific binding than did ^{125}I-labeled IL-1β in mouse hippocampus (42) (Fig. 1) and testis (43). The lower level of ^{125}I-labeled IL-1β binding in mouse hippocampus and in the other tissues described above is probably a consequence of a structural modification in the molecule incurred during the radioiodination procedure rendering the molecule less biologically active and therefore a poor radioligand to label the receptor. A loss of biological activity of recombinant human IL-1β but not

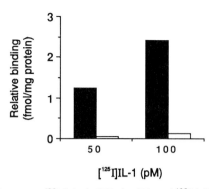

FIG. 1   Comparison between ^{125}I-labeled IL-1α (■) and ^{125}I-labeled IL-1β (□) binding in mouse hippocampus. Crude membrane preparations were incubated for 120 min at room temperature in the presence of noted concentrations of ^{125}I-labeled IL-1α or ^{125}I-labeled IL-1β. Nonspecific binding was defined in the presence of 300 nM IL-1β. Each bar represents the mean of a triplicate determination that varied by less than 10%. [Reproduced with permission from Takao *et al.* (42).]

IL-1α following radioiodination of the proteins has been reported (41). However, in view of recent reports demonstrating that IL-1α and IL-1β may have different effects on biological functions (23, 44) and the suggestion of multiple IL-1 receptors (45, 46), the detection of an ^{125}I-labeled IL-1β binding site in brain under different radioiodination or assay conditions cannot be excluded at the present time. On the basis of these experiments, all subsequent studies were performed using ^{125}I-labeled IL-1α as the radioligand.

Choice of Species

^{125}I-Labeled IL-1α binding was compared in mouse, rat and guinea pig tissues (43). In contrast to high levels of binding in mouse tissues, ^{125}I-labeled IL-1α binding to rat or guinea pig testis was barely within the range of sensitivity of the assay. These species differences in ^{125}I-labeled IL-1α binding are intriguing, especially in view of the reported effects of recombinant human IL-1α in rats to stimulate fever (23), thermogenesis (23), hypothalamic norepinephrine metabolism (47), and hypothalamic–pituitary–adrenocortical secretion (25, 47). Furthermore, evidence suggests a multiplicity of IL-1 receptors (45, 46), and the possibility exists that the radioligand used in the present study (recombinant human ^{125}I-labeled IL-1α) labels only a subtype of these receptors that is present in some species, including mouse, human, and monkey (T. Takao and E. B. De Souza, unpublished data) but is absent in

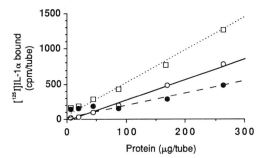

FIG. 2 ^{125}I-labeled IL-1α binding to mouse hippocampus as a function of membrane protein concentration. Direct plot of data showing the amount of ^{125}I-labeled IL-1α bound in the absence (total, □) or in the presence of 300 nM IL-1β (nonspecific, ●); specific binding (○) represents the difference between total and nonspecific binding. ^{125}I-labeled IL-1α (100 pM) was incubated for 120 min at room temperature in incubation buffer with increasing concentrations of crude membranes. Each point represents the mean of a triplicate determination that varied by less than 10%. [Reproduced with permission from Takao et al. (42).]

species such as rat and guinea pig. Additional studies using homologous ligands (i.e., rat IL-1) may be useful in resolving these species differences. Therefore, mouse tissues were used for the remainder of the studies.

Characteristics of Interleukin 1 Receptors

Effects of Tissue Protein Concentrations

Incubation of varying concentrations of membranes of mouse tissues with ^{125}I-labeled IL-1α indicated that binding of the radioligand was linear over the protein concentration range examined (0–300 μg/tube) (42, 43, 48) and representative curves in the hippocampus are shown in Fig. 2. On the basis of this study, all subsequent assays were carried out using approximately 200–300 μg protein/tube. Under these conditions, specific ^{125}I-labeled IL-1α binding (i.e., 300 nM IL-1β displaceable) in hippocampus, kidney, and testis was approximately 40–60, 30–40, and 60–80% of the total binding, respectively (42, 43, 48).

Binding Characteristics at Equilibrium

The concentration-dependent binding of ^{125}I-labeled IL-1α to mouse hippocampus (42), kidney (48), and testis (43) under equilibrium conditions was examined and representative data in the hippocampus are shown in Fig. 3.

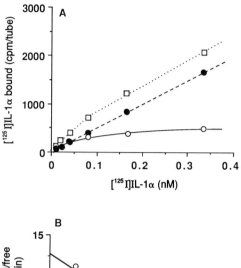

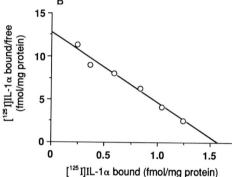

FIG. 3   The binding of ^{125}I-labeled IL-1α to mouse hippocampus as a function of increasing ligand concentration. (A) Direct plot of data showing the total amount of ^{125}I-labeled IL-1α bound (□), binding in the presence of 300 nM IL-1β (nonspecific, ●), and specific (total minus nonspecific) binding (○). (B) Scatchard plot of ^{125}I-labeled IL-1α specific binding. Crude membrane preparations of mouse hippocampus were incubated for 120 min at room temperature with increasing concentrations of ^{125}I-labeled IL-1α. [Reproduced with permission from Takao *et al.* (42).]

Specific ^{125}I-labeled IL-1α binding was saturable (Fig. 3A) and of high affinity. Scatchard analysis (Fig. 3B) of the saturation data showed comparable high-affinity binding (K_D, 60–120 pM) in all three tissues. A summary of the affinity and density of ^{125}I-labeled IL-1α binding is seen in Table I. The highest relative density of binding sites was present in the testis, with progressively lower densities evident in the hippocampus and kidney.

TABLE I   Affinity and Density of ^{125}I-Labeled
Interleukin 1α Binding in Mouse Tissues[a]

Tissue	K_D (pM)	B_{max} (fmol/mg protein)
Hippocampus	114 ± 35	2.5 ± 0.4
Kidney	66 ± 10	1.04 ± 0.24
Testis	82 ± 4	10.8 ± 1.5

[a] Crude membrane preparations of mouse tissues were incubated for
120 min at room temperature with increasing concentrations (10–500
pM) of ^{125}I-labeled IL-1α. Nonspecific binding was determined in the
presence of 300 nM IL-1β. The experiment was carried out three
times and the equilibrium dissociation constant (K_D) and maximum
number of binding site (B_{max}) values from saturation binding
experiments were calculated using the nonlinear curve-fitting
program LIGAND of Munson and Rodbard (40).

Characterization of Pharmacological Specificity

The pharmacological characteristics of the ^{125}I-labeled IL-1α-binding site
were examined by determining the relative potencies of IL-1-related and
-unrelated peptides in displacing specifically bound ^{125}I-labeled IL-1α in homogenates of mouse tissues. The results of the homogenate studies are
summarized in Table II and representative competition curves in the hippo-

TABLE II   Pharmacological Specificity of ^{125}I-Labeled Interleukin 1α Binding to
Mouse Tissues[a]

| | K_i (pM) | | | Biological activity |
Peptide	Hippocampus	Kidney	Testis	(units/ml)
IL-1α	55 ± 18 (3)	28 ± 19 (3)	14 ± 2 (3)	3.0 × 10^7
IL-1β	76 ± 20 (3)	53 ± 23 (3)	89 ± 6 (3)	2.0 × 10^7
IL-1β^+	2,940 ± 742 (3)	5,560 ± 2,098 (3)	7,183 ± 604 (3)	1.0 × 10^6
TNF	>100,000 (2)	>100,000 (2)	>100,000 (2)	8.0 × 10^2
CRF	>100,000 (2)	>100,000 (2)	>100,000 (2)	0.0

[a] Peptides at 3–10 concentrations were incubated with approximately 100 pM ^{125}I-labeled IL-1α for 120 min at room
temperature. All assays were conducted in triplicate for the number of experiments indicated in parentheses. The
K_i (inhibitory binding affinity constant) values were obtained from competition curve data analyzed using the
computer program Ligand (40). Biological activity data were obtained in a murine thymocyte assay (49).
Abbreviations: CRF, rat/human corticotropin-releasing factor; TNF, human recombinant tumor necrosis factor α.

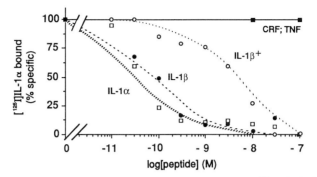

FIG. 4 Characterization of the pharmacological specificity of ^{125}I-labeled IL-1α binding in mouse hippocampus membranes. Crude membranes were incubated for 120 min at room temperature in the presence of 100 pM ^{125}I-labeled IL-1α and varying concentrations of IL-1-related and -unrelated peptides. Nonspecific binding was determined in the presence of 300 nM IL-1β. The data are from representative experiments. Each point represents the mean of a triplicate determination. Abbreviations: CRF, rat/human corticotropin-releasing factor; TNF, human recombinant tumor necrosis factor α. [Reproduced with permission from Takao *et al.* (42).]

campus are shown in Fig. 4. Interleukin 1α was more potent than IL-1β, which, in turn, was much more potent than its weak analog IL-1β$^+$. Corticotropin-releasing factor and TNF (at concentrations up to 100 nM) had no effect on ^{125}I-labeled IL-1α binding. The relative inhibitory potencies of IL-1α, IL-1β, and IL-1β$^+$ for the most part paralleled their bioactivities in a murine thymocyte costimulation assay (49) (Table II).

In Vivo Modulation of Interleukin 1 Receptors in Mouse

Effects of Hypophysectomy

In view of the effects of IL-1 on both the hypothalamic–pituitary–adrenocortical (25–27) and the hypothalamic–pituitary–gonadal (28) axis, we examined the effects of hypophysectomy on the relative density in the hippocampus and testis to define the involvement of trophic pituitary hormones on regulation of IL-1 receptors (42, 43). Two to 3 weeks after hypophysectomy, the hippocampus weighed less in hypophysectomized than in sham-operated animals. Hippocampus weights in hypophysectomized and sham-operated mice were 23.1 ± 1.92 mg ($n = 9$) and 30.6 ± 1.32 mg ($n = 7$), respectively ($p < 0.005$). A saturating concentration of ^{125}I-labeled IL-1α (120 pM) was utilized in this

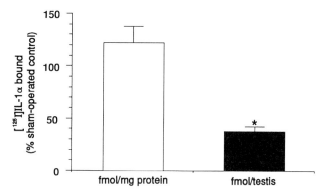

FIG. 5   Effect of hypophysectomy on ^{125}I-labeled IL-1α binding in mouse testis. Crude membrane preparations of testis from hypophysectomized and sham-operated mice were incubated for 120 min at room temperature with ^{125}I-labeled IL-1α. A saturating concentration of ^{125}I-labeled IL-1α (160 pM) was utilized in this study to detect primarily changes in receptor density rather than receptor affinity. Nonspecific binding was determined in the presence of 300 nM IL-1β. Data for hypophysectomized mice ($n = 10$) are presented as a percentage of corresponding values in sham-operated mice and are expressed both as ^{125}I-labeled IL-1α binding per milligram protein (Sham, 1.79 ± 0.19 fmol/mg protein; $n = 8$) and as ^{125}I-labeled IL-1α binding per testis (Sham, 8.04 ± 0.93 fmol/testis; $n = 8$). Asterisk indicates significant difference from sham-operated mice at $p < 0.001$. [Reproduced with permission from Takao *et al.* (43).]

study to detect primarily changes in receptor density rather than receptor affinity. There was no significant change in the relative density of receptors between sham-operated (1.15 ± 0.50 fmol/mg protein; $n = 7$) and hypophysectomized (1.04 ± 0.40 fmol/mg protein; $n = 9$) mice. Due to the multiple effects of hypophysectomy, these data do not rule out possible effects of glucocorticoids and/or sex steroids on hippocampal IL-1 receptors. On the other hand, 2 to 3 weeks after hypophysectomy the testes were significantly atrophied relative to those of sham-operated animals. Testis weights in hypophysectomized and sham-operated mice were 57.2 ± 7.2 mg ($n = 10$) and 136.1 ± 12.5 mg ($n = 8$), respectively ($p < 0.0001$). While the total number of ^{125}I-labeled IL-1α-binding sites per testis was significantly decreased in hypophysectomized mice (sham-operated versus hypophysectomized: 8.04 ± 0.93 fmol/testis versus 3.08 ± 0.31 fmol/testis, respectively; $p < 0.001$) in proportion to the reduction in testicular mass, there was no significant change in the relative density of receptors (Fig. 5). These data suggest that IL-1 receptors are present on testicular cells that are, in part, dependent on maintenance by trophic pituitary hormones. However, the observation that the relative density of IL-1-binding sites in some other regions of the testis remains the same following hypophysectomy also suggests that some receptors are also localized to cells within the testis that are not under pituitary control.

Effects of Lipopolysaccharide Treatment

In an attempt to define the involvement of endogenous IL-1 in the regulation of IL-1 receptors in mouse tissues, we examined ^{125}I-labeled IL-1α binding in the kidney after intraperitoneal (i.p.) injection of lipopolysaccharide (LPS) (48). Twenty-four hours after i.p. LPS injections, kidney weights were not statistically different between LPS-treated mice (142.2 ± 4.7 mg; $n = 6$) and saline-injected controls (136.5 ± 4.7 mg; $n = 6$). In homogenate-binding studies using a single concentration (100 pM) of radioligand, ^{125}I-labeled IL-1α binding was significantly decreased in LPS-treated mice (LPS group, 0.130 ± 0.027 fmol/mg protein; control group, 0.385 ± 0.017 fmol/mg protein; $n = 6$, $p < 0.001$). Subsequently, saturation experiments were carried out in whole-kidney homogenates to determine whether the LPS-induced decreases in ^{125}I-labeled IL-1α binding were primarily due to alterations in the affinity (i.e., K_D) and/or density of the receptor (i.e., B_{max}). The LPS treatment resulted in a significant decrease in K_D value (control, 79.1 ± 4.7 pM; LPS, 30.9 ± 6.1 pM; $n = 4$, $p < 0.001$) and a substantial reduction in B_{max} value (control, 0.91 ± 0.08 fmol/mg protein; LPS, 0.19 ± 0.02 fmol/mg protein; $n = 4$, $p < 0.005$). The data of the present study provide indirect evidence in support of the contention that LPS treatment increases endogenous IL-1 production. We observed a down regulation of IL-1 receptors following LPS treatment, an effect that is characteristically evident following hypersecretion of the homologous ligand, that is, IL-1. These effects of LPS are evident throughout the kidney (i.e., cortex and medulla), suggesting a generalized effect of the endotoxin to increase IL-1 production in the kidney. Alternatively, LPS treatment may have resulted in elevated circulating levels of IL-1 that in turn could act in kidney to down regulate the receptors. Similar effects of LPS treatment to down regulate IL-1 receptors were also observed in other tissues, such as the hippocampus and spleen. The dramatic compensatory homologous down regulation of IL-1 receptors in the kidney and other tissues further underscores the importance of the cytokine in regulating brain–endocrine–immune function.

In Vitro Modulation of Interleukin 1 Receptors in Mouse AtT-20 Pituitary Tumor Cells

To further characterize the mechanisms regulating the interactions of IL-1 and CRF, we examined ^{125}I-labeled IL-1α and ^{125}I-labeled Tyr^0-ovine CRF (oCRF) binding at 24 hr following treatment of AtT-20 cell cultures with rat/human CRF (50). The treatment of AtT-20 cells for 24 hr with CRF produced a dose-dependent increase in ^{125}I-labeled IL-1α binding and a dose-dependent decrease in ^{125}I-labeled oCRF binding. The CRF-induced increase in ^{125}I-labeled IL-1α binding in AtT-20 cells appears to be mediated through specific membrane receptors for CRF because the CRF receptor antagonist, α-helical ovine CRF(9–41), blocked the CRF-induced increase in IL-1 receptors without producing any change in ^{125}I-labeled IL-1α binding by itself. ^{125}I-Labeled IL-1α saturation assays were performed in CRF-treated and control cell cultures to determine whether the increase in ^{125}I-labeled IL-1α binding following CRF treatment is related to changes in the affinity and/or concentration of IL-1 receptors on AtT-20 cells. Scatchard analysis of the saturation data indicated that the K_D values in the control and CRF-treated cells are similar (18.8 $\pm$ 2.3 and 15.3 $\pm$ 2.6 pM, respectively), while the density of receptors in the CRF-treated cultures (B_{max}, 6.8 $\pm$ 0.8 fmol/mg protein) was significantly ($p < 0.05$, Student's t-test) higher than in the control-treated cells (B_{max}, 3.5 $\pm$ 1.8 fmol/mg protein). The increased density of IL-1 receptors following CRF treatment may involve a variety of mechanisms, including increased synthesis of IL-1 receptors, unmasking of cryptic receptors, and/or a decrease in internalization of IL-1 receptors. If increased CRF concentrations produce an up regulation of IL-1 receptors in the anterior pituitary similar to that observed in AtT-20 cells, then one might speculate that IL-1 (which increases in stressful situations) may act at the pituitary level to maintain the elevated plasma adrenocorticotropic hormone seen following stress.

Summary and Conclusions

Interleukin-1 receptors were identified and characterized in mouse brain–endocrine–immune tissues using ^{125}I-labeled IL-1α as a radioligand. ^{125}I-Labeled IL-1 binding in mouse brain–endocrine–immune tissues was linear with membrane protein concentration, saturable, reversible, and of high affinity (K_D, 60–120 pM). The binding sites for ^{125}I-labeled IL-1α exhibited a pharmacological specificity for IL-1 and its analogs in keeping with the relative biological potencies of the compounds in the thymocyte proliferation assay. The pharmacological specificity of the IL-1-binding site in brain–endocrine–immune tissues was further strengthened by the lack of inhibitory activity of peptides such as CRF and TNF. The kinetic and pharmacological characteristics of ^{125}I-labeled IL-1α binding in brain–endocrine–immune tissues were similar to those previously observe in AtT-20 corticotrophs, EL-4 6.1 mouse thymoma cells membranes (51, 52), T lymphocytes (53), and fibroblasts (54). The demonstration of the presence of high-affinity binding sites that are discretely localized in the mouse tissues provides further support for the proposed role of IL-1 in modulating the function in each tissue. Interleukin 1 receptors may play an important role in communication in the brain–endocrine–immune axis.

Acknowledgments

The data presented in this chapter involved collaborative studies with Daniel E. Tracey, William Mark Mitchell, and Elizabeth L. Webster. We thank them for their contributions.

References

1. J. J. Oppenheim, E. J. Kovacs, K. Matsushima, and S. K. Durum, *Immunol. Today* **7,** 45 (1986).
2. S. B. Mizel, *FASEB J.* **3,** 2379 (1989).
3. C. A. Dinarello, *FASEB J.* **2,** 108 (1988).
4. A. Fontana, F. Kristensen, R. Dubs, D. Gemsa, and E. Weber, *J. Immunol.* **129,** 2413 (1982).
5. D. Giulian, T. J. Baker, L. N. Shih, and L. B. Lachman, *J. Exp. Med.* **164,** 594 (1986).
6. D. Giulian, D. G. Young, J. Woodward, D. C. Brown, and L. B. Lachman, *J. Neurosci.* **8,** 709 (1988).
7. D. Giulian and L. B. Lachman, *Science* **228,** 497 (1985).
8. V. H. Perry, M. C. Brown, and S. Gordon, *J. Exp. Med.* **165,** 1218 (1987).
9. A. Fontana, E. Weber, and J. M. Dayer, *J. Immunol.* **133,** 1696 (1984).
10. F. A. Lue, M. Bail, R. Gorczynski, and H. Moldofsky, *Sleep Res.* **16,** 51 (1987).
11. M. M. Mustafa, M. H. Lebel, O. Ramio, K. D. Olsen, J. S. Reisch, B. Beutler, and G. H. McCracken, Jr., *J. Pediatr.* **115,** 208 (1989).
12. W. L. Farrar, J. M. Hill, A. Harel-Bellan, and M. Vinocour, *Immunol. Rev.* **100,** 361 (1987).
13. E. Heier, J. Ayala, P. Denefle, A. Bousseau, P. Rouget, M. Mallat, and A. Prchiantz, *J. Neurosci. Res.* **21,** 39 (1988).
14. C. D. Breder, C. A. Dinarello, and C. B. Saper, *Science* **240,** 321 (1988).
15. C. D. Breder and C. B. Saper, *Soc. Neurosci. Abstr.* **15,** 715 (1989).
16. J. M. Krueger, J. Walter, C. A. Dinarello, S. M. Wolff, and L. Chédid, *Am. J. Physiol.* **246,** R994 (1984).
17. I. Tobler, A. A. Borbely, M. Schwyzer, and A. Fontana, *Eur. J. Pharmacol.* **104,** 191 (1984).
18. D. O. McCarthy, M. J. Kluger, and A. J. Vander, *in* "The Physiologic, Metabolic and Immunological Actions of Interleukin-1" (M. J. Kluger, J. J. Oppenheim, and M. C. Powanda, eds.), p. 171. Liss, New York, 1985.

19. H. Nakamura, K. Nakanishi, A. Kita, and T. Kadokawa, *Eur. J. Pharmacol.* **149,** 49 (1988).

20. R. F. Kampschmidt, *J. Leukocyte Biol.* **36,** 341 (1984).

21. C. M. Blatteis, W. S. Hunter, Q. J. Llanos, R. A. Ahokas, and T. A. Mashburn, Jr., *Brain Res. Bull.* **12,** 689 (1984).

22. M. J. Dascombe, R. A. LeFeuvre, B. O. Sagay, N. J. Rothwell, and M. J. Stock, *Am. J. Physiol.* **256,** E7 (1989).

23. N. J. Busbridge, M. J. Dascombe, F. J. H. Tilders, J. W. A. M. Van Oers, E. A. Linton, and N. J. Rothwell, *Biochem. Biophys. Res. Commun.* **162,** 591 (1989).

24. S. K. Sundar, K. J. Becke, M. A. Cierpial, M. D. Carpenter, L. A. Rankin, S. L. Fleener, J. C. Ritchie, P. E. Simson, and J. M. Weiss, *Proc. Natl. Acad. Sci. U.S.A.* **86,** 6398 (1989).

25. R. Sapolsky, C. Rivier, G. Yamamoto, P. Plotsky, and W. Vale, *Science* **238,** 522 (1987).

26. A. Uehara, P. E. Gottschall, R. R. Dahl, and A. Arimura, *Endocrinology (Baltimore)* **121,** 1580 (1987).

27. F. Berkenbosch, J. Van Oers, A. Del Rey, F. Tilders, and H. Besedovsky, *Science* **238,** 524 (1987).

28. C. Rivier and W. Vale, *Endocrinology (Baltimore)* **124,** 2105 (1989).

29. M. D. Lumpkin, *Science* **238,** 452 (1987).

30. E. W. Bernton, J. E. Beach, J. W. Holaday, R. C. Smallridge, and H. G. Fein, *Science* **238,** 519 (1987).

31. P. Kehrer, D. Turnill, J.-M. Dayer, A. F. Muller, and R. C. Gaillard, *Neuroendocrinology* **48,** 160 (1988).

32. B. M. R. N. J. Woloski, E. M. Smith, and W. J. Meyer, III, *Science* **230,** 1035 (1985).

33. J. Fukata, T. Usui, Y. Naitoh, Y. Nakai, and H. Imura, *J. Endocrinol.* **122,** 33 (1989).

34. M. O. Fagarson, R. Eskay, and J. Axelrod, *Proc. Natl. Acad. Sci. U.S.A.* **86,** 2070 (1989).

35. J. H. Calkins, M. M. Sigel, H. R. Nankin, and T. Lin, *Endocrinology (Baltimore)* **123,** 1605 (1988).

36. B. C. J. M. Fauser, A. B. Galway, and A. J. Hsueh, *Acta Endocrinol. (Copenhagen)* **120,** 401 (1989).

37. E. B. De Souza, *J. Neurosci.* **7,** 88 (1987).

38. O. H. Lowry, N. J. Rosenbrough, A. L. Farr, and R. J. Randall, *J. Biol. Chem.* **193,** 265 (1951).

39. D. B. Carter, K. A. Curry, C.-S. Tomich, A. W. Yem, M. R. Deibel, D. E. Tracey, J. W. Paslay, J. B. Carter, N. Y. Thériault, P. K. W. Harris, I. M. Reardon, H. A. Zurcher-Neely, R. L. Heinrickson, L. L. Clancy, S. W. Muchmore, K. D. Watenpaugh, and H. M. Einspahr, *Proteins* **3,** 121 (1988).

40. P. J. Munson and D. Rodbard, *Anal. Biochem.* **297,** 220 (1980).

41. S. K. Dower, S. R. Kronheim, T. P. Hopp, M. Cantrell, M. Deeley, S. Gillis, C. S. Henney, and D. L. Urdal, *Nature (London)* **324,** 266 (1986).

42. T. Takao, D. E. Tracey, W. M. Mitchell, and E. B. De Souza, *Endocrinology (Baltimore)* **127,** 3070 (1990).

43. T. Takao, W. M. Mitchell, D. E. Tracey, and E. B. De Souza, *Endocrinology* (*Baltimore*) **127,** 251 (1990).
44. A. Uehara, P. E. Gottschall, R. R. Dahl, and A. Arimura, *Biochem. Biophys. Res. Commun.* **146,** 1286 (1987).
45. K. Bomsztyk, J. E. Sims, T. H. Stanton, J. Slack, C. J. McMahan, M. A. Valentine, and S. K. Dower, *Proc. Natl. Acad. Sci. U.S.A.* **86,** 8034 (1989).
46. R. Chizzonite, T. Truitt, P. L. Kilian, S. A. S., P. Nunes, K. P. Parker, K. L. Kaffka, A. O. Chua, D. K. Lugg, and U. Gubler, *Proc. Natl. Acad. Sci. U.S.A.* **86,** 8029 (1989).
47. A. J. Dunn, *Life Sci.* **43,** 429 (1988).
48. T. Takao, W. M. Mitchell, and E. B. De Souza, *Endocrinology* (*Baltimore*) **128,** 2618 (1991).
49. I. Gery, R. K. Gershon, and B. H. Waksman, *J. Exp. Med.* **136,** 128 (1972).
50. E. L. Webster, D. E. Tracey, and E. B. De Souza, *Endocrinology* (*Baltimore*) **129,** 2796 (1991).
51. D. E. Tracey and E. B. De Souza, *Soc. Neurosci. Abstr.* **14,** 1052 (1988).
52. E. B. De Souza, E. L. Webster, D. E. Grigoriadis, and D. E. Tracey, *Psychopharmacol. Bull.* **25,** 299 (1989).
53. J. W. Lowenthal and H. R. MacDonald, *J. Exp. Med.* **164,** 1060 (1986).
54. S. K. Dower, S. M. Call, S. Gillis, and D. L. Urdal, *Proc. Natl. Acad. Sci. U.S.A.* **83,** 1060 (1986).

[4]   Vasoactive Peptides and Their Receptors

D. Regoli, A. Cadieux, and P. D'Orléans-Juste

I. Introduction

A series of naturally occurring peptides of various sizes has been shown to act on the mammalian cardiovascular system primarily as vasoconstrictors or as vasodilators. Names, primary structures, and the discovery references of angiotensin (AT_{II}), bradykinin (BK), substance P (SP), endothelin 1 (ET-1), atrial natriuretic peptide (ANP), vasoactive intestinal peptide (VIP), neuropeptide Y (NPY), vasopressin [VSP; or ADH (antidiuretic hormone)], and calcitonin gene-related peptide (CGRP) are presented in Table I (1–10). Some of these agents emerge from the action of endopeptidases (renin and kallikreins) on protein precursors of hepatic origin (angiotensinogen and kininogens) and are released in blood and extracellular fluid (e.g., angiotensin and bradykinin); others are synthesized in peripheral tissues such as endothelia (endothelins) or cardiac myocytes (atrial natriuretic peptide) and their synthesis and release is regulated by a variety of endogenous factors and physiological stimuli (11, 12). Still, the majority of the vasoactive peptides (five of nine) are neuropeptides, coded and expressed in central and peripheral neurons (SP, VIP, NPY, VSP, and CGRP) from which they are released by neurostimuli and by factors or agents that modulate transmitter release from nerve terminals, either from sensory (SP and CGRP), motor (VIP and NPY), or both. Vasoactive peptides act as hormones (VIP, AT_{II}, BK, and ANP) distant from their site of production, or as transmitter/autacoids (SP, CGRP, NPY, and ET-1) near the site of release. Angiotensin, VSP, ET-1, and NPY are vasoconstrictors; BK, SP, ANP, VIP, and CGRP are vasodilators. The major targets of vasoactive peptides are the peripheral resistance vessels, the capillaries, and the veins, and within the vessels the endothelial cells, the smooth muscle fibers and the axons or terminals of autonomic neurons, predominantly adrenergic. Target cells code and express on their plasma membrane a variety of receptors that modulate the physiological effects of vasoactive peptides and other agents. A complete list of such functional and binding sites is given in Table II (13–32).

Two binding sites have been described for angiotensins but only AT_1 appears to be a functional receptor entity (33). Two well-defined receptors have been reported for the kinins (34), B_2 being localized in the endothelium to subserve the peripheral vasodilator effect of bradykinin in the majority of

TABLE I Primary Sequences of Vasoactive Peptides

Peptide	Number of residues	Abbreviation	Sequence	Ref.
Angiotensin	8	AT_{II}	H-Asp-Arg-Val-Tyr-Ile-His-Pro-Phe-OH	1
Bradykinin	9	BK	H-Arg-Pro-Pro-Gly-Phe-Ser-Pro-Phe-Arg-OH	2
Substance P	11	SP	H-Arg-Pro-Lys-Pro-Gln-Gln-Phe-Phe-Gly-Leu-Met-NH$_2$	3
Endothelin 1	21	ET-1	Cys-Ser-Cys-Ser-Ser-Leu-Met-Asp-Lys-Glu-Cys-Val-Tyr-Phe-Cys-His-Leu-Asp-Ile-Ile-Trp-OH	4
Atrial natriuretic peptide	28	ANP	H-Ser-Leu-Arg-Arg-Ser-Ser-Cys-Phe-Gly-Gly-Arg-Met-Asp-Arg-Ile-Gly-Ala-Gln-Ser-Gly-Leu-Gly-Cys-Asn-Ser-Phe-Arg-Tyr-OH	5
Vasoactive intestinal peptide	28	VIP	H-His-Ser-Asp-Ala-Val-Phe-Thr-Asp-Asn-Tyr-Thr-Arg-Leu-Arg-Lys-Gln-Met-Ala-Val-Lys-Lys-Tyr-Leu-Asn-Ser-Ile-Leu-Asn-NH$_2$	6
Neuropeptide Y	36	NPY	H-Tyr-Pro-Ser-Lys-Pro-Asp-Asn-Pro-Gly-Glu-Asp-Ala-Pro-Ala-Glu-Asp-Met-Ala-Arg-Tyr-Tyr-Ser-Ala-Leu-Arg-His-Tyr-Ile-Asn-Leu-Ile-Thr-Arg-Gln-Arg-Tyr-NH$_2$	7
Vasopressin	9	VSP (ADH)	Cys-Tyr-Phe-Gln-Asn-Cys-Pro-Arg-Gly-NH$_2$	8
Calcitonin gene-related peptide	37	CGRPα	H-Ala-Cys-Asp-Thr-Ala-Thr-Cys-Val-Thr-His-Arg-Leu-Ala-Gly-Leu-Leu-Ser-Arg-Ser-Gly-Gly-Val-Val-Lys-Asn-Asn-Phe-Val-Pro-Thr-Asn-Val-Gly-Ser-Lys-Ala-Phe-NH$_2$	9, 10

vascular beds. Of the three functional sites identified for the neurokinins (NKs), the most important for cardiovascular regulation appears to be the NK-1 endothelium site, which sustains the SP vasodilator effect (35); NK-2 sites may play a role in some vascular beds (e.g., pulmonary) (36) and appear to be involved in the modulation of sympathetic nerve activity (37). Both ET_A and ET_B appear to be present in vascular and other smooth muscles, but the vasoconstrictor effect of endothelins is mostly mediated by ET_A; ANP-A-R (ANP-R_1) is present in peripheral vessels and appears to be involved in the vascular effect (vasodilation) of ANP, while ANP-B-R (ANP-R_2) is a binding site without apparent function. Only one receptor has been identified for VIP (24), whereas two distinct receptors have been found for CGRP (CGRP$_1$ and CGRP$_2$) (38). The CGRP$_1$ receptors mediate the peripheral vasodilator effects of this peptide. Two NPY receptors have been reported, the first of which (Y_1) mediates postjunctional effects (e.g., vasoconstriction) while the other (Y_2) is predominantly prejunctional and inhibits neurotransmitter release (39). A third site (Y_3) has been described (40). V_1 is the vascular receptor for vasopressin (responsible for vasoconstriction) and V_2 mediates autidiuresis (41).

II. Receptors for Angiotensin: AT_1 and AT_2

Angiotensin II is the biologically active component of the renin–angiotensin system. It exerts a variety of biological effects that help to increase peripheral vascular resistance and to retain water and electrolytes. Angiotensin has been shown to play an important role in hypertension and the inhibition of its formation (by inhibitors of the converting enzyme) or the blockage of its peripheral effects (by receptor antagonists) has led to the discovery and development of new and efficient antihypertensive drugs. Peripheral effects of angiotensin include vasoconstriction, aldosterone secretion, vasopressin release, salt and water retention, activation of sympathetic nerves, and stimulation of thirst. These effects are mediated by specific receptors, of which two types (AT_1 and AT_2) have been identified by binding studies; only AT_1, however, has been shown to be a functional entity by biological *in vivo* and *in vitro* assays (42, 43).

A. Binding Assays (33)

Crude membranes are prepared from various tissues (brain, uterus, liver, etc.) by homogenization in cold buffer [generally N-2-hydroxyethylpiperazine-N'-2-ethanesulfonic acid (HEPES), 10 mM at pH 7.4] containing a

TABLE II Major Features of Receptors for Vasoactive Peptides

Peptide	Receptor	Tissue	Number of residues	Molecular weight	Mechanism	Ref.
Angiotensin	AT_1	Bovine adrenal	359	41,093	G protein	13
	AT_2	Uterus, adrenal medulla, brain	?	?	?	14
Bradykinin	B_1	—	—	—	—	—
	B_2	Rat uterus	366	41,696	G protein	15
Substance P	NK-1	Rat brain	407	46,364	G protein	16
	NK-2	Bovine stomach	390	43,851	G protein	17
	NK-3	Rat brain	452	51,104	G protein	18
Endothelin	ET_A	Bovine lung	427	48,500	G protein	19
	ET_B	Rat lung	415	46,900	G protein	20
Atrial natriuretic peptide	$ANP-R_1$	Rat brain (nM)	1,057		Guanylcyclase	21
	$ANP-R_2$	Rat brain (8.25 M)	1,047		Guanylcyclase	22
	ANP-C-R	Rat aorta	496		IP_3	23
Vasoactive intestinal peptide	VIP-R	Rat liver		56,000–80,000	Adenylcyclase	24
		HT29 (intact cells)		64,000	Adenylcyclase	25

46

Peptide	Receptor	Tissue	Amino acids	M_r	Mechanism	Reference
Calcitonin gene-related peptide	CGRP-R	Human placenta		62,000–68,000	?	26
		Porcine spinal cord		70,000	?	27
		Porcine coronary artery		70,000–90,000	Adenylcyclase	27
Neuropeptide Y	Y_1	Porcine left atria		70,000	Adenylcyclase	27
		Human neuroblastoma (MC-1XC)		70,000	G protein	28
	Y_2	Rat hippocampus		50,000	G protein	28
		Rabbit kidney		50,000	G protein	28
		Rat brain		62,000	G protein	29
	Y_3	—	—	—	—	
Vasopressin	V_1	Rat liver	394	44,202	G protein (IP$_3$)[a]	30 184
	V_2	Rat kidney	370	40,518	G protein (cAMP)	31 185
	OT	Human uterine myometrium	388	42,716	G protein (IP$_3$)	32 186

[a] IP$_3$, inositol triphosphate.

TABLE III IC_{50}[a] of Several Angiotensin-Related Peptides and
Nonpeptide Antagonists

Compound	Rat liver	Rabbit adrenal	Rabbit uterus
$[Sar^1]AT_{II}$	2.03	2.93	1.64
AT_{II}	1.02	1.51	2.50
AT_{III}	5.57	10.83	1.74
AT_I	300.0	579.0	116.0
$[Sar^1,Ala^8]AT_{II}$	3.10	6.52	1.61
$[Sar^1,Leu^8]AT_{II}$	3.22	5.72	2.56
DuP 753	7.52	38.50	35.9, >10,000[b]
PD 123319	>10,000	>10,000	21.5

[a] IC_{50}, Concentration (nM) required to displace 50% of [^{3}H]AT.
[b] Values for DuP 753 were obtained after fitting to a two-site model. [modified from
Dudley et al. (33), with permission.]

mixture of protease inhibitors (leupeptin, bestatin, captopril, pepstatin A,
etc.) at a concentration of 10 μM. Homogenates obtained in various ways
[e.g., with a Brinkmann (Westbury, NY) Polytron PT-10 at setting 7 for 20
sec] are centrifuged for 10 min at 50,000 g and 4°C and the pellets are
first washed with HEPES, recentrifuged, and then suspended in a buffer-
membrane preparation. They can be used for several days when stored at
-70°C.

^{3}H-Labeled AT_{II}, ^{125}I-labeled AT_{II}, and ^{125}I-labeled $[Sar^1,Ile^8]AT_{II}$ are the
ligands used (25 μM) to measure binding to tissues (10 mg of homogenate)
contained in a final volume of 1 ml HEPES [with 0.2% (w/v) bovine serum
albumin (BSA) and 10 mM $MgCl_2$]. Samples are incubated for 60 min at 25°C
and then filtered through Whatman (Clifton, NJ) GF/B glass filters presoaked
in 50 mM Tris buffer at pH 7.7, containing 0.2% (w/v) BSA and 100 μM
bacitracin. Filters are transferred to vials containing Formula 963 scintillation
fluid (Du Pont, Wilmington, DE) to measure radioactivity in a liquid scintillation counter (33).

Results of binding assays, performed in rat liver, rabbit adrenals, and rabbit
uterus using [^{3}H]AT_{II} as a ligand, are presented in Table III by showing the
IC_{50} of angiotensins and some antagonists. The most active agonist is AT_{II},
followed by $[Sar^1]AT_{II}$ and AT_{III}: AT_I is 100–500 times weaker. The peptide
antagonists are fairly strong and, like the natural peptides, equally active
(nonselective) on the three preparations. DuP 753 (Du Pont, Wilmington,
DE) shows high affinity for rat liver and rabbit adrenals and binds to two sites
with different affinities in rabbit uterus. PD 123319 (Parke Davis, Cambridge,
England) is inactive in the first two preparations but shows high affinity for
rabbit uterus. Thus, the use of nonpeptide antagonists reveals the existence
of two distinct sites, AT_I in the rat liver and rabbit adrenals and both AT_I

TABLE IV Characterization of the Angiotensin Receptor *in Vivo* and *in Vitro* with Agonists and Antagonists

Compound	Rat blood pressure	Rabbit aorta			Rat stomach		
		pD_2	RA^a	pA_2	pD_2	RA	pA_2
$[Asp^1,Val^5]AT_{II}$	100	8.85	100	—	7.75	100	—
$[Sar^1]AT_{II}$	110	9.10	175	—	8.21	280	—
$[Ala^3]AT_{II}$	80	7.73	7.4	—	7.33	38	—
$[Ala^5]AT_{II}$	5	6.42	0.4	—	5.50	0.6	—
$[Ala^8]AT_{II}$	0.5^b (+)[c]	—	—	7.7	—	—	7.2
$[Leu^8]AT_{II}$	0.2 (+)	—	—	8.8	—	—	8.6
$[Sar^1,Ala^8]AT_{II}$	0.15 (++)	—	—	8.6	(+)	—	8.4
$[Sar^1,Leu^8]AT_{II}$	0.04 (++)	—	—	9.0	(+)	—	9.2
DuP 753	0.78^d	—	—	8.3	—	—	8.0
$[pNH_2,Phe^6]AT_{II}$	0	0	—	0	0	—	0
PD 123319	0	0	—	0	(+)	—	0

[a] RA, relative affinity, in percent of that of $[Asp^1, Val^5]AT_{II}$.

[b] ID_{50} (μg/kg/min), by intravenous infusion.

[c] (+), (++): Residual agonistic activity.

[d] ED_{30} (mg/kg), by intravenous injection [from Timmermans *et al.* (42)].

and AT_2 in the rabbit uterus: DuP 753 is selective for AT_1 and PD 123319 for AT_2 (Table III).

B. Biological Assays

1. In Vivo Assay on Rat Blood Pressure

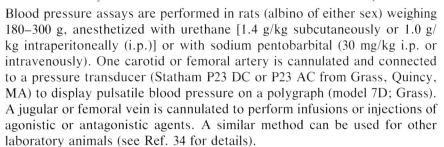

Blood pressure assays are performed in rats (albino of either sex) weighing 180–300 g, anesthetized with urethane [1.4 g/kg subcutaneously or 1.0 g/kg intraperitoneally (i.p.)] or with sodium pentobarbital (30 mg/kg i.p. or intravenously). One carotid or femoral artery is cannulated and connected to a pressure transducer (Statham P23 DC or P23 AC from Grass, Quincy, MA) to display pulsatile blood pressure on a polygraph (model 7D; Grass). A jugular or femoral vein is cannulated to perform infusions or injections of agonistic or antagonistic agents. A similar method can be used for other laboratory animals (see Ref. 34 for details).

2. In Vitro Assays on Rabbit Aorta and Rat Stomach

A variety of isolated organs have been used in pharmacological studies of angiotensin (44). The rabbit aorta and the rat stomach or the guinea pig ileum are the most frequently used to test agonists and antagonists (Table IV).

a. Rabbit Aorta

Rabbits of both sexes (1.0–2.0 kg) are killed by stunning and exsanguination. The thoracic aorta is dissected away, prepared as a strip [according to the method of Furchgott and Bhadrakom (45)], and suspended in oxygenated (95% O_2/5% CO_2) Krebs solution at 37°C. The composition of the Krebs solution is as follows (mM): NaCl, 117.5; KH_2PO_4, 1.18; KCl, 4.7; $MgSO_4$ · $7H_2O$, 1.18; $NaHCO_3$, 25.0; $CaCl_2$ · $6H_2O$, 2.5; dextrose, 5.5. Changes of tension (generally contractions) are recorded isometrically (preferably) or isotonically (see Ref. 34 for details) with special transducers and displayed on polygraphs (model 7D; Grass). Complete concentration–response curves can be measured to estimate apparent affinities of agonists in terms of pD_2 (the $-$log of the concentration of agonist required to produce 50% of the maximum effect) or of antagonists in terms of pA_2 (the concentration of antagonist required to reduce the effect of a double dose of agonist to that of a single dose) (46).

b. Rat Stomach

Rats of both sexes (150–300 g) are killed by stunning and exsanguination. The stomach is dissected away and the stomach fundus is prepared as a strip, according to the method of Vane (47). Strips of the stomach are suspended *in vitro* in 5- to 10-ml organ baths containing oxygenated Krebs solution at 37°C in order to record changes of tension as for the rabbit aorta. Agonist and antagonist activities are measured or estimated as described above (see also Ref. 34 for other details on nonvascular preparations).

Pharmacological characterization of angiotensin receptors performed *in vivo* and *in vitro* with agonists and antagonists is presented in Table IV. A good correlation is demonstrated between the results of the *in vivo* and *in vitro* assays, [Sar^1]AT$_{II}$ being the most potent agonist (pD_2 9.1) and [Sar^1, Leu^8]AT$_{II}$ the most potent antagonist (pA_2 = 9.0, 9.2). Peptide antagonists maintain a residual agonistic effect *in vivo* and on the rat stomach *in vitro*. Nonpeptide antagonists differ by the fact that DuP 753 antagonizes the effect of AT$_{II}$ in all preparations and shows good affinities, while PD 123319 (agonist, antagonist?) is inactive both as agonist and as antagonist. The same holds for [pNH$_2$Phe^6]AT$_{II}$, a compound (agonist, antagonist?) that Speth and Kim (48) showed to interact with AT$_{II}$ binding to AT$_2$ receptors.

In early studies, the existence of different receptors for angiotensin was repeatedly proposed from (a) results of binding assays performed with naturally occurring peptides (AT$_1$, AT$_{II}$, and AT$_{III}$) and showing differences in binding affinities in vascular and nonvascular (especially adrenal cortex and medulla) tissues (49), (b) from the multiplicity of signal transduction (stimulation of phosphoinositide, inhibition of adenylcyclase) (50), and (c) from the observation that disulfide-bridge-reducing agents (dithiothreitol) inactivate AT_1 but do not affect AT_2 (51).

Looking at these data today in the light of the new finding, we conclude that (a) the use of natural peptides for receptor characterization is not always appropriate because these peptides are nonselective. Indeed, the proposal by Peach (49) of three receptors has not been supported by experimental data (52); (b) the use of binding assays on plasma membranes for identification and characterization of new angiotensin antagonists shows major limitations because binding does not allow the determination if new agents interfering with the ligand are agonists or antagonists and binding to membrane does not correlate with binding evaluated by historadiography (see example concerning rat brain; Timmermans *et al.* (43)]. Moreover, some antagonists (e.g., DuP 532) bind strongly to bovine serum albumin (which is currently used in binding assays) and their affinities can be markedly underestimated (53) with respect to bioassays.

Differences in signal transduction cannot be used for angiotensin receptor classification because all biological effects of AT_{II} are mediated by AT_1 receptors, no matter what the transduction system might be. The reduction of the disulfide bridges by dithiothreitol is a rather unclear phenomenon that cannot be used for receptor differentiation.

Definite evidence for the existence of two sites has been obtained only with the new nonpeptidic compounds, DuP 753, PD 123177, and PD 123319, which are selective for either one or the other site.

From the above analysis, it is concluded that all biological effects of angiotensin are mediated by AT_1 receptors, AT_2 being a nonfunctional binding site.

III. Receptors for Bradykinin-Related Kinins: B_1 and B_2

Kinins are released in blood and extracellular fluid by the action of kallikreins (a series of serine proteases) on proteinic precursors (kininogen of high or low molecular weight), in response to inflammatory, noxious, and other types of stimuli that are able to activate prekallikrein to kallikreins (54). Bradykinin and kallidin (Lys-bradykinin) evoke a variety of biological responses, such as hypotension, edema, pain, bronchoconstriction, and cough. In the cardiovascular system, kinins exert peripheral effects on (1) arterial resistance vessels, which are brought to relax by nitric oxide (NO) and prostacyclin released from the endothelium, (2) capillaries, where kinins contract the endothelial layer and increase vascular permeability, and (3) the veins that are stimulated by kinins to contract and thus increase capillary pressure. Kinins stimulate or relax a variety of smooth muscles in the intestinal, genitourinary, and respiratory tracts and in other peripheral tissues where kinins find specific functional sites of two types, B_1 and B_2. Kinin receptors have been primarily characterized with classical pharmacological methods and by the use of isolated organs, particularly isolated vessels (34, 54–56). Both the inhibitory (indirectly mediated by the endothelium), vasodilatatory (dog carotid artery, handled according to the method of [D'Orléans-Juste *et al.* (57)], and the stimulatory venoconstrictor effects (rabbit jugular vein prepared according to the method of Gaudreau *et al.* (58)] of bradykinin have been characterized together with the stimulatory intestinal effect [cat ileum (54), guinea pig ileum (59)] and the contractile response of the B_1 receptor in the rabbit aorta (55, 56). Results are presented in Table V.

A. *Biological Assays of Bradykinin and Related Kinins*

Kinins are potent hypotensive agents in all animal species studied (54). The most common *in vivo* test for these peptides is the rat blood pressure, described previously. Vasodilator effects of kinins are measured in isolated perfused organs with intact endothelium, according to the procedure described in Section IV. The relaxant effect of the kinins in arterial vessels is evaluated *in vitro* in the dog carotid artery (57) using the method described by Regoli and Barabé (34). The venoconstrictor effect is measured *in vitro* in the rabbit jugular vein (42), according to the procedure summarized below.

The veins, taken from rabbits (1.0–2.0 kg), are cut into helicoidal strips 2 mm wide and 2 cm long and suspended in Krebs solution (oxygenated at 37°C) containing a converting enzyme inhibitor (captopril, 10 μM) to prevent kinin degradation (34). Contractions of tissue in response to kinins are recorded as described before and complete concentration–response curves are usually measured to evaluate affinities of kinins and their antagonists. The rabbit jugular vein has been shown to contain a B_2 receptor subtype (B_{2A}) (Table V).

The most commonly used nonvascular preparation is the guinea pig ileum, which is taken from guinea pigs of 250–350 g and prepared as a longitudinal smooth muscle strip, according to Rang (37). The tissue is suspended *in vitro* in Krebs solution (oxygenated at 37°C) and its changes of tension are measured as described above for the isolated vessels (see Section I). The guinea pig ileum is the preparation used to characterize the B_{2B} receptor subtype (Table V).

B_1 receptors are studied using the rabbit aorta strip, prepared and handled in the same way as for angiotensin. The tissue is almost insensitive to kinins, particularly to desArg⁹BK, the B_1 receptor agonist, at the beginning of the experiment. The sensitivity of the tissue increases over several hours (up to

TABLE V Characterization of B_2 and B_1 Kinin Receptors with Agonists and Antagonists

	Rabbit jugular vein (B_{2A})			Guinea pig ileum (B_{2B})			Rabbit aorta (B_1)		
	pD_2	RA^c	pA_2	pD_2	RA^c	pA_2	pD_2	RA^c	pA_2
Agonists									
Bradykinin (BK)	8.48	100	—	7.9	100	—	6.2	9	—
Lys-BK	8.60	141	—	7.9	100	—	7.3	100	—
[Hyp³]BK	8.88	254	—	7.3	25	—	6.2	8	—
[desArg⁹]BK		Inactive			Inactive		7.3	100	—
Lys,desArg⁹BK		<0.1			<0.1		8.6	1995	—
Antagonists									
[Leu⁸]desArg⁹BK	0.05ᵃ		0	0		0	6.2		7.3
[Thi⁵,⁸,D-Phe⁷]BK	0.3ᵃ		6.7	0.3ᵃ		5.9	0		6.2
D-Arg[Hyp³,Phe⁷]BK	0.7ᵃ		8.0	0.1ᵃ		5.4	0		6.4
D-Arg[Hyp³,D-Phe⁷,Leu⁸]BK	0.1ᵃ		8.9	—		6.8	—		5.8
Hoe 140ᵇ	—		9.2	—		8.4	0	Inactive	Inactive
D-Arg[Hyp³,Gly⁶,Leu⁸]BK	0.3ᵃ		7.60	0.3ᵃ	Partial agonist		—		<5.0
D-Arg[Tyr³,D-Phe⁷,Leu⁸]BK	8.30	66	—	0.3ᵃ		6.80	—		<5.0

ᵃ Indicates residual agonistic activity as a fraction of the maximal response to bradykinin ($\alpha^E = 1.0$).

ᵇ Hoe 140, D-Arg[Hyp³,Thi⁵,D-Tic⁷,Oic⁸]BK.

ᶜ RA, relative affinity, in percent of bradykinin.

6–10 hr) of incubation as B_1 receptors are formed *de novo* (55). The contractile effects of the kinins are recorded and analyzed using the same instruments and approaches described in Section I for angiotensin. Rabbit tissues can be sensitized to desArg⁹BK by pretreatment of the animals with lipopolysaccharide (LPS), which is injected intravenously 5 hr before killing the animal (56). The mechanism of B_1 receptor generation by LPS has been investigated (60, 61). Aortas and other tissues taken from LPS-treated rabbits respond to desArg⁹BK from the beginning of the incubation *in vitro* (56). Similarly, dog renal arteries express B_1 receptors spontaneously and show high sensitivity to desArg⁹BK (62).

Several compounds have been used to characterize kinin receptors in isolated organs, using the biological responses (contractile) of three preparations (Table V). Bradykinins and kallidin are potent stimulants of the rabbit jugular vein (RJV) and guinea pig ileum (GPI), whereas desArg⁹BK and Lys,desArg⁹BK are inactive. The opposite order of potency is observed in the rabbit aorta (RA). [Leu⁸]desArg⁹BK is an antagonist only on the RA. On these bases, Regoli and Barabé (54) proposed the two kinin receptors hypothesis, the B_1 (RA) and the B_2 (RJV, GPI, and many other preparations and tests) which was characterized initially only with agonists (54) and has subsequently (see below) been characterized with antagonists. B_2 receptor antagonists were identified by Vavrek and Stewart (63) and subsequently improved by various investigators (64–66) by the replacement of Pro³ by hydroxyproline (Hyp), by the addition of a D-Arg to the N terminus, by the substitution of Phe⁸ by Leu, and by the replacement of the dipeptide Pro⁷-Phe⁸ with D-Tic-Oic (67–69). A prototype of each antagonist series is reported in Table V to indicate that B-2-thienyl-elanine (Thi) is not needed in positions 5 and 9, while Hyp³ and D-Arg⁰ are important for affinity, particularly on the RJV. The substitution of Phe⁸ by Leu, added to the other modifications, leads to D-Arg[Hyp³,D-Phe⁷,Leu⁸]BK, which (a) is almost devoid of agonistic activity, and (b) is active on the RJV, less active on the GPI, and rather poor on the RA (B_1), and therefore is quite selective for the B_2 site. The difference among the pA_2 values (by two log units) between the RJV and the GPI is a determinant finding for the proposed (Table V) subdivision of B_2 receptors into B_{2A} (RJV) and B_{2B} (GPI). D-Arg[Hyp³,D-Phe⁷,Leu⁸]BK is a competitive antagonist, rapidly reversible both *in vivo* and *in vitro* and is different from Hoe 140, which is noncompetitive (nonequilibrium), probably because it has a prolonged interaction with both the B_{2A} and B_{2B} sites (59, 67, 68, 70). The distinction between B_{2A} and B_{2B} is supported by the results obtained with the two last compounds (Table V), which differ by the residue in the third position. The presence of Hyp favors antagonism (pA_2 7.6) on the B_{2A} and partial agonistic activity on the B_{2B}, while Tyr³ gives a potent *agonist* on the B_{2A} and fairly good antagonist (pure antagonist) on the B_{2B}. This new classification has been presented in a review article (71). Kinin functional sites are therefore B_1 and B_2 (two subtypes are contemplated). Several other receptors (B_3, B_4, and B_5) have been proposed (72–74) but their existence has not been demonstrated with solid experimental data (see critical review in Ref. 59). The kinin-induced histamine release from rat peritoneal mastocytes is a nonspecific phenomenon that has been attributed to the cationic character of the kinins (75, 76).

IV. Receptors for Substance P, Neurokinins, and Tachykinins: NK-1, NK-2, and NK-3

Three mammalian neuropeptides have been identified that bear the following C-terminal sequence: Phe-X-Gly-Leu-Met-NH$_2$. Two of them, substance P and neurokinin A, are coded for by the same gene that codes for the precursor preprotachykinin-A (PPT-A), while the other (neurokinin B) is present in another gene that codes for PPT-B (77, 78). Neurokinins show similar, but not identical, biological activities that are brought about by the activation of three different receptor types, named NK-1, NK-2, and NK-3 (79). Neurokinin 1 receptors are more sensitive to SP than to the other neurokinins and, similarly, NK-2 receptors are more sensitive to NKA and NK-3 receptors are more sensitive to NKB. The activation of receptors by neurokinins in peripheral organs leads to hypotension, plasma extravasation, increase in airway resistance, and stimulation of a variety of smooth muscles in the intestine, the urogenital tract, the respiratory system (80), and the eye (pupillary constriction). In the cardiovascular system, neurokinin peptides are both inhibitory [of the arterial smooth muscle through release of prostaglandin I_2 (PGI$_2$) and NO by NK-1 receptor activation] (35, 57) and stimulatory of some arterial smooth muscle [e.g., of the rabbit pulmonary artery (36)]: NK-2 and NK-3 receptors appear to modulate the activities of sympathetic and parasympathetic nerves in the heart (37), the intestine (37), and the vas deferens of various species. Regulation of blood pressure and heart rate by neurokinins involves spinal and central pathways, the activation of which leads to an increase in blood pressure and heart rate (81) in the rat. Neurokinins, however, are primarily sensory neuropeptides, which are released centrally and peripherally by the ortho or antidromic stimulation of sensory fibers and lead to pain transmission in the spinal cord and to plasma extravasation in the periphery, as the first most relevant manifestation of neurogenic inflammation.

Characterization of neurokinin receptors has been performed with (a) naturally occurring peptides (the three neurokinins), (b) selective agonists, and (c) antagonists, of which some are of a nonpeptidic nature. These compounds have been tested on three isolated vessels whose contractile responses to neurokinins are mediated by a single receptor type (monoreceptor systems), namely the rabbit jugular vein (NK-1), the rabbit pulmonary artery (NK-2), and the rat portal vein (NK-3) (36, 82, 83).

The rabbit jugular vein has been described (see Section III, above).

The rabbit pulmonary artery is taken from the animal and suspended *in vitro,* as described in Section I and in the original publication by D-Orléans-Juste *et al.* (36). The endothelium, which contains NK-1 receptors (vasodilatory), must be removed to eliminate this functional site and allow the study of the NK-2 sites, which are in the smooth muscle fiber. Recording of contractions and their use for NK-2 receptor characterization are the same as for the rabbit aorta (Section I). The rat portal vein is prepared according to the method of Rioux *et al.* (84) and used for NK-3 receptor studies as indicated by Mastrangelo *et al.* (85). This preparation can be used under the ordinary conditions utilized for pharmacological assays and the contractile responses are recorded as described above (see Section I), or in a microbath, by the technique described by Mastrangelo (85, 86). When used in a microbath, affinity for NK-B is increased (85, 86).

Results obtained with a series of compounds acting as agonists or antagonists on the neurokinin receptors are presented in Table VI. Most of the data have been taken from recent review papers (35, 80, 82, 83).

Substance P being the most potent on the RJV, NKA on the rabbit pulmonary artery (RPA), and NKB on the rat portal vein (RPV), naturally occurring peptides show less selectivity for the various receptors than the compounds $[Sar^9,Met(O_2)^{11}]SP$, $[\beta\text{-}Ala^8]NKA(4–10)$, and $[MePhe^7]NKB$, which have been selected from a large number of analogs of the three neurokinins (35, 83, 87) (selective agonists).

In regard to antagonists (Table VI), the first three compounds (R-544, CP 96345, and RP 67580) have been shown to be active on the NK-1 receptor and to be quite selective. Three other compounds, MEN 10207, R-396, and SR 48968, are inhibitors of NK-2 and R-486 is an antagonist of NK-3.

In pharmacological terms, by applying the Schild's criterion (order of potency of agonists and affinity of antagonists) the three neurokinin receptors can be defined as follows:

NK-1: SP > NKB > NKA
$$[Sar^9,Met(O_2)^{11}]SP > [\beta\text{-}Ala^8]NKA(4–10) > [MePhe^9]NKB$$

Neurokinin 1 receptors are blocked by a series of nonselective (88) and more selective antagonists, such as R-544 (88), as well as by two newly identified nonpeptidic compounds (CP 96345 and RP 67580), which are potent and selective for NK-1. Following the discovery of CP 96345, it has been found that subtypes of NK-1 receptors may be present in different species, CP 96345 being more active in the dog, rabbit, and guinea pig than in the

TABLE VI Characterization of NK-1, NK-2, and NK-3 Receptors with Agonists, Selective Agonists, and Antagonists

Compound	Rabbit jugular vein (NK-1)		Rabbit pulmonary artery (NK-2)		Rat portal vein (NK-3)	
	pD_2	RA	pD_2	RA	pD_2	RA
Agonist						
Substance P	8.83	100	6.13	0.8	5.82	0.5
Neurokinin A	7.65	6.7	8.22	100	6.45	5.8
Neurokinin B	7.84	10	7.45	16	7.68	100
[Sar^9,Met(O$_2$)^{11}]SP	8.86	107	Inactive	Inactive	Inactive	Inactive
[BAla^8]NKA(4–10)	6.23	0.3	8.60	239	6.13	2.8
[MePhe^7]NKB	6.23	0.3	5.24	0.1	8.30	416
Antagonist	pA_2		pA_2		pA_2	
R-544[a]	7.0		5.4		5.8	
CP 96345[b]	8.9		4.0		5.6	
RP 67580[c]	7.23		Inactive		—	
MEN 10207[d]	ND		7.9		4.9	
R-396[g]	Inactive		5.6		Inactive	
SR 48968[f]	6.1		10.1		<5.7	
R-486[g]	Inactive		Inactive		7.46	

[a] R-544, Ac-Thr-D-Trp(For)-Phe-NMeBz.

[b] CP 96345, (±)-cis-3-(2-methoxybenzylamino)-2-benzhydrylquinuclidine.

[c] RP 67580, (3aR,7aR)-7,7-diphenyl-2-[1-imino-2-(2-methoxyphenyl)-ethyl]perhydroisoindol-4-one.

[d] MEN 10207, Asp-Tyr-D-Trp-Val-D-Trp-D-Trp-Arg-NH$_2$.

[e] SR 48968, (S)-N-methyl-N[4-acetamino-4-piperidino)-2-(3,4 dichlorophenyl)butyl]benzamide.

[f] R-396, Ac-Leu-Asp-Gln-Trp-Phe-Gly-NH$_2$.

[g] R-486, [Trp^7,β-Ala^8]NKA(4–10).

mouse, rat, and chicken (89) and RP 67580 equally active in rats and guinea pigs (90).

NK-2: NKA > NKB > SP
          [β-Ala^8]NKA(4–10) > [MePhe^7]NKB > [Sar^9,Met(O$_2$)^{11}]SP

Neurokinin 2 receptors are antagonized by various compounds (MEN 10207, R-396, and SP 48968), some of which are short peptides of average potency and selectivity, while others (SR 48968) are nonpeptides, extremely potent, and selective for the NK-2 receptors (91). By the use of antagonists, two NK-2 receptor subtypes have been proposed by Maggi *et al.* (92): NK-2$_A$ is found in the rabbit pulmonary artery and is blocked by MEN 10207, and NK-2$_B$ mediates the contractile effect of NKA in the hamster trachea and is blocked by R-396. The utilization of the newly identified nonpeptidic NK-2 antagonists may contribute to clarify further the two NK-2 receptor subtypes hypothesis (92).

NK-3: NKB > NKA > SP
　　　　[MePhe^7]NKB > [β-Ala^8]NKA(4–10) > [Sar^9,Met(O$_2$)^{11}]SP

This receptor is not influenced either by CP 96345 (anti NK-1) or by SP 48968 (anti NK-2), but is inhibited by R-486, a heptapeptide analog of NKA(4–10) (93).

The existence of NK-1- and NK-3-binding sites has been demonstrated in brain homogenates of several species and abundant literature is available (78, 94–96). The presence of NK-2 receptors in the central nervous system has been proposed (97). In general, results of binding assays correlate with those of the biological tests (83, 98).

Neurokinins are tested *in vivo* on rat, guinea pig, rabbit, and dog blood pressure with the method described above (Section I) or on plasma extravasation in the rat, guinea pig, and rabbit, according to the method of Couture and Kerouac (99). Plasma extravasation produced by SP and congeners at the mucosa levels (intestine, trachea, urinary bladder, and other organs) is evaluated with the technique of Marceau *et al.* (100). Stimulation of salivary secretion in anesthetized rats is measured as described by Maggi *et al.* (101).

V. Receptors for Endothelins ET$_A$ and ET$_B$

Endothelin 1 (ET-1) is a member of the endothelin family, which consists of three isomers, ET-1, ET-2, and ET-3. Endothelin 1 is the most potent vasoactive peptide yet described. In the initial report by Yanigisawa *et al.* (4), it was suggested that ET-1 is an endogenous activator of the dihydropyridine-sensitive calcium channels. However, subsequent studies have shown that the biological effects of ET-1 occur independent of these channels (102, 103). The identification of receptors for endothelins was confirmed by Arai *et al.* (19) and Sakurai *et al.* (20), who genetically and biochemically characterized ET$_A$ and ET$_B$ receptors, respectively. The potent vasoconstrictive effects of ET-1 are mediated by ET$_A$, whereas the initial hypotension induced by ET-1 following a bolus injection into anesthetized rats appears to be mediated by ET$_B$ receptors. In general, peripheral effects of ET-1 include prolonged vasoconstriction and release of endothelium-derived relaxing factor and eicosanoids (4, 104, 105). The identification of selective ET$_A$ receptor antagonists has allowed the determination of the role of the two receptor types in various biological assays (106, 107).

A. Biological Assays

1. Measurement of Eicosanoids from Isolated Perfused Lungs

Male guinea pigs, Duncan Hartley (300–400 g), or Wistar rats (250–350 g) are anesthetized with sodium pentobarbitone or urethane and their spinal cords sectioned. Following thoracotomy, the pulmonary artery is cannulated for perfusion of the pulmonary circulation. The lungs are then suspended in a heated chamber (37°C) and perfused (5 ml/min) with oxygenated (95% O_2: 5% CO_2) Krebs solution (108). The lungs are allowed to stabilize for 40 min before ET-1 is infused at 2.5–5 nmol/min for 3 min. The effluent from the lungs is collected (1-min samples before, during, and after infusion of the peptide). The samples are stored (-20°C) and a stable, hydrolytic metabolite of eicosanoids [6-keto-$PGF_{1\alpha}$ or thromboxane B_2 (TxB_2)] is later determined by radioimmunoassay (109).

2. Rat Mesenteric Vascular Bed Perfused Simultaneously through the Arterial and Venous Vasculature

The rat mesentery is prepared as previously described by Warner (110). Male albino Wistar rats are killed by stunning and exsanguination. The abdomen is opened and the ileocolic and colic branches of the superior mesenteric artery are tied. The portal mesenteric vein is freed of connective and adipose tissues and then cannulated [Portex (Kent, U.K.) size tube 3FG] 1.0–1.3 cm distal to the portal–mesenteric junction. The superior mesenteric artery is cannulated as described previously by McGregor (111). Warm oxygenated Krebs solution, containing heparin (100 units/ml), is then perfused through the mesenteric artery at a flow of 2 ml/min for 5 min. Following this initial perfusion period, the mesentery is separated from the intestine by cutting close to the intestinal border. The venous and arterial vasculatures are subsequently perfused independently at flow rates of 2 ml/min with Krebs solution containing indomethacin (5 μM). The pressor responses of the vasculatures to the various peptides are measured with pressure transducers (model P-23A; Statham) and recorded on a Grass physiograph (model 7-D). To evaluate the endothelium-dependent relaxing effects of endothelins, the perfusion pressure on both sides of the mesenteric circulation is increased by perfusing either a thromboxomimetic (U46619: 64 nmol) on the venous side or a sympathomimetic (methoxamine: 60 μM) on the arterial side. Furthermore, the perfusion flow is increased to 5 ml/min on the arterial side to reduce spontaneous activity. When a plateau is reached on both sides, the various peptides are administered by bolus injections or infusions (50 μl/min) and changes of perfusion pressure are recorded, as described above.

3. Preparation of the Prostatic Portion of the Rat Vas Deferens (112)

Male Wistar rats (250–350 g) are sacrificed by stunning and exsanguination. Both vasa deferentia are removed, dissected from surrounding adipose tissues and blood vessels, and emptied of their contents. Segments (1.5–2.0 cm) of the prostatic portion are prepared according to Tousignant *et al.* (113) and suspended between parallel platinum electrodes in 10-ml organ baths containing oxygenated warm Krebs solution. The tissues are stretched to an initial tension of 2 g and equilibrated for 30–40 min. Change of tension is measured isometrically by force transducers and recorded on a Grass polygraph (model 7-D). Following equilibration, the tissues are electrically stimulated (square-wave pulses: 50 V, 0.1 msec) at a frequency of 0.1 Hz with a Grass stimulator (model S-8). The facilitatory or inhibitory effects of pharmacological agents (applied in increasing concentrations) are recorded to build cumulative concentration–response curves and evaluate potencies of ET-1, ET-2, and ET-3 in terms of pD_2. The tissues are exposed to the peptides for 20–40 min (112).

4. Isolated Vascular Tissues

Jugular veins are obtained from male New Zealand White rabbits anesthetized with sodium pentobarbital (30 mg/kg) and exsanguinated. The vessels are removed and cut into rings (3–4 mm wide) and the endothelium mechanically removed. Rings are suspended under a tension of 1 g in 10-ml organ baths containing indomethacin-treated Krebs solution maintained at 37°C and oxygenated (95% O_2:5% CO_2). The responses of the rings are recorded via isometric transducers. Concentrations of ET-1, -2, and -3 are added cumulatively in the organ baths.

Experiments are also performed in coronary arteries isolated from fresh porcine hearts. Connective tissues, adherent fats, and the vascular endothelium are removed before cutting into spiral strips about 10 mm long and 1 mm wide. Each strip is suspended in an organ bath containing Krebs solution, warm and oxygenated (see above). After equilibration, reference contractions are isometrically recorded with 50 mM KCl. Concentration–response curves for ET-1, -2, and -3 are obtained by cumulative additions of peptides.

5. Classification of Receptors for Endothelins

Receptors for endothelins have been characterized with agonists and with an antagonist (BQ-123) in the rabbit jugular vein (RJV), the rat vas deferens (RVD), and the porcine coronary artery (PCA) (Table VIIa). In two preparations (RJV and PCA, containing the ET_A site):

TABLE VII   Basic Pharmacologic Data on Endothelins

a. Pharmacological Characterization of ET_A and ET_B Receptors in *In Vitro* Assays

	Preparation								
	Rabbit jugular vein			Rat vas deferens			Porcine coronary artery		
Peptide	pD_2	RA	pA_2	pD_2	RA	pA_2	pD_2	RA	pA_2
ET-1	9.63	100		7.43	100		9.28	100	
ET-2	9.19	36		7.40	93		8.72	27	
ET-3	8.48	7.1		7.45	105		8.43	14	
BQ-123			7.2			<5.2			7.4

b. Pharmacological Preparations Sensitive to Endothelin-1

Tissue	Threshold	pD_2/ID_{50}	Effect[a]	Receptor type
Porcine coronary artery	10^{-10} M	9.28	C	ET_A
Rabbit jugular vein	10^{-11} M	9.63	C	ET_A
Rat vas deferens	10^{-9} M	7.47	C	ET_B
Rabbit aorta	10^{-9} M	8.47	C	ET_A
Rat perfused mesenteric bed				
Contraction				
Arterial	2 pmol	50 pmol	C	ET_A
Venous	0.1 pmol	25 pmol	C	ET_A
Vasodilation				
Arterial	1 pmol	10 pmol	R	ET_B
Rat perfused lung	10^{-9} M	—	PGI_2 release	ET_A
Guinea pig perfused lung	10^{-9} M	—	PGI_2/TxA_2 release	—
Rat arterial blood pressure	100 pmol/kg	—	Increase of blood pressure	ET_A

[a] C, Contraction; R, relaxation. Antagonist tested against ET-1.

$$ET\text{-}1 > ET\text{-}2 > ET\text{-}3$$

while in the RVD (containing the ET_B site):

$$ET\text{-}1 = ET\text{-}2 = ET\text{-}3$$

The antagonist BQ-123 is fairly active in the RJV and PCA (106) (ET_A), where it shows similar pA_2 values, but is almost inactive on the RVD (ET_B) (Table VIIa).

Threshold concentrations of ET-1, pD_2 or ID_{50} values, and the receptor type involved in the biological effects observed in various preparations are schematically analyzed in Table VIIb. Thus, isolated arteries and veins re-

TABLE VIII   Specificity of Peptide Receptor Antagonists[a]

	Preparation						
	Rabbit jugular vein				Guinea pig ileum		
Compound	AT_{II}	BK	SP	ET-1	AT_{II}	BK	SP
DuP 753	8.27	I	I	I	8.27	I	I
CP 96345	I	I	8.90	I	(+)	(+)	9.62
Hoe 140	I	9.18	I	I	I	8.94	I
BQ-123	I	I	I	7.24	—	—	—

[a] (+), CP 96345 inhibits the responses of the GPI to AT_{II} and BK when applied at concentrations of 20.6 μM or higher. I, absence of antagonism.

spond to ET-1 with contractions that are mediated by ET_A, although the presence of ET_B receptors (about 10%) must be taken into account in the RJV and the PCA (106). Peripheral vascular beds (e.g., the rat perfused mesentery) with intact endothelium shows vasodilation in the arterial side, which is mediated by ET_B [through release of endothelium-derived relaxing factor (EDRF)], while the vasoconstriction of both the arterial and venous sides is due to activation of ET_A and is blocked by BQ-123 [P. D'Orléans-Juste (183)]. In other organs (e.g., the rat lung), ET-1 promotes the release of eicosanoids, possibly through ET_A receptors (107). *In vivo*, in anesthetized rats, ET-1 induces a transient initial hypotensive effect mediated by ET_B and a prolonged increase of blood pressure mediated by ET_A (106).

The discovery of nonpeptide antagonists for angiotensin (AT_1) and neurokinins (NK-1), as well as the identification of peptide antagonists resistant to degradation and highly selective for kinin B_2 receptors and for the endothelin (ET_A) receptor, opens the way to the investigation of the pharmacological and therapeutical potential of peptide–receptor systems. The selectivity of the new compounds, especially the nonpeptidic ones, is crucial for their usefulness in physiology and physiopathology. An attempt is made below to show the selectivity of the new compounds in two preparations that are stimulated (contracted) by AT_{II}, BK, SP, and ET (Table VIII).

VI. Receptors for Atrial Natriuretic Peptides: ANP-R$_1$ and ANP-R$_2$

The atrial natriuretic peptides (ANP), which were originally isolated from mammalian atria, exhibit potent natriuretic and vasodilatory effects *in vivo* and *in vitro* (114). Two receptor types (ANP-R$_1$ and ANP-R$_2$) have been identified in vascular smooth muscles (bovine aorta). ANP-R$_1$ is responsible for the dilatory effects of ANP in the vascular smooth muscle and its natriuretic–diuretic effects *in vivo*. This receptor contains the particulate guanylate cyclase in its structure (21). The second receptor (biologically inactive), also called clearance receptor or ANP-R_2 (23), when activated, is rapidly internalized on ligand binding (115). Although the intracellular second messenger involved, following the binding of ANP to the ANP-R_2 receptor, is yet to be identified, increased phosphoinositide hydrolysis has been found in cultured bovine aortic smooth muscle cells (116).

A. Biological Assays

1. Assay for the Pharmacological Effects of Atrial Natriuretic Peptides on Rat and Rabbit Aortic Strips

Relaxation studies of atrial–natriuretic peptides are performed on rat and rabbit thoracic aortas according to Rapoport *et al.* (117). The aortas from rats (male, Sprague–Dawley, 240–260 g) and rabbits (male, New Zealand White, 2.2–2.5 kg) are removed and placed in physiological salt solution at 38°C, oxygenated with 95% O_2, 5% CO_2, and with the following composition (mM): NaCl, 130; KCl, 4.7; KH_2PO_4, 1.18; $MgSO_4$, 1.17; $CaCl_2$, 1.16; $NaHCO_3$, 14.9; dextrose, 11.0; ethylenediaminetetraacetic acid (EDTA), 0.026. Aortic ring segments (4 mm) are cut and mounted in tissue baths under optimal resting tension (2.0 *g* force). Following equilibration for 1 hr, aortic rings are contracted with methoxamine (0.7–3 μM) and cumulative concentration–relaxation curves of ANP and related peptides (Peninsula Laboratories, Belmont, CA) can be measured and recorded with the equipment described in Section II.

2. Assay for the Natriuretic–Diuretic Effects of Atrial Natriuretic Peptides in Sprague–Dawley Rats

The atrial natriuretic peptide is administered (bolus injections) in rats (average weight, 400 g) anesthetized with inactin (100 mg/kg) and maintained on a constant infusion of saline (2.2 ml/hr). Glomerular filtration rate (inulin), urine flow (V), urinary sodium ($U_{NA}V$), and urinary potassium excretion rate ($U_K V$) are measured according to Atlas *et al.* (114). Changes of each parameter induced by ANP and related peptides are evaluated from the difference between the average of three control periods (10 min each) and the experimental periods during which ANP is given.

3. Assay for the Antinatriuretic Effect of a Nonpeptidic ANP-R_1 Antagonist

Male Sprague–Dawley rats (220 g) are anesthetized with sodium pentobarbital (50 mg/kg i.p.). Catheters are inserted in the femoral artery (for measurement of blood pressure) and the femoral vein (for administration of saline or

HS-142-1, an AMP-R$_1$ antagonist) and into the bladder for collection of urine. The trachea is cannulated for artificial respiration. Constant infusion of isotonic saline (11 ml/kg/hr), containing sodium pentobarbital (34.5 mg/kg/hr), is given throughout the experiment. After equilibration, urine is collected for 30 min (control). The animal is then given an infusion of isotonic saline or the extracellular volume is expanded acutely with 4.0 ml/kg/min of saline given for 5 min and urine is collected at 10-min intervals. HS-142-1 at 3 mg/kg (i.v.) or saline (control) is injected 10 min before volume expansion. Urine volume is determined gravimetrically and electrolyte concentrations in urine are measured by flame photometry.

4. Assay for the Mitogenic and Proliferative Effects of Atrial Natriuretic Peptides in Rat Aortic Smooth Muscle Cells

Vascular smooth muscle cells are obtained from thoracic aortas of male Sprague–Dawley rats (150–175 g) and isolated and cultured as described by Garg and Hassid (118). DNA synthesis between the third and nineteenth subcultures is measured by [^{3}H]thymidine incorporation. The effects of agents under study are evaluated on the cells seeded at a density of 20 cm^2 and cultured for 2 days in 20% (v/v) serum-supplemented culture medium. After addition of peptides or saline, the cells are cultured for 8 days in medium supplemented with 5% (v/v) serum. Culture medium is changed daily. Experiments are terminated by fixing cell colonies in 2% (w/v) glutaraldehyde in phosphate-buffered saline and staining with 0.5% (w/v) Crystal Violet in water.

B. Receptor Characterization

Several naturally occurring peptides have been isolated from mammalian cardiac atria and shown to exert marked vasodilatory, natriuretic, and diuretic effects (119–122). Comparative pharmacological profiles have been reported for the 26-amino acid peptide, rat ANP(8–33), its human counterpart [Met^{17}] ANP(8–33), and the 23-amino acid peptides, atriopeptin I and II (rat sequences). As shown in Table IXa, these peptides have relaxant effects on rabbit and rat aortas, with differences in their relative affinities, particularly for the atriopeptins. Indeed, atriopeptin I is very weak in effect on rabbit, but not on rat aorta, while atriopeptin II shows an opposite pattern of activity. Such different pharmacological profiles suggest the existence of ANP-R$_1$ receptor subtypes in vascular smooth muscle of various species (117).

Other effects of ANPs, summarized in Table IXb (122–128), include inhibition of aldosterone and renin release, natriuresis, and mitogenesis in cultured

TABLE IX Basic Pharmacologic Data on Atrial Natriuretic Peptides[a]

a. Relative Potencies of Atrial Natriuretic Peptides on Rabbit and Rat Aortas

Peptide	Preparations				
	Rabbit aorta		Rat aorta		
	IC_{50} (M)	RA[b]	IC_{50} (M)	RA[b]	Ref.
R-ANP(8–33)	5.5×10^{-10}	100	1.4×10^{-9}	100	119
H-ANP(8–33)	4.6×10^{-10}	120	1.9×10^{-9}	74	119
Atriopeptin I	1.4×10^{-7}	0.4	1.6×10^{-9}	87	117
Atriopeptin II	1.4×10^{-9}	39	0.7×10^{-9}	200	117

b. Pharmacological Preparations Sensitive to Atrial Natriuretic Peptide

Preparation	Threshold	pD_2/ED_{50}	Effect	Antagonist	Receptor	Ref.
Rabbit aorta	0.1 nM	0.7 nM	Relaxation			122
Renal artery	0.1 nM	0.8 nM	Relaxation			123
Facial vein	0.025 nM	0.2 nM	Relaxation			123
Rat aorta		0.5 nM	Relaxation			119
Rat blood pressure	36 pmol/kg	360 pmol/kg	Hypotension			124
Aldosterone release	0.03 nM	0.3–10 nM	Inhibition			125
Renin release	0.0001 nM	0.01 nM	Inhibition			126
Natriuresis						
Rat	400 pmol/kg	2 nmol/kg	Increase	HS-142-1	(B) $ANP-R_1$	114, 127
Dog	3 nmol	20 nmol	Increase			120
Mitogenesis (rat aorta)	2.5 nM	100 nM	Inhibition of thymidine incorporation	C-ANP[c]	(C) $ANP-R_2$	121

[a] Modified from Winquist (128), with permission.

[b] RA, Relative potency expressed as a percentage of the affinity of R-ANP(8–33).

[c] C-ANP, [desGln^{16},Ser^{117},Gly^{118},Leu^{119},Gly^{120}]R-ANP (102–121)-NH$_2$.

smooth muscle fibers from rat aortas. The natriuretic effects in the rat appear to be mediated by ANP-R$_1$ receptors, because the nonpeptide antagonist (HS-142-1), selective for the ANP-R$_1$ receptor, has been shown to prevent ANP-induced natriuresis in anesthetized rats (127). The same receptor appears to be responsible for the *in vitro* arterial vasodilatation that has been associated with a marked increase of intracellular cyclic GMP (129).

The ANP-R$_2$ receptor, also named receptor C (clearance) (23), was considered until recently to be a nonfunctional binding site. Cahill and Hassid (121) have, however, reported that the antimitogenic effect of ANPs in rat aortic smooth muscle fibers in culture is inhibited by the selective ANP-R$_2$ antagonist, [desCys^{105},desCys^{121}] ANP (104–126) (rat sequence), and is independent of changes in intracellular cGMP.

VII. Receptor for Vasoactive Intestinal Peptide: VIP-R$_1$

Vasoactive intestinal peptide (VIP) is a 28-amino acid peptide first isolated from porcine intestine (130). This peptide is a member of a large family of peptides with marked structural homology [glucagon, secretin, gastric inhibitory peptide (GIP), and growth hormone-releasing factor (GRF)] (131, 132). In addition, this family includes helodermin and helospectin. Vasoactive intestinal peptide is a potent vasodilator and its actions are mediated via the activation of a single receptor type. This receptor is coupled with the adenylate cyclase in most target tissues (132–134). Growth hormone-releasing factors, but not glucagon or GIP, are able to interact with the VIP receptors and increase intracellular cAMP levels.

A. Biological Assays of Vasoactive Intestinal Peptide (Table Xb)

1. In Vivo Hypotensive Effect

Rats are anesthetized by intraperitoneal administration of 0.5 ml ketamine (50 mg/ml) and 0.2 ml xylazin (20 mg/ml). The left jugular vein and right femoral artery are cannulated for administration of the peptides and for continuous recording of systemic blood pressure. Experimentation is started when the blood pressure has stabilized at 110–130 mmHg. The peptide is injected or slowly infused in a volume of 100 μl, followed by washing the catheter with 100 μl saline (135). Experimental protocols and other technical details are reported by Grundemar and Hogestatt (135).

TABLE X   Basic Pharmacologic Data on Vasoactive Intestinal Peptides[a]

a. Apparent Affinities (%) of Vasoactive Intestinal Peptide

Peptide	Dog mean arterial pressure (hypotension)	Guinea pig trachea (relaxation)	Rat stomach (relaxation)
VIP	100	100	100
VIP(1–28)	100	200	100
VIP(7–28)	2–10	5–10	10–15
VIP(14–28)	2	0.1	—
VIP(15–25)	0.1	0.2	0.1
VIP(18–28)	0.05	0.05	0
VIP(1–6)	0.2	0.01	0.04

b. Pharmacological Preparations Sensitive to Vasoactive Intestinal Peptide

Preparation	Threshold	EC_{50}/IC_{50}	Effect	Ref.
Rat femoral artery	$1 \times 10^{-8} M$	$4.8 \times 10^{-8} M$	Relaxation	135
Dog carotid artery	$7.5 \times 10^{-10} M$	$7.6 \times 10^{-8} M$	Relaxation	140
Rat blood pressure	0.03 nmol/kg	0.5 nmol/kg	Hypotension	135
Human submandibular arteries	$5 \times 10^{-10} M$	$5 \times 10^{-8} M$	Relaxation	141
Cat interpulmonary artery	$1 \times 10^{-9} M$	$3.7 \times 10^{-9} M$	Relaxation	137

[a] Reproduced from Bodanszky et al. (139), with permission.

2. In Vitro Relaxant Effect

a. Rat Femoral Artery

Rats are killed by decapitation. The distal part of the femoral artery (0.2 mm in diameter) is removed and cut into 1- to 2-mm-long segments. The preparations are transferred to thermostatted baths containing oxygenated Krebs solution. The vascular segments are mounted on two L-shaped stainless steel wires (0.1 mm in diameter), one of which is connected to a force displacement transducer (Grass instrument FD03C) for continuous tension recording on a Grass polygraph. The resting tension is gradually adjusted to 2–4 mN. The contractile capacity of the tissue is examined by adding an isotonic 60 mM potassium Krebs solution (NaCl replaced by KCl). Relaxations in response to VIP are studied in preparations precontracted with phenylephrine (3 μM) or prostaglandin $F_{2\alpha}$ (3–10 μM). These agents induce contractions that are 60–80% of the maximum response to KCl (135).

b. Human Submandibular Arteries

Human submandibular arteries (diameter, 1–2 mm) are obtained as described (136) from human submandibular glands of patients operated for salivary duct calculus. Before anesthesia, maintained with halotane and NO_2, the patients are premedicated with scopolamine (0.01 mg/kg). After surgical removal, the glands are immersed in ice-cold Tyrode's solution and transported to the *in vitro* experimental set-up within 15 min. The tissues are mounted on special hooks in 2-ml organ baths for recording of circular contractions. The incubation medium (Tyrode's) has the following composition (mM): NaCl, 122; $CaCl_2$, 2.5; KCl, 4.23; KH_2PO_4, 1.14; $NaHCO_3$, 15.5; glucose, 11.5. It is warmed at 37°C and continuously gassed with 94% O_2 and 6% CO_2. After application of an initial resting tension of 5 mN (millinewtons), the vessels are allowed to equilibrate for 1 hr with repeated washings; 10^{-6} M noradrenaline (NA) is then added. When a stable contractile level is established, the peptides are added in a cumulative fashion until complete relaxation is obtained. Tests are made at 60-sec intervals.

c. Cat Interpulmonary Artery

Interpulmonary arteries are obtained, according to the method described by Altiere and Diamond (137), from adult cats (2–4 kg) of either sex, anesthetized with allobarbitone (100 mg/kg) and urethane (400 mg/kg). The interpulmonary artery is dissected, equilibrated for 2 hr in Krebs solution (with washing every 10 min), on the passive loads of 5 g. The tissues are precontracted with noradrenaline to enable the measurement of the relaxing effect of the VIP (137, 138).

B. *Structure–Activity Studies*

Several VIP-related peptides have been used to characterize VIP-R$_1$ *in vivo* on dog blood pressure and *in vitro* on guinea pig trachea and rat stomach (Table Xa) (139). Relative activities of VIP fragments, expressed as a percentage of the effect of natural VIP, indicate that both the N- and C-terminal parts of the peptide are important for the activity, because marked significant reductions of activity are observed with VIP (18–28) and VIP (1–6) (Table Xb) (140, 141). On the other hand, the changes of the relative activity of the various peptides are very similar in the three preparations, suggesting that the same receptor type may be involved in mediating the inhibitory effect of VIP *in vivo* and *in vitro*. Some antagonists have been reported, namely [4-Cl-D-Phe^6,Leu^{17}]VIP (140) and [N-Ac-Tyr^1,D-Phe^2]GRF (142), which, however, have not been tested in isolated vascular preparations. Dog blood pressure is measured in animals anesthetized with pentobarbital or with chloralose and urethane, and prepared for blood pressure recording and intravenous injections as described by Said and Mutt (130). The rat stomach preparation is described in Section II and guinea pig trachea is used according to the method of Piper *et al.* (143).

VIII. Neuropeptide Y and Its Receptors

Neuropeptide Y (NPY), originally isolated from porcine brain, belongs to a group of structurally related peptides that include peptide YY (PYY) and pancreatic polypeptides (PPs). Neuropeptide Y and PYY are characterized by the presence of tyrosine residues at both ends, the C-terminal tyrosine being amidated and essential for biological activity (144). Neuropeptide Y is widely distributed in the central and peripheral nervous system and is considered to be the most abundant neuropeptide in the mammalian brain (145). In peripheral sympathetic nerves, NPY is often colocalized with noradrenaline and cooperates with the amine both on a pre- and postjunctional level (146).

Neuropeptide Y is a potent vasoconstrictor in all species in which it has been tested. In isolated blood vessels, both NPY and PYY have been shown to induce direct concentration-dependent contractions and to potentiate the stimulatory effects of other vasoconstrictors, such as noradrenaline, histamine, and angiotensin II (39). Moreover, NPY can promote vasoconstriction by inhibiting the action of vasodilating substances (147). Finally, both peptides also act prejunctionally to inhibit the release of noradrenaline; this has been studied in the rat vas deferens (39, 148).

Neuropeptide Y is a potent stimulant of other smooth muscles (intestine, trachea) and exerts a variety of central effects, such as stimulation of food intake, modulation of thermoregulation, and central cardiovascular effects (148). These various biological effects are mediated by three different receptor types named Y_1, Y_2, and Y_3 (Table XIa).

Neuropeptide receptors are being characterized pharmacologically in three preparations: the rabbit saphenous vein (Y_1), the rat vas deferens (Y_2), and the rat descending colon (Y_3) (A. Cadieux, personal communication). The methods used for isolation and handling of the rabbit saphenous vein *in vitro* are the same as those described for the rabbit jugular vein. The rat vas deferens has been prepared as described in Section V and according to experimental procedures described by Martel *et al.* (149). The rat colon has been used according to the method of Regoli and Vane (150). Experimental protocols and analysis of data have been performed as described before [see Sections II, III, V, and Martel *et al.* (149)].

Binding assays are performed on homogenates of rat cortex and rat hippocampus according to the method of Martel *et al.* (149). Membranes from either the cortex or hippocampus are prepared by homogenization in Krebs–Ringer

TABLE XI Basic Pharmacologic Data on Neuropeptide Y

a. Characterization of Y_1, Y_2, and Y_3 Receptors in *in Vitro* Assays

| | Bioassays | | | | | | [125I]PYY CNS binding assays[a] | | | |
| | Rabbit (Y_1) saphenous vein[a] | | Rat (Y_2) vas deferens[b] | | Rat (Y_3) colon[b] | | Rat (Y_1) cortex[a] | | Rat (Y_2) hippocampus[a] | |
Peptide	EC_{50} (nM)	RA (%)	EC_{50} (nM)	RA (%)	EC_{50} (nM)	RA (%)	IC_{50} (nM)	RA (%)	IC_{50} (nM)	RA (%)
pNPY[c]	9.7 ± 0.4	100	27 ± 3	100	86 ± 6	100	0.63 ± 0.13	100	0.36 ± 0.04	100
PYY	2.3 ± 0.2	421	6 ± 1	450	44 ± 1	195	0.62 ± 0.12	102	0.07 ± 0.01	514
pNPY(2–36)	17.5 ± 0.5	55	112 ± 3	24	192 ± 38	45	12.4 ± 3.5	5	1.68 ± 0.45	21
pNPY(13–36)	>500	<2	337 ± 57	8	420 ± 42	20	63.6 ± 12.0	1	3.4 ± 1.0	11
pNPY(18–36)	187.2 ± 7.1	5	322 ± 13	8	153 ± 31	56	ND^{d}	—	ND	—
[Leu31,Pro34]pNPY	1.8 ± 0.1	538	>1000	<3	181 ± 44	47	2.4 ± 1.0	26	1058 ± 350	0.03

b. Pharmacological Preparations Sensitive to Neuropeptide Y

Preparation	Threshold	EC_{50} (M)	Effect	Receptor	Ref.
Rat blood pressure	0.25 nmol/kg	—	Hypertension	Y_1	142
Guinea pig iliac vein	3×10^{-9} M	5×10^{-8}	C	Y_1	139
Cat middle cerebral artery	2×10^{-11} M	1.3×10^{-8}	C	Y_1	144
Human pial artery	2×10^{-11} M	1×10^{-8}	C	—	144
Pig perfused spleen	10^{-9} M	10^{-7}	C	Y_2	145
Intestinal ion secretion (rat)	10^{-10} M	1.3×10^{-8}	Inhibition	Y_2	146
MSH release	10^{-9} M	6×10^{-8}	Inhibition	—	147

[a] R. Quirion and A. Cadieux, personal communications.
[b] Modified from Cadieux et al. (152) and from Martel et al. (149), with permission.
[c] pNPY, porcine Neuropeptide Y.
[d] ND, Not determined.

buffer, pH 7.4 at 25°C, using a Brinkmann Polytron (setting 6 for 15–20 sec) and centrifuged at 49,000 g for 20 min. The supernatant is discarded and the pellet washed, resuspended, and centrifuged again. The final pellet is rinsed and resuspended in Krebs buffer (15 ml) to give a protein concentration of 4 and 1 mg/ml of membrane preparation for cortex and hippocampus, respectively. For binding assays, 100 μl of membrane preparation is incubated at 25°C for 120 min, in a final volume of 500 μl containing Krebs buffer, pH 7.4, 0.1% (w/v) bovine serum albumin, 0.05% (w/v) bacitracin, and 25–30 pM ^{125}I-labeled PYY. Incubations are terminated by rapid filtration through Schleicher & Schuell (Keene, NH) No. 32 filters [previously soaked in 1.0% (v/v) polyethyleneimine], using a cell harvester filtering apparatus. Filters are rinsed three times with 3 ml of ice-cold buffer and transferred to vials to measure radioactivity in an LKB (Rockville, MD) counter.

A. Characterization of Y_1, Y_2, and Y_3 Receptors

A first characterization of Y_1 and Y_2 was proposed by Wahlestedt *et al.* in 1986 (39), based on the relative activity of a C-terminal fragment of NPY, particularly porcine NPY (pNPY) (13–36). More recently, the characterization into three sites has been made using three isolated organs (Table XIa) and binding assays, following the discovery of [Leu^{31},Pro^{34}]pNPY, which has been shown initially to bind to Y_1 receptors selectively and, second, to be more active on this receptor type than on the others (151). Using several agonists (Table XIa), Y_1 is the functional site that mediates the contraction of the rabbit saphenous vein, by a direct mechanism. In this site PYY is more active than NPY, and [Leu^{31},Pro^{34}]pNPY is extremely active whereas pNPY (13–36) is inactive. An opposite pattern of activity is observed in the Y_2 functional site, which modulates the motor response of the electrically stimulated rat vas deferens. Y_2 is therefore localized in the sympathetic nerve terminal and inhibits the release of noradrenaline. In this site, pNPY (13–36) maintains almost 10% of NPY activity, whereas [Leu^{31},Pro^{34}]pNPY is inactive. The third functional site, Y_3, which mediates the contraction of the rat colon, shows sensitivity similar to pNPY (13–36) and to [Leu^{31},Pro^{34}]pNPY. The site has been characterized by comparing the effect of pNPY and PYY, the former being antagonized by atropine, while PYY is not (152). It is therefore suggested that Y_3 is a receptor for NPY that is not activated by PYY.

Results obtained with binding assays confirm the existence of two binding sites in the rat brain (153): Y_1 in the rat cortex, whereby [Leu^{31},Pro^{34}]pNPY is much more active than pNPY (13–36), and Y_2 in the rat hippocampus, in which the opposite pattern of activity is observed (Table XIa). Moreover,

TABLE XII Receptors for Neurohypophysial Hormones

Receptor	Target tissue	Biological activity	Agonist	Antagonist
OT	Uterus	Contraction	Oxytocin	[D-Phe(4-Et)^2]OT
	Mammary gland	Milk secretion	Deamino-OT	
	Brain	Sexual behavior	Deamino[1-carba]OT	
V_1	Vascular muscle	Vasoconstriction	Vasopressin	[Et$_2$-β-Mpa^1]^{a}AVP
	Hepatocyte	Glycogenolysis		desGly(NH$_2$)-
	Platelets	Degranulation		[D-Phe(Et)^2]LVP
	Brain	Avoidance behavior?		Linear antagonist 1
	Pituitary	ACTH release		
V_2	Kidney	H$_2$O reabsorption	Vasopressin	[(CH$_2$)$_5$-β-Mpa^1,
	Urinary bladder	H$_2$O reabsorption	Desmopressin	D-Phe^2,Ile^4]AVP^b
	Vascular tissues	Vasodilatation	[B-Mpa^1,D-Arg^8]AVP (dDAVP)	
	Brain	Memory, learning		Linear antagonist^c
	Mast cell	Degranulation		SKF 105494 (169)^d

^{a} β, β-mercaptopropionic acid.
^{b} Pa-D-Tyr(Et)-Phe-Val-Asn-NVa-Pro-Arg-Arg-NH$_2$ (8.07); Pa, propionyl.
^{c} Phaa-D-Tyr(Et)-Phe-Gln-Asn-Lys-Pro-Arg-NH$_2$ (9.05); Phaa, phenylacetyl.
^{d} desGlyd(CH$_2$)$_5$-D-Tyr(Et)^{2}VAVA.

PYY is five times more active on the Y_2 than on the Y_1 receptor, when compared to pNPY.

In Table XIb (154–157) various pharmacological actions of NPY are described and an attempt has been made to indicate the types of receptors involved in the various organs or tissues. The direct vasopressor effect of NPY appears to be mediated by Y_1 receptors because the specific Y_1 receptor agonist [Leu^{31},Pro^{34}]pNPY is as potent as NPY in increasing blood pressure in the rat (151). The same receptor appears to be responsible for the *in vitro* contractile activities of NPY on isolated veins and arteries (39, 154). However, the existence of postjunctional Y_2 receptors cannot be excluded because vasopressor effects have also been reported with the C-terminal fragment pNPY (13–36) in the pig perfused spleen (155).

IX. Receptors for Vasopressin: V_1, V_2, and OT

Vasopressin and oxytocin are cyclic nonapeptides, synthetized and released into the blood stream by hypothalamic neurons and other cells within the central nervous system of vertebrates. They act as hormones in a variety of target organs (Table XII) and through three receptor types: OT (for oxytocin) and V_1 and V_2 (for vasopressin). These receptors have been characterized with data of binding and biological assays *in vivo,* as shown in Table XII (158).

A variety of pharmacological tools have been tested to compare the patterns of biological activities corresponding to the three receptor types. Three groups of compounds have been used: (a) some naturally occurring peptides, (b) some analogs, selective agonists for one or the other receptor, and (c) antagonists (Table XII) (32).

In regard to blood vessels and the circulation, V_1 acts as vasoconstrictor, V_2 as vasodilator, whereas no precise vasoactive function has been reported for OT, the oxytocin receptor that mediates uterus contraction, milk secretion, and sexual behavior. In addition to its potent vasoconstrictor effect, much accentuated in the splanchnic area and mesenteric circulation, V_1 mediates glycogenolysis, adrenocorticotropic hormone (ACTH) release, and possibly avoidance behavior, while V_2 acts on the kidney and other epithelia to promote water reabsorption and transport (158). V_2 is also responsible for important central actions, such as learning and memory, currently under investigation (159).

A pharmacological characterization of the three functional sites for the posthypophysial hormones is given below:

> *OT*
>   *Agonists* (*order of potency*)
>   Naturally occurring agonists: OT > AVP > LVP
>   Selective agonists: *d*-[1 carba]OT > *d*-[6 carba]OT > [Mpa^1]OT (32)
>   *Antagonist affinity* (*pA₂*)
>   [D-Phe(4-Et)^2]OT (8.15) or [Tyr(OMe)^2]OT (6.79) (160, 161)
> *V$_1$*
>   *Agonists* (*order of potency*)
>   Naturally occurring agonists: AVP > LVP > OT
>   Selective agonists: desGly(NH$_2$)dDAVP > [Ile$_3$]AVP (32)
>   *Antagonist affinity* (*pA₂*)
>   desGly(NH$_2$)[D-Phe(Et)^2]LVP (8.80) (160)
> *V$_2$*
>   *Agonists* (*order of potency*)
>   Naturally occurring agonists: AVP > LVP > OT
>   Selective agonists: *d*-[1 carba]AVP > [B-Mpa^1,D-Arg^8]AVP (32)
>   *Antagonist affinity* (*pA₂*)
>   [(CH$_2$)$_5$-β-Mpa^1,D-Phe^2,Ile^4]AVP (8.24) (41) (161)

The above characterization of receptors has been performed in biological assays by measuring the contraction of rat uterus for the OT site, the pressor activity in rats for the V_1 site, and the antidiuretic activity in rats for the V_2 site.

The above-mentioned activities have been evaluated with well-established classic pharmacological methods, as quoted by Berde and Boissonnas (162).

Uterotonic activity is generally measured in nonpregnant rat uterus *in vitro* but considerable variations are observed depending on the hormonal state of the organs or the ionic composition of the physiological medium. For these reasons, the assays are generally performed on tissues treated with steroids (to induce estrus artificially) and suspended in a magnesium-free physiological medium at a temperature of 30 or 32°C according to the method of Gaddum *et al.* (163). Pressor activity is measured in anesthetized rats using the procedure described in Section II.

The antidiuretic effects of vasopressin and the inhibition by antagonists are generally evaluated in rats loaded with water and treated with alcohol, according to the original suggestion of Jeffers *et al.* (164). Variations of this method have been described by Sawyer (165, 166).

Antagonists for V_1 and V_2 receptors bearing linear structure have been described and found to be fairly active (167). This observation suggests that cyclic structure is not needed for antagonism both on V_1 and V_2 receptors. Furthermore, a nonpeptidic, orally active V_1 antagonist has been reported (168) (also see Table XII, Ref. 169).

X. Calcitonin Gene-Related Peptide

Human calcitonin gene-related peptide (hCGRPα) is a mammalian, 37-amino acid peptide encoded by the calcitonin gene (9, 10). In both human and rat, this peptide is known to occur in two forms designated α- and β-CGRP, which differ in their primary sequence by three (human) and one (rat) amino acid (170). Studies on the biological role of the CGRP peptide family have shown that these peptides are the most potent vasodilators yet to be described (171). The CGRP has also been reported to increase heart rate, stimulate the release of pancreatic amylase, and inhibit gastrin acid secretion and feeding behavior (170). *In vitro,* CGRP induces relaxation of vascular and nonvascular smooth muscles via the activation of two distinct receptors, CGRP-1 and CGRP-2. CGRP-1 appears to be responsible for the vasodilatory effect while CGRP-2 has been found mostly in nonvascular tissues and inhibits mostly muscle tone. The various biological effects of CGRP and characteristics of the two receptor subtypes are analyzed in Table XIIIa and b.

A. Biological Assays for Calcitonin Gene-Related Peptide

1. Guinea Pig Ileum

The effects of CGRP and analogs are tested in the external longitudinal smooth muscle layer. Tissues are prepared in segments of 15 mm of length according to the method described by Rang (37) and as previously described in Section III.

2. Mouse Aorta

Thoracic aortas are obtained from anesthetized (pentobarbitone; 60 mg/kg i.p.) CD-1 male mice (22–30 g). Rings (3 mm) are cut and placed in 5-ml organ baths with special hooks. In some experiments, the endothelium of the aortic rings is mechanically removed. The rings are left to stabilize for 90 min under a tension of 1 g. Following the equilibration period, the reactivity of the preparations is evaluated with standard relaxant or contractile agonists, such as carbamylcholine, histamine, or norepinephrine.

3. Rat Vas Deferens

The rat vas deferens is prepared as described in Section V and according to experimental procedures described by Dennis *et al.* (172).

4. Rat Perfused Mesenteric Vasculature

The vasoactive effects of hCGRPα are assessed on both sides of the rat mesenteric vasculature (venous and arterial) according to experimental procedures described in Section V.

5. Guinea Pig Right Atrium

Guinea pigs are decapitated and the hearts removed rapidly and placed in warm (37°C) oxygenated Krebs–Ringer solution. Right atria are dissected carefully and suspended (with a resting tension of 1 g) in 10-ml organ baths filled with oxygenated (95% O_2, 5% CO_2) Krebs–Ringer solution at 37°C. The lower end of the right atrium is firmly fixed and the apex is attached to an isometric force displacement transducer (model FT03-D; Grass Instruments) with a silk thread. Spontaneous beating is recorded on a polygraph; effects of agents on tension and rate are recorded as described by Dennis *et al.* (172).

B. Characterization of Calcitonin Gene-Related Peptide Receptors: CGRP-1 and CGRP-2 Receptors

Apparent affinities of human and rat CGRP and analogs, estimated in four isolated organs, are presented in Table XIIIa (172, 173). In the guinea pig ileum, CGRP induces a biphasic effect (A. Cadieux, personal communica-

TABLE XIII Basic Pharmacologic Data on Calcitonin Gene-Related Peptide[a]

a. Characterization of CGRP$_1$ and CGRP$_2$ Receptors in *in Vitro* Assays[a]

Peptide	Guinea pig ileum contraction[b]			Mouse aorta[b]			Rat vas deferens[c]			Guinea pig right atrium[c]		
	EC$_{50}$ (nM)	RA (%)	pA$_2$	EC$_{50}$ (nM)	RA (%)	pA$_2$	EC$_{50}$ (nM)	RA (%)	pA$_2$	EC$_{50}$ (nM)	RA (%)	pA$_2$
hCGRPα	10.7 ± 1.7	100		2.7 ± 0.4	100		1.2 ± 0.1	100		7.6 ± 1.3	100	
rCGRPα	14.7 ± 4.6	73		5.7 ± 0.7	47							
rCGRPβ	23.3 ± 3.9	46		16.9 ± 2.3	16							
[Cys(ACM)^{2,7}]hCGRP	189 ± 30	6		151 ± 43	2		76 ± 13	2		>710	<0.01	
[Cyclo^{2,7}(Asp^2,Lys^7)]hCGRP	>1000	<0.1		>1000	<0.1		>1666	<0.001		>1666	<0.001	
hCGRP(8–37)	—	—	5.0	—	—	Inactive	—	—	6.24	—	—	7.22

b. Pharmacological Preparations Sensitive to Human CGRPα

Preparations	Threshold	EC$_{50}$	Effect	Endothelium dependent	Ref.
Rat					
Mesentery (arterial side)	10^{-11} mol	$\sim 3 \times 10^{-10}$ mol	Relaxation	No	174, 175
Mesentery (venous side)	10^{-8} mol		Relaxation (very weak)	No	176
Vas deferens	10^{-10} M	1.2×10^{-9} M	Inhibition of twitch response	—	173
Blood pressure	10^{-11} mol/kg	$\sim 4 \times 10^{-10}$ mol/kg	Hypotension		177
Human					
Forearm blood flow	10 ng/min	~ 100 ng/min	Increase	—	178
Coronary artery	5×10^{-9} M	2.5×10^{-8} M	Relaxation	Yes	178
Gastric artery	10^{-9} M	8×10^{-9} M	Relaxation	Yes	178
Radial artery	7.5×10^{-9} M	5×10^{-8} M	Relaxation	Yes	178
Pulmonary artery	10^{-11} M	$\sim 3 \times 10^{-9}$ M	Relaxation	No	179
Pulmonary vein	10^{-11} M	3×10^{-9} M	Relaxation	No	179
Porcine coronary arteries				—	
Large diameter	2.5×10^{-9} M	1.1×10^{-8} M	Relaxation	No	180
Small diameter	$\sim 10^{-10}$ M	1.4×10^{-9} M	Relaxation	—	180
Mouse					
Colon	10^{-9} M	3.6×10^{-8} M	Relaxation	—	181
Bovine					
Coronary artery	10^{-11} M	2×10^{-9} M	Relaxation	No	182

[a] CGRP$_2$ characterized in all assays but guinea pig right atrium (CGRP$_1$).
[b] A. Cadieux, personal communication.
[c] Modified from Dennis et al. (172, 173), with permission.

tion), namely an initial contraction followed by sustained relaxation, whereas it causes a relaxation in the mouse aorta, inhibits the twitch response of the rat vas deferens, and increases frequency (positive chronotropic effect) in the guinea pig right atrium (172). The order of agonist potency is similar in all preparations whereas affinity of the antagonist hCGRP (8–37) differs. Preparations containing CGRP-1 receptors (e.g., guinea pig right atrium) are sensitive to the antagonistic activity of hCGRP (8–37) and insensitive to the linear analog, $[Cys(ACM)^{2,7}]hCGRP\alpha$, in which the hydrogen atoms of the sulfhydryl groups of the cysteine residues in the CGRP structure have been replaced by acetamidomethyl moieties. In contrast, tissues containing CGRP-2 sites are sensitive to the agonist potential of the linear analog and the antagonist is inactive or weaker (pA_2 values of 6.2 or 5.0).

The sensitivities of various isolated organs to CGRP are presented in Table XIIIb (174–182). Characteristically, hCGRPα is a potent vasodilator in all preparations, namely in isolated human, rat, porcine, guinea pig, mouse, and bovine vessels. In these preparations, the peptide induces potent vasodilation at threshold doses or active concentrations in the nanomolar range. In addition, hCGRP is an inhibitor of field-stimulated nonvascular tissues, such as the rat vas deferens, with threshold effects in the subnanomolar range (172). Human CGRPα is a potent hypotensive agent that induces vasodilatation and increase of blood flow in the human forearm (178). In the majority of human isolated arteries, the relaxant effect of hCGRPα is dependent on the presence of endothelium, while in other arteries (e.g., the pulmonary) or in veins, and in the coronary arteries of other species, CGRP-induced relaxation is observed in the absence of endothelium and is probably due to the inhibition of vascular tone induced directly on smooth muscle fibers.

Acknowledgments

The authors acknowledge the secretarial help of H. Morin and the following graduate students for allowing the use of some experimental data in the tables: N.-E. Rhaleb, N. Rouissi, D. Jukic, and S. Télémaque. D.R. is a career investigator of the Medical Research Council of Canada. A.C. is a *chercheur-boursier* of the Fonds de la Recherche en Santé du Québec. P.D.-J. is a scholar of the Heart and Stroke Foundation of Canada.

References

1. L. T. Skeggs, K. E. Lentz, J. R. Kahn, N. P. Shumway, and K. R. Woods, *J. Exp. Med.* **104,** 193–197 (1956).
2. R. A. Boissonnas, S. Guttmann, and P. A. Jaquenoud, *Helv. Chim. Acta* **43,** 1349–1355 (1960).

3. M. M. Chang and S. E. Leeman, *J. Biol. Chem.* **245**, 4784–4790 (1970).
4. M. Yanagisawa, H. Kurihara, S. Kimura, Y. Tomobe, M. Kobayashi, Y. Mitoui, Y. Yazaki, K. Goto, and T. Masaki, *Nature (London)* **322**, 411–415 (1988).
5. A. J. De Bold and T. A. Salerno, *Can. J. Physiol. Pharmacol.* **61**, 127–130 (1983).
6. S. I. Said and V. Mutt, *Eur. J. Biochem.* **28**, 199–204 (1972).
7. K. Tatemoto, *Proc. Natl. Acad. Sci. U.S.A.* **79**, 5485–5489 (1982).
8. V. Du Vigneaud, C. Ressler, J. Swan, C. W. Roberts, P. G. Katsoyannis, and S. Gordon, *J. Am. Chem. Soc.* **75**, 4880 (1953).
9. S. G. Amara, V. Jonas, M. G. Rosenfeld, E. S. Ong, and R. M. Evans, *Nature (London)* **298**, 240–244 (1982).
10. M. G. Rosenfeld, J. J. Mermod, S. G. Amara, L. W. Swanson, P. E. Sawchenko, J. Rivier, W. W. Vale, and R. M. Evans, *Nature (London)* **304**, 129–135 (1983).
11. G. M. Rubanyi and L. H. Parker Botelho, *FASEB J.* **5P**, 2713–2720 (1991).
12. A. J. De Bold, *Can. J. Physiol. Pharmacol.* **69**, 1477–1485 (1991).
13. K. Sasaki, Y. Yamano, S. Bardhan, N. Iwai, J. J. Murray, M. Hasegawa, Y. Matsuda, and T. Inagami, *Nature (London)* **351**, 230–232 (1991).
14. T. J. Murphy, R. W. Alexander, K. K. Grinedling, M. S. Runge, and K. E. Rerustein, *Nature (London)* **351**, 233–236 (1991).
15. A. E. McEachern, E. R. Shelton, S. Bhakta, R. Obernolte, C. Bach, P. Zuppan, U. Fujisaki, R. W. Aldrich, and K. Jarnagin, *Proc. Natl. Acad. Sci. U.S.A.* **88**, 7724–7728 (1991).
16. Y. Yokota, Y. Sasai, K. Tanaka, T. Fujiwara, K. Tsuchida, R. Shigemoto, A. Kakizuka, H. Ohkubo, and S. Nakanishi, *J. Biol. Chem.* **264**(30), 17649–17652 (1989).
17. Y. Masu, K. Nakayama, H. Tamaki, Y. Harada, M. Kuno, and S. Nakanishi, *Nature (London)* **329**, 836–838 (1987).
18. R. Shigemoto, Y. Yokota, K. Tsuchida, and S. Nakanishi, *J. Biol. Chem.* **265**, 623–628 (1990).
19. H. Arai, S. Hori, I. Armmori, H. Oikabo, and S. Nakanishi, *Nature (London)* **348**, 730–732 (1990).
20. T. Sakurai, H. Yanagisawa, H. Takuwa, H. Miyazaki, S. Kimura, K. Goto, and T. Masaki, *Nature (London)* **348**, 732–735 (1990).
21. M. Chinkers, D. L. Garbers, M. S. Chang, D. G. Lowe, H. M. Chin, D. V. Goeddel, and S. Schulz, *Nature (London)* **338**, 78–83 (1989).
22. M. S. Chang, D. G. Lowe, M. Lewis, R. Hellmiss, E. Chen, and D. V. Goeddel, *Nature (London)* **341**, 68–72 (1989).
23. F. Fuller, J. G. Porter, A. E. Arfsten, J. Miller, J. W. Schilling, R. M. Scarborough, J. A. Lewicki, and D. B. Schenk, *J. Biol. Chem.* **263**, 9395–9401 (1988).
24. T. D. Nguyen, J. A. Williams, and G. M. Gray, *Biochemistry* **25**, 361–368 (1986).
25. J. M. Muller, J. Luis, J. Fantini, B. Abadie, F. Giannellini, and J. Pichon, *Eur. J. Biochem.* **151**, 411–417 (1985).
26. S. M. Foord and R. K. Craig, *Eur. J. Biochem.* **170**, 373–379 (1987).
27. Y. Sano, O. Hiroshima, T. Yuzurika, C. Yamuto, A. Saito, S. Kimura, T. Hirabayashi, and K. Goto *J. Neurochem.* **52**, 1919–1924 (1989).

28. S. P. Sheikh and J. A. Williams, *J. Biol. Chem.* **265,** 8304–8310 (1990).
29. P. J. Mannon, S. J. Mervin, and I. L. Taylor, *J. Neurochem.* **56,** 1804–1809 (1991).
30. V. J. Hrndi, M. S. Chow, and D. D. Smith, *Annu. Rev. Pharmacol. Toxicol.* **30,** 501–534 (1990).
31. F. A. Laszlo, F. Laszlo, and D. De Wied, *Pharmacol. Rev.* **43,** 73–108 (1991).
32. V. I. Hrudy, M. S. Chow, and D. D. Smith, *Annu. Rev. Pharmacol. Toxicol.* **30,** 501–534 (1990).
33. D. T. Dudley, R. L. Panek, T. C. Major, G. H. Lu, R. F. Bruns, B. A. Klinkefus, J. C. Hodges, and R. E. Weishaar, *Mol. Pharmacol.* **38,** 370–377 (1990).
34. D. Regoli and J. Barabé, *in* "Methods in Enzymology" (G. Di Sabato, ed.), Vol. 163, pp. 210–230. Academic Press, San Diego, 1988.
35. D. Regoli, N. Rouissi, and P. D'Orléans-Juste, *in* "Vascular Innervation and Receptor Mechanisms: New Perspective" (L. Edvinsson and R. Uddman, eds.). Academic Press, San Diego, 1992 (in press).
36. P. D'Orléans-Juste, S. Dion, G. Drapeau, and D. Regoli, *Eur. J. Pharmacol.* **125,** 37–44 (1986).
37. H. P. Rang, *Br. J. Pharmacol.* **22,** 356–365 (1964).
38. R. Quirion, D. Van Rossum, Y. Dumont, S. St-Pierre, and A. Fournier, *Ann. N.Y. Acad. Sci.* **657,** 88–105 (1992).
39. C. Wahlestedt, N. Yanaihara, and R. Hakanson, *Regul. Pept.* **13,** 307–318 (1986).
40. M. C. Michel, *Trends Pharmacol. Sci.* **12,** 389–394 (1991).
41. M. Manning, A. Olma, W. A. Klis, J. Seto, and W. H. Sawyer, *J. Med. Chem.* **28,** 1607–1613 (1983).
42. P. B. M. W. M. Timmermans, P. C. Wang, A. T. Chiu, and W. F. Herblin, *Trends Pharmacol. Sci.* **12,** 55–62 (1991).
43. P. B. M. W. M. Timmermans, W. F. Herblin, R. J. Ardecky, D. J. Carini, J. V. Duncia, P. C. Wong, R. R. Wexler, R. D. Smith, A. L. Johnson, and A. T. Chin, *in* "Receptor Data for Biological Experiments" (H. N. Doods and J. H. C. A. Van Meel, eds.), pp. 96–100. Ellis Harwood, New York, 1991.
44. D. Regoli, W. K. Park, and F. Rioux, *Pharmacol. Rev.* **26,** 69–123 (1974).
45. R. F. Furchgott and S. Bhadrakom, *J. Pharmacol. Exp. Ther.* **108,** 129–143 (1953).
46. H. O. Schild, *Br. J. Pharmacol.* **2,** 189–206 (1947).
47. J. R. Vane, Br. J. Pharmacol. **12,** 344–349 (1957).
48. R. C. Speth and K. H. Kim, *Biochem. Biophys. Res. Commun.* **169,** 997–1006 (1990).
49. M. J. Peach, *Physiol. Rev.* **57,** 313–370 (1977).
50. M. J. Peach and D. E. Dostal, *J. Cardiovasc. Pharmacol.* **16,** S25–S30 (1990).
51. S. M. Whitebread, M. Mele, B. Kamber, and M. de Gasparo, *Biochem. Biophys. Res. Commun.* **163,** 289–291 (1989).
52. D. Regoli, *Can. J. Physiol. Pharmacol.* **57,** 129–139 (1979).
53. A. T. Chiu, D. E. McCall, P. E. Aldrich, and P. B. M. W. M. Timmermans, *Biochem. Biophys. Res. Commun.* **172**(3), 1195–1202 (1990).

54. D. Regoli and J. Barabé, *Pharmacol. Rev.* **32**, 1–46 (1980).
55. D. Regoli, J. Barabé, and W. K. Park, *Can. J. Physiol. Pharmacol.* **55**, 855–867 (1977).
56. D. Regoli, F. Marceau, and L. Lavigne, *Eur. J. Pharmacol.* **71**, 105–115 (1981).
57. P. D'Orléans-Juste, S. Dion, J. Mizrahi, and D. Regoli, *Eur. J. Pharmacol.* **114**, 9–21 (1985).
58. P. Gaudreau, J. Barabé, S. St-Pierre, and D. Regoli, *Can. J. Physiol. Pharmacol.* **59**, 371–379 (1985).
59. D. Regoli and N.-E. Rhaleb, *Can. J. Gen. Pharmacol.* (in press).
60. D. Deblois, J. Bouthillier, and F. Marceau, *Br. J. Pharmacol.* **93**(4), 969–977 (1988).
61. J. M. Bathon, D. C. Manning, D. W. Goldman, M. C. Towns, and D. Proud, *J. Pharmacol. Exp. Ther.* **260**, 384–392 (1992).
62. N.-E. Rhaleb, S. Dion, J. Barabé, N. Rouissi, D. Jukič, G. Drapeau, and D. Regoli, *Eur. J. Pharmacol.* **162**(3), 419–427 (1989).
63. R. I. Vavrek and J. M. Stewart, *Peptides (N.Y.)* **6**, 161–169 (1985).
64. D. Regoli, N.-E. Rhaleb, G. Drapeau, and S. Dion, *J. Cardiovasc. Pharmacol.* **15**, S30–S38 (1990).
65. D. Regoli, N.-E. Rhaleb, S. Dion, and G. Drapeau, *Trends Pharmacol. Sci.* **11**, 156–161 (1990).
66. J. M. Stewart and R. J. Vavrek, *in* "Bradykinin Antagonists" (R. M. Burch, ed.), pp. 51–96. Dekker, New York, 1991.
67. F. J. Hock, K. Wirth, U. Albus, W. Linz, H. J. Gerhards, G. Wiemer, S. Henke, G. Breipohl, W. Konig, J. Knolle, and B. A. Scholkens, *Br. J. Pharmacol.* **102**, 769–773 (1991).
68. K. Wirth, F. J. Hock, M. Albus, W. Linz, H. G. Alpermann, H. Anagnosto-poulos, S. Henke, G. Breipohl, W. Konig, J. Knolle, and B. A. Scholkens, *Br. J. Pharmacol.* **102**, 774–777 (1991).
69. S. G. Farmer, R. M. Burch, C. J. Dehaas, J. Tog, and L. R. Steranka, *J. Pharmacol. Exp. Ther.* **248**, 677–681 (1989).
70. N.-E. Rhaleb, N. Rouissi, D. Jukič, D. Regoli, S. Henke, G. Breipohl, and J. Knolle, *Eur. J. Pharmacol.* **210**(2), 115–121 (1991).
71. D. Regoli, D. Jukič, C. Tousignant, and N.-E. Rhaleb, *Agents Actions* **34**, 138–141 (1991).
72. I. Llona, R. Vavrek, J. Stewart, and J. P. Huidobro-Toro, *J. Pharmacol. Exp. Ther.* **241**, 608–614 (1987).
73. S. G. Farmer, R. M. Burch, S. N. Mecker, and D. E. Wilkins, *Mol. Pharmacol.* **36**, 1–8 (1989).
74. J. K. Saha, J. N. Sengupta, and R. K. Goyal, *J. Pharmacol. Exp. Ther.* **259**, 265–273 (1991).
75. P. Devillier, M. Renoux, J. P. Giroud, and D. Regoli, *Eur. J. Pharmacol.* **117**, 89–96 (1985).
76. M. Mousli, J. L. Bueb, C. Bronner, B. Rovot, and Y. Landry, *Trends Pharmacol. Sci.* **11**, 358–362 (1990).
77. S. Nakanishi, *Physiol. Rev.* **67**, 1117–1142 (1987).
78. S. Guard and S. P. Watson, *Neurochem. Int.* **18**, 149–165 (1991).

79. J. L. Henry, R. Couture, A. C. Cuello, G. Pelletier, R. Quirion, and D. Regoli, "Substance P and Neurokinins," pp. 17–18. Springer-Verlag, New York, 1987.
80. C. A. Maggi, S. Giuliani, P. Santicioli, D. Regoli, and A. Meli, *J. Auton. Pharmacol.* **7,** 11–32 (1987).
81. T. Unger, S. Carolus, J. Demert, D. Ganten, R. E. Long, C. Maserglut, H. Steinberg, and R. Veelken, *Circ. Res.* **63,** 812–820 (1988).
82. D. Regoli, G. Drapeau, S. Dion, and P. D-Orléans-Juste, *Life Sci.* **40,** 109–117 (1987).
83. D. Regoli, G. Drapeau, S. Dion, and P. D'Orléans-Juste, *Pharmacology* **38,** 1–15 (1989).
84. F. Rioux, R. Quirion, D. Regoli, M. A. Leblanc, and S. St-Pierre, *Eur. J. Pharmacol.* **66,** 273–279 (1980).
85. D. Mastrangelo, R. Mathison, H. J. Huggel, S. Dion, P. D-Orléans-Juste, N. E. Rhaleb, G. Drapeau, P. Rovero, and D. Regoli, *Eur. J. Pharmacol.* **134**(3), 321–326 (1987).
86. D. Mastrangelo, Ph.D. Thesis, Geneva University (1986).
87. G. Drapeau, P. D'Orléans-Juste, S. Dion, N.-E. Rhaleb, N. Rouissi, and D. Regoli, *Neuropeptides* (*Edinburgh*) **10,** 43–54 (1987).
88. D. Jukič, N. Rouissi, R. Laprise, M. Boussougou, and D. Regoli, *Life Sci.* **49,** 1463–1469 (1991).
89. B. D. Gitter, D. C. Waters, R. F. Burns, N. R. Mason, J. A. Nixon, and J. J. Howbert, *Eur. J. Pharmacol.* **197,** 237–238 (1991).
90. N. Rouissi, A. Claing, M. Nicolau, D. Jukič, P. D-Orléans-Juste, and D. Regoli, *Life Sci.* (in press).
91. C. Advenier, N. Rouissi, Q. T. Nguyen, X. Emonds-Alt, J. C. Brelier, G. Neliat, E. Naline, and D. Regoli, *Biochem. Biophys. Res. Commun.* **184,** 1418–1424 (1992).
92. C. A. Maggi, R. Patacchini, S. Giuliani, P. Rovero, S. Dion, D. Regoli, A. Giachetti, and A. Meli, *Br. J. Pharmacol.* **100,** 588–592 (1990).
93. G. Drapeau, H. Rouissi, F. Nantel, N.-E. Rhaleb, C. Tousignant, and D. Regoli, *Regul. Pept.* **31,** 125–135 (1990).
94. A. Viger, J. C. Baujouan, Y. Torrens, and J. Glowinski, *J. Neurochem.* **40,** 1030–1038 (1983).
95. S. Buck, Y. Maurin, T. F. Burks, and H. I. Yamamura, *Life Sci.* **34,** 497–507 (1984).
96. C. Tousignant, G. Guillemette, and D. Regoli, *Brain Res.* **560,** 1–11 (1991).
97. R. Quirion and T. V. Dam, *Neuropeptides* (*Edinburgh*) **6,** 191–204 (1985).
98. S. Dion, G. Drapeau, N.-E. Rhaleb, P. D'Orléans-Juste, and D. Regoli, *Eur. J. Pharmacol.* **138,** 125–128 (1987).
99. R. Couture and R. Kerouac, *Br. J. Pharmacol.* **91,** 265–273 (1987).
100. F. Marceau, M. Knap, and D. Regoli, *Can. J. Physiol. Pharmacol.* **59,** 921–926 (1981).
101. G. A. Maggi, P. Santicioli, S. Giuliani, D. Regoli, and A. Meli, *Eur. J. Pharmacol.* **113,** 291–294 (1985).
102. M. Auguet, S. De Laflotte, P. E. Chabrier, E. Pirotsky, F. Clostre, and P. Braquet, *Biochem. Biophys. Res. Commun.* **156,** 186–192 (1988).

103. P. D'Orléans-Juste, G. de Nucci, and J. R. Vane, *Eur. J. Pharmacol.* **165,** 289–293 (1989).
104. G. De Nucci, R. Thomas, P. D'Orléans-Juste, E. Antunes, C. Walder, T. D. Warner, and J. R. Vane, *Proc. Natl. Acad. Sci. U.S.A.* **85,** 9797–9800 (1988).
105. J. W. Barnard, S. W. Barman, W. K. Adkins, G. L. Longenecker, and A. E. Taylor, *Am. J. Physiol.* **261,** 4479 (1991).
106. M. Ihara, K. Noguchi, T. Saeki, T. Fukuroda, S. Tsuchida, S. Kimura, T. Fukami, K. Ishikawa, M. Nishikibe, and M. Yano. *Life Sci.* **50,** 247–255 (1992).
107. P. D'Orléans-Juste, S. Télémaque, A. Claing, M. Ihara, and M. Yano, *Br. J. Pharmacol.* **104,** 773–775 (1992).
108. Y. S. Bakhle, A. M. Reynard, and J. R. Vane, *Nature* (*London*) **222,** 956–959 (1969).
109. J. A. Salmon, *Prostaglandins* **15,** 383–397 (1978).
110. T. D. Warner, *Br. J. Pharmacol.* **99,** 427–431 (1990).
111. D. D. McGregor, *J. Physiol.* (*London*) **177,** 21–30 (1965).
112. S. Télémaque and P. D'Orléans-Juste, *Naunyn-Schmiedeberg's Arch. Pharmacol.* **344,** 505–507 (1991).
113. C. Tousignant, S. Dion, G. Drapeau, and D. Regoli, *Neuropeptides* (*Edinburgh*) **9,** 333–343 (1987).
114. S. A. Atlas, H. D. Kleinert, M. J. Camargo, A. Januszewick, J. E. Sealey, J. H. Laragh, J. W. Schilling, J. A. Lewicki, L. K. Johnson, and T. Maack, *Nature* (*London*) **309,** 717–719 (1984).
115. T. Maack, M. Suzuki, F. A. Almeida, D. Nussenzveig, R. M. Scarborough, G. A. McEnroe, and J. A. Lewicki, *Science* **238,** 675–678 (1987).
116. M. Hirata, C. Chang, and F. Murad, *Biochim. Biophys. Acta* **1010,** 346–351 (1989).
117. R. M. Rapoport, R. J. Winquist, E. P. Baskin, E. P. Faison, S. A. Waldman, and F. Murad, *Eur. J. Pharmacol.* **120,** 123–126 (1986).
118. V. C. Garg and A. Hassid, *J. Clin. Invest.* **83,** 1774–1777 (1989).
119. E. Baskin, E. Faison, A. Wallace, T. Schafield, and R. Winquist, *J. Clin. Pharmacol.* **25,** 467 (1985).
120. K. Wakitani, T. Ohshima, A. D. Loewy, S. W. Holmberg, B. R. Cole, S. P. Adams, K. F. Fox, M. G. Carrie, and P. Needleman, *Circ. Res.* **56,** 621–627 (1985).
121. P. A. Cahill and A. Hassid, *Biochem. Biophys. Res. Commun.* **179,** 1606–1613 (1991).
122. R. J. Winquist, *Life Sci.* **37,** 1081–1087 (1985).
123. E. P. Faison, P. K. S. Sigel, G. Morgan, and R. J. Winquist, *Life Sci.* **37,** 1073–1079 (1985).
124. R. W. Lappe, J. A. Todd, and R. L. Wendt, *Hypertension* **8,** 866–873 (1986).
125. W. B. Campbell, M. G. Currie, and P. Needleman, *Circ. Res.* **57,** 113–118 (1985).
126. A. Kurtz, R. D. Bruna, J. Pfeilschifter, R. Tangner, and C. Bauer, *Proc. Natl. Acad. Sci. U.S.A.* **83,** 4769–4773 (1986).
127. T. Sano, Y. Morischita, K. Yamada, and Y. Matsuda, *Biochem. Biophys. Res. Commun.* **182,** 824–829 (1992).

128. R. J. Winquist, in "Atrial Natriuretic Factor" (M. Rosenblatt and J. W. Jacob, eds.), Endocrinol. Metab.: Clin. North Am., Vol. 16, No. 1, pp. 163–182. Saunders, Philadelphia, 1987.

129. R. M. Scarborough, D. B. Schenk, G. A. MacEnroe, A. Arfsten, L. L. Kang, K. Schwartz, and G. A. Lewicki, *J. Biol. Chem.* **261,** 12960–12964 (1986).

130. S. I. Said and V. Mutt, *Science* **169,** 1217–1218 (1970).

131. J. Luis, J. M. Martin, A. el Battari, J. Marvaldi, and J. Pichon, *Biochimie* **70,** 1311 (1988).

132. M. Laburthe, A. Couvineau, and C. Rouyer-Fessard, *Mol. Pharmacol.* **29,** 23–27 (1986).

133. M. Laburthe, N. Amiranoff, C. Boize, C. Rouyer-Fessard, K. Tatemoto, and L. Moroder, *FEBS Lett.* **159,** 89–92 (1983).

134. J. D. Gardner and A. J. Rothman, *Biochim. Biophys. Acta* **627,** 230–243 (1980).

135. L. Grundemar and E. D. Hogestatt, *Br. J. Pharmacol.* **99,** 526–528 (1990).

136. D. Larson, M. Duner-Engström, J. M. Lundberg, B. B. Fredholm, and A. Anggard, *Regul. Pept.* **13,** 319–326 (1986).

137. R. J. Altiere and L. Diamond, *Br. J. Pharmacol.* **82,** 321–328 (1984).

138. R. J. Altiere, and L. Diamond, *Eur. J. Pharmacol.* **93,** 121–124 (1983).

139. M. Bodanszky, Y. S. Klausner, and S. Said, *Proc. Natl. Acad. Sci. U.S.A.* **70,** 372–382 (1973).

140. S. J. Pandol, K. Dharmsathaphorn, M. S. Schoeffield, W. Vale, and J. Rivier, *Am. J. Physiol.* **250,** G553–G557 (1986).

141. V. Larsson, M. Duner-Engström, J. M. Lundberg, B. B. Fredholm, and A. Anggard, *Regul. Pept.* **13,** 319–326 (1986).

142. H. P. Parkman, J. C. Reynolds, and D. H. Coy, *Gastroenterology* **92,** 1566 (1987).

143. P. Piper, S. I. Said, and J. R. Vane, *Nature (London)* **225,** 1144–1145 (1970).

144. K. Tatemoto, M. Carlquist, and V. Mutt, *Nature (London)* **296,** 659–660 (1982).

145. T. E. Adrian, J. M. Allen, S. R. Bloom, M. A. Ghatei, M. N. Rossor, G. W. Roberts, T. J. Crow, K. Tatemoto, and J. M. Polak, *Nature (London)* **306,** 584–586 (1983).

146. E. Ekblad, L. Edvinsson, C. Wahlestedt, R. Uddman, R. Hakanson, and F. Sundler, *Regul. Pept.* **8,** 225–235 (1984).

147. C. Han and P. W. Abel, *J. Cardiovasc. Pharmacol.* **9,** 675–681 (1987).

148. Y. Dumont, J. C. Martel, A. Fournier, S. St-Pierre, and R. Quirion, *Prog. Neurobiol.* **38,** 125–167 (1992).

149. J. C. Martel, A. Fournier, S. St-Pierre, Y. Dumont, M. Forest, and R. Quirion, *Mol. Pharmacol.* **38,** 494–502 (1990).

150. D. Regoli, and J. R. Vane, *Br. J. Pharmacol.* **23,** 351–359 (1964).

151. J. Fuhlendorff, U. Gether, L. Aakerlund, N. Langeland-Johansen, H. Thogersen, S. G. Melberg, U. B. Olsen, O. Thastrup, and T. W. Schwartz, *Proc. Natl. Acad. Sci. U.S.A.* **87,** 182–186 (1990).

152. A. Cadieux, M. T-Benchekroun, A. Fournier, and S. St-Pierre, *Ann. N.Y. Acad. Sci.* **611,** 372–375 (1990).

153. Y. Dumont, A. Fournier, S. St-Pierre, T. W. Schwartz, and R. Quirion, *Eur. J. Pharmacol.* **191,** 501–503 (1990).

154. L. Edvinsson, J. R. Copeland, P. C. Emson, J. McCulloch, and R. Uddman, *J. Cerebral Blood Flow Metab.* **7,** 45–57 (1987).
155. J. M. Lundberg, A. Hemsen, O. Larsson, A. Rudehill, A. Saria, and B. B. Fredholm, *Eur. J. Pharmacol.* **145,** 21–29 (1988).
156. H. M. Cox and A. W. Cuthbert, *Br. J. Pharmacol.* **101,** 247–252 (1990).
157. J. M. Danger, M. C. Tonon, M. Lamacz, J. C. Martel, S. St-Pierre, G. Pelletier, and H. Vaudry, *Life Sci.* **40,** 1875–1880 (1987).
158. L. B. Kinter, S. Caltabiano, and W. F. Huffman, *in* "Receptor Data for Biological Experiments" (H. N. Doods and J. C. A. Van Meel, eds.), pp. 62–68. Ellis Harwood, New York, 1991.
159. F. A. Laszlo, F. Laszlo, Jr., and D. De Wied, *Pharmacol. Rev.* **43,** 73–108 (1991).
160. M. Lebl, T. Barth, L. Servitova, J. Slaminova, and K. Jost, *in* "Peptides 1982" (K. Bhaha and P. Malon, eds.), pp. 456–460. de Gruyter, Berlin, 1983.
161. V. J. Hruby, *in* "Topic in Molecular Pharmacology" (A. S. V. Burgen and G. C. K. Roberts, eds.), pp. 99–126. Elsevier, Amsterdam, 1981.
162. B. Berde and R. A. Boissonnas, *Handb. Exp. Pharmacol.* **23,** 802–870 (1968).
163. J. H. Gaddum, W. S. Peart, and M. Vogt, *J. Physiol. (London)* **108,** 467–480 (1949).
164. W. A. Jeffers, M. M. Livezey, and J. H. Austin, *Proc. Soc. Exp. Biol. Med.* **50,** 184–190 (1942).
165. W. H. Sawyer, *Endocrinology (Baltimore)* **63,** 694–698 (1958).
166. W. H. Sawyer, P. K. T. Pang, J. Seto, M. McEnroe, B. Lammex, and M. Manning, *Science* **212,** 49–51 (1981).
167. M. Manning, J. P. Przybylski, A. Olma, W. A. Klis, M. Kruszynski, N. C. Wo, G. H. Pelton, and W. H. Sawyer, *Nature (London)* **329,** 839–840 (1987).
168. Y. Yamamura, H. Ogawa, T. Chihara, K. Kondo, T. Onogawa, S. Nakamura, T. Mori, M. Tominaga, and Y. Yabouchi, *Science* **252,** 572–576 (1991).
169. M. L. Moore, C. Albrightson, B. Brickson, H. C. Bryan, N. Caldwell, J. F. Callahan, J. Foster, L. B. Kinter, N. C. F. Newlander, D. B. Schmidt, E. Sorenson, F. L. Stassen, N. C. F. Yim, and W. F. Huffman, *J. Med. Chem.* **31,** 1487–1489 (1988).
170. L. H. Breimer, I. MacIntyre, and M. Zaidi, *Biochem. J.* **255,** 377–390 (1988).
171. S. D. Brain, T. J. Williams, J. R. Trippins, H. R. Morris, and I. MacIntyre, *Nature (London),* **313,** 54–56 (1985).
172. T. Dennis, A. Fournier, S. St-Pierre, and R. Quirion, *J. Pharmacol. Exp. Ther.* **251,** 718–725 (1989).
173. T. Denis, A. Fournier, A. Cadieux, F. Pomerleau, F. B. Jolicoeur, S. St-Pierre, and R. Quirion, *J. Pharmacol. Exp. Ther.* **254,** 123–128 (1990).
174. I. Marshall, S. J. Al-Kazwini, J. J. Holman, and R. K. Craig, *Eur. J. Pharmacol.* **123,** 217–222 (1986).
175. Y. Li and S. P. Duckles, *Eur. J. Pharmacol.* **210,** 23–30 (1992).
176. A. Claing, S. Télémaque, A. Cadieux, A. Fournier, D. Regoli, and P. D'Orléans-Juste, *J. Pharmacol. Exp. Ther.* **263,** (in press) (1992).
177. I. Marshall, S. J. Al-Kazwinin, P. N. Roberts, N. B. Shipperson, M. Adams, and R. K. Craig, *Eur. J. Pharmacol.* **123,** 207–216 (1986).

178. S. McG. Thom, A. D. Hughes, P. Goldberg, G. Martin, M. Schachter, and P. S. Sever, *Br. J. Clin. Pharmacol.* **24,** 139–144 (1987).
179. D. McCormick, J. C. W. Mak, M. D. Coupe, and P. J. Barnes, *J. Appl. Physiol.* **67,** 1265–1270 (1989).
180. R. Foulkes, N. Shaw, C. Bose, and B. Hughes, *Eur. J. Pharmacol.* **201,** 143–149 (1991).
181. A. Cadieux, F. Pomerleau, S. St-Pierre, and A. Fournier, *J. Pharm. Pharmacol.* **42,** 520–521 (1990).
182. B. Greenburg, K. Rhoden, and P. J. Barnes, *Br. J. Pharmacol.* **92,** 789–794 (1987).
183. P. D'Orleans-Juste, A. Claing, T. D. Warner, M. Yano, and S. Telamaque, *Br. J. Pharmacol.* (submitted, 1993).
184. A. Morel, A. M. O'Carroll, M. J. Brownstein, and S. J. Lolait, *Nature (London)* **356,** 523–526 (1992).
185. S. J. Lolait, A. M. O'Carroll, O. W. McBride, M. Konig, A. Morel, and M. J. Brownstein, *Nature (London)* **28,** 336–339 (1992).
186. T. Kimura, O. Tanizawa, K. Mori, M. J. Brownstein, and H. Okayama, *Nature (London)* **28,** 526–529 (1992).

[5] Melanotropin Receptors of the Brain

Jeffrey B. Tatro

Introduction

The classic melanotropin, α-melanocyte-stimulating hormone (α-MSH), is a hormone of the pituitary intermediate lobe that is secreted in most vertebrates, and was identified by and named for its ability to stimulate pigmentation in specialized cells of the integument. Native melanotropins are derived from several homologous coding sequences within the proopiomelanocortin (POMC) gene (1, 2), following cell type-specific posttranslational processing (3). The melanotropin peptide family now includes numerous natural and synthetic structural analogs, each containing a sequence bearing homology to the core heptapeptide sequence of α-MSH (-Met-Glu-His-Phe-Arg-Trp-). α-Melanocyte-stimulating hormone itself is 13 residues in length, and represents the amino-terminal fragment of adrenocorticotropic hormone (ACTH), N-terminally acetylated and C-terminally amidated (3).

Central administration of melanotropins modulates diverse functions, including hypophysial hormone secretion (4–6), thermoregulation and fever (7), cardiovascular functions (8), learning, memory, attention, and motivation (9–11), behavior (9, 10), and functional recovery from nerve damage (12). A network of POMC-expressing neurons, originating primarily within the hypothalamic arcuate nucleus and certain medullary cell groups, innervates numerous structures within and outside of the hypothalamus and septum, and is known to produce α-MSH, γ-MSH and ACTH (13, 14). Moreover, selective central deficiency of α-MSH modulates neuroendocrine functions (15), febrile responses to pyrogens (7), and functional recovery from nerve damage (16), supporting the hypothesis that endogenous melanotropins are physiological regulators of brain functions.

Nevertheless, methods for the detection of putative melanotropin receptors in the brain have only recently been described (17), and the characterization of these receptors is at a relatively early stage. This chapter describes radioligand-based methods for the detection, localization, and pharmacological characterization of brain melanotropin receptors. Critical methodological points are emphasized, and specialized apparatus and specific suppliers are indicated when helpful. Most of the techniques have been adapted from standard methods that have been extensively described and annotated by others, and the reader is referred to the references cited for underlying principles and additional methodological details. A brief discussion of advances in knowledge of the structural and signaling properties of melanotropin receptors is presented.

Methodology

Characterization of melanotropin receptors by radioreceptor (17–22) and autoradiographic (18, 22–24) methods has been made possible with the development of biologically active radioligands. Because native MSH is highly susceptible to loss of biological activity due to oxidative and enzymatic damage (25), the superpotent synthetic analog of α-MSH, Nle[4]-, D-Phe[7]-α-MSH (NDP-MSH), developed by Sawyer, Hruby, and colleagues (26), in which the oxidation-sensitive Met[4] residue is substituted by Nle, and in which the substitution of D- for L-phenylalanine confers resistance to enzymatic degradation, is advantageous for radioligand preparation (17). NDP-MSH is the most potent known melanotropin, both in stimulating melanocytes (18, 19) and in at least one central action, inhibition of fever (27). When radioiodinated and partially purified as described below, ^{125}I-labeled NDP-MSH has a specific activity of $1.2–2.0 \times 10^6$ Ci/mol, and retains full biological activity and potency as assessed by its ability to stimulate melanogenesis in B16 mouse melanoma cells (17).

Preparation of ^{125}I-Labeled NDP-MSH

NDP-MSH is radioiodinated enzymatically, and partially purified by reversed-phase chromatography. The method is designed to minimize peptide losses by adsorption and to minimize contamination hazards by using a system composed only of disposable components.

The following ingredients are added to a 1.5-ml conical polypropylene tube: (1) 4 μg NDP-MSH dissolved in 4 μl 0.001 N HCl; (2) 50 μl Enzymobeads (Bio-Rad, Richmond, CA); (3) 10 μl Na^{125}I (approximately 1 mCi; specific activity, 15 mCi/μg) (Amersham, Arlington Heights, IL), (4) 25 μl of an aqueous 1% (w/v) β-D-glucose solution. Na^{125}I and β-D-glucose are dispensed using microliter syringes (Hamilton, Reno, NV) with Luer hubs, each fitted with either an intravenous catheter or a length of polyethylene tubing (PE-100, Intramedic; Clay-Adams, Becton, Dickinson and Co., Parsippinany, NJ) affixed to a 19-gauge needle. The reaction mixture is agitated gently, tapped to move all contents into the tip, then incubated for 25 min at room temperature. The contents are transferred to a 400-μl narrow polypropylene microfuge tube using a siliconized Pasteur pipette or PE-100 tubing. The reaction is stopped by centrifuging for 1 min in a microfuge to remove the beads, then carefully transferring the supernatant (approximately 85 μl) into the longer Luer port of a Sep-Pak C_{18} cartridge (Waters Associates, Milford, MA) that has been prewetted with 3 ml of acetonitrile followed by 4 ml of water. A length of PE-100 tubing fitted to a 19-gauge needle and tuberculin syringe is convenient for this transfer.

The radiolabeled peptide is loaded and the column rinsed by slowly flushing 2 ml of 0.05 M ammonium acetate (pH 5.8) through the column, using a disposable syringe; the eluate contains most of the unreacted Na^{125}I. ^{125}I-Labeled NDP-MSH is eluted using a continuous gradient of 15–40% acetonitrile in 0.05 M ammonium acetate, at a flow rate of 1.5 ml/min. A dual-pump high-performance liquid chromatography (HPLC) system is used for elution, and 0.75-ml fractions are collected. A glass gradient maker (LKB, Rockville, MD) in combination with a peristaltic pump (Rabbit; Rainin Instruments, Inc., Woburn, MA) and silicone manifold tubing (Rainin) has also been successfully used. The radioactivity elution profile is determined in 10-μl aliquots by γ scintillation. Fifty microliters of a 5% (w/v) solution of bovine serum albumin (BSA) (Cat. No. A-4503; Sigma Chemical Co., St. Louis, MO) in phosphate-buffered saline (PBS: 0.01 M sodium phosphates, 0.15 M NaCl, pH 7.2) is added to each fraction of interest to prevent adsorptive losses, and the fractions are transferred to polyethylene culture tubes. The acetonitrile is removed by vacuum centrifugation for about 25 min or by evaporation under a stream of nitrogen. The completeness of acetonitrile removal is easily monitored by marking the level of the liquid meniscus, and waiting until the volumes have been reduced by at least 40%. The fractions in the midportion of the descending limb of the ^{125}I-labeled NDP-MSH elution curve (typically four to six fractions) consistently show the greatest immunoreactivity, specific activity [as assessed by radioimmunoassay (RIA)], and biological activity (as assessed by stimulation of melanogenesis in cultured mouse melanoma cells), and are therefore routinely pooled for use as tracer (Fig. 1) (17). The tracer can be stored frozen in aliquots or stored at 4°C, preferably under N_2 atmosphere, and should be used as soon as possible, within 2–3 weeks at the latest.

In Situ Binding and Autoradiography

The principal means by which brain melanotropin receptors have been characterized to date is *in vitro* radioligand binding to tissue sections followed by film or liquid nuclear track emulsion autoradiography (23). This approach has given an indication of the anatomical distribution of brain structures potentially responsive to melanotropins, has allowed assessment of the degree of codistribution of putative melanotropin receptors with the terminal

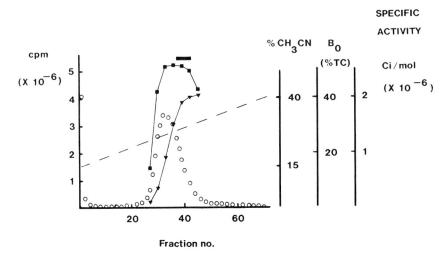

FIG. 1   Elution profiles of ^{125}I-labeled NDP-MSH total radioactivity (○), immunoreactivity (■), and specific radioactivity (▼) after reversed-phase chromatography. The dashed line represents the concentration gradient of acetonitrile. Immunoreactivity is represented as specific zero binding (percentage of total counts), as measured by RIA. The fractions indicated by the bar were pooled for use in *in vitro* and *in vivo* studies. B_0, Bound; TC, total counts. [© The Endocrine Society. From Tatro and Reichlin (17).]

fields of melanotropin-containing neurons, and has allowed initial pharmacological assessment of ligand specificity by competitive binding experiments. Methods for *in situ* binding and autoradiographic localization of receptors have been described in excellent detail by others (28–33); our methods were adapted from those described by Herkenham and Pert (33).

Preparation of Tissue Sections

Proper handling and cryosectioning of brain tissue are critical steps that must be perfected and standardized. Brains of 200- to 300-g Sprague-Dawley rats are rapidly and carefully removed, then dropped into isopentane (2-methylbutane; Kodak, Rochester, NY) maintained at approximately −30°C by alternately removing and replacing the beaker on dry ice. Each brain is left about 30 sec, just until it becomes firm, as detected by tapping it gently with the thermometer or other instrument, and it is then removed from the bath and placed on aluminum foil on a bed of crushed dry ice. After the solvent has evaporated and the brain has hardened, the brain is wrapped tightly in Parafilm to prevent desiccation of the tissue margins, sealed in a small, airtight plastic bag (coin envelope), and stored at −70°C. Brain tissue specimens are trimmed grossly with a razor blade, then mounted onto cryostat chucks at $-20°C$ in the desired orientation, using a small amount of embedding matrix (OCT; Miles Scientific, Div. Miles Laboratories, Naperville, IL), and are allowed 1–2 hr to equilibrate to cryostat temperature before sectioning. We routinely use 8-μm-thick cryosections, prepared at a cutting temperature of $-20°C$ on a Reichert-Jung 2040 cryostat (Cambridge Instruments GmBH, Nussloch, Germany). This thickness allows good counterstaining, fairly sharp resolution of anatomical structures, and serial sectioning of small structures. Gelatin-coated slides for tissue section mounting are prepared by the following steps: 10-min immersion in Chromerge (Mallinckrodt, St. Louis, MO), 30-min wash in hot running tap water; rinse with deionized/distilled water; 30-min immersion in a solution of 1% (w/v) gelatin–0.1% (w/v) chromium potassium sulfate at 40°C; and air drying overnight, loosely covered. The cryosections are positioned on chilled slides, then quickly thaw-mounted, briefly warming the slide if necessary by moving a finger along its underside. Slides are then immediately placed in racks in a supercooled ice bath constructed of alternating layers of ice and salt in a styrofoam box, and stored until all sections are mounted. To prevent histological and biochemical damage, it is critical to keep the tissue sections chilled, but to prevent refreezing, prior to desiccation. The sections are finally dried in the cold by placing in a desiccator jar containing desiccant, introducing a slight vacuum, and storing overnight at 4°C. The slides are then transferred to slide boxes containing packets of desiccant, and the boxes stored in sealed bags at a temperature of $-20°C$ or lower until use. Tissue sections retain binding activity for months when stored under these conditions (34). To prevent condensation, the slide boxes should be allowed to equilibrate to room temperature for 1–2 hr before opening.

Binding Incubations

Slides are preincubated for 15 min at 23°C in the following buffer: Tris-HCl (50 mM), NaCl (140 mM), CaCl$_2$ (2.5 mM), MgCl$_2$ (1.2 mM), pH 7.2, then incubated for 120 min in a similar buffer with the addition of BSA (0.25%, w/v), ascorbic acid (0.6%, w/v), aprotinin (500 KIU/ml), and ^{125}I-labeled NDP-MSH (0.25–1.0 $\times$ 10^6 cpm/ml; ~0.15–0.6 nM), in the presence or absence of competing peptides or other test substances. Binding incubations are terminated by washing in ice-cold wash buffer [sodium phosphate (10 mM), NaCl (154 mM), MgCl$_2$ (1.2 mM), pH 7.2], followed by rapid drying. The slides are dipped briefly in two fresh changes of wash buffer, followed by four successive 2-min washes in 200 ml wash buffer, then dried as rapidly as possible by blotting the edges and placing in a cold air stream from a hair dryer. The tissues are fixed in hot formaldehyde vapors, by placing the slide racks in a desiccator jar containing paraformaldehyde powder, introducing a slight vacuum, and placing the desiccator in an oven at 80°C for 2 hr. The slide racks are then rapidly removed, well inside a fume hood, and ventilated overnight.

Radioreceptor Assay and Autoradiography

For radioreceptor assay, sections are scraped carefully from the slides, using a moistened applicator stick and cotton swab, and counted by γ scintillation. Using serial sections, the technique is useful for optimization of binding conditions. For macroscopic autoradiographic analysis, binding is determined using X-ray film ([^{3}H]Ultrofilm; Leica Inc., Deerfield, IL). Slides are directly apposed to the film for 1–3 weeks. Films are developed under safe-light at 20°C by the following sequence of steps: 5-min immersion in D-19 developer (Kodak), 30 sec in 2% (v/v) acetic acid, 5 min in fixer (Kodak), and 20 min of washing in cold running tap water. Automatic X-ray film developers should not be used, as this film lacks a scratch-resistant coating. It has been reported (29) that less expensive, standard X-ray films are also suitable for use with ^{125}I-labeled ligands. Uniform contact pressure between film and tissue sections is accomplished with use of cardboard X-ray cassettes (Kodak), covered during exposure with thick plate glass and lead weights. Following autoradiography, tissue sections are rehydrated and counter-stained for 6 min in 0.1% (w/v) Cresyl Violet or for 30–60 sec in 0.5% (w/v) thionin. They are then rinsed quickly in water, dehydrated by passage through a series of ethanol concentrations (70, 90, 90, 100, and 100%; about 1 min each) cleared in Histosol (National Diagnostics, Manville, NJ), and cover-slips are mounted using Histomount (National Diagnostics).

Specific binding of ^{125}I-labeled NDP-MSH has also been localized successfully at the microscopic level in brain tissue sections coated directly with liquid nuclear track emulsion (NTB2; Kodak) and exposed for 1–2 weeks (34) as described previously (33). Liquid emulsion autoradiography can be performed after initial film autoradiography of the same tissue sections. Alternatively, the radiolabeled, dried tissue sections can be autoradiographed by apposition to emulsion-coated coverslips, which prevents diffusive losses and redistribution of bound radioligand and may allow improved counterstaining (28).

Analysis of Autoradiograms

Binding has routinely been quantified by computerized analysis of digitized autoradiographic images. Detailed discussions of methodology have been published (32, 35–38). The image analysis system in our laboratory includes the following components: a MOS-5300 video camera (General Imaging, Gainesville, FL) fitted with a Micro-Nikkor 55-mm $f/2.8$ lens, a Northern Light fluorescent transilluminator (Imaging Research, Inc., St. Catharines,

Ontario, Canada), a Macintosh II computer, and a Quick-Capture digitizer (Data Translation Systems, Marlborough, MA). Image files are conveniently stored on an external cartridge-based hard-drive system. Image analysis is performed using the IMAGE program (gift of Dr. W. Rasband, National Institutes of Health) (23, 38). Autoradiographic images are digitized under standardized conditions of aperture, light source intensity, and field width, designed to optimize resolution and to achieve maximal nonsaturating illumination, and corrected for shading and fixed pattern video camera noise by blank field subtraction (a feature of the IMAGE program).

To identify areas of interest and tissue landmarks, each stained tissue section is examined both microscopically and using a low-power magnifier ($\times 8$ or $\times 10$) on the light box. Autoradiographic signal intensity is then measured in film areas overlying specific tissue structures, using the technique of redirected sampling (a feature of the IMAGE program). After bringing the video image into sharp focus on the plane of the autoradiogram, each stained slide is physically superimposed and aligned carefully over its autoradiographic image, and the film is repositioned under the camera and secured in place with tape. Paired images are digitized and saved, first with the counterstained tissue superimposed on the film, and then with the autoradiogram alone. With the use of redirected sampling, the digitized macroscopic image of each stained tissue section is used as a template for sampling of signal intensity within the corresponding image of its autoradiogram alone. Many anatomical landmarks are visible in the image of the tissue section, allowing accurate sampling from known tissue structures, and analysis is restricted to areas free of tears and folds. Nevertheless, because the method depends on physical alignment of tissue section and autoradiogram, sampling should be sufficiently conservative to ensure that the areas sampled are located within the margins of the intended structures.

For each autoradiogram, optical densities (OD; gray levels on a 256-level scale) are determined in the structures of interest, and the local film background signal is determined in a field neighboring each autoradiogram image. The mean tissue-associated binding signal is calculated by subtracting the mean local film background level. Optical density values are either converted into radioactivity concentrations using a calibration curve entered directly into the IMAGE program or, for greater flexibility and convenience in data analysis, all values can be exported from IMAGE for analysis using spreadsheet (we use Microsoft Excel) and/or statistics software (STATVIEW; Abacus Concepts, Inc., Berkeley, CA).

Radioactivity concentrations, expressed in terms of disintegrations per minute per milligram tissue, are interpolated from radioactivity concentration standard curves using STATVIEW. We use a series of reference standards prepared by mixing known amounts of ^{125}I-labeled NDP-MSH with known amounts (by weight) of brain paste, arranged into multilayered frozen blocks, and sectioned and mounted on gelatin-coated slides exactly as done for tissue specimens (35, 38). Two such reference slides, each containing 1 section each of 12 different concentration standards, are exposed to each X-ray film along with each set of brain tissue slides, and individual standard curves are constructed for each film using the duplicate values determined for each standard. Reference standards are corrected for radioactive decay before curve fitting. We have found that, while the concentration–response curve for radioactivity concentration vs film optical density is near linear in the lower and midportions of the curve, film optical density of the highest radioactivity concentrations approaches saturation, and the data, even at the lowest concentration standards, are optimally fitted using a third-order polynomial regression that includes the entire range of standards (38).

Receptor Characterization

Binding assay conditions were established in preliminary experiments, and adapted from methods developed in earlier studies of melanotropin receptors in melanoma (18, 24) and lacrimal (22) cells and tissues. By radioreceptor assay in whole-brain tissue sections, 55–70% of ^{125}I-labeled NDP-MSH binding was specific, as defined by its inhibition in the presence of 1 μM α-MSH. As assessed by computerized densitometry, binding within specific anatomical structures was up to 95% specific or more (23, 34). Time course studies showed that binding of ^{125}I-labeled NDP-MSH at 23°C reached maximal levels within 2–4 hr. Nearly 100% of ^{125}I-labeled NDP-MSH in the bathing solution remained intact after a 2-hr incubation of brain tissue sections under standard conditions, as assessed by testing the ability of the tracer pool to bind specifically to a fresh set of serial sections (34).

Anatomic Distribution

The distribution of specific melanotropin binding was determined in serial sections prepared from a total of 25 male rat brains in coronal, parasagittal, and horizontal planes. The specificity of ^{125}I-labeled NDP-MSH binding in each section was determined by its inhibition in the presence of 1 μM α-MSH in paired serial sections (23). A standard stereotaxic atlas was used as an anatomical reference (39). Specific melanotropin binding was found to be differentially distributed in a highly region-specific pattern among numerous structures in the brain (Fig. 2) (23). Binding is predominantly localized in subcortical structures of the forebrain and midbrain, and its anatomical distribution correlates closely with the known distribution of melanotropinergic nerve terminals, suggesting that potential melanotropin-responsive cells lie in close proximity to the relevant innervating neurons. Furthermore, many of the structures bearing specific melanotropin-binding sites (23) and receiving melanotropinergic innervation (13, 14, 40), such as the septum (7, 13), medial preoptic area (7, 13, 40), and periaqueductal gray area (13, 14, 41), are thought to be involved in mediating the effects of exogenous melanotropins (discussed in Ref. 23). Specific melanotropin binding is generally absent from white matter (Fig. 2). The only known exception is the fasciculus retroflexus, a major fiber tract projecting from the habenular complex (Fig. 2e) to the interpeduncular nucleus (Fig. 2a), structures that also bear intense levels of melanotropin binding, and to other midbrain sites (42). The potential functional significance of melanotropin receptors in this system is not known.

Presumably, cells in the central nervous system (CNS) that were physiologically responsive to melanotropins *in vivo* would receive their principal melanotropinergic inputs from intrinsic central melanotropinergic neurons. Nevertheless, systemic, pituitary-derived melanotropins may have access to central melanotropin receptors in certain circumventricular organs that lack a functional blood–brain barrier (43). This hypothesis has been tested in part using *in vitro* and *in vivo* approaches (17, 23, 44). *In situ* binding and autoradiography studies have demonstrated specific melanotropin-binding sites in the median eminence (Fig. 2e) (23) and subfornical organ (Fig. 2c). *In vivo* (17), pentobarbital-anesthetized C3H/HeJ mice ($N = 21$) and Sprague-Dawley rats ($N = 16$) were injected intrajugularly with ^{125}I-labeled NDP-MSH (2×10^6 cpm; 1–3 pmol) in the absence or presence of an excess of α-MSH. After 10 min (mice) or 5 min (rats) blood samples were collected, the animals were killed, brains were removed and the medial basal hypothalami and samples of frontal cortex were removed and weighed, and radioactivity levels were determined. Hypothalamic tissue : plasma radioactivity concentration ratios were decreased by 67% in the presence of excess α-MSH in both mice and rats. This demonstration of specific ^{125}I-labeled NDP-MSH uptake in the medial basal hypothalamus suggested the presence of melanotropin receptors and/or transport systems in this area (17). In contrast, cortical tissue showed no detectable uptake (17), in agreement with results of binding and autoradiography studies *in vitro* (23). It is not known if this *in vivo* uptake was restricted to the median eminence, or the extent to which blood-borne MSH localizes specifically in other circumventricular organs *in vivo*. After intravenous injection in rats, ^{125}I-labeled ACTH$_{1-24}$ was demonstrated autoradiographically to localize specifically in the median eminence (44), conceivably binding to the same sites as ^{125}I-labeled NDP-MSH, because

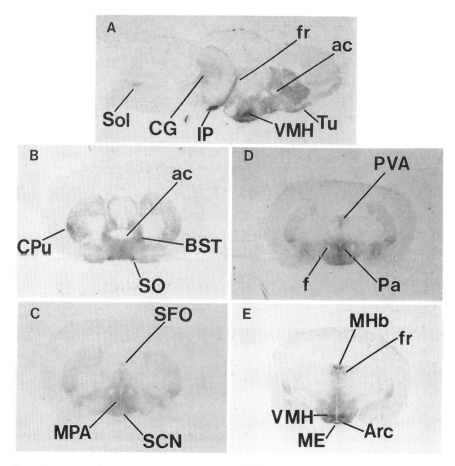

FIG. 2   Anatomical distribution of specific ^{125}I-labeled NDP-MSH binding in rat brain. Shown are X-ray film autoradiograms of parasagittal (a) and coronal (b–e) tissue sections incubated with ^{125}I-labeled NDP-MSH as described in text. Relative darkness indicates relative binding intensity in a given area. All of the binding shown is specific, as it was virtually eliminated in the presence of 1 μM α-MSH (23). The series shown in (b–e) progresses anteriorly to posteriorly. Abbreviations (39): ac, anterior commissure; Arc, arcuate nucleus; BST, bed nucleus of stria terminalis; CPu, caudate putamen; CG, central gray; f, fornix; fr, fasciculus retroflexus; IP, interpeduncular nucleus; ME, median eminence; MHb, medial habenular nucleus; MPA, medial preoptic area; Pa, hypothalamic paraventricular nucleus; PVA, thalamic paraventricular nucleus, anterior; SCN, suprachiasmatic nucleus; SFO, subfornical organ; SO, supraoptic nucleus; Sol, nucleus of the solitary tract; Tu, olfactory tubercle; VMH, hypothalamic ventromedial nucleus. [See Tatro (23) for additional data.]

ACTH competes with ^{125}I-labeled NDP-MSH for binding *in vitro* (23, 45) (see below).

Ligand Specificity and Selectivity

To assess ligand specificity and relative binding affinities, the relative potencies of melanotropins in inhibiting binding of ^{125}I-labeled NDP-MSH were determined in competitive binding studies. In a large series of brain structures, all specific binding sites detected with the use of ^{125}I-labeled NDP-MSH recognized the series of melanotropins NDP-MSH, α-MSH, des-acetyl-α-MSH, β-MSH, γ-MSH, ACTH$_{1-24}$, and ACTH$_{1-39}$: when present at a concentration of 1 μM, each peptide inhibited tracer binding to background levels in all anatomical sites studied (23, 45). In the nucleus accumbens, caudate putamen, lateral hypothalamus, ventromedial nucleus (Fig. 3a), and medial habenular nucleus (Fig. 3b), NDP-MSH, α-MSH, and ACTH$_{1-39}$ each inhibited ^{125}I-labeled NDP-MSH binding in a concentration-related manner, with the order of potency (IC$_{50}$) as follows: NDP-MSH (1.7 nM) > ACTH $\geq$ α-MSH (50 nM) (23). The respective competition curves appeared similar among different brain structures (Fig. 3), suggesting that the marked differences in binding intensity observed among different brain structures probably reflect differences in tissue receptor concentrations rather than differences in receptor affinities. Taken together, the results suggest that multiple melanotropic peptides may bind to a common specific melanotropin-binding site.

It is possible that additional classes of specific melanotropin-binding proteins, which do not bind ^{125}I-labeled NDP-MSH, may exist in the brain. Only a few of the known biologically active native and synthetic melanotropins have been tested for ability to compete with ^{125}I-labeled NDP-MSH for binding, and certain central actions of NDP-MSH are qualitatively distinct from those of α-MSH (10, 11). Therefore it is not clear whether specific binding detected with this ligand could theoretically represent receptors capable of mediating all of the known actions of melanotropins in the brain. Studies employing alternative melanotropins as radioligands or competitors may be helpful in resolving this issue, but only limited data are presently available. In a preliminary report, one group used [^{3}H]Nva^{13}-α-MSH as tracer, and detected high-affinity (K_D = 4–8 nM) and low-affinity (K_D = 5 μM) binding sites for α-MSH by radioreceptor assay in rat brain membranes (46). High levels of the high-affinity sites were detected autoradiographically in hippocampus, dentate gyrus, cortex, and cerebellum (46), structures in which specific ^{125}I-labeled NDP-MSH binding is not detectable (Fig. 2; 23). If confirmed, these findings (46) suggest the existence of another melanotropin receptor subtype, which has a distinct distribution and does not recognize

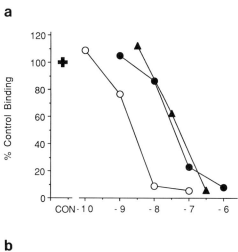

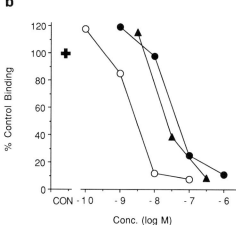

FIG. 3 Concentration–response relationships for inhibition of ^{125}I-labeled NDP-MSH binding to brain structures *in situ* [(a) hypothalamic ventromedial nucleus; (b) medial habenular nucleus] by NDP-MSH (○), α-MSH (●), and human $ACTH_{1-39}$ (▲). Binding is represented on the *y* axis as a percentage of control values (competing peptides absent). Similar results were observed in additional brain structures (23, 34). Abbreviations as in Fig. 2, CON (+).

NDP-MSH. Another group reported binding of ^{125}I-labeled Phe^2, Nle^4-$ACTH_{1-24}$ to rat brain membranes that was 30–40% specific, and was inhibited not only by ACTH but also by vasoactive intestinal polypeptide (VIP), growth hormone-releasing factor (GRF), and dynorphin. Adrenocorticotropic hormone also inhibited binding of ^{125}I-labeled VIP (47). The significance of these findings remains to be established.

Based on results of binding studies alone, it is likely that multiple classes of melanotropin receptor-binding proteins do exist, at least in different target organs. Thus, in brain, α-MSH and ACTH$_{1-39}$ were approximately equipotent in inhibiting ^{125}I-labeled NDP-MSH binding (23; Fig. 3), whereas in cultured cells (18, 19) and tissue sections (18) of melanoma, the classic MSH-responsive mammalian target tissue, α-MSH was at least 20 times as potent as ACTH$_{1-39}$. In contrast, α-MSH did not compete with ^{125}I-labeled ACTH for binding to adrenal ACTH receptors (48).

Recently, murine and human genes encoding melanoma melanotropin receptors and adrenal ACTH receptors were cloned. Transfection of the genes into normally unresponsive kidney-derived cells conferred responsiveness of adenylate cyclase to α-MSH and ACTH. The results demonstrated the existence of structurally distinct forms of melanotropin receptors with apparently distinct ligand selectivities, and also provided evidence for the existence of additional forms of the receptors (49).

Functional and Biochemical Characterization

Several lines of indirect evidence support the hypothesis that the specific ^{125}I-labeled NDP-MSH-binding sites detected in brain represent functional receptors. First, the differential and highly reproducible anatomical distribution of ^{125}I-labeled NDP-MSH binding, predominantly among brain structures known to be innervated by melanotropinergic neurons and believed to be involved in mediating the actions of centrally administered melanotropins, suggests that the binding reflects the presence of biologically relevant receptors (23). In mouse melanoma cells, the potencies of NDP-MSH, α-MSH, and ACTH in inhibiting ^{125}I-labeled NDP-MSH binding were virtually identical to their respective potencies in inducing cyclic AMP accumulation, strongly suggesting that ^{125}I-labeled NDP-MSH binding represents binding to functional receptors (18). Similar respective cAMP-inducing potencies were observed for the three peptides in a kidney epithelial cell line transfected with the mouse melanoma MSH receptor gene (49). In the brain, NDP-MSH showed the highest binding affinity among a series of melanotropins (23, 34), as was observed in both melanoma cells (18, 19) and lacrimal acinar cells (22), in which melanotropins are potent secretagogues (50), suggesting some degree of similarity between the melanotropin-binding sites in brain and the receptors of melanoma and lacrimal acinar cells.

Current knowledge of melanotropin receptor signaling mechanisms in the brain is limited. Studies of melanotropin-stimulated cAMP accumulation *in vivo* (51, 52) and *in vitro* (34, 51, 53–55) suggest that adenylate cyclase may be involved in melanotropin receptor signaling in brain cells, as in melanoma

(18, 21) and lacrimal acinar cells (22, 50). A series of melanotropins, including α-MSH and ACTH, stimulated cAMP accumulation in neuron-enriched (55) and astrocyte-enriched (54) fetal rodent brain cell cultures, suggesting that both neurons and glia may be capable of expressing melanotropin receptors. NDP-MSH likewise stimulated cAMP production in both glial-enriched and mixed neuronal–glial fetal rat brain cultures (34).

Nevertheless, other melanotropin signaling systems have been implicated in brain (56, 57) as well as in melanoma models (58–60). In the brain, ACTH has been proposed to act in part by decreasing the activity of protein kinase C (PKC), leading to decreased phosphorylation of a major PKC substrate, identified as B-50 protein or growth-associated protein 43 (GAP-43) (56, 61). GAP-43 is tightly associated with PKC, is localized subcellularly at the presynaptic membrane (56), and is distributed among a majority of the brain structures that exhibit specific melanotropin binding (62). The phosphorylation state of B-50 has been proposed to regulate phosphatidylinositol-4-phosphate (PIP) kinase activity, and thereby polyphosphoinositol metabolism, in brain (56). In mouse melanoma cells, NDP-MSH induced adenylate cyclase-independent morphological (58) and melanogenic (59) responses. α-Melanocyte-stimulating hormone was also reported to induce production of novel phosphomonoesters, primarily phosphoethanolamine, in M2R mouse melanoma cells, suggesting that a specific phospholipase may participate in a distinct α-MSH signaling pathway by mediating the hydrolysis of membrane phospholipids, including phosphatidylethanolamine (60).

Melanoma melanotropin receptors and adrenal corticotropin receptors are encoded by distinct genes (49). Further, the structural requirements for ligand binding are distinct between corticotropin receptors of adrenal glands (48) and the melanotropin receptors of melanoma cells (18–20) and lacrimal acinar cells (22). Nevertheless, receptors in these respective cell types share a number of common properties. Specific melanotropin-binding proteins (M_r 43K–46K) have been identified by photoaffinity cross-linking of ^{125}I-labeled Trp(Naps)[9]-NDP-MSH (20, 63) to melanoma cells and photochemical cross-linking of ^{125}I-labeled β-MSH (64) to melanoma cell membranes followed by sodium dodecyl sulfate-polyacrylamide gel electrophoresis (SDS-PAGE). Similarly, a specific ACTH-binding protein (43 kDa) was identified in bovine adrenal membranes by photochemical cross-linking (65). Molecular weights of the protein components of both receptor types, determined from the amino acid sequences predicted from the cloned receptor genes (total lengths of about 300 residues), are somewhat smaller (49). Both melanoma cell melanotropin receptors (21) and adrenal corticotropin receptors (66) are coupled to adenylate cyclase through GTP-dependent mechanisms. Important facilitory roles of Ca^{2+} in both ligand-binding and postreceptor functions have been demonstrated, for melanotropin receptors of melanophores (67, 68) and melanoma cells (21), as well as for adrenal ACTH receptors (69). Furthermore, based on studies with calmodulin antagonists and/or antibodies, calmodulin or a similar calcium-binding protein is thought to participate in melanotropin receptor functioning in melanoma cells (64), lacrimal cells (64), and adrenal cells (70, 71).

Summary and Conclusions

The neuroanatomical distribution of specific melanotropin binding in the rat brain has been determined with use of a radiolabeled α-MSH analog. The binding sites recognize multiple melanotropic ligands, and are extensively codistributed with known melanotropinergic neuron terminal fields, providing a likely anatomical basis for many of the diverse biological actions of melanotropins in the brain.

It is likely that new research tools will become available in the near future, including molecular probes for brain melanotropin receptor gene structure and expression (49), anti-receptor antibodies, and receptor antagonists (71). These, in combination with further structure–function analysis of ligand–receptor interactions, should allow rapid progress in understanding the molecular basis of melanotropin receptor structure, function, and regulation. Nevertheless, considering the multiplicity of known and potential endogenous melanotropins, and the recognition of multiple melanotropic ligands by common receptors, the greater challenge may be to identify the relevant endogenous melanotropic ligands and to define their respective physiological roles.

Acknowledgments

The author gratefully acknowledges the expert technical assistance of Margaret Entwistle. This work was supported by National Institute of Mental Health Grant No. RO1-MH-44694, and by a grant from the Elsa U. Pardee Foundation.

References

1. S. Nakanishi, A. Inoue, T. Kita, M. Nakamura, A. C. Y. Chang, S. N. Cohen, and S. Numa, *Nature* (*London*) **278,** 423 (1979).
2. J. Drouin and H. M. Goodman, *Nature* (*London*) **288,** 610 (1980).
3. A. I. Smith and J. W. Funder, *Endocr. Rev.* **9,** 159 (1988).
4. O. Khorram, L. R. DePalatis, and S. M. McCann, *Endocrinology* (*Baltimore*) **114,** 277 (1984).

5. S. E. Lindley, K. J. Lookingland, and K. E. Moore, *Neuroendocrinology* **51,** 394 (1990).
6. T. Scimonelli and M. E. Celis, *J. Endocrinol.* **124,** 127 (1990).
7. J. M. Lipton, *Yale J. Biol. Med.* **63,** 173 (1990).
8. K. A. Gruber and M. F. Callahan, *Am. J. Physiol.* **257,** R681 (1989).
9. D. de Wied and J. Jollès, *Physiol. Rev.* **62,** 976 (1982).
10. K. Kobobun, T. L. O'Donohue, G. E. Handelmann, T. K. Sawyer, V. J. Hruby, and M. E. Hadley, *Peptides (N.Y.)* **4,** 721 (1983).
11. B. E. Beckwith, T. P. Tinius, V. J. Hruby, F. Al-Obeidi, T. K. Sawyer, and J. A. Affholter, *Peptides (N.Y.)* **10,** 361 (1989).
12. D. de Wied, *Acta Neurobiol. Exp.* **50,** 353 (1990).
13. T. L. O'Donohue and D. M. Dorsa, *Peptides (N.Y.)* **3,** 353 (1982).
14. M. Palkovits, E. Mezey, and R. L. Eskay, *Brain Res.* **436,** 323 (1987).
15. O. Khorram, J. C. Bedran De Castro, and S. M. McCann, *Proc. Natl. Acad. Sci. U.S.A.* **81,** 8004 (1984).
16. G. Wolterink, E. Van Zanten, and J. M. Van Ree, *Brain Res.* **507,** 115 (1990).
17. J. B. Tatro and S. Reichlin, *Endocrinology (Baltimore)* **121,** 1900 (1987).
18. J. B. Tatro, M. L. Entwistle, B. R. Lester, and S. Reichlin, *Cancer Res.* **50,** 1237 (1990).
19. W. Siegrist, M. Oestreicher, S. Stutz, J. Girard, and A. N. Eberle, *J. Recept. Res.* **8,** 323 (1988).
20. W. Siegrist, F. Solca, S. Stutz, L. Guiffré, S. Carrel, J. Girard, and A. N. Eberle, *Cancer Res.* **49,** 6352 (1989).
21. J. E. Gerst, J. Sole, and Y. Salomon, *Mol. Pharmacol.* **31,** 81 (1987).
22. M. L. Entwistle, D. A. Sullivan, L. E. Hann, and J. B. Tatro, *Peptides (N.Y.)* **11,** 477 (1990).
23. J. B. Tatro, *Brain Res.* **536,** 124 (1990).
24. J. B. Tatro, M. Atkins, J. W. Mier, S. Hardarson, H. Wolfe, T. Smith, M. L. Entwistle, and S. Reichlin, *J. Clin. Invest.* **85,** 1825 (1990).
25. C. B. Heward, Y. C. S. Yang, T. K. Sawyer, M. D. Bregman, B. B. Fuller, V. J. Hruby, and M. E. Hadley, *Biochem. Biophys. Res. Commun.* **88,** 266 (1979).
26. T. K. Sawyer, P. J. Sanfilippo, V. J. Hruby, M. H. Engel, C. B. Heward, J. B. Burnett, and M. E. Hadley, *Proc. Natl. Acad. Sci. U.S.A.* **77,** 5754 (1980).
27. M. Holdeman and J. M. Lipton, *Peptides (N.Y.)* **6,** 273 (1985).
28. Y. S. Young, III and M. J. Kuhar, *Brain Res.* **179,** 255 (1979).
29. W. E. Stumpf and G. E. Duncan, this series, Vol. 3, p. 35.
30. D. R. Gehlert and H. I. Yamamura, this series, Vol. 3, p. 425.
31. E. B. De Souza and M. J. Kuhar, *in* "Methods in Enzymology" (P. Conn, ed.), Vol. 124, p. 560. Academic Press, Orlando, FL, 1986.
32. A. W. Rogers, "Techniques of Autoradiography." Elsevier, New York, 1973.
33. M. Herkenham and C. B. Pert, *J. Neurosci.* **28,** 1129 (1982).
34. J. B. Tatro, unpublished observations.
35. J. R. Unnerstall, M. J. Kuhar, D. L. Niehoff, and J. M. Palacios, *J. Pharmacol. Exp. Ther.* **218,** 797 (1981).
36. M. J. Kuhar and J. R. Unnerstall, *Trends Neurosci.* **8,** 49 (1985).

37. A. Schleicher and K. Zilles, *in* "Molecular Neuroanatomy" (F. W. Van Leeuwen, R. M. Buijs, C. W. Pool, and O. Pach, eds.), p. 147. Elsevier, Amsterdam, 1988.

38. J. B. Tatro, Z. Wen, M. L. Entwistle, M. B. Atkins, T. J. Smith, S. Reichlin, and J. R. Murphy, *Cancer Res.* **52,** 2545 (1992).

39. G. Paxinos and C. Watson, "The Rat Brain in Stereotaxic Coordinates." Academic Press, Orlando, FL, 1986.

40. E. Mezey, J. Z. Kiss, G. P. Mueller, R. Eskay, T. L. O'Donohue, and M. Palkovits, *Brain Res.* **328,** 341 (1985).

41. B. M. Spruijt, A. R. Cools, B. A. Ellenbroek, and W. H. Gispen, *Eur. J. Pharmacol.* **120,** 249 (1986).

42. R. J. Sutherland, *Neurosci. Biobehav. Rev.* **6,** 1 (1982).

43. W. M. Pardridge, *Annu. Rev. Physiol.* **45,** 73 (1983).

44. M. Van Houten, M. N. Khan, R. J. Khan, and B. I. Posner, *Endocrinology (Baltimore)* **108,** 2385 (1981).

45. J. B. Tatro, *Ann. N.Y. Acad. Sci.* (in press).

46. W. Lichtensteiger, M. Schlumpf, and A. Eberle, *Proc. Ann. Neurosci. Meet.* **14,** 564 (abstr.) (1988).

47. Z.-G. Li, G. Queen, and F. S. LaBella, *Endocrinology (Baltimore)* **126,** 1327 (1990).

48. H. G. Klemcke and W. G. Pond, *Endocrinology (Baltimore)* **128,** 2476 (1991).

49. K. G. Mountjoy, L. S. Robbins, M. T. Mortrud, and R. D. Cone, *Science* **257,** 1248 (1992).

50. R. Jahn, U. Padel, P. H. Porsch, and H. D. Soling, *Eur. J. Biochem.* **126,** 623 (1982).

51. V. M. Wiegant, A. J. Dunn, P. Schotman, and W. H. Gispen, *Brain Res.* **168,** 565 (1979).

52. D. Rudman and J. W. Isaacs, *Endocrinology (Baltimore)* **97,** 1476 (1975).

53. D. Rudman, *Endocrinology (Baltimore)* **103,** 1556 (1978).

54. D. Van Calker, F. Loffler, and B. Hamprecht, *J. Neurochem.* **40,** 418 (1983).

55. S. Weiss, M. Sebben, and J. Bockaert, *J. Neurochem.* **45,** 869 (1985).

56. W. H. Gispen, D. L. Colbern, and B. M. Spruijt, *in* "Psychopharmacology, Series 4: Transduction Mechanisms of Drug Stimuli" (Colpaert and Balster, eds.), p. 216. Springer-Verlag, Berlin, 1988.

57. M. Zohar and Y. Salomon, *Brain Res.* **576,** 49 (1992).

58. S. F. Preston, M. Volpi, C. M. Pearson, and R. D. Berlin, *Proc. Natl. Acad. Sci. U.S.A.* **84,** 5247 (1987).

59. Z. A. Abdel-Malek, V. B. Swope, L. S. Trinkle, and J. J. Nordlund, *Exp. Cell Res.* **180,** 198 (1989).

60. H. Degani, J. O. DeJordy, and Y. Salomon, *Proc. Natl. Acad. Sci. U.S.A.* **88,** 1506 (1991).

61. L. I. Benowitz and A. Routtenberg, *Trends Neurosci.* **10,** 527 (1987).

62. L. I. Benowitz, P. J. Apostolides, N. Perrone-Bizzozero, S. P. Finkelstein, and H. Zwiers, *J. Neurosci.* **8,** 339 (1988).

63. F. F. A. Solca, Y. Salomon, and A. N. Eberle, *J. Recept. Res.* **11,** 379 (1991).

64. Y. Salomon, *Mol. Cell. Endocrinol.* **70,** 139 (1990).

65. K. Hofmann, C. J. Stehle, and F. M. Finn, *Endocrinology* (*Baltimore*) **123,** 1355 (1988).

66. C. Londos and M. Rodbell, *J. Biol. Chem.* **250,** 3459 (1975).

67. M. E. Hadley, B. Anderson, and C. B. Heward, *Science* **213,** 1025 (1981).

68. P. N. E. DeGraan, A. J. van de Kamp, D. R. W. Hup, W. H. Gispen, and F. C. G. van de Veerdonk, *J. Recept. Res.* **4,** 521 (1984).

69. R. Cheitlin, D. I. Buckley, and J. Ramachandran, *J. Biol. Chem.* **260,** 5323–5327 (1985).

70. V. Papadopoulos, E. P. Widmaier, and P. F. Hall, *Endocrinology* (*Baltimore*) **126,** 2465 (1990).

71. J. X. Wilson, G. Aguilera, and K. J. Catt, *Endocrinology* (*Baltimore*) **115,** 1357 (1984).

72. T. K. Sawyer, D. J. Staples, A. M. L. Castrucci, M. E. Hadley, F. A. Al-Obeidi, W. L. Cody, and V. J. Hruby, *Peptides* (*N.Y.*) **11,** 351 (1990).

[6] Melatonin Binding Sites

Eric L. Bittman

Melatonin (*N*-acetyl-5-methoxytryptamine) is synthesized in vertebrate photoreceptors and constitutes the major known secretory product of the pineal gland. The synthesis and secretion of melatonin are photically regulated, being restricted to the hours of darkness and inhibited by exposure to light during the night. Production of melatonin is also controlled by an endogenous daily clock: when animals are maintained in constant darkness, concentrations within the pineal gland, eye, and blood show marked circadian variations.

Melatonin exerts a variety of actions throughout the vertebrates. Control of disk shedding and pigment migration within photoreceptors represent local, and perhaps primitive, functions of this indoleamine. The entrained pattern of melatonin synthesis and secretion reflects the light–dark cycle and carries information about the photic environment to target organs at some distance from its site of production. This signal regulates melanosome aggregation in some fishes and amphibian tadpoles, influences sun compass orientation in salamanders, and coordinates multiple physiological and behavioral functions in some reptiles and birds (1). By far the best understood functions of melatonin concern aspects of mammalian reproduction, metabolism, and behavior that are regulated by seasonal variations in day length (2, 3). In many species, pinealectomy eliminates photoperiodic control of these functions and replacement of physiological doses of melatonin in precise temporal patterns reinstates responses appropriate to the day length they represent. Significantly, the nature of several of these effects of melatonin (e.g., on pulsatile gonadotropin secretion and sexual behavior) indicates a direct or indirect action on the central nervous system.

Each of these actions of melatonin is presumed to be triggered by binding to one or more receptor types. Within the past several years, our knowledge about the mechanisms of melatonin action has increased greatly. This chapter will review methods in use for detection and characterization of melatonin binding sites.

Preparation of Radiolabeled Melatonin

Three forms of isotopically labeled melatonin are commercially available. While the [3]H- and ^{14}C-labeled forms constitute authentic melatonin and thus pose an advantage for binding studies, they are available only at relatively

Methods in Neurosciences, Volume 11

low specific activities and thus are of severely limited value. The introduction by Vakkuri *et al.* (4) of [2-^{125}I]iodomelatonin (IMEL), which can be radiolabeled to high specific activity (on the order of 2000 Ci/mmol), has permitted great progress in the localization and characterization of binding sites. Fortunately, halogenation at the 2-position does not interfere with at least some of the effects of melatonin, and the analog can cross the blood–brain barrier after systemic injection (5, 6).

While IMEL is commercially available from Amersham (Arlington Heights, IL) and Du Pont (New England Nuclear, Boston, MA), it can be prepared in the laboratory with relative ease and modest expense (7–10). Radioiodination is accomplished in a microfuge tube in which 0.1–8 mg Iodogen (Pierce Chemical Corp., Rockford, IL) in 10–20 μl of methylene chloride or chloroform is evaporated under a stream of nitrogen. Iodogen-coated tubes should be used within a few weeks, and open bottles of Iodogen lose their potency over longer periods even when stored at $-80°C$. Once the organic solvent is evaporated, melatonin (Sigma, St. Louis, MO, 10 μg in 10 μl of ethanolic 0.05 M sodium phosphate, pH 6.0) and Na[125]I (0.2–2.5 mCi in 1 μl of NaOH solution) are added. After 1 min at room temperature without agitation, the labeled product may be extraced in 200–500 μl chloroform and dried under nitrogen. After resuspension in methanol and dilution (1 : 4, v/v) in distilled water, the product must be purified. Although partial purification is possible using silica gel chromatography or thin-layer chromatography (TLC), the yield and purity of the resulting peak are inferior to that achieved using high-performance liquid chromatography (HPLC). A reversed-phase ODS column (5-μm particle size) may be run either under isocratic conditions [45% (v/v) methanol; Fig. 1], in a 10–40% (v/v) gradient of 2-propanol, or in a gradient of 15–55% methanol in trifluoroacetic acid.

In Vivo Labeling of Melatonin Binding Sites

Studies of the fate and metabolism of intravenously, intraventricularly, or intracisternally administered [3]H- or ^{14}C-labeled melatonin suggest significant retention in brain, pituitary, pineal, gonads, uterus, muscle, liver, and kidney (11–15). Melatonin in the latter two organs is most likely in the process of metabolism to more polar compounds in preparation for clearance. Unfortunately, the low specific activity of these radioligands has often required use of high (nanomolar) concentrations to yield detectable binding and uptake was not always saturable. While radiolabeled IMEL might provide a suitable alternative for *in vivo* labeling, the quantities of isotope that would have to be injected to achieve physiological concentrations even in a small animal make this an expensive undertaking. IMEL binds specifically to fetal hamster hypothalamic slices incubated at 36°C for several hours in Dulbecco's modi-

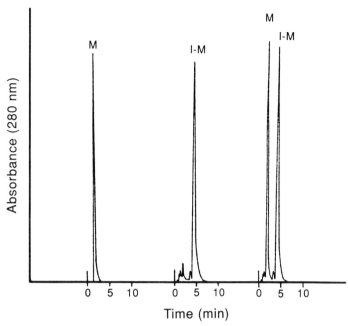

FIG. 1   Although IMEL is commercially available at reasonable cost, it may be made in the laboratory and purified by HPLC. After iodination of melatonin using Iodogen, radiolabeled IMEL is dried under nitrogen, reconstituted with methanol, injected into a 12.5 × 0.40 cm ODS reversed-phase column, and eluted with 45% methanol in distilled water at a flow rate of 2 ml/min. Retention times for melatonin (M) and IMEL (I-M) were 2.1 and 4.4 min, respectively. [Reproduced, with permission, from Niles *et al.* (8).]

fied Eagle's medium which has been gassed with 95% O_2/5% CO_2, supplemented with glucose (to 6 g/liter), bovine serum albumin (0.1%, v/v), and sodium pyrivate (1 m*M*), and adjusted to pH 7.35 by addition of sodium bicarbonate (E. L. Bittman and M. H. Hastings, unpublished results, 1992). This may provide an indication of physiologically relevant binding *in vivo* because some neurons maintain responsiveness to melatonin under similar conditions (16).

In Vitro Labeling of Melatonin Binding Sites

Choice of Isotope

Attempts to localize and characterize melatonin receptors also utilized [³H]melatonin for many years (17–19). Although it is not clear that binding of [³H]melatonin is saturable at the concentrations used, specific binding was reported to occur in nuclear, microsomal, and mitochondrial membrane fractions and, in two reports, in cytosol. Binding affinities in pineal, retina, brain, and ovary were reported in the 6–80 nM range. Because physiological serum concentrations rarely if ever exceed 1 nM, it is doubtful that a significant number of these sites would ever be occupied *in vivo*. The use of IMEL has superseded these earlier approaches, and it is now the ligand of choice for studies of melatonin binding sites.

Homogenization and Incubation Conditions

Characterization and cellular localization of melatonin binding sites have generally proceeded through cell fractionation using standard techniques (20). Typically, tissue is removed rapidly and homogenized in 0.05 M Tris buffer (pH 7.4) at 0–4°C using a Polytron (Brinkmann Instruments, Westbury, NY), although a glass homogenizer with Teflon pestle may be used instead (21, 22). In many studies 4 mM $CaCl_2$ has been added to this buffer, and ascorbic acid is sometimes included to bring its concentration to 0.1%. In other studies, $MgCl_2$ has been substituted for $CaCl_2$ and ethylenediaminetetraacetic acid (EDTA) has been included in millimolar concentrations (23, 24). It is not clear that any of these additions is necessary. Fractionation may be performed by differential centrifugation, but binding characteristics of such preparations closely resemble those in crude membrane fractions or whole homogenates. Most if not all binding is found in the membrane fraction, although it has not been absolutely established whether intracellular (including mitochondrial, microsomal, and nuclear) membranes contribute. Membrane fractions may be stored frozen (-20°C or lower) for at least several days without loss of binding activity.

Binding assays are typically performed using a similar buffer (0.05 M Tris plus 4 mM $CaCl_2$). Addition of ascorbate or 0.01% (v/v) bovine serum albumin (BSA) to incubation and wash buffers is compatible with successful binding studies, although systematic studies of the effects of these reagents have not been reported (25, 26). Studies of binding in homogenates or partially purified membrane preparations have also been conducted in higher concentrations of Tris buffer (up to 0.15 M) or using phosphate buffer (0.02 M) containing 0.15 M NaCl and 1% BSA. Although autoradiographic studies indicate a depression of binding by millimolar concentrations of sodium, lithium, or choline chloride (27, 28; see below), the characteristics of binding sites inferred from these procedures seem comparable. Incubations are typically performed using a volume of 100 μl of homogenate, to which a similar volume of radioligand and competitors or drugs is added. Specific binding typically reaches an asymptote at concentrations at or below 200 pM. For single-point assays of high-affinity sites the use of concentrations above 100 pM is unnecessary and not advisable. Specific binding is typically linear over a wide range of protein concentrations but incubations are most often performed in tubes containing 50–100 μg protein.

Specificity, Affinity, and Capacity of Binding Sites

Incubations have been carried out for periods ranging from 30 min to 5 hr. Specific binding, which usually constitutes in excess of 50% of total binding, typically reaches an asymptote within an hour at 22–37°C and remains stable thereafter. While the result depends on the temperature of incubation, rates of association (k_{+1}) have been reported from 13.5 pM to 1.63 nM/min. Addition of excess unlabeled melatonin demonstrates reversibility of binding and provides estimates of a dissociation rate (k_{-1}) that may be used in kinetic estimates of binding site affinity. These estimates (k_{+1}/k_{-1}) have characteristically agreed well with estimates provided by Scatchard plots of saturation data (21–26).

A parallel set of incubations must be carried out using unlabeled melatonin or other appropriate competitors if specificity of the binding reaction is to be assessed. Typically assays of melatonin binding sites use micromolar concentrations of cold melatonin for this purpose. Specificity studies using a range of indoles and other potential agonists or antagonists uniformly show melatonin, 6-chloromelatonin, and 2-iodomelatonin to be the most effective competitors for IMEL binding sites. Other drugs, including known monoamine receptor agonists/antagonists, almost invariably confirm specificity of the binding site. The one exception is the report in which prazosin, but not other α-adrenergic agonists or antagonists, had a low K_i (high affinity) for IMEL binding sites (24, 29). This has not been confirmed in several studies performed in other laboratories.

Termination of Incubations

Incubations are most typically terminated by rapid vacuum filtration in a standard apparatus. Whatman (Clifton, NJ) GF/B or GF/C filters serve well for this purpose. Membranes are typically washed several times with ice-cold Tris buffer (at least 20 incubation volumes) before counting. As an alternative, incubations may be terminated by protein precipitation at 0–4°C, utilizing 1% (v/v) sheep gamma globulin in Tris buffer and 24% (v/v) polyethylene glycol (PEG) 8000 in distilled water prior to centrifugation at

1800 g or higher (22, 30). In this method, the supernatant containing unbound IMEL is discarded prior to γ counting.

Receptor Subtypes

Differences between laboratories in the concentrations of IMEL used and the temperature at which the incubations have been conducted have contributed to apparent discrepancies in the literature. Binding is stable, saturable, and reversible at physiological temperatures of 20–37°C. Impressive unanimity exists among reports from laboratories executing binding studies at these temperatures (K_d, 20–72 pM; B_{max}, 2–81 fmol/mg protein; Table I). This binding site is highly specific (Fig. 2) and undoubtedly a large proportion of these sites is occupied at physiological concentrations of circulating melatonin.

Incubations performed at 0–4°C provide evidence for as many as two classes of saturable and specific binding sites, both of lower affinity and higher capacity than those demonstrable at higher temperatures (31–33). Lower affinity binding sites may also be demonstrated when incubations are performed at warmer temperatures by abbreviating the postincubation wash procedures in autoradiographic studies (27) or by application of curve-fitting procedures to nonlinear Scatchard plots which occasionally arise after incubation with a wide range of concentrations of IMEL (24). There is some indication that the specificity of binding sites revealed by incubations at 0°C differs slightly from those demonstrated at higher temperatures. Although it has been suggested (34) that binding of melatonin to the lower affinity site may be less readily displaced by 6-methoxymelatonin and N-acetylserotonin than is binding to the higher affinity IMEL binding site, this has not been demonstrated in parallel incubations of homogenates of the same tissue at higher temperatures (Fig. 2). The possibility that the high- and low-affinity sites are related or interconvertible has not yet been eliminated.

While the paucity of pharmacological tools has been a hindrance to the study of melatonin action, some analogs may discriminate between types of melatonin binding sites. The ability of a range of compounds to displace IMEL from membrane binding sites under these conditions of low-temperature incubation correlates well with their potency in inhibiting electrically or K^+- and Ca^{2+}-stimulated dopamine release from chick and rabbit retina (31–34). Dubocovich (31) argues on the basis of pharmacological studies in retina that ML-23 (N-2,4-dinitrophenyl-5-methoxytryptamine) antagonizes melatonin action at the site revealed by incubation with IMEL at or near 0°C. Despite its apparent ability to antagonize effects of melatonin on estrous cycles in rats (36), ML-23 appears ineffective as an antagonist to melatonin-

TABLE I   Reported Characteristics of 2-[^{125}I]Iodomelatonin Binding Sites[a]

Species and tissue	Buffer	Temp. (°C)	Time (hr)	K_d (pM)	B_{max} (fmol/mg)	Ref.
High-affinity binding sites						
Rat brain	Tris/CaCl$_2$	22	1	34–72	15–72	27, 28
Sheep pars tuberalis	Tris/EGTA	37	0.5–4	29–33	103	9, 22
	Tris/CaCl$_2$ ascorbate	20	2–3	21–104	0.6–3.25[b]	25, 49
Rodent, sheep, sparrow brain	PBS/BSA	22	1	28–43	6–20	2, 43–46
Hamster brain, pituitary	Tris/CaCl$_2$	28	0.5	60–133	9–26	21, 53
Chick retina, sheep pars tuberalis	Tris/EGTA/ PMSF/leupeptin	25–37	1	20–34	10–76	23
Hamster brain	Tris/MgCl$_2$	30–37	0.5–3	28–320	2–61	8, 24
Low-affinity binding sites						
Hamster brain, chick retina	Tris/BSA	0	1–5	260–3340	56–110	26, 31–35
Hamster brain	Tris/EDTA/ MgCl$_2$/ascorbate	0–4	1	700–3580	18–195	24
Quail brain	Tris	4	5	890	45	51[c]
Rat, hamster brain	Tris/CaCl$_2$	37	0.5	3200–9300	115	40–42[c]

[a] This table contains a nonexhaustive list of results from various laboratories using variations of methods described in text. Some studies used whole homogenates, synaptosomes, or membrane fractions; others employed autoradiographic analyses of tissue sections. It is not clear whether species differences in B_{max} represent authentic variations in density of binding sites or dissimilar lability under conditions of isolation and incubation. Note that incubations at 20–37°C routinely reveal high-affinity sites, provided IMEL concentrations of less than 200 pM are used.

[b] Number of binding sites presented as femtomoles per square millimeter.

[c] Only high concentrations of IMEL (200 pM–50 nM) were used in these studies, so high-affinity sites may have been missed.

induced testicular growth in Soay rams and is a poor competitor for IMEL when incubated with sheep pars tuberalis or rat hypothalamus at 37°C (Fig. 2; 22, 37, 38). Similarly, luzindole (2-benzyl-N-acetyltryptamine; Nelson Research, Irvine, CA) antagonizes some of the pharmacological effects of melatonin but has a low affinity for the binding site labeled by IMEL (39).

Some laboratories have employed high (nanomolar) concentrations of IMEL in incubation studies (40–42). These experiments have not always demonstrated saturability and estimation of the affinity of binding sites in

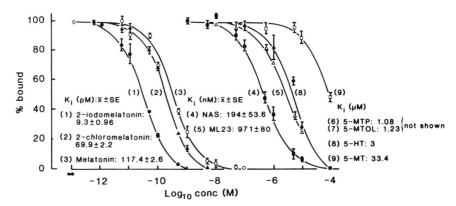

FIG. 2 Displacement of IMEL (60 pM) from ovine pars tuberalis membranes by coincubation with various concentrations of nine different indoleamines. Inhibition constants (K_i) are indicated as calculated from IC_{50} values derived from such data (59). These findings indicate the specificity for melatonin of the high-affinity IMEL binding site. [Reproduced, by permission of Oxford University Press, from Morgan *et al.* (9).]

this work has relied on assumptions other than those used in the standard kinetic and saturation procedures. It is not clear whether these binding sites correspond to those described using IMEL at low temperatures, or whether physiological concentrations of circulating melatonin would result in occupancy of a significant proportion of sites with low (nanomolar) affinities. Furthermore, the absence of autoradiographic localization and evidence for cellular effects of occupation of such sites makes their physiological role questionable at present. Nevertheless, melatonin may be present at high concentrations near its site of synthesis in the retina or pineal gland, and these low-affinity, high-capacity sites could reflect a paracrine function at such loci.

Autoradiographic Studies

Considerable attention has focused on the localization of melatonin binding sites within the central nervous system (CNS), and *in vitro* autoradiographic techniques have loaned themselves to this purpose. In these studies, animals are most typically rapidly decapitated using a guillotine. There is no evidence, however, that barbiturate anesthesia prior to removal of the brain depresses IMEL binding. Tissue is rapidly frozen using powdered dry ice or immersion in 2-methylbutane at or below −20°C. Brains have been stored for many months prior to sectioning without obvious loss of binding activity. Tissue is equilibrated to cutting temperature (typically about $-20°C$) in a cryostat and sections are thaw-mounted onto slides that have been previously subbed with chrome alum [$CrK(SO_4)_2$, 1.25 g/liter] and gelatin (12.5 g/liter). Alternatively, slides may be precoated with Vectabond (Vector Laboratories, Burlingame CA) to ensure optimal adhesion of unfixed sections through long periods of dipping in multiple buffers. Section thickness is typically in the range of 15–20 μm; for subsequent quantitation it is necessary to cut tissue at a thickness that corresponds to that of the radioactive standards that are to be used. Commercial plastic ^{125}I standards available from Amersham are 20 μm thick, and tissue sections of this thickness provide excellent resolution in most species (Fig. 3).

Once mounted on slides, sections may be returned to the freezer and stored until the time of incubation. We have noticed no obvious loss of binding when sections are stored with desiccant for periods up to several months at $-80°C$. When the incubation is to be performed, slides are laid on the bench at room temperature under a stream of air for 10–15 min to allow drying. Slides are preincubated in buffer at 20–22°C before their transfer to IMEL. Different laboratories have used preincubation periods as short as 15 min and as long as 1 hr with no obvious differences in results. The effects of drying and preincubating the slide-mounted sections at room temperature have not been explored; it is possible that some receptor degradation occurs. This could be assessed by systematically varying the time or temperature of drying and preincubation or by comparing the results of *in vitro* procedures with *in vivo* IMEL labeling (see above). Until such studies are performed it should be kept in mind that, while they offer unparalleled anatomical resolution, *in vitro* autoradiographic methods may underestimate the density of receptors.

As for assays of subcellular fractions, 50 mM Tris buffer containing 4 mM $CaCl_2$ has been most widely used. Good results have been obtained with Tris concentrations up to 170 mM (21). Use of 20 mM phosphate-buffered saline (PBS) containing 150 mM NaCl and 1% (w/v) bovine serum albumin (BSA) provides similar estimates of the distribution, affinity, and number of binding sites (43–46). Nevertheless, binding is inhibited by sodium, lithium, and choline at concentrations above 50 mM (27; Fig. 4). Inclusion of $CaCl_2$ provides partial protection against the inhibition of IMEL binding by Na^+ (28). Thus the experimenter must balance the merits of optimizing binding, that is, by use of Tris buffer without sodium, against those of using a physiological buffer, that is, by use of PBS/BSA. The decision is best made with the aims of the specific study in mind. For quantitative studies it is essential to be consistent in the preincubation and incubation buffers used, and the cation content of drugs used in experimental manipulations of binding should be considered and controlled.

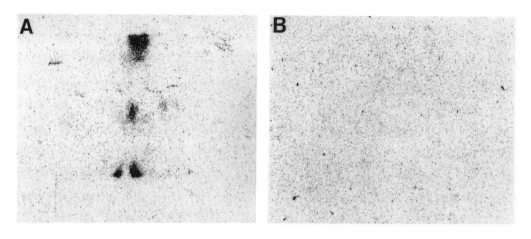

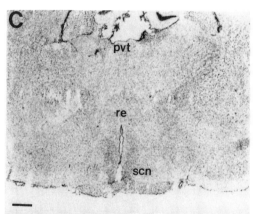

FIG. 3   (A) Autoradiographic image of coronal section of Siberian hamster diencephalon, illustrating total IMEL binding. (B) Nonspecific binding in an adjacent 20-μm section, assessed by coincubation of an equivalent (40 pM) concentration of radiolabeled IMEL with 1 μM unlabeled melatonin. (C) Cresyl Violet-stained section which generated the image shown in (A). Abbreviations: scn, suprachiasmatic nucleus; re, nucleus reuniens; pvt, paraventricular nucleus of the thalamus. Scale bar = 500 μm.

Incubation of slide-mounted sections has most often been carried out at or around 22°C for a period of 1 hr. As for studies of membranes or homogenates, IMEL concentrations of 200–300 pM are typically sufficient to saturate binding sites under these conditions, and for single-point studies a concentration of 60–100 pM is adequate. Postincubation washes are necessary to improve signal : noise ratios. Good results are obtained with cold (0°C) 5-min washes in 50 mM Tris buffer without CaCl$_2$, followed by a brief wash in distilled

AP

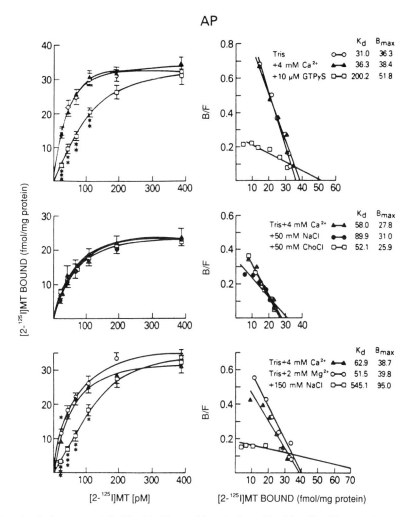

FIG. 4   Influences of CaCl$_2$, NaCl, MgCl$_2$, choline chloride (ChoCl), and GTP-γS on IMEL binding in slide-mounted sections of rat area postrema (AP) incubated in 50 mM Tris buffer. *Left:* Saturation curves. *Right:* Scatchard isotherms. Asterisks indicate statistically significant suppression of IMEL binding by GTP-γS (top) or NaCl (bottom). [Reproduced, with permission, from Laitenen *et al.* (27), Karger, Basel.]

water. When 0.02 M PBS/1% BSA is used as preincubation and incubation buffer, 15-min postincubation washes in ice-cold PBS/BSA followed by PBS are used. Brief washes are more likely to preserve IMEL binding to lower affinity sites, but IMEL binding to the high-affinity site is stable for at least

2 hr (44). On completion of the wash step, slides are again dried under a stream of cold air.

Sections to which IMEL is bound may be loaded onto film casettes in a standard manner. Double-sided tape or spray adhesive may be used to fix the backs of the slides to a cardboard surface that fits into the casette. Film is loaded into the casette under a safelight. LKB (Rockville, MD) Ultrofilm or Amersham Hyperfilm provides excellent resolution, but films such as Kodak (Rochester, NY) SB-5 are nearly as good and much less expensive. It is wise to make up a few test casettes containing representative sections that can be developed at intervals of several days so that the optimal exposure time for the casettes containing the bulk of slides in the experiment can be estimated. While the appropriate exposure interval depends on the film, the concentration of ligand used in the incubations, the species under study, and other factors, the high specific activity of IMEL permits visualization of binding sites within 2–3 weeks of exposure. Film is developed following the directions provided by the manufacturer. For most films, a 5- to 6-min immersion in Kodak D-19 is followed by a 1-min wash in distilled water or a stop bath and an 8- to 10-min incubation in Kodak fixer, all at 22°C. Use of lower temperatures may improve resolution. Films are rinsed for several minutes under running tap water, followed by a rinse in distilled water, and hung to dry.

Quantitation of binding may be performed using any of several computerized densitometric analysis programs. Particularly good software is available in the form of the Image program written by Dr. W. Rasband (National Institutes of Health, Bethesda, MD). This versatile and user-friendly program, which is rapidly becoming the standard among neurobiologists performing quantitative imaging studies on Macintosh-based systems, is updated frequently and is available without charge by file transfer over the internet. Using the mouse, it is easy to compile a standard curve from commercial or brain-mash ^{125}I standards mounted on each film casette in parallel with the slides containing the brain sections. Total binding is estimated in individual brain nuclei from images of sections incubated with IMEL alone, and subtraction of nonspecific binding as estimated from slides coincubated with excess unlabeled melatonin allows estimation of specific melatonin binding within individual brain regions. Saturation analysis leading to Scatchard isotherms can be performed using slide-mounted sections, particularly if care is taken to use exposure intervals short enough to ensure that the film is not saturated. Final values may be expressed as femtomoles per milligram plastic standard. If a more physiologically relevant measure is desired, these values may be converted to femtomoles per milligram protein using the conversion factor of 7.34 derived by Nazarali *et al.* (47).

In analyzing the distribution of IMEL binding sites on film, it is most useful to compare the image to the original tissue section. After a satisfactory autoradiogram is obtained, sections are typically postfixed in formalin and stained with Cresyl Violet or other appropriate agents. It appears that only limited studies have been carried out on the ability of these binding sites to withstand exposure to fixatives before or after incubation with IMEL. It has been reported that exposure to 10% (v/v) neutral buffered paraformaldehyde eliminates IMEL binding activity in rat median eminence/pars tuberalis (ME/PT) (32), but this is not the case for sheep pars tuberalis or hamster suprachiasmatic nucleus (SCN) lightly fixed in 4% (v/v) phosphate-buffered paraformaldehyde (pH 7.4; M. H. Hastings and E. L. Bittman, unpublished observations, 1992). IMEL bound to rat pars tuberalis is not displaced on exposure to high concentrations of glutaraldehyde (30). Such treatments may be useful in attempts to describe the neuronal connections and/or the immunocytochemical profile (e.g., the peptide phenotype) of cells that bind melatonin.

General Considerations for Experimental Design in Melatonin Receptor-Labeling Studies

In light of the rhythmicity of melatonin synthesis and secretion and its role in circadian and seasonal aspects of physiology, careful attention should be devoted to the time of day and year at which tissue is prepared for labeling studies. Variability in the results of such experiments may result from fluctuations in the timing of the distribution, number, or properties of melatonin binding sites and/or effects of seasonally changing endocrine or metabolic status on melatonin targets. Indeed, effects of time of day, light exposure, and photoperiod on IMEL binding site density have been described (38, 48–53). It should be noted that not all species respond to melatonin. For example, seasonally breeding rodents offer a better experimental model than some of the more commonly used laboratory animals (e.g., white rats) if the aim is to provide physiologically interpretable results. Furthermore, the annual reproductive cycle of some species includes phases during which they are refractory to photoperiodic signals and unresponsive to exogenous melatonin (53). While these properties may offer an exciting opportunity for probes of the cellular functions of melatonin, they may also lead to inconsistencies in results obtained within and between laboratories. At the very least, parameters such as time of day of sacrifice and seasonal state should be reported in all publications describing melatonin binding sites.

Coupling of Melatonin Receptor Complexes to G Proteins and Effects on Target Cell Physiology

The hypothesis that IMEL binding sites function as *bona fide* receptors is strongly supported by (1) their distinct and selective localization in pars tuberalis and neuroendocrine regions of the CNS, (2) the correlation of binding affinity with *in vivo* concentrations, and (3) the correspondence between their specificity and *in vivo* actions of a range of methoxyindoles. Demonstration of a cellular response to occupation of these binding sites, however, constitutes the most critical evidence for their physiological role as receptors. The discovery of a high density of binding sites in the pars tuberalis has permitted several groups to demonstrate that melatonin binding to the site labeled by IMEL regulates adenylate cyclase activity through coupling to membrane proteins of the G_i class.

In such studies, IMEL incubations are carried out in parallel with or without a GTP analog. Millimolar quantities of GTPγS, a nonhydrolyzable GTP analog, are often used for this purpose (22, 27, 43). The decrease in the affinity and number of IMEL binding sites under these conditions provides presumptive evidence for coupling to a G protein. This evidence is consistent with demonstrations that pertussis toxin, which catalyzes NAD-dependent ADP ribosylation of G_i proteins, interferes with the inhibition by melatonin of forskolin-stimulated pigment aggregation in *Xenopus* melanophores and cAMP accumulation in rat, deermouse, and sheep pars tuberalis *in vitro* (54–56). In related experiments, physiological concentrations of melatonin are capable of inhibiting the activation of adenylate cyclase by forskolin in receptor-rich tissues. Typically, cAMP accumulation or activation of protein kinase A is measured in cultures of pars tuberalis obtained from sheep or hamsters (2, 55, 56). While this goes beyond the topic of binding assays and probably does not exhaust the range of melatonin action on target cells, it provides important confirmation that high-affinity IMEL binding sites represent *bona fide* receptors and indicates directions for investigation of CNS regions in which these sites are concentrated.

Ultimately, understanding of melatonin binding sites must await full characterization of their biochemical nature. Affinity purification has been used to obtain relatively homogeneous membrane preparations that promise to prove useful in such studies (7). Analogs of IMEL that bind tightly to receptor proteins may prove useful in their isolation for subsequent characterization (57). Isolation of mRNA for melatonin receptor proteins has been difficult, but such studies may provide a sequence from which the structure of the receptor protein may be inferred and with which its expression may be studied using *in situ* hybridization or immunocytochemistry (58).

Acknowledgments

Preparation of this manuscript and unpublished results reported herein were supported by National Institutes of Health Grant MH44132 and Science and Engineering Research Council Grants GR/H08754 and H08716. I thank Drs. Francis J. P. Ebling, Michael H. Hastings, Elizabeth Maywood, Peter J. Morgan, and Shaun McNulty for their critical reading of the manuscript and helpful suggestions for improvements and Mr. John Bashford for assistance in preparation of photomicrographs.

References

1. H. Underwood, *Experientia* **45,** 914–922 (1989).
2. D. R. Weaver, S. A. Rivkees, L. L. Carlson, and S. M. Reppert, *in* "Suprachiasmatic Nucleus: The Mind's Clock" (D. C. Klein, R. Y. Moore, and S. M. Reppert, eds.), p. 289–308. Oxford Univ. Press, London, 1991.
3. E. L. Bittman, *Am. Zool.,* in press (1993).
4. O. Vakkuri, E. Lämsä, E. Rahkamaa, H. Ruotsalainen, and J. Leppäluoto, *Anal. Biochem.* **142,** 284–289 (1984).
5. D. R. Weaver, M. A. A. Namboodiri, and S. M. Reppert, *FEBS Lett.* **228,** 123–127 (1988).
6. D. Sugden, *J. Pineal Res.* **7,** 205–209 (1990).
7. S. A. Rivkees, L. L. Carlson, and S. M. Reppert, *Proc. Natl. Acad. Sci. U.S.A.* **86,** 3883–3886 (1989).
8. L. P. Niles, D. S. Pickering, and B. G. Sayer, *Biochem. Biophys. Res. Commun.* **147,** 949–956 (1987).
9. P. J. Morgan, L. M. Williams, G. Davidson, W. Lawson, and E. Howell, *J. Neuroendocrinol.* **1,** 1–4 (1989).
10. O. Vakkuri, J. Leppäluoto, and O. Vuolteenaho, *Acta Endocrinol. (Copenhagen)* **106,** 152–157 (1984).
11. R. J. Wurtman, J. Axelrod, and L. T. Potter, *J. Pharmacol. Exp. Ther.* **143,** 314–318 (1964).
12. F. Anton-Tay and R. J. Wurtman, *Nature (London)* **221,** 474–475 (1969).
13. P. A. Vitte, C. Harthe, P. Pevet, and B. Claustrat, *Neurosci. Lett.* **110,** 1–5 (1990).
14. B. Withyachumnarkul, M. Limpanawattanakul, and W. Trakulrungsi, *Life Sci.* **38,** 1757–1765 (1986).
15. M. Berria and R. A. Mead, *J. Pineal Res.* **8,** 129–136 (1990).
16. R. Mason and A. Brooks, *Neurosci. Lett.* **95,** 296–301 (1988).
17. D. P. Cardinali, M. I. Vacas, and E. Esteves-Boyer, *Endocrinology (Baltimore)* **103,** 437–441 (1979).
18. M. Cohen, D. Roselle, B. Chabner, T. J. Schmidt, and M. Lippman, *Nature (London)* **274,** 894–895 (1978).

19. A. F. Weichman, D. Bok, and J. Horwitz, *Invest. Ophthalmol. Visual Sci.* **27,** 153–163 (1986).

20. R. M. Marchbanks, *in* "Methods in Brain Research" (P. R. Bradley, ed.), pp. 113–172. Wiley, London, 1975.

21. J. Vanecek, *J. Neurochem.* **51,** 1436–1440 (1988).

22. L. M. Williams, P. J. Morgan, M. H. Hastings, W. Lawson, G. Davidson, and H. E. Howell, *J. Neuroendocrinol.* **1,** 315–320 (1989).

23. D. Sugden and N. W. S. Chong, *Brain Res.* **539,** 151–154 (1991).

24. L. P. Niles, *Eur. J. Pharmacol.* **189,** 95–98 (1990).

25. M. M. de Reviers, J. P. Ravault, Y. Tillet, and J. Pelletier, *Neurosci. Lett.* **100,** 89–93 (1989).

26. M. L. Dubocovich and J. S. Takahashi, *Proc. Natl. Acad. Sci. U.S.A.* **84,** 3916–3920 (1987).

27. J. T. Laitinen, G. Flügge, and J. M. Saavedra, *Neuroendocrinology* **51,** 619–624 (1990).

28. J. T. Laitinen and J. M. Saavedra, *J. Neurochem.* **55,** 1450–1453 (1990).

29. D. S. Pickering and L. P. Niles, *J. Pharm. Pharmacol.* **41,** 356–357 (1989).

30. L. M. Williams and P. J. Morgan, *J. Endocrinol.* **119,** R1–R3 (1988).

31. M. L. Dubocovich, *FASEB J.* **2,** 2765–2773 (1988).

32. M. L. Dubocovich, *J. Pharmacol. Exp. Ther.* **234,** 395–401 (1985).

33. M. L. Dubocovich, G. Shankar, and M. Michel, *Eur. J. Pharmacol.* **162,** 289–299 (1989).

34. M. L. Dubocovich, *J. Pharmacol. Exp. Ther.* **246,** 902 (1988).

35. C. Blazynski and M. L. Dubocovich, *J. Neurochem.* **56,** 1873–1880 (1991).

36. M. Laudon, Z. Yaron, and N. Zisapel, *J. Endocrinol.* **116,** 43–53 (1988).

37. G. A. Lincoln and R. W. Kelly, *J. Reprod. Fertil.* **86,** 737–743 (1989).

38. J. English and J. Arendt, *J. Reprod. Fertil., Suppl.* **1,** 8 (1988).

39. M. L. Dubocovich, E. Mogilnicka, and P. M. Areso, *Eur. J. Pharmacol.* **182,** 313–325 (1990).

40. M. Laudon and N. Zisapel, *FEBS Lett.* **197,** 9–12 (1986).

41. M. Laudon and N. Zisapel, *Neuroendocrinology* **48,** 577–583 (1988).

42. N. Zisapel, M. Shaharabani, and M. Laudon, *Neuroendocrinology* **46,** 207–216 (1987).

43. D. R. Weaver, S. A. Rivkees, and S. M. Reppert, *J. Neurosci.* **9,** 2581–2590 (1989).

44. S. A. Rivkees, V. M. Cassone, D. R. Weaver, and S. M. Reppert, *Endocrinology (Baltimore)* **125,** 363–368 (1989).

45. E. L. Bittman and D. R. Weaver, *Biol. Reprod.* **43,** 986–993 (1990).

46. V. M. Cassone and D. S. Brooks, *J. Exp. Zool.* **260,** 302–309 (1991).

47. A. J. Nazarali, J. S. Gutkind, and J. M. Saavedra, *J. Neurosci. Methods* **30,** 247–253 (1989).

48. J. Vanecek, E. Kosar, and J. Vorlicek, *Mol. Cell. Endocrinol.* **73,** 165–170 (1990).

49. J. Pelletier, B. Castro, G. Roblot, R. Wylde, and M. M. de Reviers, *Acta Endocrinol. (Copenhagen)* **123,** 557–562 (1990).

50. J. T. Laitinen, E. Castren, O. L. Vakkuri, and J. M. Saavedra, *Endocrinology (Baltimore)* **124,** 1585–1587 (1989).

51. H. Yuan and S. F. Pang, *Acta Endocrinol.* (*Copenhagen*) **122,** 633–639 (1990).
52. L. Jun and V. M. Cassone, *Neurosci. Abstr.* **17,** 265.10 (1991).
53. J. Vanecek and L. Jansky, *Brain Res.* **477,** 387–390 (1989).
54. B. H. White, R. D. Sekura, and M. D. Rollag, *J. Comp. Physiol.* **157,** 153–159 (1987).
55. P. J. Morgan, G. Davidson, W. Lawson, and P. Barrett, *J. Neuroendocrinol.* **2,** 773–776 (1990).
56. D. G. Hazelrigg, P. J. Morgan, W. Lawson, and M. H. Hastings, *J. Neuroendocrinol.* **3,** 597–604 (1991).
57. Y. Anis and N. Zisapel, *Biochem. Biophys. Res. Commun.* **178,** 1147–1152 (1991).
58. S. P. Fraser, P. Barrett, M. B. A. Djamgoz, and P. J. Morgan, *Neurosci. Lett.* **124,** 242–245 (1991).
59. Y. C. Cheng and W. H. Prusoff, *Biochem. Pharmacol.* **22,** 3099–3108 (1973).

[7] Transferrin Receptors in the Central Nervous System

Bruno Giometto, Paolo Gallo, and Bruno Tavolato

Transferrin (Tf), a glycoprotein of 79.5 kDa, contains two homologous iron-binding domains, each of which binds one Fe^{3+} (1). Transferrin transports iron in the blood stream and delivers it to various tissues, after binding to a specific receptor (TfR) on the cell surface.

Recycling of Transferrin during Receptor-Mediated Endocytosis

After binding to specific cell surface receptors, the ligands follow two different pathways: (1) some are degraded within the cells after dissociation from the receptors; (2) others are not degraded but exocytosed intact into the extracellular space. This is the fate of Tf that leaves the iron within the cells in endocytosed vesicles and, as apotransferrin, comes back to the membrane.

The intracellular Tf cycle is strictly pH dependent and can be divided into four stages (2, 3) (Fig. 1): (1) iron-loaded Tf binds with high affinity to its receptor; (2) the receptor–Tf complex (Tf–TfR) is internalized via coated vesicles; (3) the Tf–TfR complex is exposed to a low pH (5.0) within the lysosome, which allows the release of iron from Tf while Tf remains bound to its receptor; (4) finally, when the Tf–TfR complex reaches the external membrane Tf dissociates from its receptor at neutral pH and is released into the circulation as an intact, iron-free protein, apotransferrin.

Structure of the Transferrin Receptor

The TfR is a glycoprotein consisting of two identical 95.0-kDa polypeptides held together by a disulfide bridge. The TfR contains both N-asparagine-linked oligosaccharides and covalently attached fatty acid chains (3).

The TfR has a somewhat unusual configuration, with a small N-terminal cytoplasmic domain and a large C-terminal extracellular domain (4). In fact, the receptor spans the plasma membrane close to its N-terminal ending,

Methods in Neurosciences, Volume 11

FIG. 1   The transferrin (Tf) cycle. Iron-loaded Tf enters the cells by receptor-mediated endocytosis, delivers the iron, and reemerges into the blood stream. ⋎, Transferrin receptor (TfR); ○, transferrin (Tf); ×, iron.

exposing it in the cytoplasm (Fig. 2). The cytoplasmic domain comprises 62 amino acids and contains 4 serine residues that can act as acceptors for phosphate modification; the extracellular domain comprises 648 amino acids and contains the transferrin-binding site. This is in contrast to most membrane proteins, which span the membrane close to the carboxyl end, exposing it on the cytoplasmic side. The receptor exists as a dimer in the plasma membrane, and self-interactions of the transmembrane segments within the lipid bilayer could help to stabilize the dimer structure. The extracellular domain of the TfR contains three of five possible sites for asparagine-linked glycosylation.

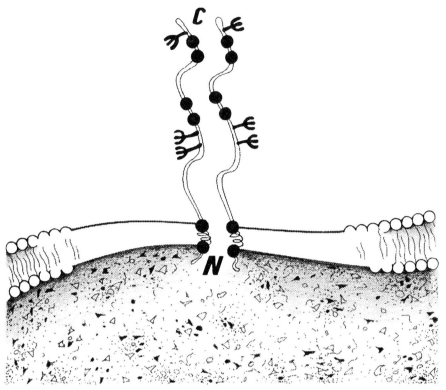

FIG. 2   Structure and membrane orientation of the human transferrin receptor (TfR). N, N-terminal end; C, C-terminal end; ●, cysteine residues; Ψ, N-asparagine-linked oligosaccharides.

Distribution of Transferrin Receptor in Tissues

The distribution of TfR in tissues reflects the cell iron requirement. This requirement varies considerably. As a general rule, the rapidly proliferating cells (compared to cells in resting state) express larger amounts of TfR. The first analysis of the distribution of TfR was performed by studying the binding of radiolabeled ^{125}I-labeled transferrin to human cell lines (5, 6).

Later, in 1980, the production by Reinherz of a monoclonal antibody (MAb) against a cell surface glycoprotein (OK T9) and by the Salk Institute of another MAb against the same glycoprotein (B3/25, T56/14, T58/1) (7), allowed a better characterization, at the morphological level, of the distribution of these receptors that were recognized to be TfR. In the studies in which the distribution of TfR in tissues was analyzed, a restricted expression pattern was detected. The tissues most susceptible to excessive iron deposition in primary hemocromatosis are the sites that express more numerous TfRs (8).

Normal resting lymphocytes express very few or no TfR, while transformed lymphocytes have larger numbers of TfRs. Lymphocytes, after mitogenic stimulation, express TfR, and their expression precedes the initiation of DNA synthesis (9).

Macrophages are the cells that express TfR diffusely in any tissue in which they are located, such as the Kuppfer cells in the liver (Fig. 3); on the other hand, parenchymal cells show a restricted pattern within the tissues (Table I): that is, in the skin only the basal layers express TfR, while more superficial layers do not; in the pancreas only the endocrine portion expresses these

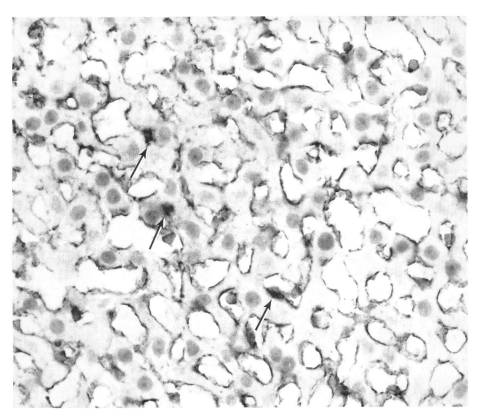

FIG. 3   Rat liver section stained by MAb OX26. The membranes of hepatocytes and Kupffer cells (arrows) are clearly outlined by the MAb. The section was counterstained with hematoxylin. (×400)

TABLE I   Expression of Transferrin Receptors in
Different Tissues

Tissue	Expression site
Skin	Basal layer of epidermis
Kidney	Tubular epithelium
Placenta	Syncytiotrophoblast
Pancreas	Islet of Langerhans
Testis	Seminiferous tubules
Anterior pituitary	Scattered cells throughout tissue
Breast	Scattered duct epithelial cells
Liver	Kuppfer cells, hepatocytes (Fig. 3)
Brain	Endothelial cells, oligodendrocytes (Fig. 4), neurons (Fig. 5)

receptors. Usually, the stained cells show a linear reaction product marking
the membranes of cells (Fig. 3); moreover, a diffuse cytoplasmic positivity
is seen, suggesting that TfR can be also detected in the cytoplasm (8).

Transendothelial Transport of Transferrin: Role of Blood–Brain Barrier

Iron-loaded Tf must cross the blood–tissue barrier to reach the parenchymal
space. Iron-loaded Tf crosses the endothelium via a vescicular transport
system. This process is called *transcytosis* and implies a regulatory function
for endothelium in the transport (10). In cerebrospinal fluid (CSF), Tf is more
concentrated than could be predicted from the molecular weight and the
hydrodynamic radius of the protein; in fact, it has a concentration of about
14 mg/liter (i.e., 4–6% of the total proteins) (11).

Such a high concentration of Tf in the CSF could mean a *de novo* synthesis
of the peptide and/or transport of the peptide through the choroid plexus
(i.e., the blood–CSF barrier), or through the brain capillary wall (i.e., the
blood–brain barrier). The observation that an anti-TfR MAb binds human
and rat brain capillaries (12) supports these concepts; the same study showed
that TfR is selectively enriched in the brain capillaries, compared to the
endothelia of other tissues. Using isolated brain capillaries it has been demonstrated that receptor-mediated endocytosis occurs at the luminal border of
brain endothelial cells; this endocytosis is followed by receptor-mediated
exocytosis of transferrin at the antiluminal border in the same manner as in
the tissue–blood barrier (13). This transcytosis occurs in the blood–brain
barrier not only for Tf, but also for insulin and insulin-like growth factor.

In the case of Tf transport through the endothelial cells, the endocytosis of Tf is not accompanied by iron dissociation from Tf within the endothelial cytoplasm.

Transferrin in the Cerebrospinal Fluid

In addition to the high concentration, Tf in the CSF has several special features. By means of electrophoretic techniques, it has been observed that Tf in the CSF comprises two fractions: a major one, with β_1 electrophoretic mobility corresponding to serum Tf; and a minor one, with a slightly lower mobility than β_2 absent in serum Tf. The latter, still retaining iron-binding capacity, was called the *Tau fraction* and was shown to have the same antigenic properties as Tf. The intrathecal synthesis of the Tau fraction was suggested, and the term *cerebrogenic Tf* has been used in the past. Subsequently, it was observed that the electrophoretic Tf band(s) could be "transformed" to the Tau band(s) by desialization with neuraminidase (14).

In a previous study done with agarose isoelectric focusing (AIEF) and two-dimensional polyacrylamide gel electrophoresis (2D-PAGE) followed by specific immunofixation, we analyzed the microheterogeneity of the CSF Tf-Tau pattern and the effects of desialization and iron saturation. We found that the AIEF and 2D-PAGE patterns of the Tau fraction were similar but not equal to that of Tf. When a genetic variant of Tf was present in the serum, the same variant was also observed in the corresponding CSF-Tf and in the Tau fraction. After neuraminidase treatment, both serum and CSF moved to the Tau position on AIEF and 2D-PAGE. On 2D-PAGE, no desialized precursors were detected. No synthesis of the Tau fraction within the brain could, therefore, be inferred.

Moreover, we found that in CSF not treated with neuraminidase, Tf appeared to be the only sialoglycoprotein clearly desialized, suggesting that the Tau fraction could not be generated by neuraminidase activity at the CSF level.

These findings strongly support the hypothesis that Tau is derived from the action of neuraminidase activity at the brain tissue level, and then is "washed" into the CSF. Brain utilization of Tf, meeting the cerebral iron requirement (intracerebral cycle), seems very likely (15).

Transferrin Receptor in the Central Nervous System

For the "intracerebral Tf cycle" to occur the expression of TfR on the membrane of CNS cells is required. The analysis of TfR in the CNS was performed using immunohistochemical and radiolabeling methods.

Radiolabeling

Using autoradiography with ^{125}I-labeled Tf, Hill *et al.* (16) characterized the TfR in whole sections of rat brain. In this study many areas of Tf accumulation were shown. Binding sites were more dense in the superficial molecular layers, in the olfactory bulb and tubercle, in pyriform cortex, dentate girus, hippocampus, and cerebellar cortex. Surprisingly, the brain sections stained for iron histochemistry showed a different pattern of staining, and the areas with dense TfR had little or no iron. Interestingly, the areas with a high concentration of iron receive neuronal input from sites with more numerous TfR, thus suggesting a neuronal transport of iron. The same findings, using radiolabeling methods, were also obtained in humans (17); the human forebrain (insula cortex, amygdala, and claustrum) showed higher binding sites for Tf. The distribution of iron in human brain showed an inverse correlation with TfR density, just as in rats.

Immunohistochemistry

Immunohistochemical methods allowed characterization, at the morphological level, of cells expressing TfR. In rats, many authors investigated TfR using a MAb (clone OX26) reported to be specific for TfR, because it recognized a detergent-soluble molecule that can bind ^{125}I-labeled Tf and precipitates a dimer of glycoprotein with an apparent molecular weight of 95,000 that correspond to the molecular weight of Tf (18).

Brain Capillaries
Jefferies *et al.* (12) demonstrated with this MAb (clone OX26) the presence of TfR on brain capillaries and in the choroid plexus cells of rats. These authors also reported weak staining in scattered cells having the morphology of neurons. Many other articles have confirmed these findings in rats (19–21) (Fig. 4) and also in human brain (22).

Oligodendrocytes
Although Tf has been localized in oligodendrocytes (23) these cells express only a little TfR. Their expression seems to play an important role during development, because among rats it declines after a few days after birth (24). The production of Tf by oligodendrocytes may account for high levels of Tf in the CSF.

   A weak staining of oligodendrocytes was obtained by immunohistochemistry using the anti-TfR MAb OX26 (21); these arrange in clusters at the

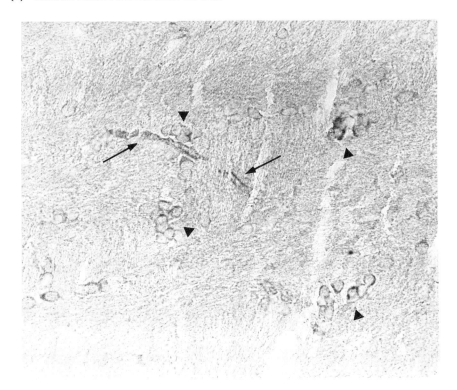

FIG. 4   Brain capillary (arrows) and cluster of oligodendrocytes (arrowheads) stained by MAb OX26 in the cerebral white matter. Among the cells only the membranes are outlined by the reaction. (×200)

interfascicular and perivascular levels, especially in the white matter of the cerebral cortex (Fig. 4).

Astrocytes

No expression of TfR is reported on the membranes of astrocytes under normal conditions. However, in experimentally induced brain injuries, reactive astrocytes, in addition to endothelial cells, expressed TfR in rats (20).

Neurons

In developing chicken neurons TfR was detected by immunocytochemistry, using peroxidase and anti-peroxidase methods (25). Their expression became gradually weaker in postnatal neurons, suggesting that Tf plays a role only during early neuronal development.

Using a more amplified immunocytochemical method with avidin–biotin, we showed in rat brain the presence of TfR in cortical and brainstem postnatal neurons (21). In our study, neuronal reactivity was highlighted by treatment of the sections with trypsin; this showed TfR immunoreactivity, mainly in the cytoplasm of neurons. In fact, TfR present on the cell surface may be partially destroyed or masked by fixatives or by postmortem modification, and the epitopes recognized by the MAb might become accessible to the antibody only after there has been an increase in tissue permeability induced by enzymatic digestion. On the other hand, the presence of TfR in the cytoplasm of neurons is not surprising, if we consider the intracellular cycle of Tf/TfR. Other authors have reported the presence of TfR, particularly in the cytoplasm of CNS cells.

In these cases, a nonspecific staining induced by enzymatic treatment could be excluded by the finding of other MAbs of the same immunoglobulin class that fail to stain neurons.

With these technical procedures and using MAb OX26 we demonstrated the presence of TfR on neurons of all cerebral layers of the motor cortex, especially those of layer V. In these cells the labeling was mainly confined to the cell membrane and the proximal portion of the apical dendrites (Fig. 5A and B). Pontine neurons showed intense TfR immunoreactivity, which extended to the entire cytoplasm (Fig. 5C). In the cerebellum, the Purkinje cells were weakly stained, while no reactivity was present in the granular and molecular layers. Scattered neurons were faintly stained in the cervical gray matter of the spinal cord. No particular laminar distribution of reactivity has been observed; white matter remained unstained.

Conclusions

The detection of TfR in the central nervous system has several important implications.

1. The transcytosis mediated by TfR across the blood–brain barrier may also have utility as a drug delivery system when antibody-conjugated drug is used instead of Tf. In fact, delivery of nonlipophilic drugs to the brain is hindered by the blood–brain barrier. The TfR may shuttle molecules across the blood–brain barrier, considering the high density of these receptors on brain endothelial cells. Preliminary experiments demonstrated that the drug levels in brain parenchyma are enhanced when the drug is conjugated to the antibody OX26 (26).

2. Data show that in oligodendrocytes, derived from developing rat optic nerve, there is a temporal association between TfR expression–Tf accumula-

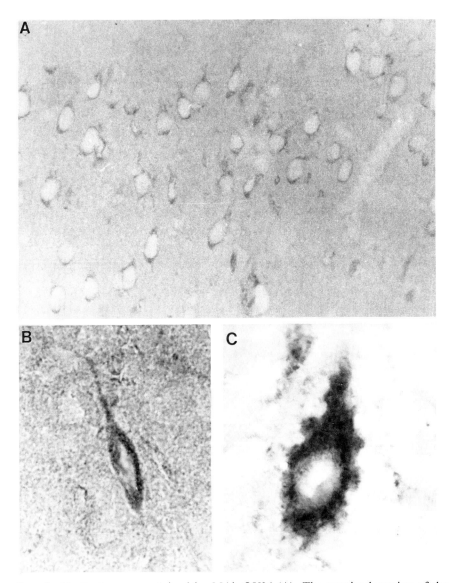

FIG. 5 Cortical neurons stained by MAb OX26 (A). The proximal portion of the apical dendrite is also positive. At the higher magnification (B and C) it is possible to recognize the cytoplasm of other neurons fully occupied by the reaction. (A) ×200; (B and C) ×800.

tion and myelin production. In the myelin mutant strain of rats characterized by a lack of myelin production, TfR expression and Tf accumulation are absent in oligodendrocytes and confined to the vasculature. These findings suggest that iron and Tf may play a permissive role in myelination and TfR expression may modulate this process (27).

3. Besides normal proliferating cells and a few resting cell types, tumor cells express a high number of TfRs. Moreover, the expression of TfR correlates with the proliferating rate of neoplastic elements, and in some cases TfR can be used as a marker to distinguish between tumor cells and normal tissue. For this reason, the use of anti-TfR MAb as a carrier in immunotoxin cytotoxicity has been proposed for tumor therapy (28). This treatment has been suggested for tumors that arise in organs with low TfR basal expression, such as the brain (29). However, the presence of TfR on neurons implies that this therapy could also destroy normal neurons, leading to important neurological syndromes. The therapeutic window should be considered to minimize the neurological side effects.

Immunohistochemical Procedures

1. Adult Sprague–Dawley rats, anesthetized with pentobarbitone, are perfused through the ascending aorta with 100 ml cold saline followed by 500 ml 4% (v/v) paraformaldehyde (4°C) in 0.1 M phosphate buffer, pH 7.4.

2. The cerebral and cerebellar hemispheres, brainstem, and spinal cord are dissected out and stored in cold fixative for 4 hr; the tissue is then kept overnight in 10% (w/v) sucrose.

3. Ten-micrometer-thick frozen sections of cerebral cortex, cerebellar cortex, brainstem, and spinal cord are cut and placed on poly-L-lysine-coated slides.

4. Subsequently, the sections are treated with 0.1% (v/v) H_2O_2 for 10 min, followed by 0.5% (w/v) trypsin (100 ml distilled water, 0.05 g of trypsin, 0.5 g Ca_2Cl, pH 7.8) for 10 min at 37°C.

5. The slides are then incubated overnight at 4°C with the IgG_{2a} MAb OX26 (SeraLab, England) diluted 1 : 100 in phosphate-buffered saline (PBS), pH 7.4.

6. The sections are washed three times in PBS, and then covered with an intermediate layer of biotinylated rabbit anti-mouse immunoglobulin (Dako, Denmark) diluted 1 : 200 in PBS for 1 hr at room temperature.

7. After further washing, a layer of horseradish peroxidase-conjugated avidin (Dako) diluted 1 : 500 is added for 30 min at room temperature.

8. The substrate reaction is developed with 0.05% (w/v) diaminobenzidine tetrahydrochloride (Sigma, St. Louis, OH) and 0.01% (v/v) H_2O_2 in PBS.

9. Finally, the slides are washed and mounted in glycerol gelatin (E. Merck, AG, Darmstadt, Germany).

References

1. R. T. A. MacGillivray, E. Mendez, S. K. Sinha, M. R. Sutton, J. Lineback-Zins, and K. Brew, *Proc. Natl. Acad. Sci. U.S.A.* **79,** 2504 (1982).
2. A. Dautry-Varsat, A. Ciechanover, and H. F. Lodish, *Proc. Natl. Acad. Sci. U.S.A.* **80,** 2258 (1983).
3. J. W. Goding, *Surv. Immunol. Res.* **2,** 129 (1983).
4. C. Schneider, M. J. Owen, D. Banville, and J. G. Williams, *Nature (London)* **311,** 675 (1984).
5. J. W. Larrick and P. Cresswell, *Biochim. Biophys. Acta* **583,** 483 (1979).
6. P. A. Seligman, R. B. Schleicher, and R. H. Allen, *J. Biol. Chem.* **254,** 9943 (1979).
7. M. B. Omary, I. S. Trowbridge, and J. Minowada, *Nature (London)* **286,** 888 (1980).
8. K. C. Gatter, G. Brown, I. S. Trowbridge, R. E. Woolston, and D. Y. Mason, *J. Clin. Pathol.* **36,** 539 (1983).
9. J. W. Larrick and P. Cresswell, *J. Supramol. Struct.* **11,** 579 (1979).
10. R. Soda and M. Tavassoli, *J. Ultrastruct. Res.* **88,** 18 (1984).
11. K. Felgenhauer, *Klin. Wochenschr.* **52,** 1158 (1974).
12. W. A. Jefferies, M. R. Brandon, S. V. Hunt, F. A. Williams, K. C. Gatter, and D. Y. Mason, *Nature (London)* **312,** 162 (1984).
13. W. M. Pardridge, J. Eisenberg, and J. Yang, *Metab. Clin. Exp.* **36,** 892 (1987).
14. J. Clausen and T. Munkner, *Nature (London)* **189,** 60 (1961).
15. P. Gallo, F. Bracco, S. Morara, L. Battistin, and B. Tavolato, *J. Neurol. Sci.* **70,** 81 (1985).
16. J. M. Hill, M. R. Ruff, R. J. Weber, and C. B. Pert, *Proc. Natl. Acad. Sci. U.S.A.* **82,** 4553 (1985).
17. C. M. Morris, J. M. Candy, A. E. Oakley, G. A. Taylor, S. Mountfort, H. Bishop, M. K. Ward, C. A. Bloxham, and J. A. Edwardson, *J. Neurol. Sci.* **94,** 295 (1989).
18. W. A. Jefferies, M. R. Brandon, A. F. Williams, and S. V. Hunt, *Immunology* **54,** 333 (1985).
19. H. H. Lin and J. R. Connor, *Dev. Brain Res.* **49,** 281 (1989).
20. T. Orita, T. Akimura, T. Nishizaki, T. Kamiryo, Y. Ikeyama, H. Aoki, and H. Ito, *Acta Neuropathol.* **79,** 686 (1990).
21. B. Giometto, F. Bozza, V. Argentiero, P. Gallo, S. Pagni, M. G. Piccinno, and B. Tavolato, *J. Neurol. Sci.* **98,** 81 (1990).
22. L. Recht, C. O. Torres, T. W. Smith, V. Raso, and T. W. Griffin, *J. Neurosurg.* **72,** 941 (1990).
23. J. R. Connor and R. E. Fine, *Brain Res.* **368,** 319 (1986).
24. A. Espinosa de los Monteros and B. Foucaud, *Dev. Brain Res.* **35,** 123 (1987).

25. T. H. Oh, G. J. Markelonis, G. M. Royal, and B. S. Bregman, *Dev. Brain Res.* **30,** 207 (1986).

26. P. M. Friden, L. R. Walus, G. F. Musso, M. A. Taylor, B. Malfroy, and R. M. Starzyk, *Proc. Natl. Acad. Sci. U.S.A.* **88,** 4771 (1991).

27. H. H. Lin and J. R. Connor, *Dev. Brain Res.* **49,** 281 (1989).

28. J. S. Trowbridge and D. L. Domingo, *Nature (London)* **294,** 171 (1981).

29. M. Colombatti, M. Bisconti, L. Dell'Arciprete, M. A. Gerosa, and G. Tridente, *Int. J. Cancer* **42,** 441 (1988).

[8] Binding Sites of Pituitary Adenylate Cyclase-Activating Polypeptide in Human Brain

David M. Smith and Stephen R. Bloom

I. Introduction

Pituitary adenylate cyclase activating polypeptide (PACAP) was isolated in 1989 by Arimura and colleagues from ovine hypothalamus as a 38-amino acid amidated peptide, PACAP 38 (1), and a C-terminally deleted minor form of 27 amino acids, PACAP 27 (2). Its name derives from its ability to increase cyclic AMP production and hormone release in superfused rat pituitary cells (1). PACAP shows sequence homology with a number of members of the secretin/glucagon family of peptides (Table I), in particular the first 28 amino acids of PACAP and vasoactive intestinal polypeptide (VIP) show a 68% homology. Specific receptors for PACAP have been demonstrated in a number of tissues and species, including rat central nervous system (3), rat astrocytes (4), human neuroblastoma cells (5), rat pancreatic acinar AR4-2J cells (6), bovine hypothalamus (7), and human brain (8). These receptors show a much greater affinity for PACAP (in the nanomolar range) than VIP (micromolar range). PACAP-binding sites have also been demonstrated in mouse splenocytes (9) and rat liver (10) and lung (3), which are displaced by VIP at nanomolar concentrations. It has been suggested that specific PACAP receptors be referred to as type I and those shared with VIP as type II (11). The distribution of immunoreactive PACAP in rat tissues has been determined (12).

PACAP is highly abundant in the brain (especially the hypothalamus) and the testes. The possible neurotransmitter/neuromodulator role of PACAP has led us to examine PACAP receptors in the human brain.

Receptor-Binding Assay

Human Brain Tissue

Human postmortem brain is dissected into the various anatomical regions (hypothalamus, cortex, cerebellum, brainstem, and basal ganglia) and frozen in liquid nitrogen for transport. Samples can be stored at −70°C for mem-

TABLE I   Amino Acid Sequence of PACAP 38, PACAP 27, and Related Peptides

Peptide	Sequence[a]			
	1 10 20 30 38			
PACAP 38	H-S-D-G-I-F-T-D-S-Y-S-R-Y-R-K-Q-M-A-V-K-K-Y-L-A-A-V-L-G-K-R-Y-K-Q-R-V-K-N-K-NH$_2$			
PACAP 27	H-S-D-G-I-F-T-D-S-Y-S-R-Y-R-K-Q-M-A-V-K-K-Y-L-A-A-V-L-NH$_2$			
VIP	H-S-D-A-V-F-T-D-N-Y-T-R-L-R-K-Q-M-A-V-K-K-Y-K-N-S-I-L-N-NH$_2$			
Glucagon	H-S-Q-G-T-F-T-S-D-Y-S-K-Y-L-D-S-R-R-A-Q-D-F-V-Q-W-L-M-N-T			
PHM	H-A-D-G-V-F-T-S-D-Y-S-R-L-L-G-Q-L-S-A-K-K-Y-L-E-S-L-L-M-NH$_2$			

[a] The N terminal of the peptide is to the left and designated residue 1. Single-letter amino acid codes are as follow: H, His; S, Ser; D, Asp; G, Gly; I, Ile; F, Phe; T, Thr; Y, Tyr; R, Arg; K, Lys; Q, Gln; M, Met; A, Ala; V, Val; L, Leu; N, Asn; W, Trp; E, Glu.

brane preparation for up to 4 months without deterioration. Samples are taken from both male and female subjects without previous history of neurological or psychiatric disorder. There is no apparent difference in receptors from male or female subjects. Time after death before dissection appears critical and we have not obtained good preparations from brains more than 20 hr postmortem.

Preparation of a Crude Membrane Fraction

Most of our binding studies on specific PACAP receptors have measured binding in a crude membrane fraction (3, 8, 13). This has been the policy of most researchers (4, 6, 11, 14, 15) but PACAP-binding assays on intact mouse splenocytes (9) and rat pituitary GH$_3$ cells (16) have been reported. All the membrane preparations used are similar and based on simple differential centrifugation.

The methodology we use is as follows: All procedures are carried out at 4°C. Buffer A is 50 mM Tris-HCl, pH 7.6, plus 10 μg/ml soybean trypsin inhibitor, 0.5 μg/ml pepstatin, 0.25 μg/ml leupeptin, 0.25 μg/ml antipain, 0.1 mg/ml benzamidine, 1 mg/ml bacitracin, and 30 μg/ml aprotinin. All chemicals and protease inhibitors are from Sigma (St. Louis, MO).

1. Tissues (1–5 g wet weight) are homogenized in ice-cold buffer A plus 0.25 M sucrose with three 1-min bursts (three-quarters speed), with 1-min intervals in between, using an Ultra-Turrax T25 homogenizer (BDH, Poole, Dorset, England). The ratio of tissue wet weight to homogenization buffer volume is 5 g tissue/20 ml.

2. The homogenates are centrifuged at 1500 g for 20 min at 4°C in 30-ml polypropylene tubes using a Sorvall (Norwalk, CT) RT6000B centrifuge.

3. The supernatant from the first spin is centrifuged at 100,000 g for 60 min at 4°C in 30-ml "Oak Ridge"-style polycarbonate tubes using a Sorvall A841 rotor in a Sorvall OTD55B centrifuge.

4. The pellets from the high-speed spin are resuspended in 10 vol of buffer A (to wash out the sucrose) by hand homogenization using glass/Teflon homogenizers (Jencons, Leighton Buzzard, Bedfordshire, England) and centrifuged as in step 3.

5. The pellets are resuspended in buffer A to a final protein concentration of 3–6 mg protein/ml in 250- to 500-μl aliquots and stored at $-70°C$ for up to 5 months.

We routinely use the biuret method (17) for determination of membrane protein concentration, as lower concentrations are given by the commonly used Bradford method (18), possibly because of insufficient solubilization of the membranes. Final yields are approximately 4 mg of membrane per gram wet weight tissue. We have replaced the Tris-HCl with 50 mM N-2-hydroxy-ethylpiperazine-N'-2-ethanesulfonic acid (HEPES), pH 7.6, with no change in results. This is desirable if the membranes are to be used in cross-linking with the N-hydroxysuccinimide ester reagents, which are reported to react with primary amine groups present in Tris but not HEPES (information from reagent manufacturer). The membrane preparations reported in the literature differ from the protocol in two aspects. First, sucrose may be omitted from the homogenization buffer (15), and second, membranes are prepared using 1 mM NaHCO$_3$ without sucrose or protease inhibitors (6). Both of these protocols yield good results, with the NaHCO$_3$ method being useful for preparation of membranes from cell culture as a hypotonic lysis buffer.

Preparation of Labeled Peptide

PACAP-binding sites are most often detected using ^{125}I-labeled PACAP 27, as complete ^{125}I-PACAP 38 gives very high nonspecific binding (4, 6). Three different oxidation reagents for iodination have been employed, namely Iodogen (19), chloramine-T (20, 21), and lactoperoxidase (15, 22). All three methods yield effective iodinated PACAP 27 for receptor studies. We routinely use the Iodogen method for all receptor radioligands to avoid the loss of biological activity sometimes associated with the strong oxidizing conditions of the chloramine-T method.

Materials

PACAP 27 is custom synthesized by Peptide Products (Southampton, Hampshire, England). Iodogen reagent (1,3,4,6-tetrachloro-3α,6α-diphenylglycoluril) is from Pierce (Rockford, IL). Na ^{125}I (specific activity, 629 GBq/mg) is from Du Pont (Wilmington, DE).

Protocol

1. PACAP 27 (7 nmol) is freshly dissolved in 10 μl 0.2 M phosphate buffer, pH 7.4, and added to a polypropylene tube coated with 10 μg of Iodogen reagent. These tubes are prepared by adding 10 μg of Iodogen reagent in 20 μl of chloroform to the tube and allowing the chloroform to evaporate under nitrogen. The capped tube is stored at $-20°$C in a desiccator and used within 2 months.

2. Add 1 mCi (10 μl) of Na ^{125}I and incubate on ice for 10 min.

3. The reaction is stopped by adding 500 μl of 10% acetonitrile/0.1% trifluoroacetic acid in H$_2$O and injecting the sample onto a reversed phase C$_{18}$ high-performance liquid chromatography (HPLC) column (Nova-Pak C$_{18}$, 8 mm $\times$ 10 cm radial PAK cartridge; Waters Associates, Milford, MA).

4. The iodinated peptide is separated from unlabeled peptide using a 15–35% acetonitrile/0.1% trifluoroacetic acid/water gradient over 90 min. Fractions (1.5 ml) are collected into tubes containing 1 ml of 0.1 M Tris-HCl, pH 11.00, plus 0.3% (w/v) bovine serum albumen (BSA).

5. Peak fractions of radioactivity are tested in the binding assay and those showing high specific binding are diluted with 500 μl (total volume, 2 ml) of 5% BSA (v/v) plus 300 μg/ml aprotinin in water (to inhibit proteases present in the BSA). Aliquots of approximately 20,000 Bq are added to 2-ml siliconized glass vials, freeze-dried overnight, and stoppered. Using siliconized vials and BSA added to the label prevents the label adhering to the vial wall. Repeated freezing and thawing destroys the labeled peptide; freeze-drying is therefore preferable.

Fractions showing the best binding are eluted from the column at about 32% acetonitrile. PACAP 27 has three tyrosine residues (see Table I) that could be iodinated. We routinely see three peaks of iodinated peptide (see Fig. 1); the first shows no binding and the second peak shows the greatest specific binding. Samples of label dissolved in binding buffer are analyzed by fast protein liquid chromatography (FPLC) using a Pep RPC C$_{18}$ column (Pharmacia, Piscataway, NJ) and a 30-min 20–45% acetonitrile in 0.1% trifluoroacetic acid/water gradient. A single peak of undegraded label is observed at approximately 32% acetonitrile (see Fig. 2). The specific activity of the label is 108 Ci/mmol. The production of Iodogen-labeled ^{125}I-labeled

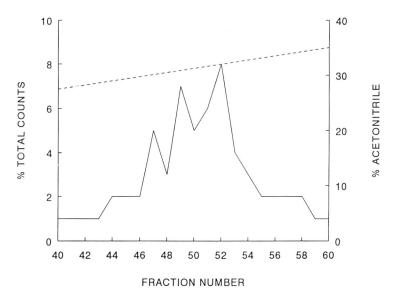

FIG. 1   HPLC profile of PACAP 27 iodinated by the Iodogen method. PACAP 27 (10 nmol) was iodinated and HPLC performed as described in text. This result is typical of 10 iodinations. –––, Acetonitrile gradient.

PACAP 38 of high specific activity and low nonspecific binding has been reported (23). This could be important, because the authors demonstrate the existence of receptors that bind only PACAP 38 with high affinity.

Binding Assay Procedure and Expected Results

Standard Protocol

   1. Membrane protein (60 μg) is incubated at 37°C for 90 min with 0.25 nM ^{125}I-labeled PACAP 27 (500 Bq) in binding buffer [50 mM HEPES, pH 7.6, 1 mM ethylenediaminetetraacetic acid (EDTA), 0.25 mg/ml bacitracin and 3% (v/v) bovine serum albumen] in a 1.5-ml polypropylene microfuge tube. The final assay volume is 500 μl. Nonspecific binding is determined by the addition of 0.2 μM PACAP 27 (i.e., approximately 1000 times the concentration of labeled PACAP 27).

   2. The receptor/^{125}I-labeled PACAP 27 complex is separated from free label by centrifugation at 15,000 g for 2 min in an IEC (Needham Heights, MA) Centra M at 4°C.

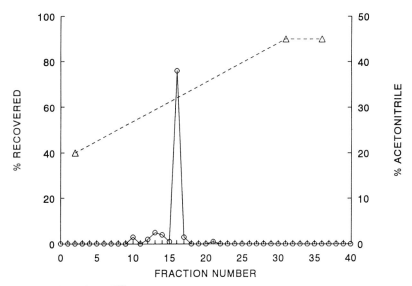

FIG. 2   FPLC profile of ^{125}I-labeled PACAP 27 reconstituted from freeze-dried label. FPLC was performed as described in the text. This result is typical of six runs. It can clearly be seen that the label is a single peak (80%). –––, Acetonitrile gradient.

3. The supernatant is removed and the pellets are washed at 4°C with 0.5 ml of ice-cold binding buffer and recentrifuged as in step 2.

4. The supernatant is removed and the dry tubes counted for 2 min in a Nuclear Enterprises NE1600 multiple well γ counter.

5. All tubes and pipette tips are siliconized to reduce nonspecific binding of PACAP. Results are expressed as specific binding, that is, total binding minus nonspecific binding.

We have experimented with different concentrations of membrane (see Fig. 3) and shown that 60 μg of membrane protein gives the best compromise between high specific binding and adequate precipitation of the membrane. The effect of buffer pH is shown in Fig. 4, the optimum pH being around pH 7.6 (3, 8). The effect of incubation temperature and time is shown in Fig. 5. We routinely use a 90-min incubation at 37°C for human brain membranes but these parameters should be checked for each tissue, for example, for rat brain we have found that a 60-min incubation at 22°C is optimum.

The main differences between our protocol and those of others lie in the buffers used and the method for separation of receptor bound and free label. Tris-maleate (50 mM), pH 7.4 (6), Tris-HCl (50 mM), pH 7.4 (14), and phosphate-buffered saline, pH 7.4 (7), all appear to give good results. Separa-

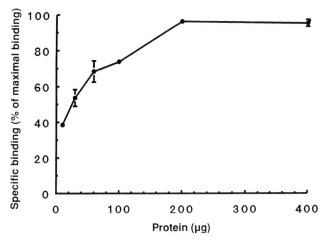

FIG. 3 Effect of quantity of membrane protein on specific binding of ^{125}I-labeled
PACAP 27. Increasing amounts of membrane were incubated under standard binding
assay conditions. Values are a percentage of maximal specific binding and mean ±
SEM of three experiments using human hypothalamic membranes. [Reproduced from
Suda *et al.* (8) with permission).]

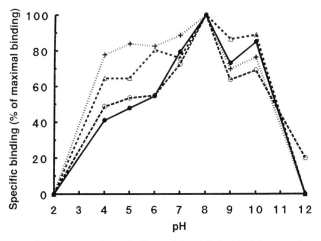

FIG. 4 Effect of pH on specific binding of ^{125}I-labeled PACAP 27 in hypothalamic
(●), brainstem, (△), cerebellar (○), and pituitary gland (+) membranes. The pH of
the assay buffer was adjusted with HCl and NaOH as required. Values are expressed
as a percentage of maximal specific binding. [Reproduced from Suda *et al.* (8) with
permission.]

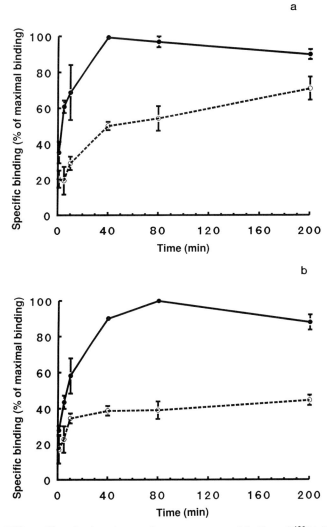

FIG. 5   Effect of incubation time and temperature on binding of ^{125}I-labeled PACAP 27 to hypothalamic (a), brainstem (b), and cerebellar (c) membranes. Binding assays were carried out at 37°C (●) and 4°C (○). Values are a percentage of maximal specific binding and mean ± SEM of three experiments using different membranes. [Reproduced from Suda *et al.* (8) by permission.]

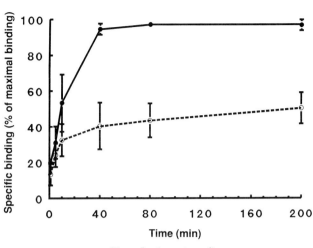

FIG. 5 (*continued*)

tion of bound from free label has been achieved by aliquoting the binding mixture onto either Whatman (Clifton, NJ) GF/C filters presoaked in 0.1% polyethyleneimine (23) or Whatman GF/B filters presoaked in 0.5% polyethyleneimine (11), followed by washing of the filters using a cell harvester and counting. This method is theoretically superior to our centrifugation procedure because the high-speed washing causes minimum disruption of the equilibrium between bound and free label. However, the results do not seem qualitatively or quantitatively different, and our method requires less specialized equipment and is easier to perform.

The PACAP-binding sites in human brain are specific for PACAP and have a low affinity for VIP, that is, they are type I. We have demonstrated the existence of smaller numbers of type II receptors in human brain using labeled VIP (13). Type I human brain PACAP receptors show a K_D for PACAP 27 of 0.5–1.0 nM, which is typical of type I PACAP receptors. GTP (10 μM) increases the rate of dissociation of ^{125}I-labeled PACAP 27 from cerebellar membranes, indicating that the receptor is G protein linked, as might be expected of a receptor that activates adenylate cyclase (8).

Molecular Identification of PACAP Receptors: Chemical Cross-Linking Studies

These studies have proved useful to determine the physical identity of peptide receptors. Reagents for chemical cross-linking of ligands to receptors may be homobifunctional or heterobifunctional and may utilize either a spontaneous reaction pathway or be photoreactive or both. The most widely used homobifunctional reagents utilize the *N*-hydroxysuccinimide group for coupling to amine groups on the ligand and receptor. We have found that best results are obtained using disuccinimidyl suberate (DSS) as the cross-linking reagent.

Protocol

1. Receptor binding is performed as described in the previous section, except that 100 μg of membrane protein is incubated with 5 nM (10,000 Bq) of ^{125}I-labeled PACAP 27. Nonspecific binding is determined in the presence of 1 μM unlabeled PACAP 27.

2. The washed pellets are counted for 2 min in a γ counter to determine specific binding and resuspended in 200 μl of 50 mM HEPES, pH 7.4. Freshly made DSS (100 mM in dimethylsulfoxide; Pierce) is added to a final concentration of 3 mM and allowed to react for 30 min at 22°C.

3. The reaction is stopped by the addition of 1 ml of ice-cold 50 mM Tris-HCl, pH 7.4, and centrifugation at 15,000 g for 3 min. The supernatant is removed and the pellet washed with a further 1 ml of 50 mM Tris-HCl, pH 7.4. Centrifugation is repeated and the pellets counted as above to check if the cross-linking reaction is successful.

4. The pellet is resuspended in 50 μl of fresh electrophoresis sample buffer [62.5 mM Tris-HCl, pH 7.4, 2% (w/v) sodium dodecyl sulfate (SDS), 0.1% (w/v) bromphenol blue, and 0.1 M dithiothreitol] and boiled for 2 min.

5. Electrophoresis is performed under reducing conditions as used by Smith *et al.* (24). Sucrose is added to a final concentration of 20% (w/v) and the samples loaded onto 4% (w/v) acrylamide stacking and 10% (w/v) acrylamide resolving gels (20 cm $\times$ 20 cm $\times$ 1.5 mm). A series of protein standards (carbonate dehydratase, M_r 29,000; ovalbumin, M_r 45,000; bovine serum albumen, M_r 66,000; phosphorylase b, M_r 97,400; β-galactosidase, M_r 116,000; and myosin, M_r 205,000; Sigma) are run concurrently with the samples. Gels are run at a constant 8 mA for 15 hr at room temperature.

6. The stacking gel is removed and the resolving gel stained for 10 min in 0.25% (w/v) Coomassie Brilliant Blue R250/50% (w/v) trichloroacetic acid. Destaining is with 45% (v/v) methanol/5% (v/v) acetic acid in water. Finally, the acetic acid is removed by immersion in 4% (v/v) glycerol in water for 1 hr at room temperature and the gel dried at 80°C for 2 hr with a Flowgen Gel Dryer (Flowgen Instruments, Ltd., Sittingbourne, Kent, England).

7. Autoradiographs are obtained at -70°C for 3 days–3 weeks within cassettes containing intensifying screens (Genetic Research Instruments, Ltd., Essex, England) using Kodak (Rochester, NY) X-Omat AR film.

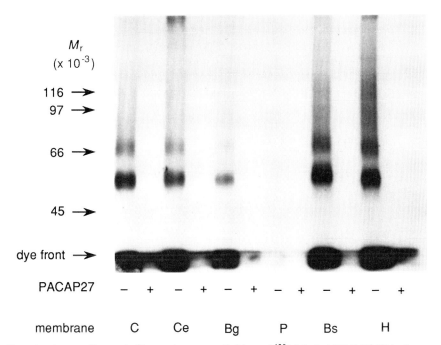

FIG. 6   Autoradiograph illustrating cross-linking of ^{125}I-labeled PACAP 27 to human brain membranes using DSS. Cross-linking was performed as described in text using membranes from cortex (C), cerebellum (Ce), basal ganglia (Bg), pituitary gland (P), brainstem (Bs), and hypothalamus (H) in the presence and absence of 0.2 μM PACAP 27. The positions of molecular weight markers are shown on the left of the figure. [Reproduced from Suda *et al.* (8) with permission.]

Using this method we obtained molecular weights for human brain PACAP receptors of 48,000 [major band (M_r 3000) subtracted for one PACAP 27 molecule] and 67,000 (see Fig. 6). Labeling of both receptor bands were reduced in the presence of unlabeled PACAP 27, PACAP 38 (but not VIP), and GTP, as expected (8). We have also used the homobifunctional cross-linking reagents disuccinimidyl tartrate (DST), ethylene glycol bis(succinimi-dylsuccinate) (EGS), bis[2-(succinimidooxycarbonyloxy)ethyl]sulfone (BSOCOES) (all three are *N*-hydroxysuccinimide reagents), and dimethyl suberimidate (DMS; an imido ester reagent). None of these reagents was better than DSS, with the imido ester being completely ineffective. Chemical cross-linking of PACAP 27 to its binding sites has been performed using membranes from a number of different tissues. In bovine brain (7) an M_r 57,000 receptor was observed using phosphate-buffered saline containing

DSS (which gave best results) or the photoreactive compounds N-hydroxy-succinimidyl-4-azidobenzoate (HSAB) and N-succinimidyl-6 (4'-azido-2'-nitrophenylamino) hexanoate (SANPAH). Interestingly the molecular weight of the putative receptor did not change when gels were run under nonreducing conditions, indicating that there are no other subunits of the receptor linked by disulfide bridges. In human neuroblastoma NB-OK cells (5) and rat pancreatic acinar AR4-2J cells (6), DSS cross-linking in reducing conditions showed single PACAP-binding sites of M_r 65,000. Using bis(sulfosuccinimidyl)suberate (BS3) under reducing conditions, the rat hypothalamic PACAP-binding site was of M_r 57,000 (14). None of these PACAP-binding sites appears to relate closely to the major 48,000 band in the human brain although the larger, M_r 67,000 band may be similar to that seen in the NB-OK cells. Differences in size of the various PACAP receptors described may be due to differential glycosylation but this has not yet been examined. Further characterization of PACAP receptors will require molecular cloning and sequencing of the receptor. Functional studies of PACAP in neural systems need the development of effective and specific antagonists. These should soon be available and the pharmacology of PACAP receptors properly established.

Acknowledgments

D.M.S. thanks the Medical Research Council and the Nuffield Foundation for supporting this work. We also wish to thank Dr. K. Suda for help in setting up the assays.

References

1. A. Miyata, A. Arimura, R. R. Dahl, N. Minamino, A. Vehara, L. Jiang, M. D. Culler, and D. H. Coy, *Biochem. Biophys. Res. Commun.* **164,** 567 (1989).
2. A. Miyata, L. Jiang, R. R. Dahl, C. Kitada, K. Kubo, M. Fujino, N. Minamino, and A. Arimura, *Biochem. Biophys. Res. Commun.* **170,** 643 (1990).
3. H.-C. Lam, K. Takahashi, M. A. Ghatei, S. M. Kanse, J. M. Polak, and S. R. Bloom, *Eur. J. Biochem.* **193,** 725 (1990).
4. I. Tatsuno, P. E. Gottschall, K. Köves, and A. Arimura, *Biochem. Biophys. Res. Commun.* **168,** 1027 (1990).
5. A. Cauvin, L. Buscail, P. Gourlet, P. De Neef, D. Gossen, A. Arimura, A. Miyata, D. H. Coy, P. Robberecht, and J. Christophe, *Peptides (N.Y.)* **11,** 773 (1990).
6. L. Buscail, P. Gourlet, A. Cuavin, P. De Neef, D. Gossen, A. Arimura, A. Miyata, D. H. Coy, P. Robberecht, and J. Christophe, *FEBS Lett.* **262,** 77 (1990).
7. T. Ohtaki, T. Watanabe, Y. Ishibashi, C. Kitada, M. Tsuda, P. E. Gottschall, A. Arimura, and M. Fujino, *Biochem. Biophys. Res. Commun.* **171,** 838 (1990).

8. K. Suda, D. M. Smith, M. A. Ghatei, J. K. Murphy, and S. R. Bloom, *J. Clin. Endocrinol. Metab.* **72,** 958 (1991).

9. I. Tatsuno, P. E. Gottschall, and A. Arimura, *Endocrinology* (*Baltimore*) **128,** 728 (1991).

10. P. Robberecht, P. Gourlet, A. Cauvin, L. Buscail, P. De Neef, A. Arimura, and J. Christophe, *Am. J. Physiol.* **260,** G97 (1991).

11. B. D. Shivers, T. J. Görcs, P. E. Gottschall, and A. Arimura, *Endocrinology* (*Baltimore*) **128,** 3055 (1991).

12. A. Arimura, A. Somogyvari-Vigh, A. Miyata, K. Mizuno, D. H. Coy, and C. Kitada, *Endocrinology* (*Baltimore*) **129,** 2787 (1991).

13. K. Suda, D. M. Smith, M. A. Ghatei, and S. R. Bloom, *Neurosci. Lett.* **137,** 19 (1992).

14. P. E. Gottschall, I. Tatsuno, and A. Arimura, *FASEB J.* **5,** 194 (1991).

15. P. E. Gottschall, I. Tatsuno, A. Miyata, and A. Arimura, *Endocrinology* (*Baltimore*) **127,** 272 (1990).

16. R. Propato-Mussafiri, D. M. Smith, and S. R. Bloom, *Regul. Pept.* **35,** 254 (1991).

17. A. G. Gornall, C. J. Bardawill, and M. M. David, *J. Biol. Chem.* **177,** 751 (1949).

18. M. Bradford, *Anal. Biochem.* **72,** 248 (1976).

19. P. J. Fracker and J. C. Speck, *Biochem. Biophys. Res. Commun.* **86,** 849 (1978).

20. W. H. Hunter and F. C. Greenwood, *Nature* (*London*) **194,** 495 (1962).

21. P. Gourlet, M.-C. Woussen-Colle, P. Robberecht, P. De Neef, A. Cauvin, M.-C. Vandermeers-Piret, A. Vandermeers, and J. Christophe, *Eur. J. Biochem.* **195,** 535 (1991).

22. K. N. Holohan, R. F. Murphy, R. W. J. Flanagan, K. D. Buchanan, and D. T. Elmore, *Biochim. Biophys. Acta* **322,** 178 (1973).

23. P. Robberecht, M.-C. Woussen-Colle, P. De Neef, P. Gourlet, L. Buscail, A. Vandermeers, M.-C. Vandermeers-Piret, and J. Christophe, *FEBS Lett.* **286,** 133 (1991).

24. D. M. Smith, M. J. King, and G. J. Sale, *Biochem. J.* **250,** 509 (1988).

[9] Role of Cholecystokinin Type B Receptor in Nociception Studied with Peptide Agonists and Antagonists

Zsuzsanna Wiesenfeld-Hallin and Xiao-Jun Xu

I. Introduction

Cholecystokinin (CCK) (1) is present in many areas of the central nervous system (CNS), primarily as the sulfated C-terminal fragment CCK-8 (2–4). This peptide fulfills many of the criteria for a neurotransmitter and may have a role in various CNS functions (5). In the rat spinal cord genuine CCK is probably not found in primary afferent terminals (6–8), but has been described in local dorsal horn neurons and in neurons in lamina X (9–11), areas that have a role in nociception. Studies on the effect of exogenously applied CCK and related peptides on pain modulation in rodents have given variable results (12). While most electrophysiological studies revealed that CCK had an excitatory effect on spinal neurons and spinal reflexes (13–15), behavioral studies have reported both analgesic and hyperalgesic effects of intrathecal (i.t.) CCK (16, 17). It has, however, been shown that CCK antagonized the analgesic effect of morphine, β-endorphin, and electroacupuncture after systemic, i.t., or intracerebroventricular (i.c.v.) injection and CCK antagonists potentiated opioid-mediated analgesia (18–23), indicating that CCK may be a physiological endogenous opioid antagonist.

It has been proposed that CCK receptors are heterogeneous, with receptors in the periphery that differ from those found in the CNS (24). Moran *et al.* (25) provided the first direct autoradiographical evidence for the existence in rat brain of CCK receptors that resembled those in peripheral tissues. They termed the peripheral site type A to distinguish it from classical brain (type B) receptors. Potent and highly selective antagonists toward types A and B CCK receptors have been developed that provided a firm basis for studying the biological functions of CCK (26).

Our interest in this area has been to study the spinal mechanisms through which the CCK system is involved in nociception. We have used two experimental approaches in the course of these experiments. One is a decebrate, spinalized, unanesthetized rat preparation in which the spinal nociceptive flexor reflex was examined. The second is a behavioral test of nociception, the hot plate test, which is an integrated response requiring an intact neu-

Methods in Neurosciences, Volume 11

roaxis. We have been able to demonstrate that spinal application of CCK caused excitation of spinal reflex excitability and antagonized morphine-induced analgesia in rats (15) and that these effects were mediated by B-type CCK receptors (27). CI988, a CCK-B receptor antagonist, depressed spinal reflex excitability in a naloxone-reversible fashion, potentiated the spinal analgesic effect of morphine (27), and prevented morphine tolerance (28). Furthermore, we have found that i.t. galanin (GAL), which is present in primary sensory afferents and spinal cord interneurons, potentiated the reflex depressive effect of CI988 and CI988 combined with morphine (27).

Materials and Methods

Electrophysiological Experiments

The physiological experiments were carried out on Sprague–Dawley rats of both sexes weighing 200–250 g (Alab, Stockholm, Sweden). The magnitude of the polysynaptic hamstring flexor reflex in response to activation of high-threshold afferents was examined in decerebrate, spinalized, unanesthetized rats. The animals are initially briefly anesthetized with i.p. methohexital (70 mg/kg; Eli Lilly, Indianapolis, IN) and a tracheal cannula is inserted. In some experiments one jugular vein is cannulated for systemic drug administration. The rats are decerebrated by aspiration of the forebrain and midbrain and then ventilated. The spinal cord is exposed by a laminectomy at midthoracic level and sectioned at Th8–9. An i.t. catheter (PE 10, Becton Dickinson and Co., Parsippany, NJ) is implanted caudally to the transection with its tip on the lumbar spinal cord (L4–5). The flexor reflex is elicited by supramaximal test stimuli to the sural nerve or its innervation area in the left foot with electric shocks (0.5 msec, 10 mA, 1/min) of sufficient strength to activate C-afferents. The flexor reflex is recorded as electromyograph (EMG) activity via stainless steel needle electrodes inserted into the ipsilateral posterior biceps femoris/semitendinosus muscles. The number of action potentials elicited during the reflex is integrated over 2 sec. During the experiments the heart rate and rectal temperature are monitored. The proper location of the i.t. catheter is confirmed by laminectomy after the experiments.

Behavioral Analgesic Testing

The behavioral experiments were performed on male rats. The antinociceptive effect of the drugs is assessed with a hot plate (IITC, Woodland Hills, CA) at 54 ± 0.2°C. The latency to licking a hindpaw is determined to an accuracy of 0.1 sec. Before any drugs are administered, the rats are habituated by being tested on the hot plate for 5 days to obtain a stable control response value. In our experience this procedure is important to obtain a stable baseline response because the lick latency of the rats decreases by about 50% on repeated testing. On the day of drug administration the rats are pretested on the hot plate and the values are taken as baseline latency (BL). The animals are then tested at 10-min intervals and the postdrug latency (DL) is recorded.

Tolerance Studies

Two series of experiments were conducted. In series I, 30 rats are randomly divided into 4 treatment groups. Morphine tolerance is induced by a 6-day schedule of twice daily injection of incremental doses of morphine, beginning with 1 mg/kg and culminating with 32 mg/kg on the morning prior to the analgesia test (group 1). Other animals are injected daily with intraperitoneal (i.p.) saline (group 2), CI988 (0.5 mg/kg) plus morphine (group 3), or CI988 plus saline (group 4). On the afternoon of day 6 the rats are challenged with 1 mg/kg morphine and the analgesic effect is evaluated.

In series II, 50 rats are divided into 5 groups. The analgesic effect of 3 mg/kg i.p. morphine is assessed on day 1 in four groups and the animals are then treated with a daily i.p. injection of 3 mg/kg morphine plus saline (group 1), morphine plus 1 mg/kg CI988 (group 2), CI988 plus saline (group 3), or saline plus saline (group 4). The analgesic effect of morphine is tested in these four groups of rats on days 8, 15, 22, and 29 to follow the development of tolerance. In group 5, 10 rats received daily i.p. injection of saline and weekly analgesic testing without morphine. On day 29, these rats are injected i.p. with 3 mg/kg morphine and its analgesic effect is examined.

Naloxone-precipitated withdrawal is tested 24 hr after the completion of both series I and series II. All testing is carried out in a blind fashion with respect to which drug is administered.

Drugs

The following drugs were used: sulfated and desulfated CCK (26–33) (Cambridge Research Biochemicals, Cambridge, UK), CI988 (PD 134308; Parke-Davis & Research Unit, Cambridge, UK) (see Ref. 29 for structure), GAL (Bachem, Bubendorff, Switzerland), morphine hydrochloride (Apoteksbolaget, Stockholm, Sweden) and naloxone hydrochloride (Endo, Garden City, NJ). All drugs are dissolved in saline and injected through three routes: (1) intrathecally in a volume of 10 μl followed by 10 μl saline to flush the catheter, (2) intravenously in a volume of 0.2 ml, or (3) intraperitoneally in a volume of 0.5 ml.

Statistics

The effects of drugs on the magnitude of the flexor reflex are expressed as the percentage change from baseline, which is defined as 100%. The analgesic effect of drugs on the hot plate test is calculated as the percentage change in reaction time from baseline latency values by using the formula [(DL-BL)/ BL] $\times$ 100%. Statistics are derived with one- and two-way analysis of variance (ANOVA), which is followed by the Scheffe F test, Dunnett's test, or Newman Keuls test. All data are presented as means $\pm$ SEM.

Results

The Effects of Intrathecal Cholecystokinin on the Flexor Reflex

Five doses of CCK were injected intrathecally: 1 ng, 10 ng, 100 ng, 1 μg, and 10 μg. The lowest dose caused no change in reflex excitability. Otherwise CCK always had a facilitatory effect, leading to an increase in reflex magnitude (Fig. 1A and B). Facilitation of the flexor reflex by i.t. CCK was prevented by i.v. preadministration of the CCK-B antagonist CI988 (Fig. 1B).

The Effects of Intrathecal Cholecystokinin on Intrathecal Morphine-Induced Depression of the Flexor Reflex

The effect of 5 μg morphine on the flexor reflex was examined. Morphine evoked an initial enhancement of the reflex, followed by prolonged depression (Fig. 2A). The initial facilitation had a duration of 2.6 $\pm$ 0.4 min followed by a reduction in reflex magnitude by 87.0 $\pm$ 7.1% at about 30 min postinjection. The depression lasted over 2 hr. Intrathecal naloxone (25 μg), but not CCK (10 ng–1 μg), reversed the reflex depressive effect of morphine (Fig. 2A).

Injected 2–3 min prior to i.t. morphine, CCK at low doses (10 and 100 ng) had no effect on the development of morphine-induced depression of the flexor reflex. One microgram CCK had a dramatically different effect. Morphine-induced reflex enhancement became greater and much longer lasting (24.3 $\pm$ 6.6 min) and the subsequent depression was less than after only morphine or morphine plus lower doses of CCK (Fig. 2B and C). The blocking effect of CCK on morphine-induced reflex depression was mimicked by naloxone and by desulfated CCK at a much higher dose than sulfated CCK (Fig. 2C).

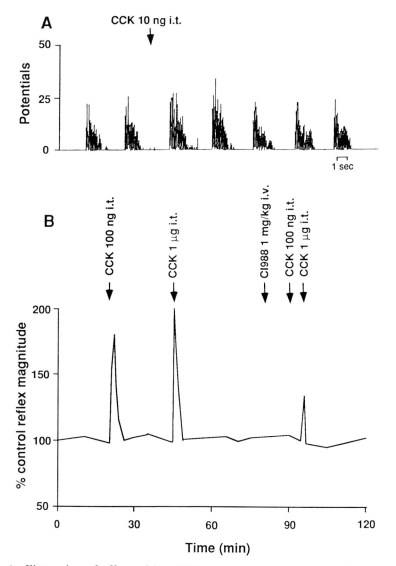

Fig. 1 Illustration of effect of i.t. CCK on the flexor reflex excitability in two experiments. (A) The flexor reflex responses recorded as EMG potentials to electrical stimulation of the ipsilateral foot. The number of potentials were summated in 100-msec bins. The time base refers to the duration of the reflex response. The reflex was evoked at 1-min intervals. The arrow indicates when 10 ng CCK was injected i.t. Note the increase in response magnitude at 1 and 2 min postinjection. [Reproduced from Wiesenfeld-Hallin and Duranti (15).] (B) CCK (100 ng and 1 μg) facilitated the flexor reflex. CI988 administered i.v. 10 min prior to i.t. CCK totally antagonized the effect of 100 ng CCK and significantly reduced facilitation by 1 μg of CCK. [Reproduced from Wiesenfeld-Hallin et al. (27).]

Effect of Systemic CI988 on Flexor Reflex Excitability and Intravenous Morphine-Induced Depression of the Reflex

CI988 (1 mg/kg) injected intravenously depressed the flexor reflex by about 25% below control level for about 30 min (Fig. 3B; Table I). This effect was readily reversed by i.v. naloxone (1 mg/kg; Fig. 3B). CI988 (1 mg/kg) and morphine (1 mg/kg) interacted synergistically to depress the flexor reflex (Fig. 3B; Table I). After their coadministration the reflex was depressed about twice as much as to the drug alone and the duration of the depression was about three times as long as after morphine alone (Table I).

Effects of Intrathecal Galanin on CI988 and CI988 Plus Morphine-Induced Reflex Depression

Intrathecal GAL (100 ng) briefly facilitated the flexor reflex. We have previously demonstrated that this dose of GAL potentiated the depressive effect of morphine (Table I; see also Ref. 30). When 100 ng i.t. GAL and 1 mg/kg i.v. CI988 were coadministered, the magnitude and duration of reflex depression by CI988 were significantly potentiated by GAL (Fig. 3C; Table I). In fact, reflex depression by CI988 plus GAL was significantly stronger than to 1 mg/kg morphine. Furthermore, the depressive effect of GAL plus CI988 was reversed by naloxone. An extremely strong potentiation of the effect of i.v. CI988 plus i.v. morphine was observed after i.t. administration of GAL (Table I; Fig. 3D).

Effects of Systemic CI988 on the Hot Plate Test and on Morphine-Induced Analgesia

CI988 at low doses (0.1 and 0.3 mg/kg) had no effect on lick latency in the hot plate test, whereas larger doses had a weak, but significant, analgesic effect for 20 min (1 mg/kg) or 40 min (3 mg/kg) (Fig. 4A). Morphine at 1 mg/kg caused moderate analgesia for about 50 min and CI988 potentiated the analgesic effect of morphine in a dose-dependent fashion (Fig. 4B). With the three higher doses of CI988 the analgesic effect of morphine was significantly potentiated at all intervals examined, starting 10 min after injection. The duration of analgesia with 1 mg/kg morphine was increased from 50 to 90 min with the addition of 0.3 mg/kg CI988 and to 130 min with 1 and 3 mg/kg CI988.

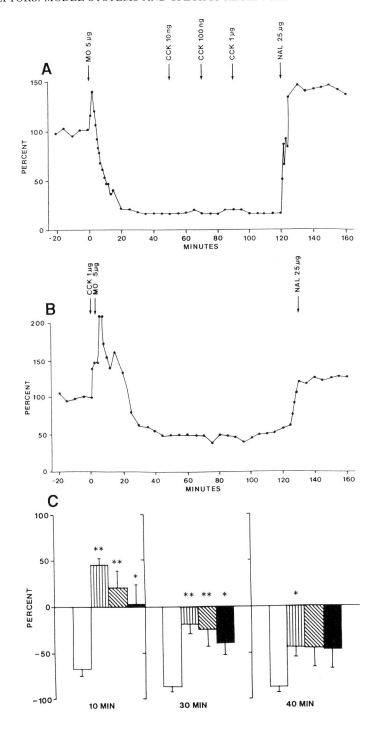

Prevention of Tolerance to Morphine Analgesia by CI988

In series I, 1 mg/kg morphine i.p. elicited moderate analgesia for 50 min in group 2, which received twice-daily injections of saline (Fig. 5A). The effect was similar to that seen in normal rats (27). In contrast, in group 1, which received incremental doses of morphine for 6 days, the challenge dose of 1 mg/kg morphine did not evoke an analgesic effect (Fig. 5A). Morphine caused analgesia in rats in group 3, which were administered CI988 prior to injection with morphine (Fig. 5A). Chronic administration of CI988 by itself (group 4) did not influence morphine-induced analgesia (Fig. 5A). The analgesic effect of morphine was significantly different when all four groups were compared, but there was no difference among groups 2 (saline only), 3 (CI988 plus morphine), and 4 (CI988 only), indicating a lack of morphine tolerance in those rats that received CI988 along with morphine.

In series II morphine at a dose of 3 mg/kg i.p. had a strong analgesic effect for about 2 hr on the first testing occasion. Daily injection of i.p. saline and weekly analgesic testing for 4 weeks (group 5) did not reduce the analgesic effect of morphine on day 29. After daily i.p. injection of 3 mg/kg morphine (group 1) the analgesic effect of morphine was significantly diminished on day 8 and totally disappeared by day 15 and thereafter (Fig. 5B). In the other three groups of rats, which were daily administered morphine plus CI988, CI988 plus saline, or only saline (groups 2, 3, and 4 respectively), the analgesic effect to morphine was unchanged on day 8. A significant reduction of the analgesic effect of morphine was observed in groups 2, 3, and 4 on day 15 (Fig. 5B). The effect of morphine in groups 2, 3, and 4 was, however, still significantly stronger than in group 1, which received daily injections of

FIG. 2   The effects of morphine (MO), CCK, and naloxone (NAL) on flexor reflex magnitude. (A) Morphine (5 μg i.t.) initially facilitated the reflex during the first 3 min postinjection, then successively inhibited it, with a maximum inhibition at 30 min postinjection. Note that 25 μg i.t. NAL, but not CCK (10–1000 ng), rapidly reversed the morphine-induced inhibition. (B) Administered prior to 5 μg morphine, 1 μg i.t. CCK potentiated the facilitatory effect of morphine, but reduced morphine-induced inhibition. (C) Comparison of the effects of 5 μg morphine (open bars), 1 μg CCK plus 5 μg morphine (striped bars), 10 μg desulfated CCK plus 5 μg morphine (hatched bars), and 50 μg naloxone plus 5 μg morphine (black bars) at 10, 30, and 40 min postinjection. The data are presented as the percentage change compared to baseline level. The positive values represent facilitation of the reflex, the negative values depression. The statistically different values are comparisons with the effect of morphine. *$p < 0.05$; **$p < 0.01$. [Reproduced from Wiesenfeld-Hallin and Duranti (15).]

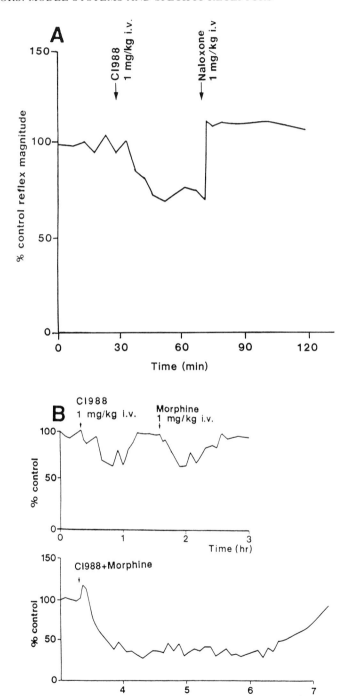

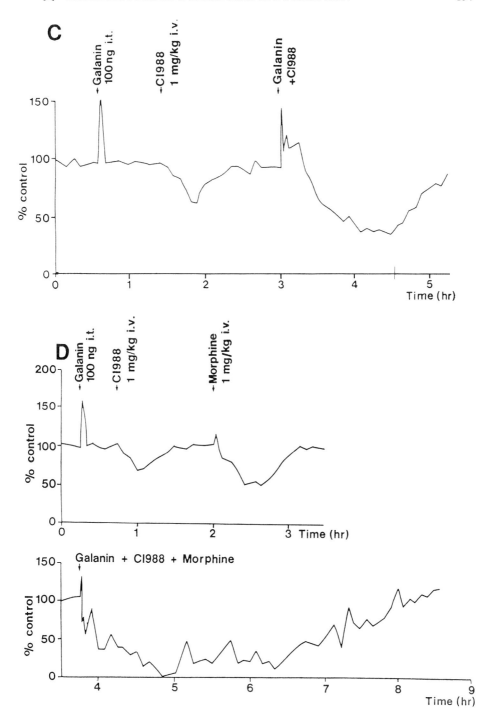

morphine, and no difference was found between groups 2, 3, and 4 ($F_{2,27}$ = 0.399; $F > 0.5$). There was no further reduction of the analgesic effect of morphine in these three groups of rats up to 29 days, when the experiments were terminated. Two-factor ANOVA (treatment groups vs time) indicated that the difference in the analgesic effect of morphine among the four groups over the entire experimental period was significant ($F_{3,180}$ = 38.176; $p <$ 0.001). The reduction of the analgesic effect of morphine over time was also significant ($F_{4,180}$ = 30.688, $p < 0.001$). ANOVA applied to data from rats in groups 2, 3, and 4 revealed that there was no significant difference in the analgesic effect of morphine ($F_{2,135}$ = 0.645, $p > 0.5$), but the decrease of the analgesic effect of morphine over time was significant ($F_{4,135}$ = 10.731, $p <$ 0.001) among these three groups (Fig. 5B).

We also examined the effect of CI988 on naloxone-precipitated withdrawal (1 mg/kg naloxone i.p.) 24 hr after the termination of testing rats in series I and II. We found that CI988 did not prevent the expression of withdrawal symptoms (Table II) and that the few symptoms observed in rats administered only CI988 were not significantly above saline control levels.

Discussion

Effects of Exogenously Applied Cholecystokinin on Spinal Nociception

The effect of CCK on flexor reflex excitability was examined over a 10^5 dose range. It was found that all effective doses (10 ng–1 μg) increased reflex magnitude. Cholecystokinin has been shown to have an excitatory effect on dorsal horn neurons (13, 14), which supports the results of the present study. The 10-μg dose caused an initial enhancement followed by depression in some experiments. A similar pattern of facilitation–inhibition has been found with high doses of i.t. somatostatin (31), substance P (Z. Wiesenfeld-Hallin,

---

FIG. 3   The effects of i.v. CI988, morphine, and i.t. GAL on flexor reflex magnitude. (A) CI988 (1 mg/kg) caused a moderate depression of the flexor reflex, which was naloxone reversible. (B) Coadmistration of 1 mg/kg morphine and 1 mg/kg CI988 induced synergistic depression of flexor reflex magnitude. (C) GAL (100 ng i.t.) by itself briefly facilitated the reflex and potentiated reflex depression by 1 mg/kg i.v. CI988. (D) Effects of coadministration of 1 mg/kg i.v. CI988, 1 mg/kg i.v. morphine, and 100 ng i.t. GAL on the flexor reflex in a single experiment. Note the strong and prolonged depression caused by combination of all three drugs. [Reproduced from Wiesenfeld-Hallin *et al.* (27).]

TABLE I   The Magnitude and Duration of the Depressive Effect of CI988,
           Morphine, Galanin, and a Combination of These Drugs, on the
           Flexor Reflex[a]

Drugs	N	Percent reflex depression	Duration of depression (min)
CI988 (1 mg/kg i.v.)	6	24.5 ± 5.9	28.6 ± 7.6
Morphine (1 mg/kg i.v.)	8	38.1 ± 10.7	60.5 ± 27.2
CI988 (1 mg/kg i.v.) plus morphine (1 mg/kg i.v.)	6	62.5 ± 11.2[b,c]	195.3 ± 24.2[b,c]
GAL (100 ng i.t.)	15	0	0
GAL (100 ng i.t.) plus morphine (1 μg i.t.)	5	58.5 ± 15.1[d]	80.1 ± 15.2
GAL (100 ng i.t.) plus CI988 (1 mg/kg i.v.)	4	66.0 ± 15.9[b,c]	152.2 ± 38.9[c,d]
GAL (100 ng i.t.) plus morphine (1 mg/kg i.v.) plus CI988 (1 mg/kg i.v.)	4	85.6 ± 13.7[e,f]	250.2 ± 14.1[e,g,h]

[a] Statistics were derived by two-way ANOVA followed by Scheffe F test. [Reproduced from Wiesenfeld-Hallin *et al.* (27).]

[b] Compared to morphine, $p < 0.01$.

[c] Compared to CI988, $p < 0.01$.

[d] Compared to morphine, $p < 0.05$.

[e] Compared to morphine plus CI988, $p < 0.05$.

[f] Compared to morphine plus GAL, $p < 0.05$.

[g] Compared to morphine plus GAL, $p < 0.01$.

[h] Compared to CI988 plus GAL, $p < 0.01$.

unpublished observations), and some substance P antagonists (32) and probably reflects toxicity or an overdose. Because the only effect at physiological doses was incresed spinal excitability, it is unlikely that CCK has an analgesic effect in conscious animals, at least not at the spinal level (16). The i.t. CCK-induced reflex facilitation was readily blocked by pretreatment with CI988, indicating that this effect was mediated through the CCK-B receptor, which is supported by the observation that the receptor for CCK in rat spinal cord is the B type (33).

The initial effect of 5 μg morphine was brief facilitation of the reflex. This excitatory effect on morphine has been even more clearly observed with lower doses of i.t. morphine (34). A brief facilitory effect of low doses of i.t. morphine on C fiber-evoked activity in dorsal horn neurons has been reported as well (35). We have demonstrated that the excitatory effect of morphine on the flexor reflex is due to the release of neuropeptides, primarily tachykinins, in the dorsal horn by low concentrations of morphine (34). However, the predominant effect on the flexor reflex of this dose of i.t. morphine is a profound, prolonged depression. Intrathecal preadministration of both CCK

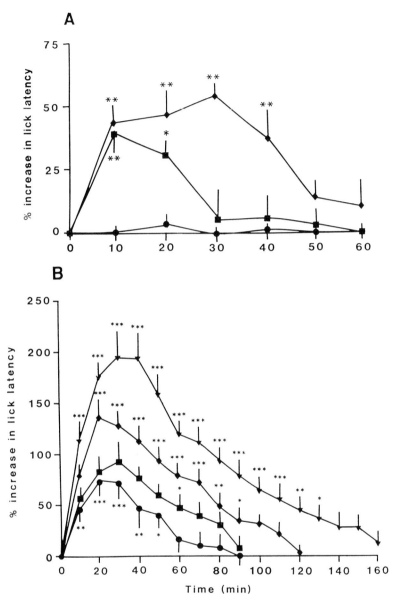

FIG. 4   (A) Effect of CI988 at 0.3 (●), 1 (■), and 3 (◆) mg/kg i.p. on the hot plate test. The two highest doses had a moderate antinociceptive effect, while no effect was observed with 0.1 mg/kg (not shown) or 0.3 mg/kg. $n = 5$ in each group. One-way ANOVA was followed by Dunnett's test. $*p < 0.05$; $**p < 0.01$. (B). Effect of 1 mg/kg morphine by itself (●) and combined with CI988 at 0.1 (■), 0.3 (◆), or 1 (▼)

and naloxone antagonized the reflex depressive effect of morphine, but only naloxone reversed it, indicating that CCK did not replace morphine from opioid-binding sites, but rather physiologically augmented the excitatory effect of morphine and prevented its depressive effect on the spinal cord. Our results are consistent with previous behavioral observations that CCK antagonized the analgesic effect of morphine and endogenous opioids (18–20) and with electrophysiological experiments in which it was shown that the depressive effect of morphine on dorsal horn neurons was attenuated by CCK (36, 37).

Endogenous Role for Cholecystokinin in Opioid Analgesia

To establish whether the antagonistic effect of CCK operates under physiological conditions, experiments with CCK receptor antagonists are essential. Previous antagonists for the CCK receptor, represented by proglumide and benzotript, have been used extensively to study the physiological role of CCK in nociception. Thus, these drugs have been shown to enhance opioid analgesia elicited by systemic, intrathecal, or supraspinal morphine in experimental animals (21, 22) and in humans (38, 39) and to prevent morphine tolerance (21, 40, 41). However, because of the lack of potency and selectivity of these drugs it was not entirely convincing that their effects on opioid analgesia were due to CCK receptor blockade. Furthermore, other evidence suggested that proglumide may possess opioid agonistic property (42, 43), which could account for its potentiation of morphine analgesia. Potentiation of morphine-induced analgesia by proglumide had a bell-shaped dose-dependent effect (22) and it was reported that long-term treatment with proglumide may reverse its acute enhancement of morphine-induced analgesia (44), suggesting a limited usefulness of these compounds as tools to study the physiological role of CCK.

Highly selective antagonists for CCK-A (MK-329 and L-365,031) and CCK-B (L-365,260 and CI988) receptors have been developed (29, 45, 46), making it possible to examine the role of CCK and the subtypes of CCK receptors involved in nociception. Thus, Dourish et al. (47, 48) have shown that MK-

---

mg/kg on the hot plate test. The effect of morphine alone was compared with predrug latency with one-way ANOVA. The effects of morphine plus various doses of CI988 were compared with the effect of morphine alone with two-way ANOVA followed by Dunnett's test. $*p < 0.05$; $**p < 0.01$; $***p < 0.001$. $n = 10$ in each group. [Reproduced from Wiesenfeld-Hallin et al. (27).]

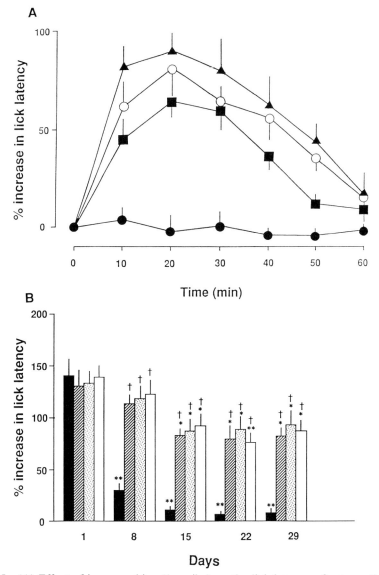

FIG. 5   (A) Effect of i.p. morphine (1 mg/kg) on the lick latency of rats on the hot plate on day 6 of series I in groups of rats that received twice daily i.p. injection of increasing doses of morphine (●), saline (○), morphine plus CI988 (0.5 mg/kg) (■), or CI988 (▲). The challenge dose of morphine was injected at time 0 and vertical bars represent the SEM. $N = 5$–10 in each group. ANOVA with repeated measures

329, L-365,031, and L-365,260 potentiated morphine analgesia and prevented morphine tolerance in rats with the rank order of potency L-365,260 > MK-329 > L-365,031, which corresponded to their potency to block the central CCK-B receptors, indicating a critical role for these receptors in modulation of the opioid system. We demonstrated that CI988 strongly enhanced the analgesic effect of morphine, supporting the hypothesis that CCK, through acting on B-type CCK receptors, behaves as a physiologically active antagonist for opioid-mediated analgesia. Our results that systemic CI988 caused naloxone reversible analgesia and potentiated the effect of morphine have been confirmed with the mouse tail immersion test (49).

Direct analgesia has not been reported with other CCK receptor antagonists. Because CI988 was inactive in the displacement of the binding of radioligands to all subtypes of opioid receptors (29), it is unlikely that its analgesic effect was due to a direct interaction of CI988 with an opioid receptor. It is possible that the antagonism by CCK on opioid analgesia operates tonically at the spinal level and removal of this antagonism by CI988 increases opioid release. This hypothesis was supported by the fact that CI988-induced reflex depression was potentiated by the neuropeptide GAL, which has been shown to potentiate the spinal analgesic effect of morphine (30).

The site of the effect of CI988 appeared to be within the spinal cord, because we observed a similar effect in intact and in spinalized rats. Strong evidence for a direct spinal effect of systemic CI988 is that it effectively antagonized the facilitatory effect of i.t. CCK and interacted with i.t. GAL to cause synergistic reflex depression. Previous experiments have documented a spinal site of interaction between CCK and opioids (15, 22, 36, 37) and extensive systems containing genuine CCK peptide (9–11) and CCK mRNA (50) are represented in the rat dorsal horn. However, CCK receptors

---

indicated that the analgesic effect of morphine was significantly different when all four groups were compared ($F_{3,130}$ = 9.669, $p < 0.0001$), but there was no difference in groups that received saline, CI988 plus morphine, or CI988 ($F_{2,110}$ = 2.865, $p > 0.05$). (B) Effect of i.p. morphine (3 mg/kg) on the lick latency of rats on the hot plate in groups of rats in series II that received daily injection of morphine (solid bars), morphine plus 1 mg/kg CI988 (hatched bars), CI988 alone (stippled bars), or saline alone (open bars). The time from the beginning of the chronic treatment is indicated under the bars. The maximal increase in lick latency for each rat, usually at 40 or 60 min after injection of morphine, is presented. The vertical lines indicate the SEM. $n = 10$ in each group. †$p < 0.005$ compared to the group that received a daily injection of morphine; *$p < 0.05$; **$p < 0.01$ compared to the respective group on day 1. [Reproduced from Xu *et al.* (28).]

TABLE II Effects of CI988 on Naloxone-Precipitated Morphine Withdrawal in Rats in Series I and II

Withdrawal symptoms	Groups in series I[a]				Groups in series II[b]			
	Morphine + saline	Saline + saline	Morphine + CI988	Saline + CI988	Morphine + saline	Morphine + CI988	Saline + CI988	Saline + saline
Ptosis	100	0	90	20	70	70	20	0
Irritability	100	0	100	20	60	60	20	0
Diarrhea	80	0	60	10	0	0	0	0
Teeth chattering	100	0	100	20	80	80	0	0
Writhing	60	0	40	0	10	0	0	0
Wet dog shakes	8.0 ± 1.4*	0	6.7 ± 1.1*	2.4 ± 0.6	3.9 ± 1.4*	3.3 ± 0.9*	1.7 ± 0.6	0.2 ± 0.2

[a] Rats were injected twice daily with increasing doses of morphine (group 1), saline (group 2), morphine plus CI988 (group 3), and CI988 (group 4) for 6 days. Naloxone-precipitated withdrawal was assessed on day 7. All rats were injected i.p. with naloxone (1 mg/kg) prior to ε 20-min observation period. The frequency of wet dog shakes (means ± SEM) during 20 min is indicated; other values are the percentages of animals in each group showing the symptom during the test ($n = 5$–10 in each group). ANOVA indicated that the frequency of wet dog shakes was significantly different among the four groups ($F_{3,26} = 12.785$, $p < 0.001$). *$p < 0.01$ compared to group 2 and group 4 with Newman–Keuls test.

[b] Rats were injected daily with morphine (group 1), CI988 plus morphine (group 2), CI988 (group 3), and saline (group 4) for 29 days. Naloxone-precipitated withdrawal was assessed on day 30. ANOVA indicated that the frequency of wet dog shakes was significantly different among the four groups ($F_{3,36} = 3.457$, $p < 0.05$). *$p < 0.05$ compared with group 4. [Reproduced from Xu et al. (28).]

also exist in many other regions in the CNS, including the periaqueductal gray (33), known to be involved in opioid analgesia, and the interaction between CCK, its antagonists, and opioids has been reported after intracerebral and i.c.v. injections as well (20, 22). We thus cannot rule out the possibility that the potentiation of morphine-induced analgesia on the hot plate test may be partially mediated by CCK-B receptors in the brain.

Cholecystokinin and Opioid Tolerance

We have presented evidence that indicated that chronic treatment with CI988 prevented the development of tolerance to the analgesic effect of morphine in rats. These data support the results from previous studies, in which a number of selective and nonselective CCK antagonists were shown to prevent or reverse tolerance to morphine (21, 40, 41, 47, 48). Our results also supported the notion that the CCK–opioid interaction occurred through CCK-B receptors in rodents (48).

We observed in series II that the analgesic effect of morphine was reduced over time in rats that received daily injections of CI988 plus morphine. Because similar phenomena also occurred in rats that received daily injections of saline only, it is clear that this effect did not reflect the failure of CI988 to prevent morphine tolerance, but of some other factors. A number of previous studies have shown that repeated nociceptive testing could induce behavioral tolerance to morphine analgesia (51, 52). We tested for the occurrence of behavioral tolerance by including another group of rats that received daily injections of saline and a weekly nociceptive test and were challenged with morphine only once, after 4 weeks. The observation that the analgesic effect of morphine on this group was similar to the effect on rats examined at the beginning of the experiments failed to support the hypothesis of behavioral tolerance to nociceptive testing in rats that were injected with morphine weekly, but not daily. Thus, it is possible that a weekly injection of morphine caused the development of some tolerance, albeit significantly less than that caused by daily injections. This tolerance development was not prevented by CI988, as on the day of nociceptive testing CI988 was injected 2–3 hr later than morphine to avoid the acute potentiation of the analgesic effect of morphine by the CCK-B antagonist (27). However, we cannot exclude the possibility that the single morphine injection had a discriminative stimulus property, which led to the full analgesic effect of the opioid. Nonetheless, the analgesic effect of morphine was only partially diminished in rats that received a weekly injection of morphine and was significantly stronger than in rats that received a daily injection during the entire 29-day experimental period (Fig. 5B). It should be noted that our procedure of habituating the animals on the hot plate test for 5 days before data collection may have contributed to the increased sensitivity of this assay of the analgesic effect of morphine, because unhabituated animals would respond with a longer latency at the first testing session than in later sessions, which may be incorrectly interpreted as tolerance.

The observation that there was no difference between groups of rats that received daily CI988, saline, and CI988 plus morphine therefore indicated that (1) tolerance induced by daily morphine injection was prevented by CI988 and (2) chronic treatment with CI988 only did not reduce morphine analgesia. The latter conclusion was at variance with the report by Kellstein and Meyer (44), who showed that chronic treatment with the CCK antagonists proglumide and lorglumide reduced the analgesic effect of morphine. Although differences in route of drug administration (intrathecal vs systemic) or in nociceptive tests used (tail flick vs hot plate) may contribute to this difference, it should be noted that the use of proglumide and its analogs as tools to study the function of CCK has been questioned because of the poor potency and low selectivity of such drugs for the CCK-B receptor (42, 43).

The possible mechanisms for the prevention of morphine tolerance by CCK antagonists has not been studied in detail. Because exogenously applied CCK antagonizes morphine-induced analgesia and the injection of morphine increases the release of CCK in the spinal cord *in vivo* (40, 53), it is possible that chronic treatment with morphine may incude up regulation of the endogenous CCK system, which antagonizes the action of morphine, leading to tolerance development. Chronic treatment with CCK antagonists may suppress such an up regulation, thus preventing the development of morphine tolerance. Neurochemical studies examining changes in CCK levels in the CNS after injection of morphine have given inconsistent results. While Faris *et al.* (54) reported that acute or chronic morphine increased the level of CCK in the hypothalamus in rats, Rosén and Brodin (55) failed to observe significant changes in CCK content in brain and spinal cord after acute morphine injection. However, it should be pointed out that examination of changes in CCK synthesis after acute and chronic morphine treatment may be more relevant in this context, because changes in tissue CCK content may have been masked by increased release of this neuropeptide.

There are, however, other possibilities by which a CCK-B antagonist may prevent morphine tolerance. For example, tolerance to the analgesic effect of morphine has been suggested to be related to classical conditioning (56). According to this theory, the administration of morphine can be viewed as a conditioning trial, with environmental cues present at the time of drug administration constituting the conditioned stimulus, and the acute pharmacological stimulation constituting the unconditioned stimulus. According to this theory tolerance is interpreted as a manifestation of the acquisition of a compensatory conditioned response between the pharmacological effects of the drug and those environmental cues that always precede these pharmacological effects. Because CI988 is a strong anxiolytic agent (29), it may depress the reaction and memory of animals to negative environmental cues, resulting in the prevention of tolerance.

Conclusions

The present series of experiments, combining behavioral and electrophysiological methods, demonstrated that activation of CCK-B receptors by exogenous and endogenous CCK peptide antagonized opioid-mediated analgesia and that blockade of this receptor enhanced morphine analgesia and tolerance. Should similar mechanisms operate in humans, application of CCK antagonists in combination with opioids may offer a new approach in controlling painful states, especially in chronic pain, in which the ineffectiveness of opioids and tolerance development block effective pain relief.

Acknowledgments

These studies were supported by the Swedish MRC (project No. 07913), the Bank of Sweden Tercentenary Foundation, the Wenner-Gren Center Foundation, and the Parke-Davis Research Unit, Cambridge, England. We are grateful to Dr. J. Hughes for providing us with CI988.

References

1. V. Mutt and J. E. Jorpes, *Eur. J. Biochem.* **6,** 156 (1968).
2. J. J. Vanderhaeghen, J. C. Signeau, and W. Gepts, *Nature (London)* **257,** 604 (1975).
3. J. F. Rehfeld, *J. Biol. Chem.* **253,** 4022 (1978).
4. G. J. Dockray, *Brain Res.* **188,** 155 (1980).
5. J. J. Vanderhaeghen and J. N. Crawley, "Neural Cholecystokinin." N. Y. Acad. Sci., New York, 1985.
6. G. Ju, T. Hökfelt, J. A. Fischer, P. Frey, J. F. Reheld, and D. J. Dockray, *Neurosci. Lett.* **68,** 305 (1986).
7. P. D. Marley, J. E. Nagy, P. C. Emson, and J. F. Rehfeld, *Brain Res.* **238,** 494 (1982).
8. M. Schultzberg, G. J. Dockary, and R. G. Williams, *Brain Res.* **235,** 198 (1982).
9. K. Fuji, E. Senba, S. Fuji, I. Nomura, J.-Y. Wu, Y. Ueda, and M. Tohyama, *Neuroscience* **14,** 881 (1985).

10. R. G. Williams, R. Dimaline, A. Varro, A. M. Isetta, D. Trizio, and G. J. Dockray, *Neurochem. Int.* **11,** 433 (1987).
11. T. Hökfelt, M. Herrera-Marchitz, K. Seroogy, G. Ju, W. A. Staines, V. Holets, M. Schalling, U. Understedt, C. Post, J. F. Rehfeld, P. Frey, J. Fischer, G. J. Dockray, T. Hamaoka, J. H. Walsh, and M. Goldstein, *J. Chem. Neuroanat.* **1,** 11 (1988).
12. N. S. Baber, C. T. Dourish, and D. R. Hill, *Pain* **39,** 307 (1989).
13. S. Jeftinija, V. Miletič, and M. Randič, *Brain Res.* **213,** 231 (1981).
14. J. Willetts, L. Urban, K. Murase, and M. Randič, *in* ''Neural Cholecystokinin'' (J. J. Vanderhashgen and J. N. Crawley, eds.), p. 385. N. Y. Acad. Sci., New York, 1985.
15. Z. Wiesenfeld-Hallin and R. Duranti, *Peptides* (*N. Y.*) **8,** 153 (1987).
16. I. Jurna and G. Zetler, *Eur. J. Pharmacol.* **73,** 323 (1981).
17. K. M. Pittaway, R. E. Rodriguez, J. Hughes, and R. G. Hill, *Neuropeptides* **10,** 87 (1987).
18. S. Itoh, G. Katsuura, and Y. Maeda, *Eur. J. Pharmacol.* **80,** 421 (1982).
19. P. L. Faris, B. R. Komisaruk, L. R. Watkins, and D. J. Mayer, *Science* **219,** 310 (1983).
20. J.-S. Han, X.-Z. Ding, and S.-G. Fan, *Neuropeptides* **5,** 399 (1985).
21. L. R. Watkins, I. B. Kinscheck, and D. J. Meyer, *Science* **224,** 395 (1984).
22. L. R. Watkins, I. B. Kinscheck, and D. J. Meyer, *Brain Res.* **327,** 169 (1985).
23. G. Katsuura and S. Itoh, *Eur. J. Pharmacol.* **107,** 363 (1985).
24. R. B. Innis and S. H. Snyder, *Proc. Natl. Acad. Sci. U.S.A.* **77,** 6917 (1980).
25. T. H. Moran, M. S. Robinson, M. S. Goldrich, and P. R. McHugh, *Brain Res.* **362,** 175 (1986).
26. R. Y. Wang and R. Schoenfeld, ''Cholecystokinin Antagonists.'' Liss, New York, 1988.
27. Z. Wiesenfeld-Halin, X.-J. Xu, J. Hughes, D. C. Horwell, and T. Hökfelt, *Proc. Natl. Acad. Sci. U.S.A.* **87,** 7105 (1990).
28. X.-J. Xu, Z. Wiesenfeld-Hallin, J. Hughes, D. C. Horwell, and T. Hökfelt, *Br. J. Pharmacol.* **105,** 591 (1992).
29. J. Hughes, P. Boden, B. Costall, A. Domeney, E. Kelly, D. C. Horwell, J. C. Hunter, R. D. Pinnock, and G. N. Woodruff, *Proc. Natl. Acad. Sci. U.S.A.* **87,** 6728 (1990).
30. Z. Wiesenfeld-Hallin, X.-J. Xu, M. J. Villar, and T. Hökfelt, *Neurosci. Lett.* **109,** 217 (1990).
31. Z. Wiesenfeld-Hallin, *Neurosci. Lett.* **62,** 69 (1985).
32. Z. Wiesenfeld-Hallin and R. Duranti, *Acta Physiol Scand.* **129,** 55 (1987).
33. D. R. Hill and G. N. Woodruff, *Brain Res.* **526,** 276 (1990).
34. Z. Wiesenfeld-Hallin, X.-J. Xu, R. Håkanson, D.-M. Feng, and K. Folkers, *Brain Res.* **551,** 157 (1991).
35. A. H. Dickenson and A. F. Sullivan, *Pain* **24,** 211 (1986).
36. D. S. K. Magnuson, A. F. Sullivan, G. Simonnet, B. P. Roques, and A. H. Dickenson, *Neuropeptides* **16,** 213 (1990).
37. D. E. Kellstein, D. D. Price, and D. J. Meyer, *Brain Res.* **540,** 302 (1991).

38. D. D. Price, A. Vondergruen, J. Miller, A. Rafii, and C. Price, *Anesth. Analg.* (*Cleveland*) **64,** 801 (1985).
39. G. J. Lavigne, K. M. Hargreaves, E. S. Schmidt, and R. A. Dionne, *Clin. Pharmacol. Ther.* **45,** 666 (1989).
40. J. Tang, J. Chou, M. Iadarola, H.-Y. T. Yang, and E. Costa, *Neuropharmacology* **23,** 715 (1984).
41. A. E. Panerai, L. C. Rovati, E. Cocco, P. Sacerdote, and P. Mantegazza, *Brain Res.* **410,** 52 (1987).
42. A. Rezvani, K. B. Strokes, D. L. Rhoads, and E. L. Way, *Alcohol Drug Res.* **7,** 135 (1987).
43. P. Gaudreau, G. J. Lavigne, and R. Quirion, *Neuropeptides* **16,** 51 (1990).
44. D. E. Kellstein and D. J. Meyer, *Brain Res.* **516,** 263 (1990).
45. R. S. L. Chang and V. J. Lotti, *Proc. Natl. Acad. Sci. U.S.A.* **83,** 4923 (1986).
46. B. E. Evans, M. G. Bock, K. E. Rittle, R. M. DiPardo, W. L. Whitter, D. F. Veber, P. S. Anderson, and R. M. Freidinger, *Proc. Natl. Acad. Sci. U.S.A.* **83,** 4918 (1986).
47. C. T. Dourish, D. Hawley, and S. D. Iversen, *Eur. J. Pharmacol.* **147,** 469 (1988).
48. C. T. Dourish, M. F. O'Neill, J. Coughlan, S. J. Kitchener, D. Hawley, and S. D. Iversen, *Eur. J. Pharmacol.* **176,** 35 (1990).
49. H. Chen and D. A. Downs, *Abstr. Soc. Neurosci.* **17,** 1012 (1991).
50. S. N. Schiffmann, E. Teugels, P. Halleux, R. Menu, and J.-J. Vanderhaeghen, *Neurosci. Lett.* **123,** 123 (1991).
51. C. Advokat, *Biochem. Behav.* **14,** 133 (1981).
52. R. J. Milne, G. D. Gamble, and N. H. G. Holford, *Brain Res.* **491,** 316 (1989).
53. J. J. Bonoliel, S. Bourgoin, A. Mauborgne, J. C. Legrand, M. Hamon, and F. Cesselin, *Neurosci. Lett.* **124,** 204 (1991).
54. P. L. Faris, M. C. Beinfeld, A. C. Scallet, J. N. Johannessen, and J. W. Olney, *Brain Res.* **367,** 404 (1986).
55. A. Rosén and E. Brodin, *Acta Physiol. Scand.* **136,** 493 (1989).
56. S. Siegel, *Science* **193,** 323 (1976).

[10] Cholecystokinin Receptors: Radioligand Binding and Affinity Labeling

Manfred P. Lutz and Laurence J. Miller

Introduction

Cholecystokinin (CCK) is a linear polypeptide hormone of neural and gastrointestinal origin that was discovered over 60 years ago by Ivy and Oldberg (1). The 33-amino acid form of this peptide was initially purified to homogeneity and sequenced by Jorpes and Mutt (2). It has subsequently been appreciated that this hormone, like many others, is found as a number of molecular forms of different length, ranging from 58 to 4 amino acids in length. All hormones of this family, which includes the gastrin peptides and the frog skin peptide cerulein, share a common carboxyl-terminal domain. It is this carboxyl-terminal domain that binds to receptors in this family (3).

Receptors for cholecystokinin have been reported in various regions of the brain and spinal cord, as well as in numerous locations along the gastrointestinal tract, including pancreatic acinar cells and islets, gallbladder smooth muscle, sphincter of Oddi, and smooth muscle and intrinsic nerves at the levels of the esophagus, stomach, small intestine, and colon (3). The classic physiological responses to cholecystokinin have been studied in contraction of gallbladder smooth muscle and secretion of zymogens by the exocrine pancreas, as well as ileal strip contraction. Interest in potential effects of CCK in the central nervous system has focused on three topics: (i) analgesia, (ii) feeding, and (iii) panic/anxiety (4). There is evidence that CCK may act as a functional antagonist of opiates; that it may play an important role as a satiety factor; and that it can elicit panic attacks in prone individuals.

All of the receptors for CCK and gastrin recognize all of the peptides in this family to some extent. There are two major types of CCK/gastrin receptors. These have been classified as the "A" or "alimentary"-type receptor and the "B" or predominant "brain"-type receptor (5). The type A receptor is that present on the pancreatic acinar cell and gallbladder smooth muscle, as well as on pyloric smooth muscle, some peripheral neurons, and a few select brain nuclei. It is most selective, requiring the carboxyl-terminal heptapeptide domain of CCK, including a sulfated tyrosine residue, for high-affinity binding. Desulfation of the tyrosine or shortening of the peptide lead to dramatic decreases in affinity and potency at this receptor. The type B receptor is widely distributed throughout the brain and represents the

Methods in Neurosciences, Volume 11

predominant CCK-binding receptor there. Only subtle differences in agonist binding have been reported that may be able to distinguish the type B receptor from the classic gastrin receptor on the gastric parietal cell. The type B/ gastrin receptor recognizes CCK and gastrin with approximately similar affinities, and shortening of these peptides to the tetrapeptide only leads to approximately one order of magnitude lower affinity. Nonpeptide antagonists are now available that can clearly distinguish between the type A and type B/ gastrin receptors (6); to date, however, they have not been able to distinguish between type B and gastrin receptors.

In this chapter, we describe the design and selection of probes for radioligand binding and affinity labeling of CCK receptors, the radiolabeling of these probes, and their use in binding assays and affinity-labeling studies, using bifunctional cross-linking as well as photoaffinity labeling.

Characteristics of Radioligand Probes for Cholecystokinin Receptors

The techniques of radioligand binding and affinity labeling of receptors are both based on the specific interaction of receptors and hormones. In a first step, radioactively labeled ligands are incubated with receptor-bearing tissue preparations under conditions that allow specific binding. After binding equilibrium has been reached, unbound ligand is separated and removed. The remaining receptor-bound ligand can then be either quantified directly, as in binding studies, or can be covalently attached to adjacent molecules, as in affinity-labeling studies.

In the design and selection of a probe for radioligand binding and affinity labeling, it is desirable to identify a molecule that binds specifically and with high affinity to the receptor of choice, and to have that probe radiolabeled to a high specific radioactivity. Based on the structure–activity considerations discussed above for type A CCK receptors and type B CCK/gastrin receptors, it is clear that an interest in the type A receptor would require a probe to bind in a manner similar to peptides larger than the carboxyl-terminal heptapeptide of CCK (Table I). Probes for the type B CCK/gastrin receptor need only include the carboxyl-terminal tetrapeptide, although the probes listed for the type A receptor are equally useful at the type B receptor.

Depending on the type of radioactive labeling technique used, the ligand needs either a free amino group that can react with the Bolton–Hunter (BH) reagent or an unsubstituted tyrosyl residue for oxidative iodination. Additionally, when choosing a radioligand for affinity-labeling studies, it is critical to utilize a probe with a potential site for covalent attachment. This can represent a free amino group or a sulfhydryl group that is able to react with commonly available bifunctional chemical cross-linking reagents (a large

TABLE I   Cholecystokinin Peptides and Radioligands

Native Ligands

CCK-33 (1-33)

Lys-Ala-Pro-Ser-Gly-Arg-Val-Ser-Met-Ile-Lys-Asn-Leu-Gln-Ser-Leu-Asp-

$$\overset{\displaystyle SO_3H}{\diagup}$$
Pro-Ser-His-Arg-Ile-Ser-Asp-Arg-Asp-Tyr-Met-Gly-Trp-Met-Asp-Phe-NH2

CCK-8 (26-33)

$$\overset{\displaystyle SO_3H}{\diagup}$$
Asp-Tyr-Met-Gly-Trp-Met-Asp-Phe-NH2

Gastrin I

pGlu-Gly-Pro-Trp-Leu-Glu-Glu-Glu-Glu-Glu-Ala-Tyr-Gly-Trp-Met-Asp-Phe-NH2

Radioligands

[125]I-Bolton-Hunter-CCK-33

^{125}I-BH-(Lys)-Ala-Pro-Ser-Gly-Arg-Val-Ser-Met-Ile-(Lys)....

$$\overset{\displaystyle SO_3H}{\diagup}$$
.....-Asp-Tyr-Met-Gly-Trp-Met-Asp-Phe-NH2

[125]I-Bolton-Hunter-CCK-8

$$\overset{\displaystyle SO_3H}{\diagup}$$
[125] I-BH-Asp-Tyr-Met-Gly-Trp-Met-Asp-Phe-NH2

[125]I-Bolton-Hunter-Lys-Gly-CCK-8

$$\overset{\displaystyle SO_3H}{\diagup}$$
[125] I-BH-(Lys)-Gly-Asp-Tyr-Met-Gly-Trp-Met-Asp-Phe-NH2

[125]I-D-Tyr-Gly-[(Nle[28,31])CCK-26-33]

[125]I

(D-Tyr)-Gly-Asp-Tyr- $\overset{\displaystyle SO_3H}{\diagup}$ Nle-Gly-Trp- Nle-Asp-Phe-NH2

Photoreactive Radioligand

[125]I-D-Tyr-Gly-[(Nle[28,31],pNO2-Phe[33])CCK-26-33]

[125]I

D-Tyr-Gly-Asp-Tyr-Nle -Gly-Trp-Nle-Asp-(Phe)-NH2

with $\overset{\displaystyle SO_3H}{\diagup}$ on Tyr and pNO2 on Phe

[a] The shaded area indicates the regions of the ligands that bind to receptor molecules. Circled are amino acid residues available for chemical or photoreactive cross-linking.

TABLE II   Cross-Linking Reagents

Reagent	Characteristic
Heterobifunctional	
m-Maleimidobenzoyl-N-hydroxysuccinimide ester (MBS)	Primary amine (NH$_2$)-reactive group Free sulfhydryl (SH)-reactive group

N-5-azido-2-nitrobenzoyloxysuccinimide (ANB-NOS)	Primary amine (NH$_2$)-reactive group Relatively nonselective photoreactive group

Homobifunctional	
Disuccinimidyl suberate (DSS)	Two primary amine (NH$_2$)-reactive groups

series of such reagents is available from Pierce Chemical Company, Rockford, IL) (a few representative agents are illustrated in Table II). Also, this site can be used for the covalent attachment of a photolabile residue which can later be used in photoaffinity labeling.

Historically, the first analog of CCK radiolabeled to high-specific radioactivity that was useful for direct radioligand binding studies was Bolton–Hunter-labeled CCK-33 (7). This probe requires radioiodination via an acylation-type reaction with the Bolton–Hunter reagent, because it cannot be radiolabeled oxidatively. This is based on the critical nature of the methionines within the carboxyl-terminal receptor-binding domain, which must remain in a reduced state for maximum binding efficacy, and also on the absence of an unsubstituted tyrosine necessary for oxidative iodination (native CCK contains only a tyrosine sulfate, not amenable to oxidative labeling). CCK-33 possesses two lysine residues in positions 1 and 11. The Bolton–Hunter reagent likely occupies the α-amino group of the lysine in position 1, and the amino groups in the ε position of residues 1 and 11 are still available and useful nucleophilic groups for bifunctional cross-linking experiments.

Because only the carboxyl-terminal heptapeptide is necessary for high-affinity, specific binding to the CCK receptor, shorter probes were subsequently developed. The next to reach widespread popularity was Bolton–Hunter-labeled CCK-8 (8). Again, this maintained the reduced state of the critical methionines in this peptide. Of note, in Bolton–Hunter-labeled CCK-8, there is no available nucleophilic group for bifunctional cross-linking experiments.

A logical step to provide an additional amino group available for bifunctional cross-linking was taken when CCK-8 was extended with a glycine spacer and a lysine residue on its amino terminus (9). This molecule was amenable to Bolton–Hunter radiolabeling as well as amino-reactive bifunctional cross-linking experiments.

A major advance occurred with the demonstration that the methionine residues in CCK could be replaced by threonine or norleucine residues, while maintaining high-affinity binding and biological activity. This led to further modification of CCK by adding a tyrosine residue to the amino terminus, which could be used for oxidative labeling. A further advance included the exchange of a D-tyrosine for a L-tyrosine at the amino terminus of such a derivative, making the peptide probe resistant to aminoproteases (10). All of the above-described peptides can be cross-linked via amino groups, utilizing a series of readily available bifunctional chemical cross-linking reagents (Table II).

Photoaffinity labeling is a technique in which a photolabile residue is either attached to or incorporated within a probe that is allowed to bind specifically to its receptor in the dark. After binding, photolysis induces the generation of a highly reactive intermediate that can insert into adjacent bonds, thus generating a covalent bond to associated proteins (11). Most useful for these types of experiments are nitrene and carbene precursors. Such reagents have the added advantage of not leading to the matting of proteins generated by high concentrations of bifunctional cross-linking reagents. Additionally, such photolabile residues are much more reactive than common amino-reactive and sulfhydryl-reactive chemical cross-linkers. The more reactive the group, the higher the efficiency of cross-linking to be expected. Highly photoreactive groups are, however, difficult to work with, because they have a short effective functional half-life in the laboratory, and they adsorb nonspecifically to tubes and proteins in solutions, therefore generating high nonspecific background labeling.

It is possible to perform photoaffinity labeling with the above peptides by derivatizing their free amino group with a bifunctional cross-linker such as *N*-5-azido-2-nitrobenzoyloxysuccinimide (ANB-NOS), which has an amino-reactive group as well a photolabile residue (Table II). Additionally, CCK analogs with intrinsic photolabile residues have been described and are useful for photoaffinity labeling of CCK receptors (although these are not yet commercially available) (12, 13).

Key in the affinity labeling of binding proteins is the approximation of appropriately reactive groups on probe and target. This includes both their spacial approximation as well as the correct orientation of reactive groups. Utilizing cross-linkers of different lengths may be necessary to facilitate the labeling, and variation of the amount of cross-linking reagent added is often needed to optimize the ratio of specific signal to nonspecific background.

Any probe utilized to characterize a receptor should be validated to demonstrate appropriate binding specificity utilizing competition-binding experiments. Photoaffinity-labeling experiments should include controls performed without photolysis and with prephotolyzed ligand, in addition to the appropriate competition controls with the structurally related and unrelated ligands. If possible, demonstration of biological activity at the receptor of interest also helps confirm appropriate binding of ligand probe to the biologically relevant receptor.

Radioligands

Based on the above-described characteristics of radioactive ligands for CCK receptors, two molecules are best suited for ligand binding and cross-linking studies: (i) ^{125}I-Bolton–Hunter-labeled CCK-8, which is commercially available from at least two different sources [Amersham, Arlington Heights, IL (Cat. No. JM.159) and New England Nuclear, Boston, MA (Cat. No. NEX203)], and which is sufficient for ligand binding and competition-binding experiments; and (ii) ^{125}I-D-Tyr-Gly-[(Nle^{28,31})CCK-26–33] (method below), which is an appropriate ligand for both competition binding and affinity-labeling experiments. The techniques for the oxidative iodination and subsequent purification of this ligand are described below. After iodination, the radioligand can be purified by two simple methods, depending on the availability of instrumentation. Purification by high-performance liquid chromatography (HPLC) will yield a radioiodinated peptide with higher specific radioactivity, but requires an HPLC system capable of using radioactive peptides. In contrast, purification by gel filtration does not require sophisticated equipment, but will yield a product with somewhat lower specific radioactivity. Nevertheless, this technique is sufficient for most applications.

Oxidative Radioiodination of D-Tyr-Gly-[(Nle^{28,31})CCK-26–33]

Materials

> D-Tyr-Gly-[(Nle^{28,31})CCK-26–33] (Cat. No. 20-2721-02; Research Plus, Bayonne, NJ), lyophilized and stored in 5- to 10-μg aliquots at $-70°C$
> Na^{125}I, 1 mCi
> Iodobeads (Cat. No. 28665; Pierce Chemical Company), stored at 4°C
> Polypropylene tubes, 12 × 75 mm
> Disposable syringe (1 ml), with blunted 22-gauge needle

For purification by HPLC separation:

> HPLC system with Vydac C$_{18}$ column (Cat. No. 218 TP54; The Separations Group, Hesperia, CA)

For purification by gel filtration:

> Sephadex G-15 (Pharmacia, Piscataway, NJ), preswollen in elution buffer
> Serological pipette, 5 ml
> Glass wool

Solutions

> Methanol
> Sodium borate (0.2 *M*), pH 9.0
> Triethylamine acetate (TEA-A) (0.1 *M*), pH 5 (pump A)
> CH$_3$CN (pump B)

Methods

The peptide is dissolved by suspension in 10 μl methanol with gentle shaking, followed by addition of 20 μl borate buffer, and transferred into a 12 × 75 mm polypropylene tube. Another 20 μl of borate buffer is used to transfer all of the remaining peptide into the reaction tube. One millicurie of Na^{125}I is added to the tube and the total radioactivity is determined in a gamma counter. One Iodobead is then added to the mixture, and gently shaken for 30 sec.

Purification by High-Performance Liquid Chromatography

The reaction is buffered with 0.9 ml 0.1 *M* TEA-A, pH 5.0, and the resulting mixture is aspirated off the Iodobead with the syringe. This is then injected into the injection loop of the HPLC. Empty reagent tubes and syringe should be counted to calculate the amount of radioactivity bound to the peptide ($\geq 30\%$ of total radioactivity is typically bound to the peptide). Separation of labeled from unlabeled peptide is carried out using the following HPLC gradient: 30-min isocratic at 29% B; 10-min linear gradient to 40% B; 5-min linear gradient to 60% B; 10-min linear gradient back to 10% B. At a flow rate of 1 ml/min, unlabeled and labeled peptide will elute during the late isocratic portion of the elution profile. Unlabeled peptide as monitored by ultraviolet (UV) absorption at 280 nm elutes after approximately 15 min and is clearly separated from radiolabeled peptide, which elutes after approximately 23 min. This can be directly observed with a radioactive flow detector, or be determined by counting aliquots.

Purification by Gel Filtration

A Sephadex G-15 column is prepared using a 5-ml serological pipette and siliconized glass wool as a stopper at the bottom. The column should be washed and equilibrated with borate buffer. To stop the radioiodination reaction, 0.4 ml of borate buffer is added to the polypropylene tube, and the mixture is aspirated off the beads. This is loaded onto the Sephadex column, and 0.5-ml fractions are collected and monitored for radioactivity.

The purified radiolabeled peptide from either separation procedure can be tested with a simple competition-binding assay, as described below, using two sets of tubes: one with radioligand only, for determination of maximal binding, and one with the incorporation of 10^{-6} M competing cold ligand (CCK-8), to determine nonspecific binding.

Preparations of Cholecystokinin Receptor-Bearing Substrates

Two alternative preparations of receptor-bearing substrates are described. (i) The preparation of membranes by sucrose density gradient centrifugation yields highly enriched plasma membranes from rat pancreatic tissue or tissue culture cells; (ii) a crude particulate preparation can be prepared more quickly. For most studies with CCK receptors, this crude method yields adequate specific binding activity in a fast and reliable way that is quite satisfactory. However, for affinity-labeling studies and visualization of labeled peptides by sodium dodecyl sulfate-polyacrylamide gel electrophoresis (SDS-PAGE), a more highly enriched plasma membrane preparation often results in better defined labeled bands with lower background labeling.

Membrane Preparations for Rat Pancreatic Tissue

Materials

Dounce homogenizer (Cat. No. 357546; Wheaton Scientific, Millville, NJ), 40 ml, with A and B pestle

Dounce homogenizer (Cat. No. 357542; Wheaton), 7 ml, with A pestle

Ultracentrifuge with fixed angle rotor and polycarbonate bottles

Cheese cloth

Solutions

Stock solutions

Krebs–Ringer–HEPES (KRH) buffer (10×): 250 mM N-2-hydroxyethylpiperazine-N'-2-ethanesulfonic acid (HEPES), 1.04 M NaCl, 50 mM KCl, 10 mM KH_2PO_4, 12 mM $MgSO_4$

$CaCl_2$ in H_2O stock (100 mM)

Phenylmethylsulfonyl fluoride (PMSF) (100 mM in ethanol)

Prepare freshly

Sucrose solution (0.3 M) with 0.01% (w/v) soybean trypsin inhibitor (Cat. No. LS3571; Worthington, Freehold, NJ), 1 μl of PMSF stock solution per milliliter (0.1 mM)

Sucrose solution (2 M) with 0.01% (w/v) soybean trypsin inhibitor, 1 μl of PMSF stock solution per milliliter (0.1 mM)

KRH/buffer: 1× KRH (1 : 10 stock), 2 mM $CaCl_2$ (1 : 50 stock), pH 7.4 with 5 N NaOH, 0.01% (w/v) soybean trypsin inhibitor, 0.2% (w/v) bovine serum albumin, 1 μl of PMSF stock solution per milliliter (0.1 mM)

Methods

Rats are sacrificed by decapitation, and their pancreata are excised and placed into iced KRH buffer. All subsequent steps are carried out at 4°C. Mesentery and lymph nodes are carefully dissected away. Remaining pancreata are weighed, transferred into 0.3 M sucrose solution (10 ml/g tissue), and finely minced with scissors. This is then homogenized in the Dounce homogenizer, using four strokes with the B pestle, and another four strokes with the A pestle. The homogenate is filtered through a double layer of cheese cloth, and 1.43 times its volume of the 2 M sucrose solution is added and carefully mixed. The resulting homogenate (1.3 M sucrose concentration) is transferred to ultracentrifuge tubes, overlayered with 0.3 M sucrose solution, and spun at 300,000 g for 60 min, using slow acceleration and deceleration. The interface between the sucrose layers, which appears as a white membrane band, is removed, diluted with three times its volume with KRH buffer, and spun for 45 min at 300,000 g. The membrane pellet is resuspended using several strokes with the 7-ml Dounce homogenizer, and membranes are pelleted again at 150,000 g for 30 min. This pellet is resuspended in KRH buffer at a concentration of 1 mg protein/ml solution. It can be safely stored at −70°C for several months without loss of ligand-binding characteristics.

Membrane Preparations for Tissue Culture Cells

Materials

Potter Elvehjem-type Teflon–glass homogenizer (30 ml) (e.g., Cat. No. 358049; Wheaton)
Refrigerated centrifuge with swinging bucket rotor
Cell scrapers
Cell line (e.g., CHP212 human neuroblastoma cell line, or AR-42J rat pancreatic acinar tumor cell line)

Methods

Cells are harvested in cold medium or KRH buffer by scraping with a cell scraper, and they are transferred to conical tubes. After centrifugation at 200 g, the pellets containing cells are resuspended in 10 ml 0.3 M sucrose solution per milliliter packed cell volume. The cells are homogenized using eight strokes with the Teflon–glass homogenizer. The homogenate is then brought to 1.3 M sucrose by adding 1.43 times its volume of the 2 M sucrose solution. Further processing to membranes is accomplished, as described above for rat pancreatic membranes.

Alternatively, small volumes of cells can be harvested and resuspended in 40% (w/v) sucrose containing soybean trypsin inhibitor and bovine serum albumin. They are then homogenized by a 10-sec burst with a sonicator [sonifier cell disrupter, model W185 (Heat Systems, Ultrasonics Inc., Plainview, NY), at setting 7]. The resulting suspension is transferred to ultracentrifuge tubes and overlayered with a 20% (w/v) sucrose solution containing soybean trypsin inhibitor and bovine serum albumin, and fractionated as described above.

Crude Particulate for Guinea Pig Brain Tissue

Materials

Brinkmann (Westbury, NY) Polytron or Potter Elvehjem-type Teflon–glass homogenizer

Solutions

   Tris-HCl (50 mM), pH 7.4, 4°C

Methods

Guinea pigs are sacrificed, and brain tissue is removed and weighed. Ten milliliters of 50 mM Tris-HCl is added per gram of tissue, and homogenization can then be performed with either the Brinkmann Polytron, setting 5 for 30 sec, or using eight strokes with the Teflon–glass homogenizer. The resulting suspension is transferred into centrifuge tubes, and spun at 1000 g for 5 min at 4°C in a swinging bucket rotor to pellet nuclei and intact cells. The supernatant is removed and centrifuged again at 40,000 g for 20 min at 4°C. The membrane pellet is homogenized in 5 ml Tris-HCl per gram original tissue weight and pelleted by another spin at 40,000 g for 20 min at 4°C. This pellet is resuspended in KRH buffer and stored at $-70°$ until ready for use.

Competition-Binding Assay of Rat Pancreatic Membranes

Techniques for competition-binding experiments are described with two alternative possibilities for the separation of bound from unbound ligand: (i) The manual separation requires no special equipment, but it is slow, and with a large number of tubes and assays becomes time consuming. (ii) The semiautomated separation by vacuum filtration requires special equipment, but does in turn facilitate the handling of tubes substantially. Due to the more rapid separation of a whole set of 12 tubes in parallel, this method furthermore yields more reproducible results when dissociation rates of the ligands from their binding sites are high.

Materials

   Radioligand, ^{125}I labeled to 2000 Ci/mmol
   Cold, competing ligands (agonists and/or antagonists): e.g., CCK-8 (Cat. No. 7183; Peninsula Laboratories, Belmont, CA), $5 \times 10^{-5} M$ in KRH buffer or L-364,718 (Merck Sharp & Dohme, West Point, PA), $10^{-4} M$ in dimethyl sulfoxide (DMSO)
   γ counter
   Polypropylene tubes (75 $\times$ 12 mm) or polypropylene microfuge tubes (1.5 ml)
   Microcentrifuge at 4°C

For semiautomated wash and separation steps:

> Skatron cell harvester (Skatron Instruments, Sterling, VA)
> Receptor-binding filter mats (Cat. No. 11734; Skatron Instruments, Sterling, VA)

Methods

1. Incubation tubes are prepared in triplicate for each point of the displacement curve. A typical assay includes points at three different parts of a displacement curve: (i) One set of tubes is prepared with radioligand alone, and no competing cold peptide to determine total binding activity. (ii) Another control includes the radioligand and an excess amount of competing cold ligand to determine nonspecific binding. The concentration of competing ligand for this set of tubes must be above the concentration necessary for maximum displacement. This is usually at about $10^{-6} M$, or 100 times the K_d of the relevant binding site. (iii) A series of tubes must be prepared that spans the range of concentrations of the unlabeled ligand where partial displacement of radioligand is expected.
2. Add 350 μl KRH buffer to each tube.
3. Prepare 10× serial dilutions of cold ligand in KRH buffer. Add 50 μl to each set of tubes, and 50 μl KRH buffer to control tubes.
4. Prepare a 20 to 100 pM solution of radioligand in KRH buffer, and adjust to 10,000–20,000 cpm/50 μl. Add 50 μl of radioligand to all tubes.
5. Add 50 μl of membrane suspension (25–50 μg protein) to all tubes, and incubate at the temperature and time shown to be sufficient to reach steady state binding (for rat pancreatic membranes, 21°C for 30 min is adequate, although other membranes typically require 45 to 60 min).
6. Separation of bound from unbound radioligand can be performed in two ways.
   a. *For manual separation:* 500 μl of ice-cold KRH buffer is added to each tube to slow down dissociation of bound ligand from the membranes, and tubes are placed on ice. Membranes are pelleted in a microfuge at maximum speed at 4°C, and the supernatant is aspirated into a radioactive waste container. The pellets are washed twice with 500 μl of iced KRH buffer, and remaining bound counts can be measured in a γ counter.
   b. *Semiautomatic vacuum separation:* Filter mats are placed in the Skatron cell harvester at 4°C, and they are prerinsed with 0.2% (w/v) bovine serum albumin in water. Reagent tubes are placed in the sample rack without further addition of buffer or other manipulation. The membrane suspension is aspirated onto the filter sheets and washed for 9 to 10 sec with iced isotonic saline solution. Filter disks can then be cut out and directly counted in a γ counter (Fig. 1).

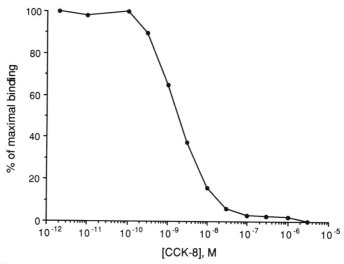

Fig. 1   Representative competition binding experiment. In this experiment, 50 μg of rat pancreatic membranes was incubated with 21,500 cpm of ^{125}I-D-Tyr-Gly-[(Nle[28,31])CCK-26–33] and varying concentrations of unlabeled CCK-8. Unbound ligand was separated from bound ligand by semiautomated vacuum separation. The maximum amount of bound ligand (100%) was 2670 cpm with a background of 320 cpm in the presence of 10^{-6} M CCK-8.

Comparable binding protocols can be used with intact cells or membranes from different sources. Necessary validation steps for the assay conditions would include time courses of binding at different temperatures to show that the amount of bound ligand reaches a steady state plateau at the temperature and time chosen for analysis. Background binding should be less than 10% of the added counts. Specificity and analysis of binding to a presumed receptor molecule can then be examined using the criteria established by Limbird (14).

Affinity Labeling of Cholecystokinin Receptor Molecules

Affinity-labeling experiments are set up in an manner analogous to binding experiments, except that more radiolabel and more receptor are used. Additionally, after binding and separation of bound from unbound ligand, samples are exposed to a cross-linking procedure. This may be either by use of a chemical bifunctional cross-linking reagent or by use of a photolabile group that is activated by UV irradiation. Examples for both methods are described below (Fig. 2).

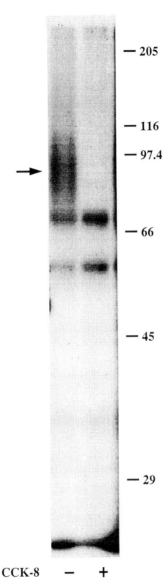

CCK-8   −   +

Fɪɢ. 2 Affinity labeling of rat pancreatic membranes with ^{125}I-ᴅ-Tyr-Gly-[(Nle^{28,31},pNO$_2$-Phe^{33})CCK-26–33]. Rat pancreatic membranes (100 μg) were incubated with 750,000 cpm of ^{125}I-ᴅ-Tyr-Gly-[(Nle^{28,31},pNO$_2$-Phe^{33})CCK-26–33] in the presence (+) or absence (−) of 10^{-6} M CCK-8. After photolysis, membrane pellets were separated by sodium dodecyl sulfate–polyacrylamide gel electrophoresis. Shown here is the autoradiograph after exposure for 24 hr. One band is labeled specifically by the ligand and represents the CCK receptor (marked with the arrow). CCK-8 is not able to compete for labeling of the other two bands, which therefore represent nonspecifically labeled proteins.

Materials

m-Maleimidobenzoyl-N-hydroxysuccinimide ester (MBS) (Cat. No. 22310 G; Pierce Chemical Co.): Amino- and sulfhydryl-reactive heterobifunctional chemical cross-linking reagent

Disuccinimidyl suberate (DSS) (Cat. No. 21555 G; Pierce Chemical Co.): Amino-reactive, homobifunctional cross-linking reagent

Siliconized 75 × 12 mm borosilicate glass tubes

UV source, such as a Hanovia lamp (Southern New England Ultraviolet Co., Hamden, CT)

Solutions

Boric acid (0.2 M), pH 9.0 with NaOH

Tris base (1 M), pH 7.0 with HCl

DMSO

KRH buffer (1×) with soybean trypsin inhibitor and bovine serum albumin

KRH buffer (1×) without added protein, 4°C

Methods

Set up the binding reaction with radioiodinated ligand in KRH buffer with bovine serum albumin in the same way as described for competition-binding experiments (above), except using a larger amount of radioligand (approximately 100,000–750,000 cpm) and receptor preparation. For photoreactive ligand binding this should be done in the dark to avoid premature activation of the reactive group. After adequate incubation to allow binding equilibrium, add 500 μl of ice-cold KRH without bovine serum albumin to the membrane suspension, and spin the tubes for 5 min in a microfuge at maximum speed. Discard the supernatants and wash the pellets once with 1 ml iced KRH buffer without added protein.

For chemical cross-linking: Resuspend the membranes carefully in 98 μl of 0.2 M borate buffer and place on ice. Dissolve the cross-linking reagent in DMSO at 5 mM, and add the appropriate amount to yield optimal labeling to the reaction mix while vortexing (e.g., 2 μl for the labeling of 50 μg of rat pancreatic membranes with ^{125}I-BH-CCK-33). Incubate for 5 min at 4°C, and quench the amino-reactive reagents with 50 μl 1 M Tris base for 15 min at 4°C. Dilute with 900 μl KRH buffer, pellet the membranes, and prepare for further evaluation (such as SDS-gel electrophoresis, and autoradiography).

For photoaffinity labeling: Resuspend the pellet in 500 μl KRH buffer at 4°C and transfer to a siliconized 75 × 12 mm borosilicate glass tube. Expose to UV irradiation (300 nm) for 30 min. The optimal exposure time for this reaction may vary depending of the strength of the UV source used, and must be determined individually in each laboratory for the radiolabel used. After the reaction, photolyzed membranes are transferred back to 1.5-ml microfuge tubes, where they are pelleted and analyzed appropriately.

Acknowledgments

This work was supported by a grant from the National Institutes of Health (DK32878). We would like to thank Marilyn LeQve for help in manuscript preparation.

References

1. C. Ivy and E. Oldberg, *Am. J. Physiol.* **86,** 599–613 (1928).
2. E. Jorpes and V. Mutt, *Acta Physiol. Scand.* **66,** 196–202 (1966).
3. V. Mutt, *in* "Gastrointestinal Hormones" (G. B. J. Glass, ed.), pp. 169–221. Raven Press, New York, 1980.
4. S. Ravard and C. T. Dourish, *Trends. Pharmacol. Sci.* **11,** 271–273 (1990).
5. T. H. Moran, P. H. Robinson, M. S. Goldrich, and P. R. McHugh, *Brain Res.* **362,** 175–179 (1986).
6. R. M. Freidinger, *Med. Res. Rev.* **9,** 271–290 (1989).
7. J. F. Rehfeld, *J. Biol. Chem.* **253,** 4016–4021 (1978).
8. L. J. Miller, S. A. Rosenzweig, and J. D. Jamieson, *J. Biol. Chem.* **256,** 12417–12423 (1981).
9. R. K. Pearson and L. J. Miller, *J. Biol. Chem.* **262,** 869–876 (1987).
10. R. K. Pearson, E. M. Hadac, and L. J. Miller, *Gastroenterology* **90,** 1985–1991 (1986).
11. A. N. Eberle and N. E. DeGraan, *in* "Methods in Enzymology" (L. Birnbaumer and B. O'Malley, eds.), Vol. 109, pp. 129–156. Academic Press, Orlando, FL, 1985.
12. S. P. Powers, D. Fourmy, H. Gaisano, and L. J. Miller, *J. Biol. Chem.* **263,** 5295–5300 (1988).
13. U. G. Klueppelberg, H. Y. Gaisano, S. P. Powers, and L. J. Miller, *Biochemistry* **28,** 3463–3468 (1989).
14. L. E. Limbird, "Cell Surface Receptors: A Short Course on Theory and Methods," pp. 1–196. Martinus Nijhoff Pub., Boston, 1986.

[11]   Endothelin Receptors in Neural Systems

Paul G. Lysko and Ponnal Nambi

Introduction

The endothelin family of 21-amino acid peptides represents the most potent series of vasoconstrictors known and contributes to the local regulation of vascular homeostasis (1, 2). Four distinct isoforms (ET-1, ET-2, ET-3, and vasoactive intestinal contractor or ET-β) differing in amino acid substitutions have been identified to date, and show widespread distribution in mammalian tissue (3–6). Vascular endothelial cells produce only ET-1 (1), but the first three types are present and/or active in brain (5–8). These neuropeptides have been ascribed functons as neuromodulators or local hormones, overseeing central nervous system regulation of cardiovascular function (6). Additionally, endothelin has been found in both posterior (9) and anterior pituitary (10), regulating anterior pituitary function by eliciting inositol trisphosphate and diacylglycerol production, calcium mobilization and influx, and gonadotropin secretion (10). Endothelin distributes in a nonvascular pattern in brain, and high densities of endothelin-binding sites are found in the granule cell layer of the cerebellum (11), where we have identified both ET-1- and ET-3-binding sites (12). These results prompted us to examine many systems of both primary cultured cells and established neural cell lines for endothelin receptors and their biochemical significance (13–17).

Methods

Cell Culture

Primary Neuronal Culture

Neurons are prepared from 8-day-old rat cerebellum as previously described (18). We have continued to use Sprague–Dawley rat pups (15–18 g) from Taconic Farms (Germantown, NY) as our sole source. Cerebella are pinched off with a forceps and placed into a 35-mm petri dish containing solution 1, which consists of 124 mM NaCl, 5.37 mM KCl, 1 mM NaH$_2$PO$_4$, 14.5 mM D-glucose, 25 mM N-2-hydroxyethylpiperazine-N'-2-ethanesulfonic acid (HEPES), 1.2 mM MgSO$_4$, 27 μM Phenol Red, 3 mg/ml of fraction V bovine serum albumin (A-4919, low endotoxin; Sigma Chemical Co., St. Louis,

Methods in Neurosciences, Volume 11

MO), adjusted to pH 7.4 with NaOH. Meninges are removed with fine forceps under magnification, aided by rolling the cerebella on moist sterile Whatman (Clifton, NJ) #1 filter paper. Groups of 10 cerebella are chopped finely in two orthogonal directions with a safety razor blade on a glass plate [both cleansed with 70% (v/v) ethanol and allowed to dry] and suspended as two groups into 30 ml of solution 1 in a 50-ml centrifuge tube. After centrifugation at 500 g for 5 min, tissue is resuspended into 30 ml of solution 1 with 0.25 mg/ml trypsin (type XII-S, T-2271; Sigma) (solution 2) and incubated 15 min at 37°C, with periodic shaking. To the contents of this tube are added 15 ml of solution 1 containing 25.6 μg/ml DNase I (D-5025; Sigma), 166 μg/ml soybean trypsin inhibitor (T-6522; Sigma), and 1.7 mM MgSO$_4$ (solution 4); contents are mixed gently, and the tube is centrifuged at 500 g for 5 min. The pellet is resuspended in 2 ml of solution 1 containing 80 μg/ml DNase I, 520 μg/ml trypsin inhibitor, and 2.8 mM MgSO$_4$ (solution 3), triturated 60 times in a Pasteur pipette, and removed to a clear 15-ml centrifuge tube. Washings of the previous tube with solution 1 containing 2.5 mM MgSO$_4$ and 0.1 mM CaCl$_2$ (solution 5) are combined to a final volume of approximately 6 ml, and the cell suspension is allowed to sit for 5 min to allow settling of cell clumps. The contents of the tube are decanted from the clumps to another centrifuge tube, the clumps are triturated again with solution 3 and, after the addition of solution 5 and settling, the cell suspensions are combined. Following centrifugation for 7 min at 500 g, the cell pellet is resuspended into approximately 200 ml of growth medium consisting of basal medium Eagle's with Earle's salts (GIBCO, Grand Island, NY) supplemented with 2 mM L-glutamine, 25 mM KCl, 100 μg/ml gentamycin (G-1397; Sigma), and 10% (v/v) heat-inactivated defined fetal bovine serum (HyClone Laboratories, Inc., Logan, UT). Cells are counted in a Coulter (Hialeah, FL) counter (model ZM) with a lower threshold setting of 15 and attenuation of 8, and the suspension is adjusted to 1.5 × 10^6 cells/ml. For endothelin-binding studies, cells are plated into 24-well culture dishes (Nunc, Roskilde, Denmark) coated with poly-L-lysine [P-1524 (Sigma), 5 μg/ml H$_2$O; incubated at least 15 min and then removed] at a seeding density of 7.5 × 10^5 cells/well, or 0.5 ml of cell suspension is added to an additional 1 ml of medium per well. For saturation analyses, cells are plated at a lesser density of approximately 2 × 10^5 cells/well. Cultures are incubated at 37°C in 5% CO$_2$ at 99% humidity, and cytosine arabinoside (C-6645; Sigma) is added to a final concentration of 13.3 μM 20–24 hr later to prevent replication of nonneuronal cells.

Established Cell Lines

The C6-BU-1 cell line is a 6-bromodeoxyuridine-resistant mutant of the rat glioma C6 cell line, while N18TG2 is a 6-thioguanine-resistant mutant of the mouse neuroblastoma clone N18. These cells are grown in Dulbecco's modified Eagle's medium (DMEM; GIBCO) containing high glucose and 10% (v/v) defined fetal bovine serum (HyClone) at 37°C with 10% CO_2. Cells are subcultured 3–5 days before experiments and are grown to confluence. N18TG2 cells are passaged after gentle agitation of the flask; the other cell lines are passaged with the aid of 0.05% (w/v) trypsin containing 0.53 mM ethylenediaminetetraacetic acid (EDTA).

NG108-15 cells are mouse neuroblastoma–rat glioma hybrids, while NCB-20 cells are hybrids of a mouse neuroblastoma–Chinese hamster embryo cortical neuron cross. Both cell lines are grown in DMEM (GIBCO) supplemented with 10% (v/v) defined fetal bovine serum (HyClone), 0.1 mM hypoxanthine, 0.4 μM aminopterin, and 16 μM thymidine (HAT media supplement; Boehringer Mannheim Biochemicals, Indianapolis, IN) at 37°C with 5% CO_2. Cells are subcultured 5–7 days before experiments and are grown to confluence.

Binding Assays

Brain Membranes

Brain tissue (approximately 100 mg) from various sites is homogenized with a motor-driven Teflon pestle at 4°C in 10 ml of 20 mM $NaHCO_3$, and the suspension centrifuged at 1000 g for 15 min at 4°C (12). The supernatant is decanted, centrifuged at 40,000 g for 30 min at 4°C, and the pellet resuspended to 0.2 mg protein/ml of 50 mM Tris/20 mM $MgCl_2$, pH 7.5. Binding assays are performed in 12 × 75 mm glass tubes with 10 μg protein in a total volume of 100 μl, containing a final concentration of 0.2–0.3 nM (3-[^{125}I]iodotyrosyl)endothelin-1 or -3 (specific activity, 2200 Ci/mmol; New England Nuclear Research Products, Du Pont Co., Boston, MA). For saturation binding experiments, membrane protein concentrations are adjusted to 0.2–0.4 μg/tube. After a 60-min incubation at 30°C, reactions are stopped by the addition of 5 ml ice-cold buffer, followed by rapid filtration through Whatman GF/C filters soaked in 0.1% (w/v) bovine serum albumin (BSA) and three 5-ml washes using a Brandel cell harvester (Brandel Biomedical Research and Development, Inc., Gaithersburg, MD). Filter papers are counted in a γ counter at 75% efficiency.

Cerebellar Granule Cells

For binding studies, cells in 24-well dishes are washed twice in 1 ml and incubated in 200 μl of buffer containing (mM): NaCl, 154; KCl, 5.6; $MgCl_2$, 1; $CaCl_2$, 2.3; glucose, 5.6; HEPES, 8.6; and 0.2% (w/v) BSA, adjusted to pH 7.4 with NaOH. Saturation endothelin-binding assays are initiated by adding 50 μl of increasing concentrations (20–500 pM) of ^{125}I-labeled ET-1 or ET-3 to a final volume of 250 μl/well. Dishes are incubated for 2 hr at 4°C in the absence (duplicate wells) or presence (singly) of 100 nM unlabeled endothelin to define nonspecific binding, which amounts to 5–15% of total binding. To terminate the reaction, cells are washed three times in 1 ml of ice-cold buffer, dissolved in 1 ml 0.1 N NaOH, and transferred to 12 × 75 mm tubes, which are capped with a cotton plug and counted in a γ counter. Scatchard analysis of ^{125}I-labeled ET-1-binding data is performed with the LUNDON 1 saturation data analysis program (Lundon Software, Inc., Cleveland, OH). For displacement studies, 10 concentrations (10^{-12}–10^{-6} M) of competitor (duplicate wells) are added to the cells before the addition of 0.2–0.3 nM ^{125}I-labeled ET-1 and results compared to untreated quadruplicate wells (total binding). Because the binding technique is performed in a relatively small well, replicate plates are seeded for the determination of cell counts and protein analysis. We find it most convenient to count cell nuclei after washing wells twice with 1 ml of buffer and lysing neurons in 1 ml of ISOTON II by the addition of 2 drops of ZAP-OGLOBIN II (both from Coulter Diagnostics). Well contents are removed into a total volume of 10 ml ISOTON II and counted as before, but at a lower threshold setting of 15 and an attenuation of 2. Cell protein is determined by the Pierce bicinchoninic acid (BCA) protein assay (Pierce, Rockford, IL) by lysing neurons with 100 μl of 0.1% (w/v) sodium dodecyl sulfate (SDS) and using the standard assay protocol with BSA as standard. Assays are performed in the 24-well dish and absorbance readings of 200 μl in a 96-well dish are made at 570 nm with a UVmax kinetic microplate reader (Molecular Devices Corp., Menlo Park, CA). Using these techniques, we measure approximately 40 μg protein/well and 2.5×10^5 cells/well, for 7- to 8-day-old neurons seeded at a cell density of 7.5×10^5/well. Therefore we may lose from one-half to two-thirds of the cells plated, due to their being nonneuronal, nonviable, or both.

Established Cell Lines

Binding experiments are performed on confluent NG108-15, NCB-20, N18TG2, and C6-BU-1 cells following a 24-hr exposure to serum-free medium in order to prevent possible down regulation of ET receptors, because serum contains endothelin. Cells are harvested by scraping (C6-BU-1) or shaking into buffer, washed once with Dulbecco's phosphate-buffered saline containing 0.2% (w/v) BSA, 5 mM glucose, and 10 mM MgCl$_2$, and resuspended to 2×10^6 cells/ml. Binding is initiated by adding $1–4 \times 10^5$ cells/tube in a total volume of 0.25 ml containing 0.2–0.3 nM ^{125}I-labeled ET-1 in the absence (total binding, in triplicate) or presence (nonspecific binding, in duplicate) of 100 nM unlabeled ET-1. Cells are incubated at 25°C for 60 min, then processed using the Brandel cell harvester as described above for brain membranes.

Measurement of Intracellular Calcium

Cells are harvested as above and suspended at 1–2 × 10^6/ml in Krebs–Ringer–Henseleit (KRH) buffer containing (mM): NaCl, 118; KCl, 4.6; MgSO$_4$, 1.1; CaCl$_2$, 1; KH$_2$PO$_4$, 1; NaHCO$_3$, 24.9; glucose, 11.1; and 0.1% (w/v) BSA, adjusted to pH 7.4 with NaOH. For measurements of intracellular calcium concentrations ([Ca^{2+}]$_i$), cells are loaded with 2 μM Fura-2/AM (Calbiochem, La Jolla, Ca) in buffer for 45 min in the dark at 37°C. For practical purposes, Fura-2 AM is made at 5 mM by dissolving 1 mg in 200 μl dimethyl sulfoxide (DMSO) and diluted to 10 μl/25 ml buffer. Cells are centrifuged at 400 g for 5 min, resuspended in buffer for 20 min to allow hydrolysis of residual ester, recentrifuged, and suspended at 2 × 10^6/ml for assay. Cells are kept on ice in the dark and should be used within 2 hr, because they lose signal with time. C6-BU-1 cells are much more stable in this regard than NG108-15 cells, but to lessen signal loss cells may be kept as pellets on ice before the final resuspension. Fluorescence is measured with a University of Pennsylvania Biomedical Instruments Group fluorometer, with excitation at 339 nm and emission at 505 nm. Cuvettes containing 2 ml of cells and a stirring bar are warmed at 37°C in a water bath for 5 min before being transferred to the fluorometer, where they are maintained at 37°C with constant stirring. Fluorescence is recorded for at least 1 min to establish a stable baseline, then endothelin is added and recording continues until stable. The F_{max} value is determined by adding 10 μl of 4% (v/v) Triton X-100 to lyse the cells, followed by F_{min} determination with the addition of 67 μl of 200 mM EGTA in 2 mM Tris, pH 10, to chelate the calcium. The [Ca^{2+}]$_i$ is calculated using the formula of Grynkiewicz $et\ al.$ (19):

$$[Ca^{2+}]_i = 224\ nM \times [(F - F_{min})/(F_{max} - F)]$$

where F is the maximum endothelin-induced fluorescence.

^{86}Rb Efflux Measurements

Measurement of K$^+$ channel activation by monitoring the movement of ^{86}Rb$^+$ is a useful index of cell function and can be used to delineate the function of ET in brain. C6-BU-1 cells are grown to confluency in 35-mm dishes (Nunc) and washed and incubated in a buffer composed of (mM): NaCl, 118; KCl, 4.7; MgSO$_4$, 1.2; CaCl$_2$, 1.2; KH$_2$PO$_4$, 1.2; NaHCO$_3$, 25; glucose, 11; and 30 μM EGTA, adjusted to pH 7.4 with NaOH. Cells are equilibrated for 2–3 hr in 1 ml of this buffer containing 2 μCi ^{86}RbCl (specific activity, ~10–30 m Ci/mg; New England Nuclear Research Products). The preloading buffer is aspirated and the cells are washed rapidly twice with 2 ml of fresh incubation buffer to remove superficial isotope. Each dish is incubated at 37°C with 1 ml of buffer, which is removed to separate scintillation vials and replaced every 2 min. Basal rates are obtained for 20 min, at which time ET is added to induce ^{86}Rb efflux and is maintained throughout. At the termination of the experiment cells are lysed with 2% (w/v) SDS, removed from the dish, and radioactivity is determined for this and the buffer samples by liquid scintillation counting in the ^{32}P window. Efflux curves are generated by summing the counts of the cell lysate and efflux buffer solutions in reverse order of collection. Rate constants (k) for ^{86}Rb efflux at each time interval are calculated using the following equation:

$$k = \ln(A_1/A_2)/(t_2 - t_1)$$

where A_1 and A_2 represent the total counts remaining in the dish at times t_1 and t_2, respectively. Most results are expressed as the rate constant k min^{-1}, with ET showing a dose-dependent increase.

Phosphoinositide Hydrolysis

For the measurement of phosphoinositide (PI) hydrolysis, confluent cells in 150 cm^2 flasks are labeled with 20 μCi/10 ml of *myo*-[2-^{3}H]inositol (specific activity, 17.4 Ci/mmol; Amersham, Des Plaines, IL) in inositol-free DMEM overnight. When used, pertussis toxin (List Biological Laboratories, Campbell, CA) was added for the same time period at a final concentration of 1 μg/ml. Cells are harvested and washed twice with KRH buffer, and resuspended at 10^6 cells/ml in KRH buffer with 10 mM LiCl. A portion of the cell suspension (0.5 ml/13 × 100 mm tube) is incubated in triplicate at 37°C for 10 min, and formation of [^{3}H]inositol monophosphate, [^{3}H]inositol diphosphate, and [^{3}H]inositol triphosphate ([^{3}H]IP$_1$, [^{3}H]IP$_2$, and [^{3}H]IP$_3$, respectively) is initiated by adding endothelin to replicate sets of tubes for dose–response analysis or for a time course. Where used, sensitivity to phorbol ester is determined by adding phorbol dibutyrate (up to 1 μM) for 15 min prior to the addition of endothelin. Reactions are stopped by adding 50 μl of 100% trichloroacetic acid (TCA) and maintaining samples on ice for 20 min. Samples are centrifuged at 1800 g for 5 min, supernatant is decanted to a new

13×100 tube, and TCA is extracted from the supernatant five times by adding 2 ml of water-saturated diethyl ether, vortexing for 1 min, and aspirating the upper ether phase. The last of the ether is evaporated under a stream of nitrogen gas and the aqueous samples are neutralized to pH 7 with 10 μl of 0.5 M Tris base. Samples may be stored at $-80°C$ until column chromatography to separate the inositol phosphates. For separation, samples are mixed with 4 ml of 5 mM sodium tetraborate containing 0.5 mM EDTA and poured onto disposable polystyrene columns (1×10 cm) containing 0.5–1 g of AG 1-$\times$8 anion-exchange resin (200–400 mesh; Bio-Rad Laboratories, Richmond, CA). The resin is easily prepared as a slurry in deionized water, and the appropriate amount added to the column, which is then washed with 5 ml of water. The sample tube is rinsed with 5 ml water and poured over the column, myo-[2-^{3}H]inositol is eluted with 5 ml of 20 mM ammonium formate, and [^{3}H]IP$_1$, [^{3}H]IP$_2$, and [^{3}H]IP$_3$ are sequentially eluted into scintillation vials with 4 ml, respectively, of 0.2, 0.4, and 0.8 M ammonium formate in 0.1 M formic acid. Scintillation fluid (10 ml, Ready Gel; Beckman, Fullerton, CA) is added to the vials, which are counted by liquid scintillation techniques.

Binding Analysis

Cell Culture

The binding of ^{125}I-labeled ET-1 to cerebellar membranes and cultured cells was saturable, time dependent, and showed a high degree of specific binding (14, 15, 17). Nonspecific binding was 10–40% of total binding, depending on the cell type and the concentration of radioligand used. There was no apparent binding to NCB-20 or N18TG2 cells (and no signal transduction; see Second Messenger Signal Transduction, below). Scatchard analysis of ^{125}I-labeled ET-1-binding data indicated a single class of high-affinity binding site with average affinities and numbers of binding sites listed in Table I. ^{125}I-Labeled ET-3 binding in cerebellar granule cells was also saturable and specific but the affinity was lower, with a K_d of 300–400 pM and fewer receptors per cell (see following section). We have also revised our original estimate (14) of receptor density in cerebellar granule cells to reflect current techniques of cell counting and protein estimation.

Displacement Studies

Where tested, ET-1 and ET-2 were equipotent diplacers of ^{125}I-labeled ET-1 binding (15, 17) with ET-3 or big ET (proET-1, 39-amino acids) being much less potent, as expected for the ET$_A$ receptor (20). Because both

TABLE I   Binding Characteristics of ^{125}I-Labeled Endothelin 1

Cells	Saturation binding		Displacement studies	
	K_d (nM)	B_{max}	ET	K_d (nM)
Cerebellar membranes	0.02	4[a]		
Cerebellar granule cell[c]	0.095	25,000[b]		
C6-BU-1[d]	0.108	12,400[b]	ET-1	0.074
			ET-2	0.167
			ET-3	261
			Big ET	187
NG108-15[e]	0.16	33,000[b]	ET-1	0.22
			ET-2	0.56
			ET-3	62
			Big ET	>1,000
NCB-20[e]	None found			
N18TG2[d]	None found			

[a] Picomoles per milligram protein.
[b] Receptors per cell.
[c] Lysko et al. (14).
[d] M. M. Gleason, et al. (15).
[e] T.-L. Yue et al. (17).

ET-1 and ET-3 bound to cerebellar granule cell neurons, we wanted to determine whether a single receptor was involved or whether these neurons contained distinct populations of ET_A and ET_B receptors. The tools for this type of analysis have only recently become available, with the development of subtype-specific alternative ligands. Sarafotoxin S_{6b}, purified from the venom of the Middle Eastern burrowing asp, *Atractaspis engaddensis,* is structurally and functionally similar to endothelin, behaving as an agonist at both ET_A and ET_B receptors. However, the highly related sarafotoxin S_{6c} is specific for ET_B receptors and can be used to define the subtypes (20). Similarly, BQ123, a new pharmaceutical agent from Banyu Pharmaceutical Co., Ltd. (Tokyo, Japan) (21), is selective for the ET_A receptor. Using these two compounds in competition binding experiments, we are able to show that both ET_A and ET_B receptors coexist on cerebellar granule cells, as they do in nonneural tissue, such as kidney medulla (20). ^{125}I-Labeled ET-1 is potently displaced by unlabeled ET-1, and less well by ET-3 (Fig. 1), as expected for the selective receptor designated as the ET_A receptor. However, analysis of ^{125}I-labeled ET-1 displacement by the ET_A-selective ligand, BQ123, shows that only 60% of the ^{125}I-labeled ET-1 binding is to an ET_A

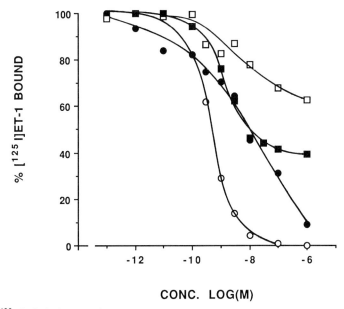

FIG. 1 ^{125}I-Labeled ET-1 displacement studies in cerebellar granule cells. Increasing concentrations of competitor [ET-1 (○), ET-3 (●), sarafotoxin$_{6c}$ (□), and BQ123 (■)] were added to cells before the addition of 0.25 nM ^{125}I-labeled ET-1 and results were compared to untreated cells. Displacement curves indicate 60% ET$_A$ and 40% ET$_B$ receptors on these neurons.

receptor. The other 40% is clearly to a coexistent ET$_B$ receptor, because the ET$_B$-selective ligand, sarafotoxin S$_{6c}$, displaces only 40% of the ^{125}I-labeled ET-1 (Fig. 1).

Second Messenger Signal Transduction

Endothelin has been shown to provoke a rise in intracellular Ca^{2+} in many types of cells and tissues (8, 10, 22–24) but has not had this effect in rat cerebellar granule cells (24). In our hands, measurements of intracellular Ca^{2+} ([Ca^{2+}]$_i$) levels with Fura-2 indicate very little increase in [Ca^{2+}]$_i$ release in response to either ET-1 or ET-3, while quisqualic acid or *trans*-ACPD (trans-(±)-1-amino-1,3-cyclopentanedicarboxylic acid) stimulate small, rapid, transient [Ca^{2+}]$_i$ increases, while N-methyl-D-aspartate causes a large, sustained calcium influx (25; and our own observations). However, robust increases in $[Ca^{2+}]_i$ were observed for C6-BU-1 and NG108-15 cell lines (13, 15, 17) with EC_{50} values listed in Table II for the various endothelin isoforms. Neither N18TG2 nor NCB-20 cells responded to ET-1, reflecting the lack of endothelin receptors shown by binding studies (above). Our results indicate that neuroblastoma cell lines or neuroblastoma–neuronal fusion hybrids lack ET receptors. The ability of NG108-15 cells to respond to ET was obviously passed on by its C6 glioma parent, which fits recent findings of functional ET receptors in astrocytes (8, 24, 26). The Ca^{2+} response in C6-BU-1 cells was totally dependent on extracellular calcium, because incubation in Ca^{2+}-free KRH abolished the response to 4% of control levels. In NG108-15 cells, removal of extracellular Ca^{2+} diminished the ET-induced response to 34% of control values (Table II), indicating true intracellular release from calcium stores, presumably generated by IP_3, as shown below. Another difference noted was that NG108-15 cells showed a transient response to ET, with full recovery to basal levels within 1 min, while the C6-BU-1 response was long lasting, indicative of possible channel activation. However, in further studies

TABLE II   Characteristics of Endothelin-
Induced Calcium Response

Cells	ET	EC_{50} (nM)
Cerebellar granule cell		No response
C6-BU-1[a]	ET-1	0.71
	ET-2	1.14
	ET-3	120
	Big ET	243
96% Inhibition of ET-1-mediated response in Ca^{2+}-free buffer		
NG108-15[b]	ET-1	6.7
	ET-2	11.2
	ET-3	71
	Big ET	No response
66% Inhibition of ET-1-mediated response in Ca^{2+}-free buffer		
NCB-20[b]	No response	
N18TG2[a]	No response	

[a] Gleason *et al.* (15).
[b] Yue *et al.* (17).

TABLE III   Characteristics of Endothelin 1-Stimulated
            Phosphoinositide Hydrolysis

Cells	EC_{50} (nM)	Conditions
Cerebellar granule cell[b]	0.8 for IP_1	PTX[a] (1 μg/ml), minimal effect on IP_1 PDBu[c] (1 μM), 57% inhibition of IP_1
NG108-15[d]	5.4 for IP_3	PTX (500 ng/ml), minimal effect on IP_1 PDBu (1 μM), 62% inhibition of IP_1

[a] PTX, Pertussis toxin.
[b] PDBu, Phorbol dibutyrate.
[c] Lysko *et al.* (14).
[d] Yue *et al.* (13).

we have noted transient responses to ET in C6-BU-1, so perhaps there is differential regulation of the response of which we are unaware.

Similarly, PI hydrolysis has been stimulated by endothelin (8, 10, 23, 26) and has been reported for rat cerebellar granule cells (14, 27). We found [^{3}H]IP_1 accumulation in these cells to be time and dose dependent (EC_{50} = 0.8 nM), and furthermore was inhibited 57% by phorbol dibutyrate but minimally by pertussis toxin (Table III). Rapid production of IP_3 in ET-induced NG108-15 cells (Table III) corroborates the Ca^{2+} influx studies mentioned above, which indicated Ca^{2+} release from internal stores. Inhibition of ET-mediated IP_1 accumulation by phorbol ester (62%) but not pertussis toxin (Table III) indicates that the ET receptor-mediated event is regulated by protein kinase C (PKC) and that the ET receptor is coupled through a GTP-binding protein that is insensitive to pertussis toxin.

^{86}Rb efflux experiments proved a convenient way to assess the activity of endothelin in cultured C6-BU-1 cells (16). Endothelin 1 stimulates a rapid, dose-dependent, transient rise in efflux rate (Table IV). Endothelin 1-stimulated efflux is reduced nearly 70% in the absence of extracellular Ca^{2+}, reflective of the requirement for [Ca^{2+}]$_i$ increase. Simultaneous measure-

TABLE IV   Characteristics of Endothelin 1-Stimulated ^{86}Rb$^+$ Efflux

Cells	EC_{50} (nM)	Conditions
C6-BU-1[a]	5.9	70% inhibition in Ca^{2+}-free buffer PTX (1 μg/ml), no effect Staurosporine (1 μM), 66% inhibition
Cerebellar granule cell	No response	

[a] Gleason *et al.* (16).

ments of ET-stimulated $^{45}Ca^{2+}$ and $^{86}Rb^+$ efflux showed similar time courses, with $^{45}Ca^{2+}$ slightly preceding $^{86}Rb^+$ efflux (16), consistent with the hypothesis that ET stimulates Ca^{2+}-activated K^+ channels in these cells. Because neither diltiazem nor nifedipine inhibits $^{86}Rb^+$ efflux (16), it seems that Ca^{2+} influx is through a ligand-gated, and not voltage-sensitive, channel. Similar arguments have been made for ET-induced Ca^{2+} signaling in glomerular mesangial cells (6; and references therein). In cerebellar granule cells, ET-1 at concentrations up to 1 μM failed to provoke $^{86}Rb^+$ efflux (Table IV), consistent with the lack of Ca^{2+} influx as measured with Fura-2 (above).

Stimulation of second messengers by ET-1 in all the neural cell systems we tested did not seem to be coupled to a pertussis toxin-sensitive GTP-binding protein, which distinguishes brain from vascular smooth muscle or glomerular mesangial cells (6). The ET-coupled GTP-binding protein in cerebellar granule cells is also distinct from the metabolotropic G_{P2} glutamate receptor-coupled G protein, which is pertussis toxin sensitive (28). Because ET-stimulated PI hydrolysis in granule cells is regulated by PKC, but does not cause $[Ca^{2+}]_i$ release or $^{86}Rb^+$ efflux, neuronal activation by ET may be independent of IP_3-mediated Ca^{2+} fluxes, with diacylglycerol produced separately via hydrolysis of PI and/or phosphatidylinositol 4-monophosphate without the release of Ca^{2+}, as found for thrombin-stimulated platelets (29, 30). It remains to be seen what functional role endothelin will play in brain physiology, but with the use of cell culture models we will continue to unravel the regulatory and pathophysiological roles of this interesting neuropeptide.

References

1. M. Yanagisawa, H. Kurihara, S. Kimura, Y. Tomobe, M. Kobayashi, Y. Mitsui, Y. Yazaki, K. Goto, and T. Masaki, *Nature (London)* **332**, 411 (1988).
2. M. Yanagisawa, A. Inoue, T. Ishikawa, Y. Kasuya, S. Kimura, S. Kumagaye, K. Nakajima, T. X. Watanabe, S. Sakakibara, K. Goto, and T. Masaki, *Proc. Natl. Acad. Sci. U.S.A.* **85**, 6964 (1988).
3. A. Inoue, M. Yanagisawa, S. Kimura, Y. Kasuya, T. Miyauchi, K. Goto, and T. Masaki, *Proc. Natl. Acad. Sci. U.S.A.* **86**, 2863 (1989).
4. K. Saida, Y. Mitsui, and N. Ishida, *J. Biol. Chem.* **264**, 14613 (1989).
5. H. Matsumoto, N. Suzuki, H. Onda, and M. Fujino, *Biochem. Biophys. Res. Commun.* **164**, 74 (1989).
6. M. S. Simonson and M. J. Dunn, *FASEB J.* **4**, 2989 (1990).
7. O. Shinmi, S. Kimura, T. Sawamura, Y. Sugita, T. Yoshizawa, Y. Uchiyama, M. Yanagisawa, K. Goto, T. Masaki, and I. Kanazawa, *Biochem. Biophys. Res. Commun.* **164**, 587 (1989).
8. R. Marsault, P. Vigne, J.-P. Breittmayer, and C. Frelin, *J. Neurochem.* **54**, 2142 (1990).

9. T. Yoshizawa, O. Shinmi, A. Giaid, M. Yanagisawa, S. J. Gibson, S. Kimura, Y. Uchigama, J. M. Polak, T. Masaki, and I. Kanazawa, *Science* **247,** 462 (1990).

10. S. S. Stojilkovič, F. Merelli, T. Iida, L. Z. Krsmanovič, and K. J. Catt, *Science* **248,** 1663 (1990).

11. C. R. Jones, C. R. Hiley, J. T. Pelton, and M. Mohr, *Neurosci. Lett.* **97,** 276 (1989).

12. P. Nambi, M. Pullen, and G. Feuerstein, *Neuropeptides* **16,** 195 (1990).

13. T.-L. Yue, M. M. Gleason, P. G. Lysko, and G. Feuerstein, *Neuropeptides* **17,** 7 (1991).

14. P. G. Lysko, G. Feuerstein, M. Pullen, H.-L. Wu, and P. Nambi, *Neuropeptides* **18,** 83 (1991).

15. M. M. Gleason, H.-L. Wu, T.-L. Yue, G. Feuerstein, and P. Nambi, *Neuropeptides* **19,** 197 (1991).

16. M. M. Gleason, E. C. Griffin, P. Nambi, and N. Aiyar, *Neuropeptides* **20,** 17 (1991).

17. T.-L. Yue, P. Nambi, H.-L. Wu, and G. Feuerstein, *Neuroscience* **44,** 215 (1991).

18. A. Novelli, J. A. Reilly, P. G. Lysko, and R. C. Henneberry, *Brain Res.* **451,** 205 (1988).

19. G. Grynkiewicz, M. Poenie, and R. Y. Tsien, *J. Biol. Chem.* **260,** 3440 (1985).

20. D. L. Williams, Jr., K. L. Jones, D. J. Pettibone, E. V. Lis, and B. V. Clineschmidt, *Biochem. Biophys. Res. Commun.* **175,** 556 (1991).

21. M. Ihara, K. Noguchi, T. Saeki, T. Fukuroda, S. Tsuchida, S. Kimura, T. Fukami, K. Ishikawa, M. Nishikibe, and M. Yano, *Life Sci.* **50,** 247 (1992).

22. Y. Hirata, H. Yoshimi, S. Takata, T. X. Watanabe, S. Kumagai, K. Nakajima, and S. Sakakibara, *Biochem. Biophys. Res. Commun.* **154,** 868 (1988).

23. P. A. Marsden, N. R. Danthuluri, B. M. Brenner, B. J. Ballermann, and T. A. Brock, *Biochem. Biophys. Res. Commun.* **158,** 86 (1989).

24. S. Supattapone, A. W. M. Simpson, and C. C. Ashley, *Biochem. Biophys. Res. Commun.* **165,** 1115 (1989).

25. M. J. Courtney, J. J. Lambert, and D. G. Nicholls, *J. Neurosci.* **10,** 3873 (1990).

26. M. W. MacCumber, C. A. Ross, and S. H. Snyder, *Proc. Natl. Acad. Sci. U.S.A.* **87,** 2359 (1990).

27. W.-W. Lin, C.-Y. Lee, and D.-M. Chuang, *J. Pharmacol. Exp. Ther.* **257,** 1053 (1991).

28. F. Nicoletti, J. T. Wroblewski, E. Fadda, and E. Costa, *Neuropharmacology* **27,** 551 (1988).

29. T. J. Rink, A. Sanchez, and T. J. Hallam, *Nature (London)* **305,** 317 (1983).

30. P. W. Majerus, T. M. Connolly, H. Deckmyn, T. S. Ross, T. E. Bross, H. Ishii, V. S. Bansal, and D. B. Wilson, *Science* **234,** 1519 (1986).

[12] Natriuretic Peptide Receptors

V. T. F. Yeung, C. S. Cockram, and M. G. Nicholls

Introduction

Atrial natriuretic peptide (ANP), a 28-amino acid peptide first isolated from rat atrial cardiocytes (1), has potent natriuretic, diuretic, and vasorelaxant properties (2–4). Additionally, it inhibits the secretion of renin, aldosterone, and vasopressin, all of which are involved in body fluid homeostasis (5). Atrial natriuretic peptide has a highly conserved amino acid sequence across mammalian species. For example, rat ANP (rANP) and mouse ANP (which are identical) differ from human ANP (hANP) by only one amino acid. In hANP a methionine residue is at position 12, whereas in rodent ANP isoleucine is at position 12 (Fig. 1) (6–8).

In keeping with evidence that many bioactive peptides, first discovered in peripheral organs, are also present in the central nervous system, both ANP and ANP-binding sites have been identified in different regions of the brain. Although binding sites for ANP have been demonstrated in cultured brain neurons (9), functional ANP receptors within the central nervous system (CNS) are located principally on astrocytes (10, 11). Stimulation of these ANP receptors elicits cyclic guanosine monophosphate (cGMP) production (10–15), which may mediate a neuromodulatory function between astrocytes and neurons.

Brain natriuretic peptide (porcine), pBNP, has marked sequence homology with ANP (Fig. 1), and biological properties similar to ANP, although amino acid substitutions suggest that the two peptides may be derived from different genes (16). Brain natriuretic peptide immunoreactivity has been demonstrated in the rat CNS, particularly within regions involved in autonomic and endocrine control (17). Intracerebroventricular (i.c.v.) injection of pBNP, as ANP, inhibits the thirst and pressor response to i.c.v. angiotensin II as well as basal and angiotensin II-stimulated vasopressin secretion. This suggests that both peptides may be involved in the central regulation of fluid balance and blood pressure control (18–20).

Our group has demonstrated that ANP and BNP act on the same receptors in cultured astrocytes, although BNP evokes a greater cGMP response (21). In this chapter, we describe the methods used for study of natriuretic peptide receptors on astrocytes. Astrocytes are increasingly recognized as being important to CNS function through astroglial–neuronal and other interac-

Methods in Neurosciences, Volume 11

```
                        1                  5              10
Human α-ANP      Ser - Leu - Arg - Arg - │Ser│- Ser -│Cys - Phe - Gly│- Gly -│Arg│- Met -

Rat ANP          Ser - Leu - Arg - Arg - │Ser│- Ser -│Cys - Phe - Gly│- Gly - │Arg│- Leu -

Porcine BNP                        Asp - │Ser│- Gly -│Cys - Phe - Gly│- Arg- │Arg│- Leu -
```

```
               15                      20
│Asp - Arg - Ile - Gly│ - Ala - Gln -│Ser - Gly - Leu - Gly - Cys - Asn│ -

│Asp - Arg - Ile - Gly│ - Ala - Gln -│Ser - Gly - Leu - Gly - Cys - Asn│ -

│Asp - Arg - Ile - Gly│ - Ser - Leu -│Ser - Gly - Leu - Gly - Cys - Asn│ -
```

```
  25
Ser - Phe -        │Arg - Tyr│

Ser - Phe -        │Arg - Tyr│

Val - Leu - Arg - │Arg - Tyr│
```

FIG. 1   Amino acid sequences of human α-ANP, rat ANP, and porcine BNP. Identical residues among the peptides are boxed.

tions. For example, they contribute to regulation of extracellular potassium that is generated by neuronal activity and to maintenance of neurotransmitter concentrations in the synaptic region (22).

Preparation of Primary Cultures of Astrocytes

Our methodology uses primary cultures of mouse astrocytes prepared according to the method of Hertz (23) with some modifications (24).

One- to 2-day old mice are killed by decapitation. Using an aseptic technique, the cerebrum is exposed and the cerebellum removed. The subependymal germinal plates from the lateral ventricles of mouse brains are then dissected free of meninges, chopped into pieces, and placed in culture medium containing minimum essential medium (MEM) with a double concentration of all amino acids except L-glutamine (2.8 mM), a quadruple concentration of MEM vitamin solution, 20% (v/v) horse serum, 200 IU/ml of penicillin, and 200 μg/ml of streptomycin. Brain tissue is vortex-mixed vigorously for

20 sec to dissociate the brain cells. Following filtration through a 10-μm membrane filter, the cell suspension is distributed into 35-mm diameter culture dishes at a plating density of 1×10^4 cells/cm^2. Cells are incubated at 37°C in a humidified incubator with a mixture of 5% CO$_2$/95% air. The culture medium is replaced 3 days later and twice weekly thereafter. Astrocyte differentiation is induced at confluency (on day 12–14 of culture) by addition of 0.25 mM dibutyryl cyclic AMP in MEM supplemented with 10% (v/v) horse serum. Binding and biological studies are carried out 2 weeks after confluency. Regular monitoring with indirect immunofluorescence using anti-glial fibrillary acidic protein (GFAP) antiserum is performed to ensure that approximately 95% of the cells are GFAP positive (Fig. 2).

Although we describe the use of primary cultures of cortical mouse astrocytes for the study of ANP receptors, other cellular preparations are also available. For instance, Beaumont and Tan (25) have utilized cultured rat cortical astrocytes without induction of differentiation with dibutyryl cAMP, whereas Fiscus *et al.* (12) and Lyall *et al.* (13) have employed human and rat glioma cell lines, respectively. Despite differences in cell preparations, similar trends in terms of binding affinities and cGMP responses to natriuretic peptides have been observed. However, in view of increasing evidence of heterogeneity among astrocytes, for example within different brain regions, caution should be maintained and overextrapolation avoided.

Preparation of ^{125}I-Labeled Natriuretic Peptides

Monoiodinated human ANP [αhANP (1–28)] of high specific activity is prepared by the Iodogen method. Iodogen (0.1 mM) (No. 28600; Pierce, Rockford, IL) is dissolved in chloroform and 100-μl aliquots (10 nmol Iodogen/tube) are added to 1.5-ml Eppendorf tubes. After evaporation of the chloroform at 37°C in an oven, the Iodogen-coated tubes are stored at -20°C until use.

Radioiodination is started by adding 65 μl of 0.2 M phosphate buffer, pH 7.4, and 15 μl Na^{125}I (No. IMS 30, 100 mCi/ml; Amersham, Arlington Heights, IL) to an Iodogen-coated tube. Twenty micrograms of hANP in 20 μl of double-distilled water is added 1 min later. The iodination mixture is allowed to react at room temperature for 5 min, then applied immediately to a C$_{18}$ μBondapak column (3.9 × 300 mm; Waters Associates, Milford, MA) equilibrated with 18% (v/v) acetonitrile. High-performance liquid chromatography (HPLC) purification of mono-^{125}I-labeled hANP with HPLC is achieved by eluting with a linear acetonitrile gradient of 18–36% in 58 mM phosphate buffer, pH 2.9, on a slope of 0.4%/min and at a flow rate of 1 ml/min. Fractions (0.5 ml) are collected into tubes containing 0.5 ml of 0.5% (w/v)

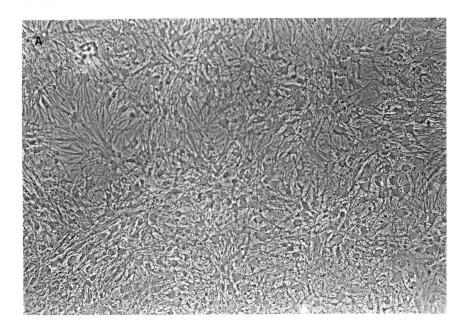

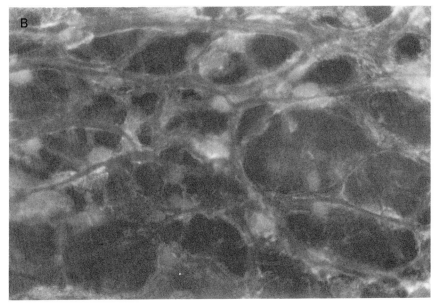

bovine serum albumin in distilled water and 10-μl aliquots taken for counting in a Beckman (Fullerton, CA) γ counter. As illustrated in the chromatogram (Fig. 3a), separation with HPLC yields pure monoiodinated hANP, totally distinct from other reaction products. The specific activity of monoiodinated hANP, calculated by self-displacement with anti-ANP antiserum, is as high as 1400 Ci/mmol. The tracer is aliquoted and stored at $-20°C$. It can be used for up to 6–8 weeks without significant loss of immunoreactivity.

[125]I-labeled pBNP of high specific activity and purity can also be prepared under similar experimental conditions except that the reaction time for iodination is longer (20 min) and that the acetonitrile gradient used for HPLC ranges from 23 to 29% in 58 mM phosphate buffer with a slope of 0.13%/min (Fig. 3b).

Atrial natriuretic peptide and BNP can be iodinated, alternatively, by the chloramine-T or lactoperoxidase methods. Both techniques yield monoiodinated ligands of high specific activity ($\sim$1200–2000 Ci/mmol) if appropriate separation techniques are applied (26–30). Readers can also refer to Chapter 28, Volume 5 of this series, for a description of ANP radioiodination with lactoperoxidase.

Binding of Natriuretic Peptides to Astrocytes

Specific Binding of Natriuretic Peptides

Duplicate samples of monolayer cultures of neonatal mouse astrocytes in 35-mm culture dishes are washed twice with binding buffer containing 5 g/liter bovine serum albumin (BSA) and 10 mM N-2-hydroxyethylpiperazine-N'-2-ethanesulfonic acid (HEPES) in serum-free MEM, pH 7.3, and incubated with 1 ml of binding buffer containing ^{125}I-labeled hANP at varying concentrations (0–2 nM) for 90 min at 22°C, with or without an excess of cold peptide (5 μM). Preliminary experiments showed that ^{125}I-labeled hANP bound to astrocytes with an estimated $T_{1/2}$ of association of 5 min. Equilibrium is

Fig. 2 Microscopy of morphologically differentiated primary cultures of mouse astrocytes 2 weeks after addition of dibutyryl cyclic AMP (28 days *in vitro*). (a) Phase-contrast micrograph of astrocytes ($\times$100). (b) Indirect immunofluorescence microscopy of astrocytes showing positive GFAP staining ($\times$250). Astrocytes are labeled with rabbit anti-GFAP antiserum, followed by goat anti-rabbit IgG conjugated to fluoroscein isothiocyanate (FITC) and counterstaining of cell nuclei with methyl green.

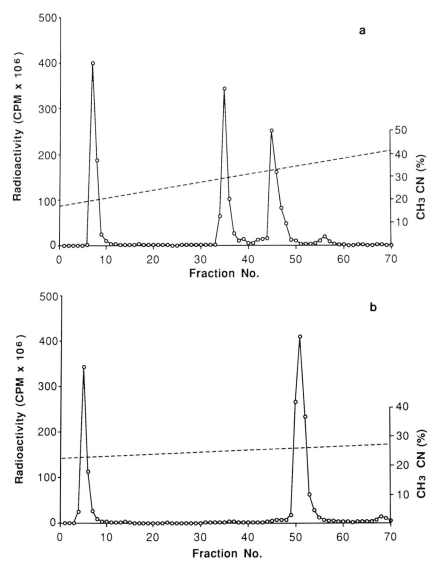

FIG. 3   (a) Reversed-phase HPLC purification of ^{125}I-labeled hANP after radiolabeling by Iodogen. The first radioactive peak corresponds to unincorporated iodine. The second radioactive peak is the iodinated methionine sulfoxide derivative of hANP, and the third major peak (fractions 45 and 46) contains the monoiodinated hANP. (b) Reversed-phase HPLC purification of ^{125}I-labeled pBNP after radiolabeling by the Iodogen method. The first peak corresponds to ^{125}I, and ^{125}I-labeled pBNP is eluted as a distinct second major peak (fractions 50–52).

reached at approximately 90 min, which therefore is the incubation period subsequently employed for binding studies. Approximately 80% of the iodinated ANP remains intact following incubation as assessed by HPLC. At the end of the incubation, cells are washed three times with ice-cold phosphate-buffered saline (PBS, pH 7.4) to remove unbound tracer and then digested with 0.5 M NaOH. Bound ^{125}I-labeled ANP is then counted in a Beckman γ counter and the protein content of the monolayer cells measured using BSA as the protein standard according to the method of Lowry (31).

Scatchard transformation of specific binding data (Fig. 4a) suggests a single class of binding sites for hANP with an apparent dissociation constant (K_D) of 0.1 nM and maximal binding capacity (B_{max}) of 90.3 fmol/mg protein, whereas rANP has a K_D of 0.06 nM and B_{max} of 86.2 fmol/mg protein (V. T. F. Yeung, unpublished data). Values of similar order of magnitude have been reported in rat astrocytes (K_D 0.018 nM; B_{max} 125 fmol/mg protein) and human glioma cell line (K_D 0.1 nM; B_{max} 105 fmol/mg protein) (13, 25). These values are comparable to those found in major ANP target tissues, namely kidney, vascular endothelium and smooth muscle, and adrenal cortex (32–34). In some early experiments trypsinized cell suspensions were used. Despite the theoretical disadvantage of denaturing the receptor protein by trypsination the data generated was comparable to those of monolayer cultures.

Under similar experimental conditions, pBNP binds to receptors on mouse astrocytes with similar kinetics ($T_{1/2}$, 4.5 min; K_D, 0.08 nM; and B_{max}, 73.8 fmol/mg protein) (Fig. 4b). Competition binding studies further indicate that both ANP and BNP interact at the same receptors with similar affinity (21).

Cellular cGMP Accumulation

Mouse astrocytes attached to 35-mm tissue culture dishes are washed twice with binding buffer, then preincubated for 10 min with 1 ml of binding buffer supplemented with 1 mM (final concentration) 3-isobutyl-1-methylxanthine (IBMX), a phosphodiesterase inhibitor. Our preliminary experiments have shown greater cGMP yields cannot be achieved with higher concentrations of IBMX. In addition, time course experiments show that cGMP levels reach a maximum at 10 min, justifying the use of this incubation time for dose–response experiments. After preincubation, hANP and pBNP at different concentrations are added to the cells in the presence of IBMX for a further 10 min at 22°C. Incubation is terminated by aspirating the solution and rinsing the cells twice with 1 ml ice-cold PBS. Intracellular cGMP is released using 1 ml 6% (w/v) trichloroacetic acid (TCA), which is subsequently removed by extraction with water-saturated diethyl ether. Following

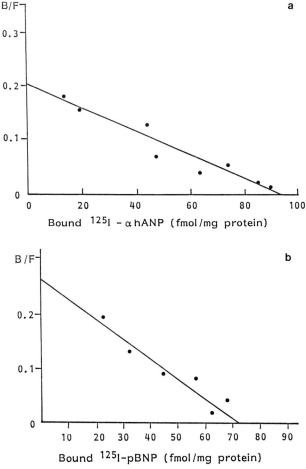

FIG. 4 (a) Scatchard transformation of specific binding of ^{125}I-hANP to mouse astrocytes: B_{max} = 90.3 fmol/mg protein; K_D = 0.01 nM. Data are means of duplicate determinations from a typical experiment. [Reprinted with permission from Yeung *et al.* (21). Copyright (1991), Raven Press, New York.] (b) Scatchard transformation of specific binding of ^{125}I-labeled pBNP to mouse astrocytes: B_{max} = 73.8 fmol/mg protein; K_D = 0.08 nM. Data are means of duplicate determinations from a typical experiment. [Reprinted with permission from Yeung *et al.* (21), with permission from Raven Press.]

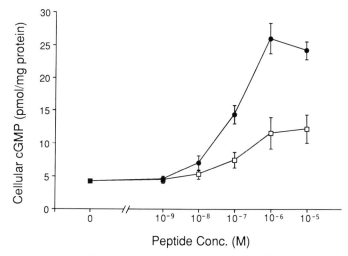

FIG. 5   Intracellular cGMP production in response to hANP (□) and pBNP (●).
Data are mean ± SEM values of duplicate determinations from three experiments.
[Reprinted with modification from Yeung *et al.* (21), with permission from Raven
Press.]

acetylation (35), cGMP in the sample is meausred by radioimmunoassay
using a commercial radioimmunoassay kit (Amersham).

Atrial natriuretic peptide and pBNP stimulate the production of cGMP in
a dose-dependent manner. The half-maximal effective dose for stimulation
of cGMP accumulation is similar for both peptides (EC_{50} = 100 nM), and
both evoke a maximal stimulatory effect at a concentration of 1 μM (Fig. 5).
However, there is a significant difference between the magnitudes of the
maximal cGMP response induced by the two peptides: pBNP elevated cGMP
level from a basal value of 4.2 ± 0.3 to 25.9 ± 2.1 pmol/mg protein, whereas
hANP stimulates cGMP only to a maximum level of 11.5 ± 2.2 pmol/mg
protein (p < 0.05). Rat ANP evokes an intermediate response, with the
cGMP level rising to a maximum of 16.5 ± 2.0 pmol/mg protein (21).

Apparently greater maximal cGMP responses have been observed with rat
cortical astrocytes cultured without addition of dibutyryl cAMP (25), yet the
concentration dependency in both astrocyte preparations is similar. The
approximately 1000-fold discrepancy between the binding affinities (K_D) of
natriuretic peptides and half-maximal stimulating concentrations (EC_{50}) for
cGMP generation agrees with results using other glial preparations and remains unexplained (13, 25), although one possible explanation is the presence
of receptor subtypes coupled to second messenger systems other than cGMP.

This discrepancy also exists in certain other cell types, such as vascular smooth muscle and endothelial cells (34, 36, 37).

Autoradiographic Localization of Natriuretic Peptide Receptors

The methodology described is that of Brown and Czarnechi (38). Male Wistar rats (200–250 g) are killed by decapitation. Their brains are removed rapidly and snap frozen in isopentane at $-40°C$. Fifteen-micrometer sections are cut in a cryostat at $-20°C$, thaw-mounted onto gelatin–chrome–alum-coated glass slides, and desiccated overnight under vacuum at 4°C. The sections are then preincubated in 50 mM Tris(hydroxymethyl)aminomethane (Tris)-HCl buffer, pH 7.4, containing 100 mM NaCl, 5 mM $MgCl_2$, 0.5% (w/v) bovine serum albumin, and 40 μg/ml bacitracin (Sigma, St. Louis, MO) for 15 min at 17°C. Sections are then incubated with 200 pM [3-^{125}I]iodo-28-tyrosyl rANP (1–28) (specific activity, 2013 Ci/mmol; Amersham) in the same buffer for 15 min at 17°C. Nonspecific binding is determined in the presence of 1 μM unlabeled rANP (1–28) or 1 μM concentrations of the unrelated peptides vasopressin, salmon calcitonin, and angiotensin II (Peninsula Laboratories, Belmont, CA). After incubation, the slide-mounted sections are taken through two successive 2.5-min washes with the preincubation buffer at 4°C, then dried rapidly in a stream of cold air. Sections are loaded in X-ray cassettes and exposed to LKB Ultrofilm (LKB, Rockville, MD) for 5 days at 4°C. After exposure, the sections are fixed in formaldehyde and stained with hematoxylin and eosin.

The X-ray films are developed in Kodak (Rochester, NY) D19 developer. Binding sites for ANP and BNP are calculated from the regional optical densities of the autoradiograms by computerized microdensitometry and comparison with optical densities produced in each of ^{125}I-labeled standards (Amersham) mounted in each cassette (39). The specific gravity of tissue blocks containing thalamus and hypothalamus from six more Wistar rats is measured directly, and their protein content is measured by a modified Lowry method (40). These measurements are used to convert values of ^{125}I-labeled ANP binding from femtomoles per square millimeter to femtomoles per milligram protein.

Comparison of autoradiographs with the corresponding stained sections of rat brain indicates that the most intense binding of ^{125}I-labeled ANP is in the subfornical organ (SFO), area postrema (AP), choroid plexus (ChP), and arachnoid mater (AM). There is also a moderate degree of binding to the median preoptic nucleus (MPN), to the supraoptic (SON) and paraventricular (PVN) nuclei, and to the ventricular lining (VL). A less intense binding is present diffusely over the rest of each section. Unlabeled ANP (1 μM) reduces binding to the specific structures noted above but leaves the diffuse background binding unaffected (Fig. 6). Unlabeled porcine BNP displaces bound ^{125}I-labeled ANP in these regions to a similar extent.

On the basis of current published information, this technique does not distinguish between binding to neurons and astrocytes.

Affinity Cross-Linking Studies of Atrial Natriuretic Peptide Receptors

Peptide hormone receptors are present at low concentrations in cellular membranes. With the advent of affinity-labeling techniques one can now identify these receptor proteins directly. The procedures enable the formation of covalent, specific bonds between radioligand and receptor protein. The radiolabeled hormone–receptor complex can then be subjected to procedures such as electrophoresis and chromatography for further study of its properties. This technique has been applied to, and has provided useful information on, astrocytic natriuretic peptide receptors.

Preparation of Cell Suspension

For this particular purpose suspensions of astrocytes have been used. A primary mouse astrocyte culture in a 75-cm^2 flask is washed once with 10 ml of PBS before trypsinization using 0.025% (w/v) trypsin (GIBCO, Grand Island, NY) in PBS at room temperature (22°C) for 2–3 min. The flask is then shaken to detach the cells. The cell suspension is washed twice with binding buffer containing 15 mM 3-(N-morpholino)propanesulfonic acid (MOPS), 150 mM NaCl, 5 mM glucose, and 1% (w/v) BSA, pH 7.6.

Chemical Cross-Linking of ^{125}I-Labeled Atrial Natriuretic Peptide to Receptors

Cells (400 μl) in suspension (4.2 × 10^5/ml) are incubated at 22°C for 1 hr with 0.4 ml binding buffer containing 0.62 nM ^{125}I-labeled ANP in the absence or presence of 1 μM (final concentration) unlabeled ANP. The MOPS binding buffer used is devoid of BSA. Binding is terminated by washing three times in ice-cold MOPS buffer and the cells are then resuspended in 1 ml of the buffer. Cross-linking is achieved by the addition of a 1 mM final concentration of the covalent linking agent disuccinimidyl suberate (DSS) (No. 21555;

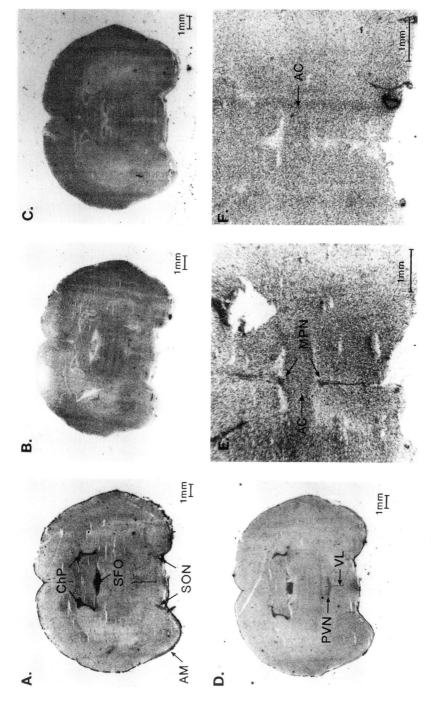

FIG. 6   Autoradiographs of ^{125}I-labeled ANP binding to rat brain. Binding is shown in the absence (A, D, and E) or presence (B, C, and F) of either 1 μM unlabeled ANP or 1 μM BNP. Binding to specific structures (except ChP) was equally displaced by 1 μM unlabeled ANP or 1 μM BNP. SFO, subfornical organ; AM, arachnoid mater; ChP, Choroid plexus; SON, supraoptic nucleus; PVN, paraventricular nucleus; VL, ventricular lining; AC, anterior commissure; MPN, median preoptic nucleus. [Reproduced from Brown and Czarnecki (38), with permission.]

Pierce) in 20 μl dimethylsulfoxide (DMSO), for 30 min at 4°C, followed by washing three times with ice-cold binding buffer.

Sodium Dodecyl Sulfate-Polyacrylamide Gel Electrophoresis

After centrifugation of the cell suspension, cell pellets containing the cross-linked receptor proteins are boiled at 100°C for 2 min in 100 μl gel sample buffer [0.12 M Tris, 4% (w/v) sodium dodecyl sulfate (SDS), 20% (w/v) glycerol, 0.14% (w/v) bromophenol blue, and 10% (w/v) 2-mercaptoethanol, pH 6.8]. Thirty microliters of samples or molecular weight standards (45K–200K; Bio-Rad, Richmond, CA) are subjected to SDS-polyacrylamide slab gel electrophoresis using the discontinuous buffer system (41) with a 4% (w/v) acrylamide stacking gel and an 8% (w/v) acrylamide resolving gel. Electrophoresis is conducted with a constant current of 50 mA at room temperature for 3 hr.

The materials and methods for preparation of polyacrylamide gel are as follows:

Stock acrylamide solution (% acrylamide = 30%, w/v): Dissolve 60 g of acrylamide and 1.6 g of bisacrylamide in 200 ml of water. The stock solution is stable for weeks in brown glass at 4°C

Stock resolving gel buffer: Dissolve 22.7 g of Trizma base and 0.5 g of SDS in water, adjust the pH to 8.8 with HCl, and make up the volume to 100 ml

Stock stacking gel buffer: Dissolve 7.57 g of Trizma and 0.5 g of SDS in water, adjust the pH to 6.8 with HCl, and make up the volume to 100 ml

Reservoir buffer: Dissolve 15.14 g of Trizma base, 72.07 g of glycine, and 5.0 g of SDS in water, adjust the pH to 8.3 with HCl, and make up the volume to 1 liter

An adequate volume of separating gel mixture (30 ml) is prepared for a gel of dimensions 170 × 120 × 1 mm (width × height × thickness). 7.92 ml of stock acrylamide solution is mixed with 6 ml of resolving gel buffer, 15.63 ml of distilled water, and 7.5 μl of N,N,N',N'-tetramethylethylene diamine (TEMED), then degassed on a water pump for 15 min. This is followed by the addition of 0.45 ml of ammonium persulfate (0.1 g/ml), and the mixture is then transferred to a slab gel chamber (gel slab casting apparatus, GSC-8; Pharmacia, Piscataway, NJ) to set in 1 hr. The degassing procedure aims at removing oxygen, which interferes with polymerization by mopping up free radicals, and preventing bubble formation when pouring the gel into the chamber.

Stacking gel is prepared by mixing 1.33 ml of stock acrylamide solution with 2 ml of stacking gel buffer, 6.52 ml of distilled water, and 2.5 μl of TEMED. After degassing for 15 min, 0.15 ml of ammonium persulfate is added. The mixture is then loaded onto the polymerized resolving gel and allowed to set with dimensions of $170 \times 15 \times 1$ mm after insertion of the comb. A detailed account of the methodology for the preparation of the SDS gel is given by Smith (42).

Gel Staining and Autoradiography

Following electrophoresis, the gel is fixed in 500 ml of a solution of methanol and acetic acid in water in a volume ratio of $25 : 6 : 19$ at room temperature for 30 min. Following silver staining (43), the gel is dried in a gel slab drier (GSD-4; Pharmacia) at 24 V overnight prior to autoradiography on Kodak X-Omat RP film with double intensifying screens at $-70°C$ for 30 days.

A typical autoradiograph is shown in Fig. 7. Following covalent linkage of ^{125}I-labeled ANP, one specifically labeled band with an apparent molecular weight of 66,000 is obtained under reducing conditions, suggesting that the major form of astrocytic natriuretic peptide receptor is a 66-kDa peptide.

Conclusions

Substantial evidence has now accumulated that natriuretic peptides could play a central role in the regulation of body fluid and electrolyte balance (18, 20, 44–46). Binding experiments and cross-linking and autoradiographic studies have confirmed the existence of receptors on astrocytes. The dissociation between the binding affinity ($K_D \sim 0.1$ nM) and cGMP responses ($EC_{50} \sim 100$ nM) remains unexplained. One possibility is the presence of astrocytic receptor subtypes to natriuretic peptides, with the 66-kDa peptide as the predominant form that is uncoupled to guanylate cyclase (47–49).

Apart from coupling to guanylate cyclase, ANP receptors have been shown to have a clearance function and to affect phosphatidylinositol metabolism in other tissues (50, 51). Using molecular cloning studies, the structure of the ANP clearance receptor and two isoforms of guanylate cyclase-linked receptors have been deduced (52–54). Natriuretic peptides have been reported to inhibit astroglial proliferation (55). However, it remains to be clarified whether this inhibitory effect is mediated through the clearance receptors, which could act by enhancing phosphatidylinositol turnover, or

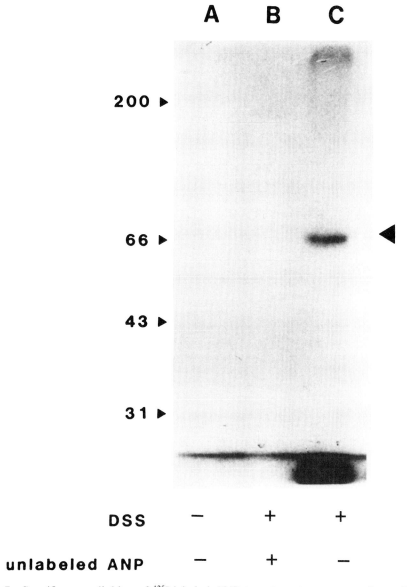

FIG. 7 Specific cross-linking of ^{125}I-labeled ANP to astrocyte receptors. Lane A shows the autoradiographic profiles of cells incubated with ^{125}I-labeled ANP without the cross-linking agent DSS; lane B, cells incubated with ^{125}I-labeled ANP, excess (2 μM) ANP, and DSS; lane C, cells incubated with ^{125}I-labeled ANP and DSS. The labeled component in lane C represents the specific astrocytic ANP receptors because no band is observed when the cross-linking agent is not used (lane A), or in the presence of excess unlabeled ANP (lane B). [Reprinted from Teoh *et al.* (15), with permission from Blackwell Scientific Publishers.]

the guanylate cyclase-coupled receptors, as in the case of other tissues (56, 57).

Thus far, limited information is available in regard to the various subtypes of ANP receptors and second messengers in the CNS and the data are primarily based on *in vitro* cell culture experiments. These findings do not necessarily reflect the real situation in intact adult animals, because the cells are derived either from perinatal animals or malignant cell lines. Moreover, they are grown in an artificial medium with loss of physiological interactions with the normal internal milieu and neurons. Nevertheless, the knowledge secured has provided the basis and logic for further studies.

A C-type natriuretic peptide (CNP) has been identified (58). It is present at high concentrations in the brain but not peripheral tissues and may act mainly as a neurotransmitter/neuromodulator (59, 60). Our studies indicate that it is 10–20 times more efficacious than ANP and BNP in its maximal stimulatory effect on cGMP release from mouse astrocytes in culture (61). Thus it is possible that the traditional natriuretic peptides (atrial and brain) may not be the most effective ligands for these receptors. Future research directed at receptor–effector coupling mechanisms of natriuretic peptides and molecular studies of their receptors, together with *in vivo* animal experiments, should help to elucidate the cellular mechanisms of actions of the natriuretic peptide family within the central nervous system.

Acknowledgments

We are most grateful to Drs. John Brown and Andrzej Czernecki for their permission to quote their methodology and for providing autoradiographs, Mr. Stanley K. S. Ho for excellent technical assistance, and Miss Hidy Yeung for typing the manuscript. The work presented in this chapter was supported, in part, by Grant 221400280 from the University Polytechnic Grant Council, Hong Kong.

References

1. A. J. de Bold, H. B. Borenstein, A. T. Veress, and H. Sonnenberg, *Life Sci.* **28,** 89 (1981).
2. T. G. Flynn, M. L. de Bold, and A. J. de Bold, *Biochem. Biophys. Res. Commun.* **117,** 859 (1983).
3. M. G. Currie, D. M. Geller, and B. R. Cole, *Science* **221,** 71 (1983).
4. R. J. Winquist, *Life Sci.* **28,** 1035 (1985).
5. B. M. Brenner, B. J. Ballermann, M. E. Gunning, and M. L. Zeidel, *Physiol. Rev.* **70**(3), 665 (1990).

6. C. E. Seidman, A. D. Duby, E. Choi, R. M. Graham, E. Haber, C. Homcy, J. A. Smith, and J. G. Seidman, *Science* **225,** 324 (1984).

7. M. Yamanaka, B. Greenberg, L. Johnson, J. Seilhamer, M. Breuner, T. Friedemann, J. Miller, S. Atlas, J. Laragh, J. Lewicki, and J. Fiddes, *Nature (London)* **309,** 719 (1984).

8. H. J. Kramer, *Gen. Pharmacol.* **19**(6), 747 (1988).

9. B. Ricard, P. Fourquet, A. Massacrier, and F. Couraud, *Biochem. Biophys. Res. Commun.* **152,** 1031 (1988).

10. G. Simonnet, M. Allard, P. Legendre, J. Gabrion, and J. D. Vincent, *Neuroscience* **29**(1), 1891 (1989).

11. J. de Vente, J. G. J. M. Bol, and H. W. M. Steinbusch, *Eur. J. Neurosci.* **1,** 436 (1989).

12. R. R. Fiscus, B. T. Robles, S. A. Waldman, and F. Murad, *J. Neurochem.* **48**(2), 522 (1987).

13. F. L. Lyall, A. J. Balmforth, and J. J. Morton, *J. Endocrinol.* **117,** 315 (1988).

14. A. Friedl, C. Harmening, F. Schmalz, B. Schuricht, M. Schiller, and B. Hamprecht, *J. Neurochem.* **52**(2), 589 (1989).

15. R. Teoh, W. Kum, C. S. Cockram, J. D. Young, and M. G. Nicholls, *Clin. Exp. Pharmacol. Physiol.* **16,** 323 (1989).

16. T. Sudoh, K. Kangawa, N. Minamino, and H. Matsuo, *Nature (London)* **332**(3), 78 (1988).

17. C. B. Saper, K. M. Hurley, M. M. Moga, H. R. Holmes, S. A. Adams, K. M. Leahy, and P. Needleman, *Neurosci. Lett.* **96,** 29 (1989).

18. H. Itoh, K. Nakao, T. Yamada, G. Shirakami, K. Kangawa, N. Minamino, H. Matsuo, and H. Imura, *Eur. J. Pharmacol.* **150,** 193 (1988).

19. G. Shirakami, K. Nakao, T. Yamada, H. Itoh, K. Mori, K. Kangawa, N. Minamino, H. Matsuo, and H. Imura, *Neuroscience* **91,** 77 (1988).

20. T. Yamada, K. Nakao, H. Itoh, G. Shirakami, K. Kangawa, N. Minamino, H. Matsuo, and H. Imura, *Neurosci. Lett.* **95,** 223 (1988).

21. V. T. F. Yeung, C. K. Lai, C. S. Cockram, J. D. Young, and M. G. Nicholls, *J. Neurochem.* **56**(5), 1684 (1991).

22. H. K. Kimelberg and M. D. Norenberg, *Sci. Am.* **260**(4), 44 (1989).

23. L. Hertz, A. Schonsboe, N. Booechler, S. Mukerji, and S. Fedoroff, *Neurochem. Res.* **3,** 1 (1978).

24. W. Kum, C. S. Cockram, S. Q. Zhu, R. Teoh, J. Vallance-Owen, and J. D. Young, *J. Neurochem.* **49,** 1293 (1987).

25. K. Beaumont and P. K. Tan, *J. Neurosci. Res.* **25,** 56 (1990).

26. H. P. von Schroeder, E. Nishimura, C. H. S. Mcintosh, A. M. J. Buchan, N. Wilson, and J. R. Ledsome, *Can. J. Physiol. Pharmacol.* **63,** 1373 (1985).

27. R. M. Scarborough, G. A. McEnroe, A. Arfsten, L. L. Kang, K. Schwartz, and J. A. Lewicki, *J. Biol. Chem.* **263**(32), 16818 (1988).

28. K. N. Pandey, S. N. Paviou, and T. Inagami, *J. Biol. Chem.* **263**(26), 13406 (1988).

29. H. Itoh, K. Nakao, Y. Saito, T. Yamada, G. Shirakam, M. Muhoyama, H. Arai, K. Hosoda, S.-I. Suga, N. Minamino, K. Kangawa, H. Matsuo, and H. Imura, *Biochem. Biophys. Res. Commun.* **158**(1), 120 (1989).

30. M. Aburaya, N. Minamino, J. Hino, K. Kangawa, and H. Matsuo, *Biochem. Biophys. Res. Commun.* **165**(2), 880 (1989).

31. O. H. Lowry, N. J. Rosebrough, A. L. Farr, and R. J. Randall, *J. Biol. Chem.* **193,** 265 (1951).

32. E. L. Schriffrin, L. Chartier, G. Thibault, J. St-Louis, M. Cantin, and J. Genest, *Circ. Res.* **56,** 801 (1985).

33. J. W. Jacobs, G. P. Vlasuk, and M. Rosenblatt, *Endocrinol. Metab. Clin. North AM.* **16**(1), 63 (1987).

34. D. C. Leitman, J. W. Andresen, R. M. Catalano, S. A. Waldman, J. J. Tuan, and F. Murad, *J. Biol. Chem.* **263**(8), 3720 (1988).

35. G. Brooker, J. F. Harper, W. L. Teraseki, and R. D. Maylan, *Adv. Cyclic Nucleotide Res.* **10,** 1 (1979).

36. T. J. Resink, T. Scott-Burden, U. Baur, C. R. Jones, and F. R. Buhler, *Eur. J. Biochem.* **172,** 499 (1988).

37. Y. Hirata, M. Shichiri, T. Emori, F. Marumo, K. Kangawa, and H. Matsuo, *FEBS Lett.* **238**(2), 415 (1988).

38. J. Brown and A. Czarnechi, *Am. J. Physiol.* **258,** R57 (1990).

39. A. Israel, F. M. A. Correa, M. Niwa, and J. M. Saavedra, *Brain Res.* **322,** 341 (1984).

40. E. F. Hartree, *Anal. Biochem.* **48,** 422 (1972).

41. U. K. Laemmli, *Nature* (*London*) **227,** 680 (1970).

42. B. J. Smith, *in Methods Mole. Biol.* **1,** 41 (1984).

43. J. H. Morrissey, *Anal. Biochem.* **254,** 3375 (1981).

44. J. Antunes-Rodrigues, S. M. McCann, and W. K. Samson, *Endocrinology* (*Baltimore*) **118,** 1726 (1986).

45. G. Katsuura, M. Nakamura, K. Inouye, M. Kono, K. Nakao, and H. Imura, *Eur. J. Pharmacol.* **121,** 285 (1986).

46. W. K. Samson, M. C. Aguila, J. Martinovič, J. Antunes-Rodrigues, and M. Norris, *Peptides* (*NY*) **8**(3), 449 (1987).

47. D. C. Leitman, J. W. Andresen, T. Kuno, Y. Kamisaki, J. K. Chang, and F. Murad, *J. Biol. Chem.* **261**(25), 11650 (1986).

48. R. Takayanagi, T. Inagami, R. M. Snajdar, T. Imada, M. Tamura, and K. S. Misono, *J. Biol. Chem.* **262**(25), 12104 (1987).

49. G. M. Olins, D. R. Patton, P. R. Bovy, and P. P. Mehta, *J. Biol. Chem.* **263**(22), 10989 (1988).

50. F. A. Almeida, M. Suzuki, R. M. Scarborough, J. A. Lewicki, and T. Maack, *Am. J. Physiol.* **256,** 469 (1989).

51. M. Hirata, C. H. Chang, and F. Murad, *Biochim. Biophys. Acta* **1010,** 346 (1989).

52. M. Chinkers, D. L. Garbers, M. S. Chang, D. G. Lowe, H. Chin, D. V. Goeddel, and S. Schulz, *Nature* (*London*) **338,** 78 (1989).

53. M. S. Chang, D. G. Lowe, M. Lewis, R. Hellmiss, E. Chen, and D. V. Goeddel, *Nature* (*London*) **341,** 68 (1989).

54. J. G. Porter, A. Arfsten, F. Fuller, J. A. Miller, L. C. Gregory, and J. A. Lweicki, *Biochem. Biophys. Res. Commun.* **171**(2), 796 (1990).

55. E. R. Levin and H. J. L. Frank, *Am. J. Physiol.* **261,** R453 (1991).

56. K. Kariya, Y. Kawahara, S. Araki, H. Fukuzaki, and Y. Takai, *Atherosclerosis* (*Limerick, Irel*.) **80,** 143 (1989).
57. R. G. Appel, *Am. J. Physiol*. **259,** E312 (1990).
58. T. Sudoh, N. Minamino, K. Kangawa, and H. Matsuo, *Biochem. Biophys. Res. Commun*. **168,** 863 (1990).
59. S. Ueda, N. Minamino, M. Aburaya, K. Kangawa, S. Matsukura, and H. Matsuo, *Biochem. Biophys. Res. Commun*. **175,** 759 (1991).
60. N. Minamino, Y. Makino, H. Tateyama, K. Kangawa, and H. Matsuo, *Biochem. Biophys. Res. Commun*. **179,** 535 (1991).
61. V. T. F. Yeung, S. K. S. Ho, C. S. Cockram, C. M. Lee, and M. G. Nicholls, *J. Neurochem*. **59,** 762 (1992).

[13] Structural and Functional Identification of Insulin-like Growth Factor Receptors

Steen Gammeltoft

Introduction

Insulin-like growth factors IGF-I and IGF-II are polypeptides structurally similar to insulin, which act as mitogens on various cell types during fetal development and postnatal growth (1–3). In the mammalian fetus IGF-I and IGF-II genes are expressed in many tissues, including the central nervous system, the levels of IGF-II mRNA being 2–600 times higher than the IGF-I mRNA levels. *In vitro* studies of primary cultures of astroglial and neuronal precursor cells from fetal rat brain show that IGF-I and IGF-II exert mitogenic activity, suggesting that they may stimulate cell proliferation *in vivo* during fetal brain development. In adult mammals IGF-I is predominantly synthesized by the liver under the control of growth hormone and secreted to the circulation whereas IGF-II is secreted mainly by the choroid plexus to the cerebrospinal fluid. In the adult brain the role of IGF-II secreted to the cerebrospinal fluid is completely unknown (4).

Insulin-like Growth Factor Receptors

Insulin-like growth factors I and II interact with two types of receptors that differ in their amino acid sequence, secondary structure, ligand-binding specificity, and signaling mechanism (3, 5). The IGF-I receptor is similar to the insulin receptor and is a heterotetramer composed of two α subunits (M_r 130,000) and two β subunits (M_r 95,000) linked by disulfide bridges. The extracellular α subunits bind IGF-I with high affinity (K_d ~1 nmol/liter), IGF-II with 2–10 times lower affinity, and insulin with 100 times lower affinity. Each β subunit is composed of a small extracellular, a transmembrane, and a large cytoplasmic domain with protein tyrosine kinase activity that is involved in intracellular signaling. The amino acid sequence of the tyrosine kinase region in the IGF-I and insulin receptors is about 80% similar, but in neither case is the mechanism of signal transduction understood. Various cellular substrates have been identified, but their role remains to be clarified.

In mammals the IGF-II receptor is identical with the mannose-6-phosphate

Methods in Neurosciences, Volume 11

(Man-6-P) receptor, which is a monomeric protein of M_r 215,000 with a large extracellular, a transmembrane, and a small cytoplasmic domain (6). The extracellular domain binds IGF-II with high affinity (K_d ~1 nmol/liter), IGF-I with 50 times lower affinity, and insulin with >1000 times lower affinity. Intracellular Man-6-P/IGF-II receptors are involved in the transport of newly synthesized Man-6-P-containing lysosomal enzymes from the Golgi to the lysosomes, whereas Man-6-P/IGF-II receptors present on the cell surface mediate endocytosis of lysosomal enzymes, as well as IGF-II. The two types of ligands bind simultaneously to the receptor, but the significance of this interaction is not understood. At present the mitogenic effect of IGF-II is believed to be mediated by the IGF-I receptor, whereas the role of the Man-6-P/IGF-II receptor in signal transduction is unknown (7).

Insulin-like Growth Factor Receptors in the Nervous System

Specific receptors for IGF-I and IGF-II have been identified on human fetal brain membranes (5), as well as in primary cultures of neuronal cells and astrocytes from fetal rat brain (8–10). Insulin-like growth factors I and II stimulate RNA and DNA synthesis in neuronal and astroglial cells by activation of the IGF-I receptor tyrosine kinase. This conclusion is based on the peptide specificity of the response and the inability of an antibody to the rat Man-6-P/IGF-II receptor to block the mitogenic effect. Both IGF-I and IGF-II are internalized and degraded following interaction with their respective receptors on neuronal and glial cells.

Insulin-like growth factor I receptors and Man-6-P/IGF-II receptors have been identified on plasma membranes from several regions in adult rat brain as well as porcine choroid plexus (11, 12). The molecular size of the IGF-I receptor as well as the Man-6-P/IGF-II receptor in adult mammalian brain is significantly smaller than the values described in other tissues (4). It has been proposed that the structural heterogeneity of the IGF-I and Man-6-P/IGF-II receptors may result from differences in N-linked glycosylation. The functional implications of these molecular variations are yet unknown.

The subject of this chapter is the state of the art methodology in studies of structure and function of IGF-I receptors and Man-6-P/IGF-II receptors. The competitive radioligand assay is fundamental and involves noncovalent association of radioisotope-labeled IGF-I or IGF-II with receptor and its competitive inhibition by unlabeled peptide. The assay was developed almost 20 years ago and is critically dependent on the preparation of bioactive tracers, availability of isolated cells, plasma membrane fractions, or purified receptors, and application of rapid centrifugation or filtration procedures. Other techniques for characterization of IGF-I receptors and Man-6-P/IGF-II receptors were developed 10 years ago and include affinity labeling, tyrosine kinase activity, and endocytosis. All the methods described are generally applicable to all cells and are not confined to neural systems.

Labeling of Insulin-like Growth Factors I and II

All receptor studies have been carried out with IGF-I and IGF-II labeled with ^{125}I. There are several advantages to this technique: the radioiodination is fairly easy to perform, a product of high specific radioactivity ($0.5–5 \times 10^{16}$ Bq/mol or $0.135–1.35 \times 10^6$ Ci/mol) is obtained, and the half-life ($T_{1/2} = 60.2$ days) is reasonably long. Iodination of a peptide is generally performed by chemical substitution of hydrogen in tyrosyl residues. In the iodination reaction, iodide (e.g., ^{125}I$^-$) must be oxidized to iodine using, for example, chloramine-T, iodate (IO_3^-), lactoperoxidase, and H_2O_2, or Iodogen (Pierce, Rockford, IL).

Chloramine-T Method

The chloramine-T method has been widely used in various modifications for iodination of many peptide hormones. The nature of the iodinated peptide depends on the iodination conditions, in particular the pH, the molar ratio of iodine to peptide, the peptide concentration, and the amount of chloramine-T. All these parameters may be varied in order to obtain an iodinated peptide preparation that is chemically homogeneous, fully biologically active, immunoreactive, and structurally unaltered. In general, the following conditions are recommended: a physiological pH of 7.4, a molar ratio of iodine to peptide below 1.0, and peptide and chloramine-T concentrations of the same order of magnitude. In particular, the chloramine-T concentration should be as low as possible to avoid oxidation damage of the peptide. The result of the iodination reaction will often be a heterogeneous mixture of various monoiodinated, and diiodinated peptide isomers as well as native peptide. These molecules can be separated using chromatographic or electrophoretic methods. The chloramine-T method has been used for iodination of IGF-I and IGF-II (13), but the products are characterized by low specific activity (40–80 μCi/g) and heterogeneity (three monoiodinated isomers).

Protocol 1: Iodination of Insulin-like Growth Factor I or II Using Chloramine-T (13, 14)

Materials

Na^{125}I: Either from New England Nuclear (Boston, MA) (Specific activity, 6.3×10^{11} Bq/mg) or from The Radiochemical Centre (Amersham,

UK) (Specific activity, 4.8–6.3 × 10^{11} Bq/mg). The ^{125}I is dissolved in NaOH, pH 7–11, at a concentration of 3.7–10 × 10^9 Bq/ml

Phosphate buffer (0.25 mol/liter), pH 7.4, freshly prepared by mixing 8 ml KH_2PO_4 (0.25 mol/liter) and 42 ml Na_2HPO_4 (0.25 mol/liter) and adjusting pH at 7.4

Phosphate buffer (0.04 mol/liter), pH 7.4, freshly prepared by diluting 10 ml (0.25 mol/liter) phosphate buffer (above) with 52.5 ml H_2O and adjusting pH at 7.4

Chloramine-T: 0.2 mg/ml in 0.04 mol/liter phosphate buffer. Dissolve 2 mg in 10 ml immediately before use. Protect the tube from light

Sodium metabisulfite: 0.6 mg/ml in 0.04 mol/liter phosphate buffer. Dissolve 6 mg in 10 ml immediately before use

Bovine serum albumin 10 mg/ml in 0.04 mol/liter phosphate buffer

Gel filtration buffer: ammonium acetate (0.1 mol/liter), pH 7.4 with bovine serum albumin 2 mg/ml

Sephadex G-50 medium (Pharmacia, Uppsala, Sweden) column (30 × 1 cm) equilibrated with gel filtration buffer (above)

IGF-I or IGF-II: 0.1 mg/ml in HCl 5 mmol/liter

Procedure

1. In an iodination vial at room temperature add the reagents in the following order:

(a) 10 μl IGF-I or IGF-II (-1 μg)

(b) 20 μl 0.25 mol/liter phosphate buffer

(c) 10 μl Na^{125}I (3.7 × 10^7 Bq $-$ 1 mCi)

(d) 50 μl 0.25 mol/liter phosphate buffer

(e) 20 μl chloramine-T (-4 μg).

2. Incubate for 45 sec while mixing vigorously on a vortex.

3. Stop the reaction by adding 20 μl sodium metabisulfite (-12 μg).

4. Add 250 μl bovine serum albumin solution.

5. ^{125}I-labeled IGF-I or ^{125}I-labeled IGF-II can be separated by gel filtration from ^{125}I-labeled aggregates and free ^{125}I-iodide. The mixture is applied on a Sephadex G-50 column and eluted with ammonium acetate and bovine serum albumin at a flow rate of 0.5 ml/min. Fractions of 1.0 ml are collected and 10 μl aliquots are counted for radioactivity. The labeled IGF-I or IGF-II preparation is stored at -20°C and is stable for up to 2 months.

Iodogen Method

Iodogen was first described as a reagent for iodination of proteins and cell membranes. Virtually insoluble in water, Iodogen (1,3,4,6-tetrachloro-3α,6α-diphenylglycouril) can be dissolved in an organic solvent and the iodination tube coated with the solution. Iodogen mediates rapid iodination in the solid phase with aqueous solutions of iodine and peptide. The reaction is stopped simply by decanting the tube. Therefore no reducing agent is needed. The advantages of the method are its simplicity and the reduced exposure of peptide to the oxidant in the two-phase system. Consequently, oxidative damage of the peptide is minimized in comparison to the previously applied chloramine-T method (13). The iodogen method has been used successfully for iodination of IGF-I, but not yet for IGF-II (15).

Protocol 2: Radioiodination of Insulin-like Growth Factor I Using Iodogen (14, 15)

Materials

Na^{125}I: Either from New England Nuclear (specific activity, 6.3×10^{11} Bq/mg) or from The Radiochemical Centre (specific activity, 4.8–6.3 10^{11} Bq/mg). The ^{125}I is dissolved in NaOH, pH 7–11, at a concentration of 3.7–7.4 MBq/μl (0.1–0.2 mCi/μl)

Iodination buffer: Sodium phosphate (0.20 M), pH 7.4, and NaCl (0.01 M)

Elution buffer: Sodium phosphate (0.04 M), pH 7.4, NaCl (0.1 M), and human albumin (2 mg/ml)

1,3,4,6-Tetrachloro-3α,6α-diphenylglycouril (Iodogen)

Methylene chloride (dichloromethane)

IGF-I or IGF-II: 5 μg dissolved in 5 μl HCl (5 mM)

Sephadex G-50 medium: In a column (1 $\times$ 50 cm) equilibrated with elution buffer

Procedure

1. Iodogen (500 μg) is dissolved in 5 ml dichloromethane and the inside of a Pyrex tube (1 $\times$ 10 cm) is coated with 50 μl of this solution (5 μg Iodogen) by gently turning the tube in warm water while the solvent evaporates.

2. Insulin-like growth factor I or II (5 μg in 5 μl) is diluted with 40 μl iodination buffer and added to the tube.

3. Na^{125}I (18.5 MBq, ~0.5 mCi) in 5 μl is added and the tube is kept on ice and gently shaken for 15 min.

4. Stop the iodination reaction by transferring the radioiodination mixture to a vial containing 1 ml elution buffer. ^{125}I-Labeled peptide is purified by gel filtration on Sephadex G-50 with elution buffer.

5. The incorporation of ^{125}I in IGF-I or IGF-II is determined by precipitation in 10% (w/v) trichloroacetic acid. It should be at least 80%. The specific

radioactivity is calculated as precipitable megabequerels (or millicuries) of ^{125}I per microgram or picomole of IGF-I or IGF-II.

Receptor Binding of Insulin-like Growth Factors I and II

A receptor-binding assay involves incubation of ^{125}I-labeled IGF-I or IGF-II with cellular, membrane, or purified receptors followed by separation of bound and free tracer either by sedimentation or filtration of cells or membranes, or by precipitation of purified receptors, or adsorption of free tracer. The assay conditions include concentration of ^{125}I-labeled IGF-I or IGF-II, amount of cells, membranes, or purified receptors, buffer composition, temperature and time of incubation, and separation procedure.

The concentration of ^{125}I-labeled IGF-I or IGF-II should not exceed one-tenth of the K_d value, that is, 50–100 pM, to obtain an optimal ratio between receptor-bound and nonspecifically bound peptide of about 10 : 1 and to avoid errors in the estimate of K_d. The amount of receptor in the assay should be at least 50 pM to ensure sufficient amounts of bound radioactivity. This can be achieved with cell concentrations of 10^5–10^8 cells/ml, or membrane protein concentrations of 0.1–1.0 mg/ml depending on the cell type and its receptor content. On the other hand, the cell or membrane concentration should be kept as low as possible to reduce proteolytic degradation of tracer, which should be minimal, to less than 5%. This may also be achieved by decreasing the temperature below 15°C and by addition of a protease inhibitor such as bacitracin (0.5–1.0 mg/ml).

Cultured cells should be incubated in Krebs–Ringer buffer, in which bicarbonate is replaced by N-2-hydroxyethylpiperazine-N'-2-ethanesulfonic acid (HEPES) (25 mM) because of its physiological pH optimum and nontoxic properties, whereas Tris or phosphate should be avoided due to their untoward effects on living cells. In contrast, membranes can be incubated in either HEPES, Tris, or phosphate buffers. The pH should be adjusted to 7.4, which is the optimum for receptor binding of IGF-I and IGF-II. Note that the pH of HEPES is highly temperature dependent, with a coefficient of $-0.01/°C$, and thus should be rigorously adjusted at the temperature of the incubation or washing step. Bovine or human serum albumin (1–10 mg/ml) should be added to reduce nonspecific adsorption of IGF-I or IGF-II and to increase viability of cultured cells. The incubation temperature should be below 15°C to reduce endocytosis of receptor-bound tracer and degradation of free tracer. The incubation time required to reach steady state for receptor-bound IGF-I or IGF-II is 2 hr at 15°C and 5 hr at 4°C. Separation of bound and free tracer is achieved by washing intact cells or membranes two to three times at 4°C, followed by harvest, sedimentation, or filtration.

Cell Receptor-Binding Assay

Protocol 3: Cell Receptor-Binding Assay (9, 14, 16, 17)
Materials

Cultured cells in monolayer in a 24-well multidish (5×10^4 cells/well)
^{125}I-Labeled IGF-I or IGF-II (10^6 cpm/ml, ~0.25–0.5 nM)
Unlabeled IGF-I or IGF-II (1 μM)
Assay buffer: Krebs–Ringer solution with HEPES (25 mM), pH 7.4 at 4–15°C, and bovine serum albumin (10 mg/ml)
Washing buffer: Krebs–Ringer solution with HEPES (25 mM), pH 7.4 at 4°C, with albumin (2 mg/ml)

Procedure

1. Cell monolayers are incubated in 200 μl of assay buffer at 4–15°C.
2. The assay is initiated by addition of 25 μl ^{125}I-labeled IGF-I or IGF-II at a final concentration of 25,000 cpm/well (10^5 cpm/ml, ~25–50 pM) and either 25 μl buffer (for determination of total binding) or 25 μl unlabeled peptide at a final concentration of 0.1 μM (for determination of nonspecific binding).
3. The incubation is continued for 2 hr at 15°C or 4–15 hr at 4°C to reach steady state.
4. The assay is terminated by cooling the culture plates on ice. An aliquot of the supernatant is collected for counting of free radioactivity, and determination of tracer degradation (see protocol 11, below). The incubation medium is removed and the cell pellets or monolayers are washed two to three times with washing buffer at 4°C.
5. The cell monolayer is harvested with 0.2 M NaOH and counted in a γ counter.

Plasma Membrane Receptor-Binding Assay

Protocol 4: Plasma Membrane Receptor-Binding Assay (11)
Materials

Plasma membranes (~10 mg protein/ml) in MgCl$_2$ (2 mM) and HEPES (25 mM), pH 7.4 at 4°C
^{125}I-Labeled IGF-I or IGF-II (10^6 cpm/ml)
Unlabeled IGF-I or IGF-II (1 μM)

Assay buffer: NaCl (150 mM), HEPES (50 mM), pH 7.4 at 20°C, and bovine serum albumin (2 mg/ml)

Washing buffer: NaCl (150 mM), HEPES (50 mM), pH 7.4 at 4°C, and albumin (1 mg/ml)

Procedure

1. Plasma membranes (50–200 μg protein in 200 μl) are incubated in Eppendorf tubes at room temperature for 2 hr with 25 μl ^{125}I-labeled IGF-I or IGF-II and cither 25 μl assay buffer or 25 μl unlabeled peptide (see protocol 3, above).

2. The assay is terminated by centrifugation of the tubes at 9000 g for 3 min. An aliquot of the supernatant is removed for counting of free radioactivity and assay of tracer degradation (see protocol 11, below). The pellets are washed twice by resuspension in washing buffer and centrifugation.

3. The tip of the tube with membrane pellet is cut and counted.

Affinity Labeling

Affinity labeling of proteins is a generally applicable technique that provides detailed structural information under appropriate conditions. One general approach has been highly successful in the identification of IGF-I receptors and Man-6-P/IGF-II receptors: chemical cross-linking of ^{125}I-labeled IGF-I or IGF-II. In the procedure described below, several features of the homobifunctional cross-linking agent disuccinimidyl suberate (DSS) should be noted. The reactive group of DSS is succinimidyl ester, which is water labile and highly reactive with primary amino groups. Therefore the use of this reagent is precluded in buffers containing primary amines (e.g., Tris buffers), and stock solutions of DSS should be prepared fresh before use. The characteristic reactivity of DSS with primary amines is taken advantage of by using Tris buffers to quench the ligand–receptor cross-linking reaction. Insulin-like growth factors I and II are single polypeptide chains, making cross-linking possible under both nonreducing and reducing conditions.

Affinity Labeling Cultured Cells or Plasma Membranes

Protocol 5: Affinity Labeling with ^{125}I-Labeled Insulin-like Growth Factor I or II (9, 11, 12, 16)

Materials

Cell monolayer at confluency in 25-cm^2 culture flasks, or plasma membranes (1–3 mg protein)

[125]I-Labeled IGF-I or IGF-II (10^8 cpm/ml = 25–50 nM)

Unlabeled IGF-I or IGF-II (1 μM)

Incubation buffer: Krebs–Ringer solution with HEPES (25 mM), pH
7.4 (adjust pH at the given incubation temperature), and bovine serum
albumin (10 mg/ml)

Cross-linking buffer: Krebs–Ringer solution with HEPES (25 mM), pH
7.4 at 4°C, *without* albumin

DSS stock solution: DSS, 5 mM in dimethyl sulfoxide (DMSO). Prepare
immediately before use by dissolving 3.7 mg DSS in 2 ml DMSO at
room temperature (DMSO freezes at 16°C)

Quenching solution: Tris (10 mM), pH 7.4, ethylenediaminetetraacetic
acid (EDTA) (1 mM)

Procedure

1. Incubate the cells or plasma membranes in 1 ml incubation buffer with
^{125}I-labeled IGF-I or IGF-II [1–3 × 10^6 cpm/ml (0.25–0.75 nM)] either alone
or with addition of unlabeled peptide (0.1 μM) for determination of nonspecific labeling for 90–120 min at room temperature or 3–5 hr at 4°C.

2. Wash the cells or membranes twice with 2–3 ml cross-linking buffer at
4°C.

3. Add 1 ml cross-linking buffer at 4°C. Add 20 μl freshly prepared DSS
stock solution [DSS (0.1 mM final concentration) and DMSO (2%, v/v, final
concentration)]. Incubate 15 min at 4°C.

4. Terminate the reaction by adding 10 ml quenching solution. Incubate 5
min at 4°C.

5. Wash the cells or membranes once with cross-linking buffer. Cells are
scraped from the flask in 1 ml of buffer and transferred to an Eppendorf tube.
Centrifuge at 9000 g for 3 min and remove the supernatant.

6. Labeled proteins are analyzed by sodium dodecylsulfate-polyacryl-
amide gel electrophoresis (SDS-PAGE) using 7.5% (IGF-I) or 5% (IGF-II)
resolving gels and autoradiography for 2–8 weeks.

Insulin-like Growth Factor I Receptor Tyrosine Kinase Activity

The IGF-I receptor shows protein tyrosine kinase activity that is intrinsic to
its β subunit and stimulated on binding of IGF-I to the α subunit. The kinase
is activated by an intramolecular autophosphorylation reaction on at least
three tyrosine residues in the β subunit and is dependent on the presence of
Mn^{2+} and ATP. By analogy with other receptor tyrosine kinases, for example, insulin and epidermal growth factor receptors, the tyrosine kinase activation represents the initial step in IGF-I action. The IGF-I receptor tyrosine

kinase is studied *in vitro* in assays of purified IGF-I receptor autophosphorylation and tyrosine kinase activity.

Purification of the Insulin-like Growth Factor I Receptor on Immobilized Wheat Germ Agglutinin

For *in vitro* assays, the partially purified IGF-I receptor eluted from a wheat germ agglutinin affinity column has been adequate. The *N*-acetylglucosamine used for elution does not interfere with any assays carried out with the receptor, so dialysis is not indicated. The preparation is stable for about 3 months at $-70°C$, but after 3 months the receptor kinase loses IGF-I sensitivity, whereas IGF-I binding is maintained. The yield of IGF-I receptor from this procedure depends on the level of expression of the receptor in the cell and is determined in a soluble receptor-binding assay.

Protocol 6: Purification of Insulin-like Growth Factor I Receptor on Wheat Germ Agglutinin (8, 11, 15, 16)

Materials

 Ten confluent dishes (15 cm) of cells: To grow, incubate the cells with serum-free medium overnight (i.e., 16 hr) before the isolation. Alternatively, use plasma membranes (30 mg protein)

 Solubilization buffer: HEPES (50 mM), pH 7.6 at 4°C, containing Triton X-100 (1.0%, w/v), EDTA (4 mM), aprotinin (400 KIU/ml), phenylmethylsulfonyl fluoride (PMSF) (1 mM), pepstatin A (1 mM), and leupeptin (1 mM)

 Washing buffer: HEPES (50 mM), pH 7.6 at 4°C, NaCl (150 mM), and Triton X-100 (0.1%, w/v)

 Elution buffer: *N*-Acetylglucosamine (0.3 M) and glycerol (10%, v/v) in washing buffer

 Wheat germ agglutinin-Sepharose (Pharmacia Code No. 27-3608-02) (2 ml) is packed in a column (0.9 × 10 cm) and washed with 50 ml SDS [0.1% (w/v) in H_2O], followed by 500 ml H_2O and 50 ml washing buffer. The column is kept and run in a cold room at 4–8°C. For long-term storage (>2 weeks) sodium azide (0.01%, w/v) should be added to the washing buffer to protect the wheat germ agglutinin from proteolysis. The column should be rinsed with 50 ml washing buffer before use, as azide inhibits tyrosine kinase activity

Procedure

 1. Remove the medium from 10 culture dishes and add 3 ml of ice-cold solubilization buffer to each dish. The cells are immediately scraped from the dish and the extracts are combined in a 50-ml plastic conical test tube at

4°C. Plasma membranes (30 mg protein) are suspended in 30 ml solubilization buffer at 4°C.

2. Mix the suspension by gentle rotation in a cold room for 90 min and sediment the insoluble material by centrifugation at 100,000 g for 60 min at 4°C in a 70.1 Ti rotor using a Beckman (Fullerton, CA) ultracentrifuge.

3. Apply the supernatant (30 ml) to the 2-ml wheat germ agglutinin-Sepharose column at 4°C. Pass the extract over the column three times and then wash the Sepharose with 100 ml of washing buffer.

4. Elute the IGF-I receptor and other membrane proteins from the column with 2 ml of elution buffer. Add to the eluate aprotinin, PMSF, pepstatin A, and leupeptin in the concentrations given for the solubilization buffer and store the partially purified IGF-I receptor at −70°C.

5. The wheat germ agglutinin-Sepharose is recovered by washing with 8 ml elution buffer followed by 50 ml washing buffer. Add sodium azide (0.01%, w/v) for long-term storage at 4°C.

Solubilized Insulin-like Growth Factor I Receptor-Binding Assay

In the solubilized receptor assay, bound and free tracer are separated either by precipitation of receptor-bound peptide with polyethylene glycol (M_r 6000) or by adsorption of free peptide with activated charcoal. Both methods give comparable results, but are hampered by a relatively large amount of nonspecifically bound tracer (approximately 30–50% of total binding).

Protocol 7: Binding Assay of the Soluble Insulin-like Growth Factor I (8, 15)

Materials

> Wheat germ agglutinin-purified proteins in elution buffer with protease inhibitors (see protocol 6, above)
> ^{125}I-Labeled IGF-I (10^6 cpm/ml = 0.25–0.50 nM)
> Unlabeled IGF-I (1 μM)
> Assay buffer: NaCl (150 mM), HEPES (50 mM), pH 7.4 at 20 or 4°C, and bovine serum albumin (1 mg/ml)
> Polyethylene glycol (M_r 6000) at concentrations of 350 and 175 mg/ml in NaCl (150 mM) and HEPES (50 mM). Readjust pH at 4°C
> Human immunoglobulin (fraction II), 3 mg/ml

Procedure

1. Incubate 5–25 μg of wheat germ agglutinin-purified protein diluted in 200 μl assay buffer in a 1.5-ml Eppendorf tube for 2 hr at room temperature or for 16 hr at 4°C with 25 μl ^{125}I-labeled IGF-I and 25 μl assay buffer or 25 μl unlabeled IGF-I.

2. The assay is terminated by addition of 100 μl immunoglobulin solution followed by 300 μl chilled polyethylene glycol solution (350 mg/ml). The tubes are vortexed and left for 10 min at 4°C.

3. The precipitate is centrifuged at 9000 g per 5 min and the supernatant aspirated. The pellet is rinsed once with polyethylene glycol solution (175 mg/ml).

4. Tips are excised and counted.

5. The total IGF-I-binding capacity of the purified receptor preparation is determined from the dependence of bound ^{125}I-labeled IGF-I on unlabeled IGF-I concentration by either graphic analysis using Scatchard plot or by computerized analysis using a nonlinear curve-fitting program. The binding capacity is expressed as picomoles per gram protein.

Autophosphorylation of the Wheat Germ Agglutinin-Purified Insulin-like Growth Factor I Receptor

Autophosphorylation of the partially purified IGF-I receptor has become a standard method used in most studies addressing the function of the IGF-I receptor and the mechanism of signal transmission. In addition, the assay gives structural information about the IGF-I receptor β subunit by its electrophoretic behavior.

Protocol 8: Autophosphorylation of Wheat Germ Agglutinin-Purified Insulin-like Growth Factor I Receptor (8, 16, 17)

Materials

Wheat germ eluate (100–200 μg protein/ml) with purified IGF-I receptor (IGF-I binding capacity, 100–200 pmol/g): See protocols 6 and 7, above.

$MnCl_2$ (50 mM)

$MgCl_2$ (125 mM)

IGF-I (1 μM)

ATP (200 μM)

[γ-^{32}P]ATP (370 MBq/ml; 10 mCi/ml): From Amersham or New England Nuclear

Laemmli buffer: 5× concentrated with dithiothreitol (DTT) (500 mmol/ liter)

Procedure

1. Mix 5 μg wheat germ agglutinin-purified protein (0.5–1.0 fmol IGF-I binding) in 50 μl with 5 μl $MnCl_2$, 5 μl $MgCl_2$, and 6 μl IGF-I or 6 μl assay buffer (see protocol 7, above). Incubate at room temperature for 45 min.

2. Initiate phosphorylation by adding 15 μl ATP mixture: 70 μl ATP and 5 μl [γ-^{32}P]ATP. Continue the incubation for 15 min at room temperature to reach steady state. (The final concentrations of the reagents in the phosphorylation reaction are as follow: MnCl$_2$, 3 mM; MgCl$_2$, 8 mM; ATP, 35 μM; and [γ-^{32}P]ATP, 125 μCi/ml.)

3. Stop the autophosphorylation reaction by adding 18 μl of Laemmli buffer (5$\times$) with DTT to the reaction mixture. Analyze phosphoproteins by SDS-PAGE using a 7.5% (w/v) gel and autoradiography for 1–2 days.

Kinase Activity of the Purified Insulin-like Growth Factor I Receptor; Measuring Kinase Activity with a Synthetic Substrate

Phosphorylation of cellular proteins on tyrosyl residues is one of the potential mechanisms of signal transmission by the IGF-I receptor. Thus an important assay to carry out on the receptor is the measurement of its phosphotransferase activity. Most investigators have used an *in vitro* assay with the synthetic substrate poly(GluNa,Tyr)4:1 based on the consensus sequence of protein tyrosine kinase substrates *in vivo*. The kinase activity of the IGF-I receptor is measured by an initial velocity experiment.

Protocol 9: Insulin-like Growth Factor I Receptor Tyrosine Kinase Activity Assay (15–17)

Materials

Wheat germ eluate (100–200 μg protein/ml) with purified IGF-I receptor (IGF-I-binding capacity, 100–200 pmol/g): Dilute with NaCl (150 mM) and HEPES (50 mM), pH 7.4 at 4°C, to an IGF-I-binding capacity of 10–20 fmol/ml, if necessary

IGF-I (1 μM)

MnCl$_2$ (1 M)

MgCl$_2$ (1 M)

ATP (1.5 mM)

[γ-^{32}P]ATP (370 MBq/ml; 10 mCi/ml) from Amersham or New England Nuclear

Poly(GluNa,Tyr)4:1 (2 mg/ml) from Sigma (St. Louis, MO): Prepare immediately before use. Weigh approximately 2 mg and dissolve in the appropriate volume of H$_2$O

Trichloroacetic acid (10 and 5%, w/v) containing sodium pyrophosphate (10 mM)

Procedure

1. Incubate 1–2 fmol IGF-I receptor in 120 μl wheat germ agglutinin eluate (10–20 μg protein) with 20 μl IGF-I in final concentrations from 10 pM to 0.1 μM or 20 μl dilution buffer for 60 min at room temperature (in duplicates).

2. Add 20 μl poly(GluNa,Tyr)4 : 1 to all tubes and incubate 30 min at room temperature. Two control tubes should be included in the assay for measurement of background phosphorylation by omission of either wheat germ agglutinin eluate or synthetic peptide substrate.

3. Prepare tracer mixture in a total volume 500 μl (for 24 samples) composed of 350 μl HEPES–NaCl buffer, 20 μl MnCl$_2$, 40 μl MgCl$_2$, 70 μl ATP, and 20 μl [γ-^{32}P]ATP, and add 20 μl to each tube at 30-sec intervals. (Final concentrations are as follow: MnCl$_2$, 4.4 mM; MgCl$_2$, 8.8 mM; ATP, 23 μM; and [γ-^{32}P]ATP, 44 μCi/ml.) Incubate 30 min at room temperature.

4. Stop the reaction by applying 75 μl of reaction mixture to 1 × 1 cm filter paper in duplicates and wash the paper twice in 200 ml 10% (w/v) trichloroacetic acid (TCA) with sodium pyrophosphate for 10 min and three times in 500 ml 5% (w/v) TCA with sodium pyrophosphate for 30–60 min each time.

5. Filters are air-dried and the radioactivity measured by Cerenkov counting.

Receptor-Mediated Endocytosis and Degradation of Insulin-like Growth Factors I and II

Two functions of the IGF-I receptor have been described: signal transduction and endocytosis of IGF-I (3, 18). Following binding on the cell surface, receptor-bound IGF-I is rapidly translocated to endosomal vesicles ($T_{1/2}$ = 5 min) via clathrin-coated pits, and after 1–2 hr about 50% of bound IGF-I is internalized. During acidification of the vesicles IGF-I is released from the receptor and degraded by aminopeptidases and endopeptidases, whereas the IGF-I receptor is recycled to the cell surface (9, 10). The internalization of the IGF-I receptor is regulated by ligand binding, tyrosine kinase activation, and receptor autophosphorylation.

The Man-6-P/IGF-II receptor mediates endocytosis of IGF-II but does not seem to be involved in signal transduction (3, 6, 7). In contrast to the IGF-I receptor, Man-6-P/IGF-II receptors are constitutively internalized and recycled to the plasma membrane independent of ligand occupancy. Receptor-bound IGF-II is rapidly taken up by the cells ($T_{1/2}$ = 3 min), and after 30 min about 80% of cell-associated IGF-II is inside the cell, where it is degraded with high efficiency (9, 10, 18).

In vitro studies of endocytosis of IGF-I and IGF-II are based on measurements of surface-bound and internalized peptide, and assays of peptide degradation. In the following, the assay of receptor-mediated endocytosis of IGF-I or IGF-II will be described. Two methods for the quantitation of IGF-I or IGF-II degradation are presented.

Surface-Binding and Internalization Assay

The assay of endocytosis of IGF-I or IGF-II is based on a differentiation between tracer associated with receptors on the cell surface and tracer accumulated inside the cell. The observation that the association between IGF-I and IGF-II and their receptors is pH sensitive led to the development of an assay in which receptor-bound peptide is released from the cell surface by washing with buffer at pH < 5, whereas internalized peptide is not affected. Receptor-mediated endocytosis of IGF-I and IGF-II is temperature sensitive and should be studied at 37°C. At lower temperatures the rate of endocytosis is significantly reduced and at 4°C the receptor-bound peptide remains at the cell surface. This may be used as a control of the efficiency of the acid treatment, which should remove all the cell-associated hormone after binding of 4°C. An alternative method for release of surface-bound IGF-I or IGF-II is mild treatment of cells with proteases like trypsin (0.2 mg/ml) or pronase (1 mg/ml) for 10 min at 37°C. In protocol 10 the procedure for acid treatment of cells is described.

Protocol 10: Receptor Internalization Assay (9, 10, 17)
Materials

 Materials used for binding of ^{125}I-labeled IGF-I or IGF-II: The same as for the cell receptor-binding assay, except that the pH of the incubation buffer should be adjusted at 37°C (see protocol 3, above)

 Acid-washing solution: Acetic acid (C_2H_5COOH) (0.2 *M*) and NaCl (0.5 *M*), pH 2.5. Alternatively, Krebs–Ringer solution with HEPES (25 m*M*), pH 3.5 at 4°C, and bovine serum albumin (10 mg/ml) may be used in studies of intracellular processing of IGF-I or IGF-II where cell viability should be maintained (9, 10)

Procedure

1. The binding of ^{125}I-labeled peptide is carried out as described in the procedure for the cell receptor-binding assay (Protocol 3, above) except that the amount of added ^{125}I-labeled peptide is increased twofold to a final concentration of 50,000 cpm/well (2×10^5 cpm/ml).

2. After termination of the incubation by removal of medium and free tracer, the cells are washed twice with washing buffer (pH 7.4) at 4°C. Acid-washing solution in a volume of 500 μl is added, and the cells are incubated 5–10 min at 4°C. The acid-washing solution, containing surface-bound radioactivity, is collected and counted.

3. The cell monolayer is washed once with washing buffer (pH 7.4) at 4°C. The cells containing the acid-resistant, that is, internalized, radioactivity are harvested with 0.2 M NaOH and counted.

Proteolytic Degradation of Insulin-like Growth Factors I and II

The major pathway of IGF-I and IGF-II degradation *in vivo* is by intracellular proteolysis following receptor-mediated endocytosis. The proteases involved in degradation of IGF-I or IGF-II have not been identified, but the insulin-specific protease may also be active in the initial cleavage of IGF-I and IGF-II, resulting in partially degraded peptides, which are subsequently degraded by less specific amino- and endopeptidases.

Degradation of IGF-I and IGF-II results in changes of the physical and biological properties of the peptide, which can be assessed by trichloroacetic acid precipitation, gel filtration, high-performance liquid chromatography (HPLC), or bioassays of receptor-binding or activity. In general, bioassays are more sensitive as they may detect the initial and partial cleavage of IGF-I and IGF-II, whereas chromatographic analysis may give molecular information about the products. The techniques of two assays (trichloroacetic acid precipitation and gel filtration) are described below; receptor-binding assays have been described above (see Protocols 3 and 4, above).

Trichloroacetic Acid Precipitation

The trichloroacetic acid precipitation assay discriminates between small soluble degradation products ($M_r < 2000$) and larger precipitable peptides. The assay is probably the least sensitive, but is also the least demanding of time and resources. The assay is limited to ^{125}I-labeled IGF-I or IGF-II and requires serum albumin (1–10 mg/ml) as carrier.

Protocol 11: Trichloroacetic Acid Precipitation as an Assay of Radioligand Degradation (10)
Materials
   ^{125}I-labeled IGF-I or IGF-II (10^6 cpm/ml, ~0.25–0.5 nM) in dilution buffer: NaCl (150 mM), HEPES (50 mM), pH 7.4, and bovine serum albumin (2 mg/ml)

Incubation buffer: Krebs–Ringer solution with HEPES (25 mM), pH
7.4 at 37°C, and bovine serum albumin (10 mg/ml)
Trichloroacetic acid (10%, w/v)

Procedure

1. Aliquots (1–2 ml) of trichloroacetic acid are distributed in 5-ml plastic tubes.

2. Aliquots (25–100 μl) of ^{125}I-labeled IGF-I or IGF-II (approximately 10^4 cpm) in dilution buffer (blank) or in buffer after incubation at 37°C with cells or membranes (sample), are added to the tubes with trichloroacetic acid. A white, coarse precipitate is formed by mixing the tubes on a vortex.

3. The tubes are centrifuged at 1500 g for 5 min ($\sim$3000 rpm at a radius of 15 cm). The supernatants and precipitates are counted in a γ counter.

4. The percentage degraded ^{125}I-labeled IGF-I or IGF-II is calculated as follows: % degraded = % soluble cpm (sample) − % soluble cpm (blank), where

$$\% \text{ soluble cpm} = \frac{\text{cpm (supernatant)} \times 100}{\text{cpm (supernatant)} + \text{cpm (precipitate)}}$$

The blank value should be as low as possible, that is, 3–10%.

Gel-Filtration Chromatographic Assay

The gel-filtration assay detects changes in the molecular size of IGF-I or IGF-II. As the molecular weight of IGF-I and IGF-II is about 7500, the gel should be Sephadex G-50 or BioGel P60, or equivalent products. The gel-filtration assay is more informative than the precipitation assay described above, because intact peptide and degraded fragments are fractionated. Aggregates of ^{125}I-labeled peptides elute in the void volume of the gel and can be subtracted. ^{125}I-Labeled tyrosine is absorbed on the gel and elutes after the salt volume of the gel. Intermediate proteolytic fragments can be identified, whereas initial cleavage products elute with the native tracer. Radioimmunoassay, radioreceptor assay, or bioassay can be applied to analyze the peaks of ^{125}I-labeled peptide further.

Protocol 12: Gel Filtration as an Assay of Radioligand Degradation
(9, 10)
Materials
[125]I-Labeled IGF-I or IGF-II (10^6 cpm/ml, $\sim$0.25–0.5 nM) in dilution buffer (see protocol 11, above)
Incubation buffer (see protocol 11, above)

Elution buffer: Ammonium acetate ($NH_4C_2H_5COO$) (0.1 M), pH 7.4, with bovine serum albumin (2 mg/ml)

Sephadex G-50 column (0.9 × 50 cm) equilibrated with elution buffer: The column should be calibrated with markers of the void volume, V_0 (Evans Blue 1640 or serum albumin), the elution volume, V_e (^{125}I-labeled IGF-I or IGF-II), and the total volume, V_t ([22]Na). The elution volume of tyrosine should also be determined, as it exceeds the total volume. Other proteins may be included as size markers. The column is run in a cold room. After use, it is conserved with addition of sodium azide (0.01%, w/v)

Procedure

1. Aliquots of ^{125}I-labeled IGF-I or IGF-II (5 × 10^4 cpm), which have been incubated with cells or membranes (sample) or diluted in dilution buffer (blank), are applied to the column.

2. The column is eluted with elution buffer at a flow rate of 0.1–0.5 ml/min. Fractions of column effluent (0.5–1.0 ml) are collected and counted in a γ counter. The recovery of radioactivity should exceed 90%.

3. The amount of degraded ^{125}I-labeled peptide can be calculated by subtracting the percentage of the total radioactivity present in the IGF-I or IGF-II peak fractions of the sample from the percentage present in these fractions of the blank.

References

1. R. E. Humbel, *Eur. J. Biochem.* **190,** 445 (1990).
2. W. H. Daughaday and P. Rotwein, *Endocr. Rev.* **10,** 68 (1989).
3. S. Gammeltoft, *in* ''Peptide Hormones as Prohormones: Processing, Biological Activity, Pharmacology'' (J. Martinez, ed.), p. 176. Ellis Horwood, Chichester, 1989.
4. S. Gammeltoft, M. Auletta, A. Danielson, E. Larsen, F. C. Nielsen, C. Nilsson, D. Senen, and E. Wang, *in* ''Growth Factors in Health and Disease'' (B. Westermark, C. Betsholtz, and B. Hökfelt, eds.), p. 227. Elsevier, Amsterdam, 1990.
5. V. R. Sara and K. Hall, *Physiol. Rev.* **70,** 591 (1990).
6. N. M. Dahms, P. Lobel, and S. Kornfeld, *J. Biol. Chem.* **264,** 12115 (1989).
7. M. P. Czech, *Cell (Cambridge, Mass.)* **59,** 235 (1989).
8. R. Ballotti, F. C. Nielsen, N. Pringle, A. Kowalski, W. D. Richardson, E. Van Obberghen, and S. Gammeltoft, *EMBO J.* **6,** 3633 (1987).
9. F. C. Nielsen, E. Wang, and S. Gammeltoft, *J. Neurochem.* **56,** 12 (1991).
10. M. Auletta, F. C. Nielsen, and S. Gammeltoft, *J. Neurosci. Res.* **31,** 14 (1992).
11. S. Gammeltoft, G. K. Haselbacher, R. E. Humbel, M. Fehlmann, and E. Van Obberghen, *EMBO J.* **4,** 3407 (1985).

12. C. Nilsson, P. Blay, F. C. Nielsen, and S. Gammeltoft, *J. Neurochem.* **58,** 923 (1992).
13. J. Zapf, E. Schoenle, and E. R. Froesch, *Eur. J. Biochem.* **87,** 285 (1978).
14. S. Gammeltoft, *in* "Peptide Hormone Action: A Practical Approach" (K. Siddle and J. C. Hutton, eds.), p. 1. IRL Press, Oxford Univ. Press, Oxford, 1990.
15. K. Drejer, V. Kruse, U. D. Larsen, P. Hougaard, S. Bjørn, and S. Gammeltoft, *Diabetes* **40,** 1488 (1991).
16. S. Gammeltoft, R. Ballotti, A. Kowalski, B. Westermark, and E. Van Obberghen, *Cancer Res.* **48,** 1233 (1988).
17. A. Danielsen, E. Larsen, and S. Gammeltoft, *Brain Res.* **518,** 95 (1990).
18. S. Gammeltoft, *in* "Degradation of Bioactive Substances: Physiology and Pathophysiology" (J. H. Henriksen, ed.), p. 81. CRC Press, Boca Raton, FL, 1991.

[14] Methods for Studying Central Serotonergic Receptors

Patricia M. Whitaker-Azmitia

Introduction

Our understanding of any central neurotransmitter receptor depends entirely on the methodologies we have for studying that receptor. In the case of serotonin (5-hydroxytryptamine, or 5-HT) receptors, for which there are multiple subtypes of receptor, we have made more progress on some than on others, simply due to the methods available. For example, the 5-HT$_{1a}$ receptor is well characterized, largely because selective pharmacological agents have long been available. On the other hand, the study of 5-HT$_4$ receptors, for which there is a lack of good selective agents, is moving more slowly.

This chapter summarizes the tools presently available for central serotonin receptor subtypes, with the intent that the reader may become aware of what work can potentially be done and how perhaps they might make a contribution to our understanding of these receptors.

Because the main purpose of this work is to discuss the methodologies available, the chapter is divided by methods rather than receptor subtypes. For those unfamiliar with serotonin receptors, a number of reviews have appeared (1, 2).

Radioligand-Binding Assays

Clearly, one of the major advances in understanding serotonin, or any other receptors, was the introduction of radiolabeled compounds of high enough specific activity that very small amounts (e.g., femtomoles) of the radioactivity could be detected. This meant that central neurotransmitter receptors, which occur in such small amounts, could be studied. Radioligand-binding assays can thus be used to determine the receptor kinetics (B_{max} or K_D) that are so important for studying so many aspects of receptors (e.g., localization, plasticity, turnover rates, and receptor reserve). Furthermore, radioligand-binding studies can be used to determine the pharmacological profile of a receptor by performing detailed competition analysis. This information can then be used to determine the structure–activity relationships (SAR) and do computer modeling to predict receptor activity of novel compounds.

Radioligand-binding assays are thus one of the most useful and technically easy assay systems for studying receptors. However, the choice of radiolabel and defining ligand is still crucial. Individual investigators should test a number of assay systems to optimize the conditions for their particular use. Several radiochemical companies offer "receptor packages"—small amounts of a variety of radiochemicals that can all be tested until one is found to be particularly useful.

Originally, serotonin receptors were studied largely with radiolabeled serotonin, but as more and more receptor subtypes were described, new selective radiolabels became available. [^{3}H]Serotonin is still useful if the study involves simply measuring the total number of 5-HT$_1$ receptors. However, it is not an easy ligand to work with. Serotonin is easily oxidized and thus an antioxidant, such as ascorbic acid, may be required. However, ascorbic acid has some specific effects on membrane proteins, which may be deleterious to the assay. [^{3}H]Serotonin cannot be used to label any of the lower affinity serotonin receptor subtypes, that is, 5-HT$_{2-4}$. Finally, the percentage of nonspecific binding with serotonin can be much higher than it is with the other, more selective ligands.

The following sections describe the methods currently available for each receptor subtype.

5-HT$_{1a}$ Receptors

Since the earliest studies of high-affinity serotonin receptors, there has been the suggestion that multiple types exist (3, 4). The 5-HT$_{1a}$ receptor was first reported on the basis of shallow displacement curves of serotonin with spiperone (5). Shortly thereafter, in 1982, the ergot congener, 8-hydroxy-2-(di-*n*-propylamino)tetralin (8-OH-DPAT) was synthesized and characterized to have central serotonergic properties on the basis of a commonly used model, the serotonin behavioral syndrome (see below) (6). When this compound became available as a radiolabel (7), it soon became apparent that the site with which 8-OH-DPAT interacted was the same as the site described by Pedigo (5) as the 5-HT$_{1a}$ site. It is the availability of this radiolabel that has advanced our understanding of this receptor far beyond our knowledge of the others, and ^{3}H-8-OH-DPAT is still the best way to label the receptor. Generally a concentration range of 0.2 to 10 nM radiolabel with a defining ligand of 1000 nM serotonin is used (8, 9). An iodinated derivative of 8-OH-DPAT (^{125}BH-8-MeO-DPAT), not commercially available, has been suggested to be more useful for autoradiography, because the exposure time is less (10).

One of the handicaps in further characterizing the 5-HT$_{1a}$ receptor and its effects is the lack of a good specific antagonist. Currently, spiroxatrine (Research Biochemicals) and NAN 190 (NOVO Industri) are the best available agents, although the efficacy of both have been questioned by some investigators (11, 12). Antagonists of the 5-HT$_2$ receptor have also proved useful to block the 5-HT$_{1a}$ receptor.

5-HT$_{1b}$ Receptors

5-HT$_{1b}$ receptors were initially characterized by Middlemiss (13), based on the effects of propranolol, a β-adrenergic antagonist, on radiolabeled serotonin binding. The ability of these antagonists to interact with the 5-HT$_{1b}$ receptor is still a hallmark of the site. RU 24969, 1-(m-trifluoromethylphenyl)piperazine (TFMPP), and m-chlorophenylpiperazine (mCPP) preferentially bind to 5-HT$_{1b}$ sites in that order of potency. However, they also interact with 5-HT$_{1a}$ and 5-HT$_{1c}$ sites. In radiolabeled binding studies, [^{125}I]iodocyanopindolol (^{125}I-CYP) is considered to be the label of choice. The usual concentration range is 50 to 500 pM. This radiolabel does not label any other serotonergic receptor but labels β-adrenergic receptors (14, 15). Using serotonin to define nonspecific binding overcomes the problem. Another option to label the sites is to use [^{3}H]serotonin, with a serotonin baseline, but in combination with 100 nM 8-OH-DPAT (to exclude binding to 5-HT$_{1a}$ sites) and 100 nM mesulergine (to exclude binding to 5-HT$_{1c}$ sites).

5-HT$_{1c}$ Receptors

The 5-HT$_{1c}$ receptor was first described in 1985 (16, 17). These researchers first found the site due to the high amount of radiolabeled binding of some serotonin labels in the choroid plexus. In particular, ^{125}I-labeled lysergic acid diethylamide (LSD) highly labeled this region. Further study, however, showed that this site did not have the pharmacology of any other known serotonin receptor. Because the receptor displayed high affinity (i.e., nanomolar) for serotonin, but was not the 5-HT$_{1a}$ or the 5-HT$_{1b}$ receptor, it was named 5-HT$_{1c}$. However, now that the receptor is further characterized, it should really be placed within the 5-HT$_2$ receptor family, because both are linked to the production of inositol phosphates and have a high degree of sequence homology.

Although the receptor can be labeled by [^{3}H]5-HT, ^{125}I-labeled LSD and [^{3}H]mesulergine are better choices (16).

5-HT$_{1d}$ Receptors

The 5-HT$_{1d}$ site is not found in rats or mice but is found in humans, guinea pigs, and rabbits. The pharmacology is similar to the 5-HT$_{1b}$ site, with the exception of a lack of effect of the β-adrenergic antagonists. This, naturally, precludes the use of [^{125}I]iodocyanopindolol as a radiolabel and leaves only [^{3}H]serotonin with the necessary addition of 100 nM 8-OH-DPAT and 100 nM mesulergine (see above) (18). The most selective agonist for 5-HT$_{1d}$ sites is sumatriptan; however, this is not yet commercially available in a radiolabeled form.

5-HT$_2$ Receptors

The first studies on the 5-HT$_2$ receptor were done largely by J. Leysen and co-workers, who used a radiolabeled form of the then novel antipsychotic spiroperidol (spiperone) to show a low-affinity (200–300 nM) binding site for serotonin (19). Although [^{3}H]spiperone can be used as a label for these sites, [^{3}H]ketanserin (20) is the more common choice because it has no dopamine component, although it has some histamine and α-adrenergic interactions. [^{3}H]Ketanserin and [^{3}H]spiperone are both antagonists, but agonists are also available. These include a number of derivatives of the hallucinogenic methoxyphenethylamines, such as [^{3}H]DOB and [^{125}I]DOI (21). There is some controversy regarding the use of these labels, as some investigators have suggested that they label only a subset of 5-HT$_2$ sites, referred to as 5-HT$_{2a}$ receptors (22). Although these agonists could prove useful in studying receptor regulation, it is probably best to use the antagonists for more routine labeling studies.

5-HT$_3$ Receptors

The earliest studies of serotonin receptors classified the receptors into D (blocked by dihydroergotamine) and M (blocked by morphine) (23). It is clear that the M receptor is what we now call the 5-HT$_3$ receptor.

There are three radiolabels for the 5-HT$_3$ receptor currently available. [^{3}H]Quipazine and [^{3}H]GR-65630 have been available for some time, and there are a number of papers published using these (24, 25). However, the nonspecific binding with these labels can be as high as 70%, making them difficult to use when small numbers of the receptor are present. More recently, [^{3}H]BRL 43694 has become available; initial reports suggest that the nonspecific binding is 50%—clearly less than the other available ligands but still enough to present some limitations.

One advantage in characterizing the 5-HT$_3$ receptor is that there are several good selective and potent antagonists. These include (with their approximate pK values for binding): zacopride (9.7), ICS 205–930 (8.5), and MDL 72222 (7.3) (26).

5-HT$_4$ Receptors

There are no radiolabels currently available for this receptor. However, several agents have been proposed as selective agonists, including cisapride (27) and the more recently described azabicycloalkyl benzimidazolone derivatives (28), which may soon be available in a radiolabeled form.

Functional Studies

Second Messengers

Adenylate Cyclase

Alterations in the production of the second messenger cAMP by interactions with the enzyme adenylate cyclase is a clearly defined function of many neurotransmitter receptors. The levels of cAMP can be inhibited (through linkage with a G_i protein) or stimulated (through linkage with a G_s protein). There are two methods for assessing the amount of cAMP produced. If the measurement of this second messenger system should become a major focus of research, the cheapest and most reliable method is to incubate the tissue with [^{32}P]ATP and separate out the resultant labeled [^{32}P]cAMP by column chromatography. However, if a small number of assays will be run, a radioimmunoassay kit for cAMP is available. The kit is prohibitively expensive for doing large numbers of assays. Several reviews on the production of cAMP by serotonergic receptors have been published (29–31). 5-HT$_{1a}$ and 5-HT$_{1b}$ receptors are generally considered to be inhibitory to the production of cAMP while the 5-HT$_4$ receptor is stimulatory.

Inositol Phosphates

In additon to the production of cAMP, many neurotransmitter systems hydrolyze membrane phosphoinositides by stimulation of the enzyme phospholipase C. Among the serotonin receptors, the 5-HT$_{1c}$ and 5-HT$_2$ receptors are coupled to this second messenger system. The most prevalent method of measuring this system is to incubate the tissue with *myo*-[^{3}H]inositol until sufficient membrane phosphoinositides are labeled. After stimulation with the drugs being tested, accumulation of [^{3}H]inositol monophosphate (IP) is determined after column chromatography. Several studies describing the methodologies are given (32–34).

Irreversible Receptor Blockers

Irreversible receptor blockers can be used in a variety of studies [e.g., studies of spare receptors (35), studies of receptor turnover time (36), and studies of *in vivo* occupancy by receptor-selective drugs (37)].

One of the most commonly used irreversible receptor blockers is *N*-ethoxycarbonyl-2-ethoxy-1,2-dihydroquinoline (EEDQ). This is an alkylating compound that has been used extensively in the study of dopamine receptors (36) but also alkylates α_1- and α_2-adrenergic receptors, muscarinic cholinergic, γ-aminobutyric acid (GABA)-ergic, and serotonergic receptors. This lack of specificity can clearly be a problem, but it can be overcome by pretreating animals with receptor blocking agents to ''protect'' the other receptors.

EEDQ is generally administered subcutaneously in an ethanol/water vehicle (1 : 1) in a dose of 10–20 mg/kg. Animals are sacrificed at various time points, after the injection, to determine turnover time of the receptors. For studies of spare receptors or *in vivo* occupancy of drugs, animals are generally sacrificed 24 hr after the injection.

Release

Serotonin receptors have been shown to play a role in regulation of neurotransmitter release, both of serotonin (5-HT$_{1a,1b,1d}$) and other neurotransmitters, including dopamine (5-HT$_3$ receptors) and acetylcholine (5-HT$_3$ receptors). The release of neurotransmitters can be assessed *in vivo*, using techniques such as *in vivo* dialysis. Although this technique can answer many interesting questions in the freely moving and behaving animal, they are not techniques that most laboratories can readily use. However, there are a number of *in vitro* techniques that are easily acquired and can be used to answer interesting questions. The source of tissue can be synaptosomes, cultured cells, or brain slices.

Release studies are most easily done by preincubating the tissue with a radiolabeled form of the neurotransmitter to be studied, for example 50 nM [^{3}H]serotonin. The concentration should be kept as low as possible or specific uptake inhibitors will have to be added to prevent accumulation of radiolabel in the terminals of other neurotransmitter neurons. The preparation is ''superfused,'' that is, bathed with large volumes of buffer, to prevent reuptake of released radiolabel. Test substances are added to the superfusion buffer. To test for released neurotransmitter and not its metabolites, enzyme inhibitors (such as inhibitors of monoamine oxidase) are often included throughout the assay buffers. If inhibition of release is being measured, release is usually stimulated by high concentrations of K$^+$.

For a detailed discussion of release studies in general, see the review by Raiteri *et al.* (38). Wolf and Kuhn (39) have presented a review of serotonin autoreceptors and release.

Behavioral Studies

The literature on behavioral effects of serotonin is considerable and unfortunately contains many contradictions. Nonetheless, the use of behavioral tests to study serotonin receptors is such an important tool that an effort to establish some agreed-on and easily reproducible behavioral models is worthwhile. The behaviors discussed in this section are also tests that can be easily implemented in most laboratories. For a more extensive review of the literature, the reader is referred to Wilkinson and Dourish (40).

5-HT$_{1a}$ Receptors

One of the earliest behavioral tests ever devised for the serotonin system was the so-called "serotonin behavioral syndrome," (41) which is used in rats. Several of the behavioral elements of the syndrome can be elicited by 8-OH-DPAT. However, not all of the behaviors can be considered direct evidence of 5-HT$_{1a}$ receptor activation. For example, the head-weaving and hyperlocomotion can be inhibited by nonserotonergic antagonists and are thus not considered selective. The reciprocal forepaw treading and flat body posture components, however, are considered to be direct measures of 5-HT$_{1a}$ receptor function (42, 43). One review has suggested that the effect of 8-OH-DPAT is on postsynaptic receptors located in the brainstem (44).

The hippocampus also contains large numbers of 5-HT$_{1a}$ receptors, and a model for quantifying these receptors would be valuable. It is possible that the studies of 5-HT$_{1a}$ receptor-active drugs in decreasing learning (45, 46) may be localized to an effect in this region.

Because 5-HT$_{1a}$ receptors also serve as autoreceptors on serotonergic cell bodies in the raphe nuclei, it is to be expected that some behavioral effects of 8-OH-DPAT are evident here as well. In this case, hyperphagia in rats is considered a quantifiable and reliable measure of activation of these receptors (47, 48). Another model of presynaptic activation of 5-HT$_{1a}$ receptors is hypothermia. These studies are usually done in mice (49), as the response is not as easily quantified or as selective in rats (50).

Many of the selective 5-HT$_{1a}$ agonists have effects in various animal models of human disease states. Models of depression, such as inescapable shock, can be attenuated or prevented by 8-OH-DPAT, buspirone, ipsapirone, and gepirone (51). Although these drugs are currently marketed as antianxiety agents, the 5-HT$_{1a}$ agonists give inconsistent results in models of anxiety. Thus, these models should not be used as routine tests to establish an action of a substance on these receptors.

For a complete summary of 5-HT$_{1a}$ receptors and behavior, see the review by Lucki and Wieland (52).

5-HT$_{1b}$ Receptors

Interestingly, 5-HT$_{1b}$ receptor agonists in many cases give effects opposite to those reported for 5-HT$_{1a}$ agonists. Thus, these drugs will cause hypophagia (53) and hyperthermia (54). In general, the best strategy to determine an effect on 5-HT$_{1b}$ receptors is to use mCPP, TFMPP, or RU 24969 as an agonist and block the effect with pindolol (55).

5-HT$_{1c}$ Receptors

There are a number of studies showing a 5-HT$_{1c}$ component in the actions of drugs often considered to be useful as 5-HT$_{1b}$ agonists. For example, mCPP and TFMPP may have their effect on feeding partly through an action on 5-HT$_{1c}$ receptors (53). The best way to discriminate between these receptors, therefore, is to test the attenuating effects of antagonists. In the case of 5-HT$_{1c}$ receptors, metergoline, mesulergine, and mianserin may all be used. There are some interesting studies suggesting that MK 212 may be useful as a selective *in vivo* agonist of 5-HT$_{1c}$ receptors (56, 57); more work in this area would be welcome.

5-HT$_2$ Receptors

There are a number of behavioral measures for 5-HT$_2$ receptor function that can easily be implemented in laboratories. The most commonly used is a head twitch response in rats, which is elicitd by selective 5-HT$_2$ agonists (58) but not by other receptor agonists (50). The response is also blocked specifically by 5-HT$_2$ antagonists (59). Rats also show a behavior referred to as "wet dog shakes" with the same pharmacological specificity as the head twitches (60). It has been suggested that this response is a more fully expressed head twitch response (40).

5-HT$_3$ Receptors

The most selective test for 5-HT$_3$ receptor function is inhibition of emesis. This work is generally done in ferrets or dogs, as rodents do not have a vomit reflex, which limits their use in many laboratories. However, 5-HT$_3$ antagonists attenuate several animal models of anxiety (61–63), which can be used as a test for changes in sensitivity of the receptor.

Human Studies

Serotonin and serotonin receptors have been implicated in a wide variety of human mental disorders, including depression, anxiety, schizophrenia, eating disorders, and alcoholism. Methods that are used to study serotonin receptors in the living human are therefore useful. In the past, investigators have used a variety of peripheral markers for serotonin receptors, such as binding to platelets. This has led to many conflicting results and, in general, is not currently considered to be a useful approach. There are, however, means of assessing central receptor function that are more useful. These include neuroendocrine challenge tests and *in vivo* imaging, such as with positron-emission tomography (PET).

Neoroendocrinological Challenge Studies

Neuroendocrine responses of serotonin receptors have been assessed in two ways: either by using directly acting receptor agonists or by using a nonspecific serotonergic agent (such as L-tryptophan or the releaser fenfluramine) and attempting to block the response with specific antagonists. A number of neuroendocrine markers have been evaluated, including adrenocorticotropic hormone (ACTH) (64), cortisol (65), growth hormone (66), and prolactin (67).

Using the nonspecific serotonergic response, Murphy (68) has suggested that the best test is intravenous L-tryptophan or 5-hydroxytryptophan to produce an increase in either prolactin or growth hormone. The prolactin response can be blocked with metergoline or methysergide but not mianserin, suggesting 5-HT$_1$ receptor involvement. Studies measuring ACTH or cortisol are more variable.

The selective 5-HT$_{1a}$ agonist buspirone (BuSpar) can be used to increase blood levels of prolactin and growth hormone (66). This is probably the easiest approach for most laboratories wishing to use the selective agonist approach, because the other commonly used agonists mCPP (for 5-HT$_1$ receptors) and MK 212 (for 5-HT$_2$ and 5-HT$_{1c}$ receptors) (69) are not Food and Drug Administration (FDA)-approved drugs and special permission is required for their use. Generally, blood samples for assay are drawn every 15 to 30 min after the drug is administered and the total response over time (i.e., area under the curve) calculated.

Imaging Studies

Positron emission tomography is the first manner of measuring discrete neurochemical parameters in the living human brain. As such, it has great potential for quantifying changes in human disease states. Because serotonin is so often implicated in mental illness, this would clearly be of great advantage to serotonin research. To date, most of the imaging studies have focused on ligands for the 5-HT$_2$ receptor. However, it has also been proposed that [^{18}F]fluorodeoxyglucose utilization patterns, after treatment with other selective agonists, could be an indicator of regions involved in the actions of those drugs. A review on PET and serotonin was given by Frost (70).

Conclusion

Like all neurotransmitter receptors, the study of serotonin receptors has been highly dependent on the available methods. The great advances in methodology since the mid-1970s are reflected in the vast increase in the depth and breadth of our knowledge of serotonin receptors.

In the mid-1970s, our major tools for studying serotonin receptors were the direct binding assay and the only known second messenger system, the production of cAMP. Today, nearly 20 years later, we have available a great array of techniques. The pharmacological information from binding assays has led to the development of highly selective pharmacological agents. This in turn has helped detect the numerous subtypes of receptors that occur and to characterize their functions, both in terms of effector systems and behaviors. The great amount of information gained by basic scientists will hopefully soon be extended to our understanding of the human disease states that may involve serotonin receptors.

References

1. S. J. Peroutka, *Pharmacol. Toxicol.* **67**(5), 373 (1990).
2. S. J. Peroutka, A. W. Schmidt, A. J. Sleight, and M. A. Harrington, *Ann. N.Y. Acad. Sci.* **600,** 104 (1990).
3. P. M. Whitaker and P. Seeman, *Proc. Natl. Acad. Sci. U.S.A.* **75,** 5783 (1978).
4. S. J. Peroutka, R. M. Lebovitz, and S. H. Snyder, *Science* **212,** 827 (1981).
5. N. W. Pedigo, H. I. Yamamura, and D. L. Nelson, *J. Neurochem.* **36,** 220 (1981).
6. S. Hjørth, A. Carlsson, P. Lindberg, D. Sanchez, H. Wikström, L. E. Arvidsson, U. Hacksell, and J. L. G. Nilsson, *J. Neural Transm.* **55,** 169 (1982).
7. M. Hamon, M. B. Emerit, S. El Mestikawy, M. C. Gallissot, and H. Gozlan, *in* "Cardiovascular Pharmacology of 5-Hydroxytryptamine: Prospective Therapeutic Application" (P. R. Saxena, D. I. Wallis, W. Wouters, and P. Bevan, eds.) pp. 41–59. Kluwer Academic Press, New York, 1990.
8. D. Hoyer, G. Engel, and H. O. Kalkman, *Eur. J. Pharmacol.* **118,** 13 (1985).
9. H. Gozlan, S. El Mestikawy, L. Pichat, J. Glowinski, and M. Hamon, *Nature (London)* **305,** 140 (1983).
10. H. Gozlan, M. Ponchant, G. Daval, D. Verge, F. Ménard, A. Vanhove, J. P. Beaucourt, and M. Hamon, *J. Pharmacol. Exp. Ther.* **244,** 751 (1988).
11. H. O. Kalkman and J. Soar, *Eur. J. Pharmacol.* **191,** 383 (1990).
12. K. M. Wozniak, M. J. Durcan, and M. Linnoila, *Eur. J. Pharmacol.* **193,** 253 (1991).
13. D. N. Middlemiss, *Eur. J. Pharmacol.* **37,** 434 (1984).
14. E. Edwards and P. Whitaker-Azmitia, *Neuropharmacology* **26,** 93 (1987).
15. D. Hoyer, G. Engel, and H. O. Kalkman, *Eur. J. Pharmacol.* **118,** 13 (1985).

16. A. Pazos, D. Hoyer, and J. M. Palacios, *Eur. J. Pharmacol.* **106,** 539 (1985).
17. N. A. Yagaloff and P. R. Hartig, *J. Neurosci.* **5,** 3178 (1985).
18. J. Gonzalez-Heydrich and S. J. Peroutka, *Exp. Neurol.* **113,** 28 (1991).
19. J. E. Leysen, C. J. E. Niemegeers, J. P. Tollenaere, and P. M. Laduron, *Nature (London)* **272,** 168 (1978).
20. J. E. Leysen, C. J. E. Niemegeers, J. M. Van Nueten, and P. M. Laduron, *Mol. Pharmacol.* **21,** 301 (1982).
21. R. A. Lyon, K. H. Davis, and M. Titeler, *Mol. Pharmacol.* **31,** 194 (1987).
22. P. A. Pierce and S. J. Peroutka, *J. Neurochem.* **52,** 656 (1989).
23. J. H. Gaddum and Z. P. Picarelli, *Br. J. Pharmacol. Chemother.* **12,** 323 (1957).
24. S. J. Peroutka and A. Hamik, *Eur. J. Pharmacol.* **148,** 297 (1988).
25. G. J. Kilpatrick, B. J. Jones, and M. B. Tyers, *Eur. J. Pharmacol.* **159,** 157 (1989).
26. M. B. Tyers, *Ann. N.Y. Acad. Sci.* **600,** 194 (1990).
27. J. Bockaert, M. Sebben, and A. Dumuis, *Mol. Pharmacol.* **37,** 408 (1990).
28. A. Dumuis, M. Sebben, E. Monferini, M. Nicola, H. Ladinski, and J. Bockaert, *Naunyn-Schmiedeberg's Arch. Pharmacol.* **343,** 245 (1991).
29. F. D. Yocca and S. Maayani, *Ann. N.Y. Acad. Sci.* **600,** 212 (1990).
30. M. De Vivo and S. Maayani, *in* ''The Serotonin Receptors'' (E. Sanders-Bush, ed.), p. 141. Humana Press, Clifton, NJ, 1988.
31. A. Frazer, S. Maayani, and B. Wolfe, *Annu. Rev. Pharmacol. Toxicol.* **30,** 307 (1990).
32. E. Sanders-Bush, M. Tsutsumi, and K. Burris, *Ann. N.Y. Acad. Sci.* **600,** 224 (1990).
33. P. J. Conn and E. Sanders-Bush, *Neuropharmacology* **23,** 993 (1984).
34. P. J. Conn and E. Sanders-Bush, *J. Neurochem.* **47,** 1754 (1986).
35. E. Meller, T. Puza, J. C. Miller, A. J. Friedhoff, and J. W. Schweitzer, *J. Pharmacol. Exp. Ther.* **257,** 668 (1991).
36. S. Xu, Y. Hatada, L. E. Black, I. Crease, and D. R. Sibley, *J. Pharmacol. Exp. Ther.* **257,** 608 (1991).
37. C. F. Saller, L. D. Kreamer, L. A. Adamovage, and A. I. Salama, *Life Sci.* **45,** 917 (1989).
38. M. Raiteri, M. Marchi, and G. Maura, *Handb. Neurochem.* **6,** 431 (1984).
39. W. A. Wolf and D. M. Kuhn, *Ann. N.Y. Acad. Sci.* **604,** 505 (1990).
40. L. O. Wilkinson and C. T. Dourish, *in* ''Serotonin Receptor Subtypes'' (S. J. Peroutka, ed.), p. 147. Wiley-Liss, New York, 1991.
41. B. L. Jacobs, *Life Sci.* **19,** 777 (1976).
42. M. D. Tricklebank, C. Forler, and J. Fozard, *Eur. J. Pharmacol.* **106,** 271 (1984).
43. M. D. Tricklebank, C. Forler, D. N. Middlemiss, and J. R. Fozard, *Eur. J. Pharmacol.* **117,** 15 (1985).
44. G. Curzon, *in* ''Neurobiology of Stereotyped Behavior'' (S. J. Cooper and C. T. Dourish, eds.), p. 142. Oxford Univ. Press, Oxford, 1990.
45. A. J. Hunter and F. F. Roberts, *in* ''Brain 5-HT$_{1a}$ Receptors: Behavioural and Neurochemical Pharmacology'' (C. T. Dourish, S. Ahlenius, and P. H. Hutson, eds.), p. 278. Ellis Horwood, Chichester, 1987.
46. J. C. Winter and D. T. Petti, *Pharmacol. Biochem. Behav.* **27,** 625 (1987).

47. P. H. Hutson, C. T. Dourish, and G. Curzon, *Eur. J. Pharmacol.* **129,** 347 (1986).
48. C. Bendotti and R. Samanin, *Eur. J. Pharmacol.* **121,** 147 (1986).
49. G. M. Goodwin, R. J. DeSouza, and A. R. Green, *Neuropharmacology* **24,** 1187 (1985).
50. A. R. Green and G. M. Goodwin, *in* "Brain 5-HT$_{1a}$ Receptors: Behavioural and Neurochemical Pharmacology" (C. T. Dourish, S. Ahlenius, and P. H. Hutson, eds.), p. 161. Ellis Horwood, Chichester, 1987.
51. P. Giral, P. Martin, P. Soubrie, and P. Simon, *Biol. Psychiatry* **23,** 237 (1988).
52. I. Lucki and S. Wieland, *Neuropsychopharmacology* **3,** 481 (1990).
53. G. A. Kennett, C. T. Dourish, and G. Curzon, *Eur. J. Pharmacol.* **141,** 429 (1987).
54. J. Maj, E. Chojnacka-Wojcik, A. Klodzinska, A. Deren, and E. Moryl, *J. Neural Transm.* **73,** 43 (1988).
55. M. O. Tricklebank, D. N. Middlemiss, and J. Neil, *Neuropharmacology* **25,** 877 (1986).
56. B. H. King, C. Brazell, C. T. Dourish, and D. N. Middlemiss, *Neurosci. Lett.* **105,** 174 (1989).
57. K. A. Cunningham, P. M. Callahan, and J. B. Appel, *Psychopharmacology* **90,** 193 (1986).
58. S. J. Peroutka, R. M. Lebovitz, and S. H. Snyder, *Science* **212,** 827 (1981).
59. I. Lucki, M. S. Nobler, and A. Frazer, *J. Pharmacol. Exp. Ther.* **228,** 133 (1984).
60. C. Y. Yap and D. A. Taylor, *Neuropharmacology* **22,** 801 (1983).
61. M. B. Tyers, B. Costall, A. M. Domeney, B. J. Jones, M. E. Kelly, R. J. Naylor, and N. R. Oakley, *Neurosci. Lett.* **29,** S68 (1987).
62. D. Piper, N. Upton, D. Thomas, and J. Nicholass, *Br. J. Pharmacol.* **94,** 314P (1988).
63. B. Costall, A. M. Domeney, P. A. Gerrard, M. E. Kelly, and R. J. Naylor, *Br. J. Pharmacol.* **93,** 195P (1988).
64. D. A. Lewis and B. M. Sherman, *J. Clin. Endocrinol. Metab.* **58,** 458 (1984).
65. M. T. Lowy and H. Y. Meltzer, *Biol. Psychiatry* **23,** 818 (1988).
66. H. Y. Meltzer, T. Flemming, and A. Robertson, *Arch. Gen. Psychiatry* **40,** 1099 (1983).
67. A. Quattrone, G. Tedeschi, U. Aguglia, F. Scopacasa, G. R. Direnzo, and L. Annunziato, *Br. J. Clin. Pharmacol.* **16,** 471 (1983).
68. D. L. Murphy, *Ann. N.Y. Acad. Sci.* **600,** 282 (1990).
69. P. J. Cowen, I. M. Anderson, and S. E. Gartside, *Ann. N.Y. Acad. Sci.* **600,** 250 (1990).
70. J. J. Frost, *Ann. N.Y. Acad. Sci.* **600,** 272 (1990).

[15] Analysis of Serotonin 5-HT$_{1A}$ Receptors in Primary Neuronal Culture

Barbara C. Swarzenski, Ann M. Benz, Janice M. Hickok, and Richard D. Todd

Introduction

Serotonin (5-hydroxytryptamine, 5-HT) is an indole monoamine found both in the periphery and in the central nervous system (CNS). Serotonin has been recognized as a fundamentally important neurotransmitter in the brain and is strongly implicated in the pathophysiology of many neuropsychiatric disorders. This compound is also thought to be involved in the regulation of neural differentiation in the early stages of embryonic development and to have neuronotrophic activity (1).

In recent years the role of serotonin in both normal and abnormal human CNS function has been of increasing interest to neuroscientists and others. In part this reflects advances in molecular biological and radioligand techniques that have permitted the distinction of several serotonin receptor subtypes based on pharmacological and physiological criteria. The mammalian brain contains at least three main classes of serotonin receptors (5-HT$_{1-3}$) (2). These three classes have been further divided into several subtypes. Receptor subtypes in the first class have been designated 5-HT$_{1A-D}$. The other two classes may likewise contain several subtypes each. Further distinction among the serotonin receptors has been noted in the association of subtypes with different second messenger systems and in the distribution of serotonin receptor subtypes within the central nervous system. With a few exceptions, there are relatively few agonists and antagonists that are selective for a particular class or subtype of serotonin receptor.

We have been interested in studying the 5-HT$_{1A}$ receptor, which is one of four subtypes of the 5-HT$_1$ receptor class. A major technical reason for choosing this receptor subtype over another is the availability of a selective 5-HT$_{1A}$ agonist, 8-hydroxy-2-(di-n-propylamino)tetralin (8-OH-DPAT) (3). This agent has few or no dopaminergic or noradrenergic receptor stimulatory properties and even at relatively high micromolar concentrations does not appear to be toxic to neurons (4). 8-OH-DPAT has nanomolar affinity for the 5-HT$_{1A}$ receptor and has high solubility in aqueous solutions (3).

5-HT$_{1A}$ receptors in the mammalian central nervous system are located predominantly in the hippocampus and raphe nuclei of the pons and upper brainstem; however a substantial proportion of this receptor subtype is also found within the cerebral cortex (5). This receptor is located postsynaptically and has been shown to modulate adenylate cyclase activity, usually by stimulation. Serotonin-producing neurons also possess somatodendritic autoreceptors which, at least in the dorsal raphe, have been identified as 5-HT$_{1A}$ receptors (6). The 5-HT$_{1A}$ receptor interacts with a guanine nucleotide-binding protein (G protein) and has been cloned (7, 8). Sequence analysis demonstrates that this 5-HT receptor shares substantial amino acid homology in its membrane-spanning domains with other members of the G protein-coupled receptor supergene family (7–9).

To investigate the developmental physiological significance of the cortical 5-HT$_{1A}$ receptor in the mammalian nervous system, we have stimulated 5-HT$_{1A}$ receptors in primary cultures of fetal rat frontal cortical neurons. We have demonstrated that 5-HT$_1$ and 5-HT$_{1A}$ receptors are present in cultured embryonic rat forebrain neurons (4) and have shown the presence in cultured neuronal cells of 5-HT$_{1A}$-specific RNA (4) (Swarzenski *et al.*, in preparation). Moreover, stimulation of 5-HT$_{1A}$ receptors with 8-OH-DPAT results in changes in neuronal morphology (4).

In this chapter we describe technical procedures for preparing primary neuronal cultures (Section 1), assaying individual cultured neurons for 5-HT$_1$ and 5-HT$_{1A}$ receptors by autoradiography (Section 2), localizing 5-HT$_{1A}$ mRNA by *in situ* hybridization by nonradioactive methods (Section 3) and quantifying changes in neurite outgrowth as a result of serotonin 5-HT$_{1A}$ receptor stimulation by 8-OH-DPAT (Section 4).

Description of Procedures

1. Procedure for Preparation of Primary Neuronal Cell Cultures

Materials

Fetal Dissection Equipment
  Dissecting microscope and light source
  Disposable plastic handled scalpel, sterile (Fisher, Pittsburgh, PA)
  Three straight forceps, very fine
  One curved forceps, very fine
  Petri dish (60 mm), sterile (for fine dissection)
  poly(D-lysine)-coated culture dishes (35 mm)

To Count Cell Viability
  Hemocytometer, coverslips, and counter
  Trypan blue stain (0.4%, w/v)

Stock Solutions
  Dulbecco's modified Eagle's medium (Sigma, St. Louis, MO)
  Minimum essential medium (Sigma)
  N-2-hydroxyethylpiperazine-N'-2-ethanesulfonic acid (HEPES), $100\times$
    $= 1\ M$
  L-Glutamine, $100\times\ =\ 200$ mM
  Poly(D-lysine), $50\times\ =\ 200\ \mu$g/ml
  Phosphate-buffered saline (PBS), calcium and magnesium free ($10\times$):
    80 g/liter NaCl, 2 g/liter KCl, 11.5 g/liter Na_2HPO_4, 2 g/liter KH_2PO_4
    at pH 7.4

Preparation of Media
  Serum medium (pH 7.2–7.4): Eagle's minimum essential medium, 5%
    (v/v) heat-inactivated fetal bovine serum, 1% (w/v) L-glutamine, 2
    mM final concentration, 1% (w/v) HEPES, 10 mM final concentration

  Storage: Serum medium kept at 4°C in the dark remains potent for 2
    weeks
  Tissue dissociation medium (pH 7.2–7.4): Dulbecco's modified Eagle's
    medium, 1% (w/v) L-glutamine, 2 mM final concentration

HEPES ($1\times$) is an optional addition to serum medium. We have found
HEPES to be useful primarily when handling a large number of plates that
are out of the incubator for a prolonged time period (e.g., when adding
chemicals or changing the medium). All solutions and materials are sterile.
We have found that cultures prepared from embryonic rat brains of ages
E17–E19 contain less than 0.1% glial cells as judged by immunocytochemical
detection of antibodies to GAF (glial fibrillary acidic protein) and galactocere-
broside C.

Preparation of Plates
Coat 35-mm sterile tissue culture plates with poly(D-lysine): Add 1 ml of 4
μg/ml poly(D-lysine) to each tissue culture dish for 1 hr at room temperature.
Remove poly(D-lysine) and wash three times with PBS. Add 1 ml of desired
medium to each plate and place into a humidified incubator under 5% CO_2 at

37°C until ready to use. *Note:* Free poly(D-Lysine) is toxic to cells, so the wash steps are critical.

Establishment of Primary Neuronal Cell Culture

The neuronal cell culture is prepared from frontal cerebral cortexes of 16- to 19-day-old rat (Sprague–Dawley) embryos. E1 is determined by the appearance of the vaginal plug. The cortexes are freed from the meninges under sterile conditions and then are mechanically dissociated to single-cell suspensions using flame-polished Pasteur pipettes of progressively smaller diameter. A given tissue sample is generally passed through a pipette three to four times and the final diameter of the pipettes is approximately 0.5–1.0 mm. At these ages, usually 7–8 cortexes are enough to prepare 20 plates. At younger ages, the amount of brain tissue is less and so more specimens may be required. The pooled, dissected cortexes are held in 2–5 ml of DMEM containing 1% (w/v) L-glutamine at room temperature until all samples are dissected. The dissociation of the cortexes is done in a 15-ml sterile polystyrene centrifuge tube that has been lightly coated with 5% (v/v) heat-inactivated fetal bovine serum. This prevents sticking of the tissue to the tube. For seven to eight cortexes, a volume of approximately 15 ml of medium is required during the dissociation. The cortex dissociation is done in DMEM containing 1% (w/v) L-glutamine. After a single-cell suspension has been produced, it is placed by pipette into a fresh tube, an additional 5 ml of dissociation medium is placed into the tube that contains the tissue sample, and the dissociation procedure is followed again. After three such dissociation cycles, there should be enough single-cell suspension for a given experiment. Cell viability is calculated using trypan blue staining and a hemacytometer. The number of cells added per plate depends on the purpose of the experiment. For single-cell analysis of neurite morphologies the plating density is about 50 cells/mm^2 of growing surface (about 50,000 cells/35-mm-diameter dish). After inoculation into 1 ml of serum medium the plates are kept in the incubator under 5% CO_2 at 37°C for 20–30 min. During this time viable cells should adhere to the poly(D-lysine) substrate. After sufficient adhesion has occurred, the medium is removed and replaced by 1 ml of fresh serum medium at 37°C. If the cell viability after tissue dissociation is under 70%, the plates are rinsed twice. This removes much of the cellular debris that accumulates at lower viabilities. Usually the viability following this procedure is between 70 and 85%. After the fresh medium is added, the plates are cultured in the incubator under 5% CO_2 at 37°C until needed. At 37°C, serum medium keeps its potency for about 2 weeks. Examples of cultured neurons are shown in Fig. 4.

2. *Measurement of the Distribution of 5-HT$_1$ and 5-HT$_{1A}$ Receptors by Autoradiography*

The distribution of serotonin 5-HT$_1$ (all 5-HT receptors with nanomolar affinity for serotonin) and 5-HT$_{1A}$ receptors in primary neuronal cultures can be determined by using the radioligand 5-[^{3}H]HT or 8-OH-[^{3}H]DPAT (respectively). Other investigators have shown that serotonin is a potent agonist at a subset of serotonin receptors. Sites that are radiolabeled by nanomolar concentrations of 5-[^{3}H]HT are designated 5-HT$_1$ sites (10) as distinct from 5-HT$_2$ receptors, which are labeled by [^{3}H]spiperone. Binding of 5-[^{3}H]HT to the class of 5-HT$_1$ receptors has been shown to be saturable, selective, and reversible (11–14). Subsequent work revealed that the different receptor subtypes within the 5-HT$_1$ class could be distinguished by a difference in ease of displacement of 5-[^{3}H]HT by spiperone, a compound that is an antagonist for serotonergic and dopamine (D$_2$) receptors: receptors to which spiperone bound with high affinity (K_i = 2–10 nM) were designated 5-HT$_{1A}$ sites (14), while low-affinity binding sites were designated 5-HT$_{non-1A}$ sites (now known to contain 5-HT$_{1B}$ and 5-HT$_{1D}$ subtypes).

In this section we describe a method for determining the distribution of 5-HT$_1$ and 5-HT$_{1A}$ receptors in primary neuronal cultures. This procedure is adapted largely from Herkenham and Pert (15), who provide more technical details. Displacement studies have shown that about one-third to one-half of 5-HT$_1$ sites radiolabeled by 5-[^{3}H]HT are expected to be 5-HT$_{1A}$ sites (3, 11, 13, 14).

Determination of the Distribution of 5-HT$_1$ Receptors in Fetal Frontal Cortical Neurons Using the Radioligands 5-[^{3}H]HT and 8-OH-[^{3}H]DPAT

1. Primary neuronal cultures are prepared as described in Section 1. Cells are plated at a density of 5.0×10^4/35-mm culture dish (50/mm^2) and cultured for 3 days. Usually 10 plates are required for a given autoradiography experiment.

2. The cultures are rinsed three times with 50 mM Tris-HCl at pH 7.4 (20°C) and preincubated for 30 min at pH 7.4 (4°C) in the same solution, to which has been added 10 mM pargyline (a monoamine oxidase inhibitor that prevents the degradation of serotonin) and 10 mM desipramine (a chemical in the antidepressant class that blocks serotonin reuptake).

3. Add either 5-[^{3}H]HT (specific activity 24.1–29.6 Ci/mmol; New England Nuclear, Boston, MA) or 8-OH-[^{3}H]DPAT (specific activity, 29.5 Ci/mmol; New England Nuclear) to a final concentration of 10 nM for 2 hr at 4°C (equilibrium is reached in 90 min).

4. The cells are rinsed quickly again three times with 50 mM Tris-HCl, pH 7.4 (4°C), to remove unbound label and the buffer is removed.

5. The moist cells are placed in an incubator saturated with glutaraldehyde vapors to cross-link the ^{3}H label to the cells and coated with NTB-2 photographic emulsion (Kodak, Rochester, NY) (15).

6. After exposure for 4 weeks (for 5-[^{3}H]HT) to 12 weeks (for 8-OH-[^{3}H]DPAT) at −70°C, the dishes are developed and the cells individually scanned for grain density using a Bioquant image analysis system (R and M Biometrics, Nashville, TN). Nonspecific binding is defined by the inclusion of 10 μM 5-HT or 1 μM spiperone. Examples of autoradiographic results are shown in Fig. 1.

Figure 2 illustrates the percentage of cells that were labeled to different degrees (little, moderate, to dense) by the ligands. Approximately three-fourths of the neurons are shown to bind 5-[^{3}H]HT to a moderate or dense degree and approximately 45% bind 8-OH-[^{3}H]DPAT to a moderate or dense degree. As discussed in the introduction to this section, this is the anticipated result. The autoradiographic process alters cell morphology, so direct comparisons of grain density and morphology are not possible.

3. In Situ Hybridization of 5-HT$_{1A}$ mRNA Using a Nonradioactive Oligonucleotide Probe

Introduction

The messenger RNA (mRNA) coding for a given receptor subtype can be detected by several methods that all rely on the nucleic acid sequence specificity of the genetic code. As described above, the gene coding for the 5-HT$_{1A}$ receptor has been cloned and sequenced in both rat and humans (7, 8). This allows the identification of unique nucleic acid sequences that can be used to detect 5-HT$_{1A}$ receptor mRNA expression. We have found that a nonradioactive method has adequate sensitivity to detect expression in individual cultured neurons. The method is essentially that described by Springer *et al.* (16), except for several modifications in the tissue preparation and wash steps. Reagents are available as a kit from Boehringer Mannheim (Indianapolis, IN), which includes detailed technical instructions. An oligodeoxyribonucleotide (usually called an oligonucleotide) complementary to the expressed sequence (and hence able to base pair with the authentic mRNA) is synthesized and end labeled with a 5- to 10-base stretch of a nucleotide derivatized with an antigen not found in nature (digoxigenin-11–dUTP : DNA tailing). This allows the detection of the bound oligonucleotide by antibodies directed against the

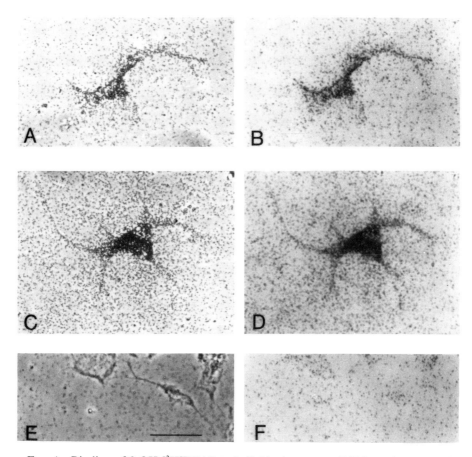

FIG. 1   Binding of 8-OH-[³H]DPAT to individual neurons. E17 frontal cortex cells
were cultured, incubated with 10 n*M* 8-OH-[³H]DPAT, and coated with photographic
emulsion as described in Section 2. Examples of two heavily labeled cells (A and C)
and one unlabeled cell (E) are shown under phase-contrast optics (which reveal both
cell morphologies and silver grains). The same cells are also shown under bright-field
optics (B, D, and F, respectively), which reveals only the silver grains. The majority
of cells were like the ones shown in (E) and (F). Scale bar = 50 μm.

tailed sequence. A convenient negative control is an oligonucleotide identical
to the mRNA (and hence unable to base pair with the expressed mRNA). If
the antibody directed against the antigen is conjugated with the enzyme
alkaline phosphatase, a simple and essentially permanent record of location
can be developed using precipitated dye.

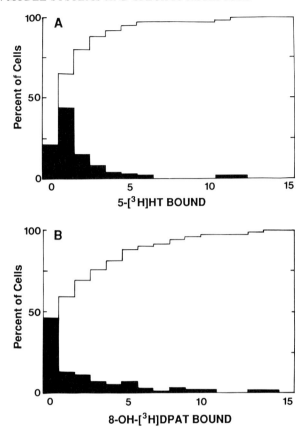

FIG. 2   Distribution of 5-HT$_1$ and 5-HT$_{1A}$ receptors on cultured rat E17 frontal cortical neurons. Each of 250 cells was measured to determine the distributions of total and nonspecific binding (see Section 2 for a description of the technique). The average nonspecific binding was subtracted from each total binding measure to produce the specific binding histogram (solid bars). The cumulative percentage distribution is also shown (line). Binding units are arbitrary and represent about 15 silver grains per unit per square micrometer of cell area. Exposure times were 4 weeks for 5-[^{3}H]HT (A) and 12 weeks for 8-OH-[^{3}H]DPAT (B). Similar results were obtained for E19 cultures with both radioligands (4).

Reagents and Materials (16)

    Genius nonradioactive nucleic acid detection kit (Boehringer Mannheim, Indianapolis, IN) (16), or equivalent DNA tailing kit
    Digoxigenin-11–dUTP (25 nmol)

Labeling Reaction

Antisense (complementary to target rat 5-HT$_{1A}$ mRNA) and sense oligonucleotides (identical to rat 5-HT$_{1A}$ mRNA)

Antisense: 5'-GCGCCCGTAGAGAACCAGCATGAGCAACAG-3'
Sense: 5'-CTGTTGCTCATGCTGGTTCTCTACGGGCGC-3'

Sodium acetate, 4.5 M
Absolute ethanol

Cell Preparation Step

Paraformaldehyde, 3% (w/v)
PBS, 0.1 M (composition given above)
Diethylpyrocarbonate, 0.02% (v/v)

Prehybridization Solution

Deionized formamide	5.0 ml
Sodium citrate saline (SSC), 20×	2.0 ml
Denhardt's solution, 50×	0.2 ml
Salmon sperm DNA, heat denatured (10 mg/ml)	0.5 ml
Yeast tRNA (10 mg/ml)	0.25 ml
Dextran sulfate, 50% (w/v)	2.0 ml
Final volume	9.95 ml

SSC (1×) consists of 150 mM NaCl, 15 mM sodium citrate, pH 7.0. Denhardt's
solution (1×) contains 0.02% (w/v) polyvinylpyrrolidone, 0.02% (w/v) bovine
serum albumin, 0.02% (w/v) Ficoll 400. Salmon sperm DNA must be denatured
immediately before use by heating it in a boiling water bath for 10 min.

Hybridization

Hybridization solution (prepared by diluting the digoxigenin-labeled oligonucleotide probe in prehybridization solution)
SSC, 20×

Immunological Detection

Buffer 1: 100 mM Tris-HCl, 150 mM NaCl, pH 7.5
Buffer 2: 100 mM Tris-HCl, 100 mM NaCl, 50 mM MgCl$_2$, pH 9.5
Buffer 3: 10 mM Tris-HCl, 1 mM ethylenediaminetetraacetic acid
(EDTA), pH 8.0
Normal sheep serum
Triton X-100
Levamisole

Procedure for in Situ Hybridization (1–7)

1. Preparation of 35-mm culture dishes: We use poly(D-lysine)-coated 35-mm culture dishes prepared in the same manner as for the preparation of the primary neuronal culture (Section 1).

2. Preparation of the neuronal culture is done in the same manner as described in Section 1. The only difference is that slightly higher cell densities are used, generally between 50,000 and 80,000 cells/35-mm culture dish.

3. Preparation of neuronal cells for *in situ* hybridization: After 48 hr of culturing in serum medium (composition described in Section 1) at 37°C under 5% CO_2 the medium is removed. Up until this step working conditions have been sterile. Subsequently, sterility of the plates and equipment need not be maintained. The cells are now fixed in 3% (w/v) paraformaldehyde dissolved in 0.1 M PBS at pH 7.4 and containing 0.02% (v/v) diethylpyrocarbonate (DEPC) for 5 min. The DEPC inactivates ribonucleases. The plates are washed with 1 ml of PBS three times, 5 min for each wash, and then incubated in 2× SSC for 10 min.

4. Preparation of probe: Oligonucleotides are end labeled with digoxigenin-11–dUTP by DNA tailing exactly as described (16).

5. The procedure for prehybridization is as follows.
   a. Prepare the prehybridization solution as described above. Salmon sperm DNA is denatured immediately before use by heating it in a boiling water bath for 10 min, then placing on ice until used.
   b. Put the prepared culture dishes in a humid chamber. We use a plastic airtight box with wet paper towels placed in the bottom. Apply 1 ml of the prehybridization solution into each dish. Incubate the cells for 1 hr.

6. The procedure for hybridization is as follows.
   a. The hybridization solution is prepared by diluting the digoxigenin-labeled oligonucleotide probe in prehybridization solution (see step 4 above for preparation of prehybridization solution). Final probe concentration is about 35 nM.
   b. The culture dishes are removed from the incubation chamber and briefly washed with 2× SSC. The SSC is removed and the bottom of the plates divided into two sections, using a marker on the outside of the dish (about 3 mm wide).
   c. Apply 30 μl of hybridization solution per side of culture dish (one-half of the dish is for the antisense oligonucleotide, the other half for the sense oligonucleotide). Cover each half of the culture separately with a piece of Parafilm. Gently flatten the Parafilm until it is completely flat. This is critical to obtain even hybridization of oligonucleotides.
   d. Incubate the culture dishes overnight at 37°C.

e. Elimination of nonspecific hybridization: The hybridization conditions are chosen to maximize hybridization of the antisense probe with the target mRNA. This also allows significant nonspecific hybridization. The specifically hybridized duplex sequences are relatively resistant to denaturation once formed. The nonspecific binding can be selectively removed by washing the culture dishes under increasingly stringent conditions that preferentially favor perfectly matched duplex sequences. A detailed discussion of the variables involved in such processes is beyond the scope of this chapter and the reader is referred to other texts such as that by Sambrook *et al.* (17) for more complete discussions. The final wash condition for the oligonucleotides described above is $1 \times$ SSC, 20 min at 37°C. In practice we usually include several final wash conditions (0.5 to $2 \times$ SSC) to ensure that the greatest discrimination between antisense and sense probes is achieved:

   i. Remove the hybridization solution.
   ii. Add 1 ml $2 \times$ SSC and incubate for 20 min at 37°C.
   iii. Remove the wash solution. Add 1 ml of $1 \times$ SSC and incubate for 20 min at 37°C.
   iv. Remove the wash solution. Add 1 ml of $1 \times$ SSC and incubate for 20 min at room temperature.

7. Detection of dioxigenin-labeled probe with enzyme-linked immunoassay: All steps are done at room temperature. Detection is done with the Genius nonradioactive nucleic acid detection kit (or equivalent).

   a. Remove the final SSC solution and wash the culture dishes for 1 min in buffer 1 (recipe under Reagents and Materials, Immunological Detection).
   b. Incubate culture dishes in buffer 1 containing 2% (v/v) normal sheep serum and 0.3% (w/v) Triton X-100 for 30–60 min to block nonspecific antibody binding.
   c. Dilute anti-digoxigenin antibody conjugate about 1 : 500 with buffer 1 containing 1% (v/v) normal sheep serum and 0.3% (w/v) Triton X-100. Apply 100 μl of diluted anti-digoxigenin antibody solution to the culture dishes, cover with a single piece of Parafilm, and incubate in a humid chamber for 3 hr. The Parafilm must be flat.
   d. Wash the dishes for 10 min with shaking in 1 ml of buffer 1.
   e. Wash the dishes for 10 min with shaking in 2 ml buffer 2 (recipe as described under Immunological Detection above).
   f. Apply 500 μl of color solution. The color solution is made by adding 45 μl Nitro Blue Tetrazolium (NBT) solution, 35 μl X-phosphate solution, and 2.4 mg levamisole to 10 ml of buffer 2. Levamisole inhibits phosphatase activity. Incubate the culture dishes in a humid chamber

in the dark for 2–24 hr. Monitor color development and stop the color reaction by adding 1 ml of buffer 3 (recipe as described under Immuno-logical Detection above) when staining is satisfactory.

g. Dehydrate the cellular preparation in a graded series of ethanol dilu-tions: 70, 80, 95, and 100% ethanol for 1 min each.

h. Preservation of specimens: Following dehydration, the specimens are covered with a drop of glycerol and a glass coverslip applied. The dishes require no special handling but strong sunlight should probably be avoided. We have stored samples on the bench for up to 4 months with no detectable loss of signal. Cultures should be viewed using an inverted microscope.

An example of E17 cultured neuronal cells hybridized with sense and antisense probes to the rat 5-HT$_{1A}$ receptor mRNA is shown in Fig. 3. There is only faint staining with the sense probe (Fig. 3A). In contrast, 80–95% of cells are stained with the antisense proble (Fig. 3C). The original staining is a deep blue color. This is similar to the percentages of neurons that bind ^{3}H-labeled ligands to 5-HT receptors or respond to 8-OH-DPAT stimulation.

4. A Method for Measuring Changes in Neuritic Outgrowth with Stimulation of the 5-HT$_{1A}$ Receptor by 8-OH-DPAT

We have been interested in determining what changes in neuronal morphol-ogy may be a consequence of 5-HT$_{1A}$ receptor stimulation in embryonic neurons. Previous work by Haydon and McCobb has shown that serotonin inhibits growth cone motility of *Helisoma* neurons B19 (18). A decrease in filopodial number and inhibited neuritic elongation were noted.

To investigate the potential effects of 5-HT$_{1A}$ receptor stimulation on mam-malian neuron morphology we have chosen the 5-HT$_{1A}$ receptor agonist 8-OH-DPAT because it is selective for this receptor and is well tolerated by fetal neurons. For morphology experiments we have used primary neuronal cultures plated at low density and grown in serum medium. We have found that 5-HT$_{1A}$ receptor stimulation by 1 μM 8-OH-DPAT significantly inhibits neuritic outgrowth *in vitro* (4). Half-maximal effects are seen at 20–200 nM. For a given experiment to determine changes in neurite growth as a consequence of 5-HT$_{1A}$ receptor stimulation we proceed as follows:

1. Preparation of the primary neuronal culture is done as described in Section 1. For a given morphology experiment three plates per condition are required. The culture plates are coated with poly(D-lysine) as described in

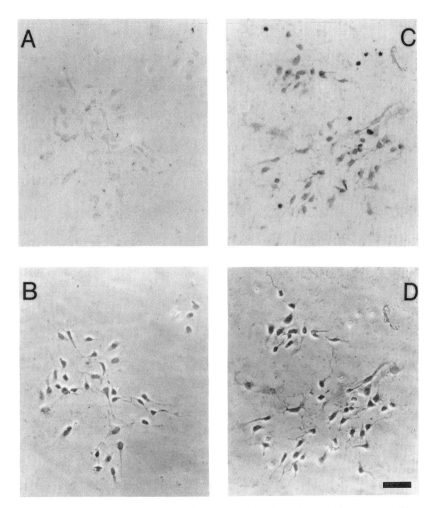

FIG. 3   Localization of 5-HT$_{1A}$-specific mRNA in cultured cortical neurons without the use of a radioactive probe. E17 neurons were cultured for 72 hr, hybridized with digoxigenin-labeled oligonucleotides, washed to a final stringency of $1 \times$ SSC at 37°C, incubated with alkaline phosphatase-conjugated anti-digoxigenin antibody, and color developed for 16 hr. (A) Sense-oligonucleotide (negative control); (B) antisense oligonucleotide. (C) and (D) are phase-contrast photos of the same cells shown in (A) and (B), respectively (to show the positions of unstained cells). Scale bar = 50 μm.

Section 1. The plating density is low at 2.5×10^4–5.0×10^4 cells/35-mm culture dish (25–50 cells/mm^2). Plating at these densities permits morphological analysis of individual cells. The plating medium is 5% (v/v) heat-inactivated serum medium (composition given in Section 1).

2. After 12–24 hr of culture in a humidified incubator at 37°C under 5% CO_2, medium containing 1 nM to 1 mM 8-OH-DPAT is added to one-half of the plates and an equal amount of medium is added to the control plates. Every 12 hr, additional 8-OH-DPAT or medium is added. The 8-OH-DPAT (M_r 328.29) is stored tightly sealed at room temperature. This chemical oxidizes easily, so exposure to room air should be kept to a minimum. Solutions are freshly prepared prior to each addition to the cultures plates, which occurs in a sterile manner. Once in solution in the incubator, 8-OH-DPAT keeps its potency for about 12 hr. Thus, 8-OH-DPAT additions to the cultures need to be done every 12 hr for the duration of the experiment.

3. After an additional 48 hr of culture in the presence of 8-OH-DPAT, phase-contrast photographs (Nikon Inc., Garden City, NY) of living cells are taken using slide film. Figure 4 shows neurons that have been cultured in the absence or presence of 8-OH-DPAT.

Although initially after plating there may be some cell death, neurite growth on viable cells occurs over 5–7 days. The cells, whether or not 8-OH-DPAT treated, appear healthy and elaborate several processes and branches. These processes are first seen after only a few hours in culture. After 2 days in culture many of the cells develop primary neurites that have an average length of 50–60 μm. By 5–7 days a substantial proportion of the cells have become very elaborate and have numerous branches. In these cells, primary neuritic length may reach well over 100 μm. For quantitative analyses, we photograph a total of 100 consecutive cells over two to three plates to avoid sampling bias.

4. We have quantified neurite outgrowth using a Bioquant image analysis system (R and M Biometrics). The Bioquant image analysis system consists of an IBM computer with installed software, a video camera, and a drawing tablet. The video camera is attached to a microscope under which we view slides obtained from photographing the primary embryonic neuronal cultures (final magnification, $\times 1640$). Parameters such as numbers of neurites, number of branch points of the neurites, total neuritic extent (length of all neurites and branches), area of the cell body, and primary neuritic length (length of the longest neurite) may be measured and quantified. The slides are coded so that the condition (i.e., 8-OH-DPAT treated or not) is not known to the person measuring the cells.

Table I shows the results of measuring 2 different control groups of 100 consecutive cells each after the same amount of time (2 days) in culture. As

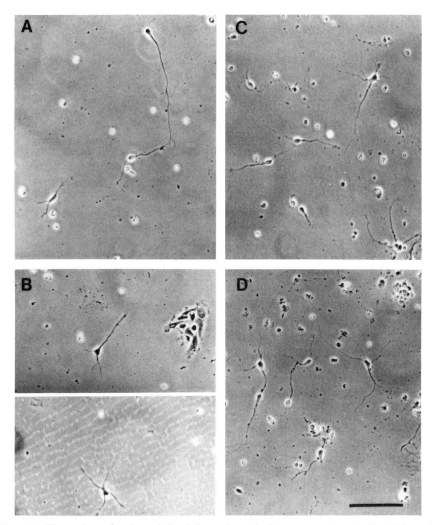

FIG. 4   Examples of cultured fetal frontal cortical neurons (A and C). Cultured neurons prepared from rats of embryonic age E16 (A) and embryonic age E18 (C). The medium is 5% (v/v) fetal bovine serum and the cells were photographed after 60.00 hr (A) and 60.75 hr (C) in culture; (B and D) Cells under embryonic age E16 (B) and cells under embryonic age E18 (D) [prepared from the same specimens as (A) and (C), respectively] are neurons that have been cultured for 60.00 hr (B) and 60.75 hr (D) in 5% (v/v) fetal bovine serum and have been treated with 1 μM 8-OH-DPAT, a selective serotonin 5-HT$_{1A}$ agonist. The 8-OH-DPAT-treated neurons in (B) and (D), compared to the neurons in (A) and (C), have fewer processes branching from the neurites that arise directly from the cell bodies and show a significant inhibition in growth. We have shown this inhibition of growth to be a direct result of 5-HT$_{1A}$ receptor stimulation by this agent (4). Scale bar = 100 μm.

TABLE I   Quantitation of Neurite Outgrowth in Untreated Cells[a]

Group	NN	BP	TNE	Area	PNL
1	2.12 ± 0.01 (SEM)	0.37 ± 0.07	72.38 ± 7.44	75.59 ± 3.17	47.71 ± 5.81
2	2.07 ± 0.10	0.41 ± 0.10	74.18 ± 6.83	71.17 ± 2.69	47.23 ± 4.65

[a] NN, Neurite number (μm); BP, branch points; TNE, total neuritic extent (μm); Area, area of cell soma (μm^2); PNL, primary neuritic extent (μm). Groups 1 and 2 are both control groups. The neuronal cultures were prepared from E16 rat fetal frontal cortexes, and the medium was 5% (v/v) heat-inactivated fetal bovine serum.

expected the results in all parameters are similar and confirm the reliability of measurements obtained by the method described (4).

In Table II typical results of a morphology experiment in which 5-HT$_{1A}$ receptors are stimulated by 8-OH-DPAT are given. As shown in Table II, 8-OH-DPAT-treated cells (group B) have undergone a striking inhibition in the number of branch points, and there is a significant inhibition in total neuritic extent as well. We have found similar results produced by both 5-HT and 8-OH-DPAT over a large number of experiments and have also shown that the inhibition in neurite growth can be completely blocked by the 5-HT$_{1A}$ antagonist spiperone (4). Examples of neuronal cells cultured in the absence and presence of 8-OH-DPAT are given in Fig. 4.

Summary

In this chapter we have detailed procedures that we have found useful in the analysis of 5-HT$_{1A}$ receptor expression and function in primary cultures of cortical neurons. Using these approaches we have documented that the

TABLE II   Results of a Morphology Experiment in Which 5-HT1A Receptors Are Stimulated by 8-OH-DPAT[a]

Group	NN	BP	TNE	Area	PNL
A	3.25 ± 0.09 (SEM)	4.88 ± 0.33	247.70 ± 18.89	94.15 ± 4.56	103.09 ± 9.10
B	2.95 ± 0.10	2.61 ± 0.27	193.36 ± 18.09	91.11 ± 3.52	87.23 ± 8.05

[a] The primary neuronal culture was prepared from E17 rat fetal frontal cortexes. One hundred consecutive cells were photographed after 84 hr in culture and measured as described above in a blinded manner. Group A, control cells; Group B, 1 μM 8-OH-DPAT-treated cells. Abbreviations for the parameters are as for Table I. The differences in the number of branch points, total neuritic extent, and the number of neurites between the control cells and the 8-OH-DPAT-treated cells were statistically significant (Student's t test; $p < 0.05$).

mRNA and protein product of the 5-HT$_{1A}$ receptor gene are expressed in cultured neurons and have demonstrated a novel developmental role for serotonin as a neural morphogen. Using different pharmacological compounds or oligonucleotides to different unique gene sequences, these same procedures should be applicable to the analysis of the developmental roles of other neurotransmitter receptors. We have used this same paradigm to demonstrate that stimulation of dopamine D$_2$ receptors enhances neurite branching and outgrowth (19). Similar studies could be conducted for any receptor that is expressed in cultured cells and for which selective compounds are available.

Acknowledgments

We wish to thank Ms. Nelly Mark for assistance with manuscript preparation.

References

1. J. M. Lauder and H. Krebs, *Dev. Neurosci.* **1,** 15–30 (1978).
2. J. Gonzalez-Heydrich and S. J. Peroutka, *J. Clin. Psychiatry* **51,** 5–18 (1990).
3. D. N. Middlemiss and J. R. Fozard, *Eur. J. Pharmacol.* **90,** 151–153 (1983).
4. L. Sikich, J. M. Hickok, and R. D. Todd, *Dev. Brain Res.* **2,** 269–274 (1990).
5. P. P. Deshmukh, H. I. Yamamura, L. Woods, and D. L. Nelson, *Brain Res.* **288,** 338–343 (1983).
6. D. Verge, G. Daval, A. Patey, H. Gozlan, S. El Mestikawy, and M. Hamon, *Eur. J. Pharmacol.* **113,** 463–464 (1985).
7. P. R. Albert, Q.-Y. Zhou, H. H. M. van Tol, J. R. Bunzow, and O. Civelli, *J. Biol. Chem.* **265,** 5825–5832 (1990).
8. A. Fargin, J. R. Raymond, M. J. Lohse, B. K. Kobilka, M. G. Caron, and R. J. Lefkowitz, *Nature (London)* **335,** 358–360 (1988).
9. F. Libert, M. Parmentier, A. Lefort, C. Dinsart, J. van Sande, C. Maenhaut, M.-J. Simons, J. E. Dumont, and G. Vassart, *Science* **244,** 569–572 (1989).
10. S. J. Peroutka, *in* ''Psychopharmacology: The Third Generation of Progress'' (H. Y. Meltzer, ed.), pp. 305–316. Raven Press, New York, 1987.
11. G. M. B. Fillion, J. Rouselle, M. Fillion, D. M. Beaudoin, M. R. Goiny, J. Deniau, and J. J. Jacob, *Mol. Pharmacol.* **14,** 50–59 (1978).
12. R. D. Todd and J. Babinski, *J. Neurochem.* **49,** 1480–1483 (1987).
13. R. D. Todd and R. D. Ciaranello, *Brain Res.* **400,** 247–258 (1982).
14. N. W. Pedigo, H. I. Yamamura, and D. L. Nelson, *J. Neurochem.* **36,** 220–226 (1981).
15. M. Herkenham and C. B. Pert, *J. Neurosci.* **2,** 1129–1137 (1982).

16. J. E. Springer, E. Robbins, B. J. Gwag, M. E. Lewis, and F. Baldino, Jr., *J. Histochem. Cytochem.* **39,** 231–234 (1991).
17. J. Sambrook, E. F. Fretsch, and T. Maniatis, ''Molecular Cloning,'' 2nd ed. Cold Spring Harbor Press, Cold Spring Harbor, New York, 1989.
18. P. G. Haydon, D. P. McCobb, and S. B. Kater, *Science* **226,** 561–564 (1984).
19. R. D. Todd, *Biol. Psychiatry* (in press) (1992).

[16] Characterization of the Bombesin/Gastrin-Releasing Peptide Receptor in Swiss 3T3 Fibroblasts

Ian Zachary, James Sinnett-Smith, and Enrique Rozengurt

Introduction

Regulatory peptides which act as local hormones or neurotransmitters are increasingly implicated in the control of cell proliferation (1–3). In particular, bombesin and mammalian peptides structurally related to bombesin, including gastrin-releasing peptide (GRP), are potent mitogens for Swiss 3T3 cells (4, 5) and may act as autocrine growth factors for small cell lung carcinoma (6–8). Prior to stimulation of DNA synthesis in 3T3 cells, bombesin and related peptides elicit a set of early responses (3), including enhanced phosphoinositide metabolism (9–11), Ca^{2+} and Na^+ fluxes (11–14), activation of protein kinase C (15–17), and induction of the cellular oncogenes c-*fos* and c-*myc* (18–20). Bombesin also stimulates the release and metabolism of arachidonic acid (21, 22). We reported that bombesin, vasopressin, and endothelin rapidly increase tyrosine and serine phosphorylation of multiple substrates in quiescent Swiss 3T3 cells (23) and stimulate tyrosine kinase activity measured in anti-phosphotyrosine immunoprecipitates of extracts from Swiss 3T3 cells (24). Biochemical studies using permeabilized cells suggest that bombesin acts through signal transduction pathways in which effector stimulation is tightly coupled to activation of a G protein(s) (25, 26).

The characterization of bombesin receptors is an essential step in elucidating the molecular basis of the mitogenic response to peptides of the bombesin family. The bombesin receptor from Swiss 3T3 cells has been cloned (27, 28) and the deduced amino acid sequence demonstrates that it belongs to the superfamily of receptors linked to GTP-binding proteins (G proteins) characterized by seven hydrophobic putative transmembrane domains. However, elucidation of the structure of neuropeptide receptors has not so far yielded information concerning the class (i.e., G_s, G_i, G_o, etc.) or number of G proteins to which they are coupled. In the present chapter we describe the procedures and techniques used for the characterization of receptors for bombesin/GRP in Swiss 3T3 fibroblasts. In particular, we will focus on the methods used to examine the functional association of this receptor to a G protein.

Binding to Intact Cells

Cell Culture

Stock cultures of Swiss 3T3 cells (29) are maintained in Dulbecco's modified Eagle's medium (DMEM) containing 10% (v/v) fetal calf serum (FCS), penicillin (100 U/ml), and streptomycin (100 μg/ml) in humidified 10% CO_2/90% air at 37°C. For experimental purposes cells are subcultured to 33-mm Nunc (Roskilde, Denmark) dishes (10^5 cells/dish) in DMEM containing 10% FCS. After 5–7 days, the cultures are confluent and quiescent as shown by autoradiography (<1% labeled nuclei) after a 40-hr exposure to [^{3}H]thymidine (29).

Radiolabeling of Gastrin-Releasing Peptide and Assay of Biological Activity

Native bombesin cannot be labeled with ^{125}I due to the absence of a tyrosine residue. Gastrin-releasing peptide labeled with ^{125}I at Tyr-15 (^{125}I-GRP) can be obtained commercially or prepared using the soluble lactoperoxidase method as described (30). The labeled peptide is separated from unreacted Na^{125}I on a Sephadex G-25 column (1 × 60 cm); Pharmacia, Piscataway, NJ) preequilibrated (24 hr) and eluted at 4°C with 0.1 M formic acid containing 0.1% (w/v) bovine serum albumin (BSA) and 50 μg/ml aprotinin (30).

Biological activity of ^{125}I-GRP is assayed by determining its ability to stimulate [^{3}H]thymidine incorporation into acid-insoluble material. ^{125}I-GRP stimulated thymidine incorporation in Swiss 3T3 cells within a concentration range similar to that for unlabeled GRP (4).

Binding Assay

For binding at 37°C, confluent and quiescent cultures of Swiss 3T3 cells in 33-mm dishes are washed twice with DMEM and incubated with 1 ml of binding medium (1 : 1, v/v, DMEM, and Waymouth medium supplemented with 1 mg of BSA per milliliter, 50 mM 2-[bis(2-hydroxyethyl)-2-amino] ethanesulfonic acid, pH 7.0), and ^{125}I-GRP at the concentration indicated. After different times of incubation, cultures are washed rapidly four times with cold (4°C) phosphate-buffered saline (PBS: 0.15 M NaCl, 5 mM KCl, 0.02 M Na$_2$HPO$_4$, pH 7.2, supplemented with BSA at 1 mg/ml). Washed cultures are extracted in 0.5 ml of 0.1 M NaOH containing 2% (w/v) Na$_2$CO$_3$ and 1%

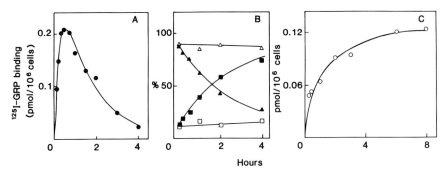

FIG. 1   (A) Time course of [^{125}I]GRP binding to Swiss 3T3 cells at 37°C. Confluent and quiescent cultures of 3T3 cells were washed and incubated with [^{125}I]GRP (1 nM). After various times cells were washed, extracted, and cell-associated radioactivity was determined. Each point represents the mean of duplicate determinations. (B) Degradation of [^{125}I]GRP by Swiss 3T3 cells. Cultures were incubated with 1 nM [^{125}I]GRP either at 37°C (closed symbols) or at 4°C (open symbols). After various times the medium was removed and the relative amounts of [^{125}I]GRP (triangles) and [^{125}I]tyrosine (squares) were measured by chromatography on Sep-Pak C18 cartridges as described (31). Each point represents a composite of three experiments. (C) Time course of [^{125}I]GRP binding to Swiss 3T3 cells at 4°C. Cells are washed once with DME medium at 4°C and incubated at 4°C for 5 min prior to the binding assay. The binding assay at 4°C is performed in 0.14 M NaCl/5 mM KCl/0.01 M Na$_2$HPO$_4$/1.8 mM KH$_2$PO$_4$/1.8 mM CaCl$_2$/1 mM MgCl$_2$/25 mM HEPES, pH 7.0, supplemented with BSA at 1 mg/ml. Confluent cultures were incubated in this medium supplemented with 1 nM [^{125}I]GRP at 4°C for various times. Other experimental details are described in text. Each point represents the mean of two determinations.

(w/v) sodium dodecyl sulfate (SDS) and total cell-associated radioactivity determined in a γ counter. Nonspecific binding, defined as the cell-associated radioactivity not displaced in the presence of either bombesin or GRP at 1 μM, is directly proportional to the concentration of ^{125}I-GRP and varied from 23% of total binding at the highest concentrations (3 nM) of ^{125}I-GRP to 5% at low concentrations (0.05 nM). Figure 1A shows the time course of ^{125}I-GRP binding to Swiss 3T3 cells at 37°C. Binding is rapid and reaches a maximum after 30 min. The marked decline in binding after this time is primarily due to rapid internalization of receptor–ligand complexes and subsequent degradation of the ligand, as shown by the release of ^{125}I-labeled tyrosine (Fig. 1B) (31). The inhibition of ^{125}I-GRP degradation by weak bases suggests that ligand degradation occurs via a lysosomal patheay (31). In contrast, binding occurs more slowly at 4°C and the rates of both ligand internalization and degradation are markedly reduced (Fig. 1B and C).

Characterization of Bombesin Receptor in Membranes

Studies in membranes permit analysis of ^{125}I-GRP binding under equilibrium conditions, and hence the derivative of constants of association, dissociation, and equilibrium dissociation.

Membrane fractions of Swiss 3T3 cells prepared according to procedures used for other growth factor receptors failed to exhibit any consistent specific binding of ^{125}I-GRP (32). However, addition of Mg^{2+} (5 mM) during the homogenization of the cells as well as during the binding assay resulted in a striking increase in the specific binding of ^{125}I-GRP to membranes (32). $MnCl_2$ at 2.5 mM only partially substituted for $MgCl_2$ (30% of maximum binding) whereas $CaCl_2$ had no effect. $MgSO_4$ was as effective as $MgCl_2$. Specific ^{125}I-GRP binding as a function of membrane concentration was linear up to 50 μg protein.

Membrane Preparation

For the preparation of membranes, 3×10^6 cells are subcultured into 1850-cm^2 Falcon (Becton Dickinson, Oxnard, CA) roller bottles with 200 ml of the same culture medium and are grown to confluence without a change of medium for 6–7 days. The final cell density is 3×10^7 cells/flask. The cultures are washed twice with 150 ml PBS at room temperature and harvested at 4°C by scraping into ice-cold PBS containing 5 mM $MgCl_2$, 1 mM [ethylenebis(oxyethylenenitrilo)]tetraacetic acid (EGTA), 1 mg/ml bacitracin, 10 μg/ml aprotonin, 1 mg/ml soybean trypsin inhibitor, and 50 μM phenylmethylsulfonyl fluoride (PMSF). All subsequent steps are carried out at 4°C. The cells are pelleted by centrifugation at 750 g for 10 min and resuspended at 5×10^6/ml in solution A [50 mM 4-(2-hydroxyethyl)-1-piperazine-2-ethanesulfonic acid (HEPES), 5 mM $MgCl_2$, 1 mM EGTA, 1 mg/ml bacitracin, 10 μg/ml aprotonin, 1 mg/ml soybean trypsin inhibitor, and 50 μM PMSF, adjusted to pH 7.4 with NaOH at 4°C]. Cells are disrupted using a Dounce (Wheaton, Millville, NJ) homogenizer (A pestle; 75 strokes) and nuclear material and intact cells removed by centrifugation at 500 g for 10 min. The supernatant is then centrifuged again at 30,000 g for 30 min and the resulting membrane-enriched pellet resuspended at a protein concentration of 5 to 10 mg/ml in solution A and stored in liquid nitrogen. For experiments, membranes are thawed and diluted to a concentration of 1 mg/ml with solution A. Protein concentration in the membrane preparations is measured by the method of Bradford (33), using bovine serum albumin as the protein standard.

Receptor-Binding Assay

Binding assays are carried out in a total volume of 100 μl in binding medium containing 50 mM HEPES, 5 mM MgCl$_2$, 1 mg/ml bacitracin, and 1% (w/v) BSA, adjusted to pH 7.4 with NaOH, unless otherwise indicated. The assays contained 25 μg of membrane protein plus 85,000–125,000 cpm of ^{125}I-GRP (0.5 nM) plus the reagents specified in the individual experiments. Nonspecific binding (5–10% of the total binding) is subtracted from total binding to obtain specific binding. Equilibrium binding is obtained by incubation for either 10 min at 37°C or 30 min at 15°C.

Binding reactions are terminated by rapid filtration on GF/B glass fiber filters (1.0 μm pore size; Whatman, Clifton, NJ) that have been presoaked for 24 hr in 5% polyethyleneimine at 4°C and washed with 5 ml of PBS containing 1% (w/v) BSA immediately prior to use. Each filter is washed five times with 5 ml of PBS containing 1% BSA at 4°C (total time, 15 sec) using a Millipore (Bedford, MA) filtration apparatus. Identical results are obtained when the assays are terminated by centrifugation for 1 min at 14,000 rpm in an MSE (Fisons, U.K.) microfuge at 4°C followed by three 1.0-ml washes with PBS containing 1.0% BSA. The recovery of measurable binding sites in the membrane preparation expressed as a percentage of total sites determined in intact 3T3 cells is approximately 50%. The specific binding activity increases from 204 ± 30 fmol/mg protein in the intact cells to 564 ± 50 fmol/mg protein in the membrane preparation.

Scatchard analysis of equilibrium binding data gave a K_d of 2.1 × 10^{-10} M (Fig. 2a). This is in excellent agreement with the apparent K_d of 1.9 × 10^{-10} M (5) obtained from rate constants of association (k_1; Fig. 2b) (34) and dissociation (k_2; Fig. 2c).

Affinity Cross-Linking of ^{125}I-Labeled Gastrin-Releasing Peptide

Bombesin/GRP receptors are chemically cross-linked to their ligand by incubating Swiss 3T3 cells that have been prebound with ^{125}I-GRP with homobifunctional cross-linking reagents. Although this can be achieved using a variety of different agents, including ethylene glycolbis(succinimidyl succinate) (EGS), disuccinimidyl suberate (DSS), dithobis(succinimidyl propionate) (DSP) and bis[2-(succimidooxycarbamylethyl] (BSCOES), we consistently found that EGS was the most efficient reagent for labeling this receptor. The rank order of efficiency (EGS > DSS > DSP > BSCOES) may be related to the chain length of the arms of these bifunctional molecules.

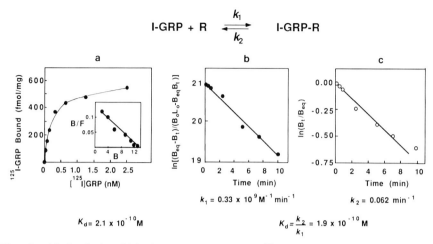

FIG. 2 (a) Analysis of binding as a function of ^{125}I-GRP concentration to Swiss 3T3 membranes. Membranes were incubated in the presence of various concentrations of ^{125}I-GRP at 15°C. Specific binding was determined after 30 min at 15°C using 25 μg of membrane protein. Nonspecific binding was measured by the additon of at least 1000-fold excess unlabeled bombesin or 1 μM bombesin for concentrations of ^{125}I GRP below 1 nM. Binding reactions were terminated by rapid filtration on glass fiber filters. *Inset:* Scatchard analysis of the data. (b) Semilogarithmic plot of the time course of ^{125}I-GRP association to Swiss 3T3 membranes. ^{125}I-GRP (0.5 nM) was incubated with 25 μg of membrane protein in 100 μl of binding medium at 15°C for the indicated times. Time was plotted on the abscissa and $\ln[(B_{eq} - B_t)/(B_o L_o - B_{eq}B_t)]$ was plotted on the ordinate. The initial concentration of free receptors (B_o) was estimated from the Scatchard analysis (a) to be 0.137 nM. The equilibrium concentration of occupied receptors (B_{eq}) was taken as 0.095 nM, that obtained after 30 min. The initial ligand concentration, L_o, was 0.5 nM. The slope of the linear regression line through the initial points (0 to 8 min) gives the second-order association rate constant k_1 according to relationship k_1 = slope $\times$ $(B_{eq}/B_{eq}^2 - B_o L_o)$. Derivation of the equation is presented by Maelicke *et al.* (34). (C) Semilogarithmic plot of the time course of ^{125}I-GRP dissociation from Swiss 3T3 membranes. Membranes were incubated with ^{125}I-GRP (0.5 nM) in 100 μl of binding medium at 15°C for 30 min. Excess bombesin (1 μM) was then added to each tube, and ^{125}I-GRP-specific binding was determined at the indicated times. Time was plotted on the abscissa and $\ln(B_t/B_{eq})$ was plotted on the ordinate. The slope of the line gave the first-order rate constant (k_2).

The procedure for intact cells is as follows. Confluent and quiescent cultures of Swiss 3T3 cells are incubated at 15°C in 1 ml of binding medium (as described for binding at 4°C in the caption to Fig. 1C) supplemented with 1 nM ^{125}I-GRP in the presence or absence of 1 μM unlabeled GRP. After 2.5 hr the cells are washed three times at 15°C with PBS and then incubated for 15 min at 15°C in 1 ml of binding medium, pH 7.4, in the presence of 4 mM EGS. EGS is dissolved in dimethyl sulfoxide immediately prior to use and added to medium to give a final concentration of dimethyl sulfoxide of 1–2% (v/v). The cultures are rapidly rinsed twice with PBS at 4°C and solubilized in 0.1 ml of 2× sample buffer [0.2 M Tris-HCl, pH 6.8, 10% (w/v) glycerol, 6% SDS (w/v), 4% (v/v) 2-mercaptoethanol, and 2 mM ethylenediaminetetraacetic acid]. Samples are immediately heated at 100°C for 3–5 min and analyzed by either one or two-dimensional gel electrophoresis.

For affinity labeling of the receptor in membranes, membrane protein (150 μg) from Swiss 3T3 cells as described above is incubated at 30 or 15°C for 10 or 30 min, respectively, in 500 μl of cross-linking medium (50 mM HEPES, 5 mM MgCl$_2$, 1 mg/ml bacitracin, pH 7.4) containing 0.5 nM ^{125}I-GRP. Bovine serum albumin was omitted from all solutions used in the cross-linking studies. At the end of the incubation the membranes are centrifuged at 14,000 rpm for 1 min in a microfuge at room temperature. The pellets are then resuspended in cross-linking medium containing 4 mM EGS and incubated at 37 or 15°C for 5 or 15 min, respectively. The reaction is terminated by centrifugation for 1 min followed by one wash with cross-linking medium and centrifugation. Samples are solubilized in 200 μl of 2× sample buffer, immediately heated to 100°C for 10 min, and analyzed by one-dimensional electrophoresis.

Both in intact cells and membranes the affinity-labeled bombesin/GRP receptor migrates as a single major band of M_r 75,000–85,000 (30, 35, 36). As shown in Fig. 3, the addition of unlabeled GRP to the incubation of membranes with radiolabeled ligand decreased the affinity labeling of this band in a concentration-dependent manner. The broad, diffuse appearance of the M_r 75,000–85,000 band is characteristic of heterogeneity in molecular weight resulting from glycosylation (Fig. 3) (30, 35, 36). This possibility was substantiated by chromatography on wheat germ lectin-Sepharose and treatment of the affinity-labeled receptor with endo-β-N-acetylglucosaminidase F (endo F), which cleaves N-linked oligosaccharides from glycoproteins (35). Treatment with endo F reduced the M_r 75,000–85,000 affinity-labeled band to a core polypeptide of M_r 43,000 (35, 36). This result is consistent with the cloning of the cDNA for the bombesin receptor, which predicts a protein of 43,200 Da with three potential N-linked glycosylation sites (27, 28).

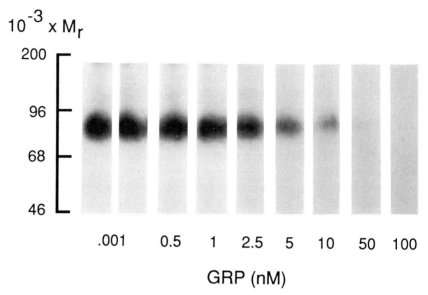

FIG. 3   Affinity labeling of the bombesin/GRP receptor with the homobifunctional cross-linking agent EGS. Membranes prepared from Swiss 3T3 cells were incubated with 0.5 nM ^{125}I-GRP at 37°C for 10 min in the presence of unlabeled GRP at the concentrations indicated. Chemical cross-linking using EGS (4 mM) and analysis of samples by SDS-PAGE were carried out as described in text.

Solubilization of Bombesin/Gastrin-Releasing Peptide Receptors

The molecular and regulatory characterization of plasma membrane receptors requires a procedure for their solubilization in a functional state. This involves solubilization from Swiss 3T3 membranes prebound with ^{125}I-GRP followed by separation of unbound free ^{125}I-GRP from ligand–receptor complexes by gel filtration (37). ^{125}I-GRP–receptor complexes are solubilized from membranes by using the detergents taurodeoxycholate (TDOC) or deoxycholate (DOC). A variety of other detergents, including Triton X-100, octylglucoside, dodecyl-β-D-maltoside, digitonin, cholate, and CHAPS, are much less effective than either TDOC or DOC in promoting ^{125}I-GRP–receptor solubilization.

Membranes (0.8–1 mg) are incubated with 1 ml of binding medium (defined under Receptor-Binding Assay, above) containing 0.5 nM ^{125}I-GRP at 37°C for 10 min. Following centrifugation at 16,000 g for 30 min to remove unbound ^{125}I-GRP, the pellet is resuspended at 4°C in 250 μl of solubilization buffer consisting of 30 mM HEPES (pH 7.4), 5 mM MgCl$_2$, 0.25 M sucrose, 10%

(v/v) glycerol, 1 mg/ml bacitracin, 10 μg/ml aprotonin, and 0.5% TDOC. The optimum detergent concentration is dependent on the detergent-to-protein ratios; a lower TDOC concentration (0.15%) is required for maximum solubilization in the presence of lower membrane protein. After 30 min at 4°C, the solubilized proteins are separated from nonextractable membrane material by centrifugation for 1 hr at 100,000 g.

^{125}I-GRP associated with macromolecular components is separated from any free ^{125}I-GRP by gel filtration on a Sephadex G-100 column (20 $\times$ 1 cm; Pharmacia). The column is equilibrated and eluted at 4°C with 30 mM HEPES, pH 7.4, containing 5 mM MgCl$_2$, 1% (w/v) BSA, and 0.1% (w/v) TDOC. Fractions of 0.5 ml are collected at a flow rate of 7 ml/hr and radioactivity is determined. Specific solubilized counts are in each case the difference between the total counts in the fractions representing the complex (typically 12, 13, and 14; see Fig. 4) obtained in the absence of bombesin during prelabeling and the total counts of the corresponding fractions from an identical column obtained in the presence of 1 μM bombesin during prelabeling. The percentage of solubilization is then calculated with respect to the total specific binding of ^{125}I-GRP to equivalent amounts of membranes, determined as described previously. The results of a typical experiment are shown in Fig. 4. A sharp peak of radioactivity is eluted in the void volume while the remaining radioactivity coelutes with free ^{125}I-GRP, indicating that only a partial dissociation of the solubilized ligand–receptor complex occurs during the chromatographic separation (Fig. 4A). This procedure results in the solubilization of 46.3 $\pm$ 2.7% ($n = 10$) of the available receptors in the intact membranes. A similar chromatographic profile is obtained when 0.5% DOC is used instead of TDOC (Fig. 4B). In each case, the sharp peak of radioactivity eluting in the void volume of the G-100 column is abolished by adding an excess of unlabeled bombesin (or GRP) together with ^{125}I-GRP during the labeling of the membrane. In this case, the radioactivity elutes in the position of free ^{125}I-GRP (Fig. 4A and B).

When membranes are treated with TDOC and the solubilized material is incubated with 1 nM ^{125}I-GRP for 30 min at 37°C prior to chromatography, no peak of specifically bound radioactivity is eluted in the void volume of the column (Fig. 4C). This indicates that TDOC and DOC extract a ligand–receptor complex formed on intact membranes prior to detergent solubilization and rules out the possibility that ^{125}I-GRP becomes bound to nonspecific macromolecular components such as mixed micelles present in the elution buffer. When the peak of radioactivity that elutes in the void volume (Fig. 4D, inset) is incubated at 37°C for 60 min and then rechromatographed, the radioactivity is markedly shifted to the position of free ^{125}I-GRP (Fig. 4D), indicating dissociation of the ligand–receptor complex.

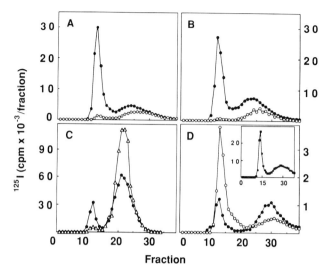

FIG. 4   Gel-filtration profiles of solubilized ^{125}I-GRP-receptor complexes (A and B). Swiss 3T3 membranes (0.9 mg) were incubated in binding medium for 10 min at 37°C with ^{125}I-GRP (0.5 nM) in the absence (closed symbols) and presence (open symbols) of 10 μM bombesin. After centrifugation, the membranes were solubilized with 0.5% TDOC (A) or 0.5% DOC (B) at a final protein concentration of 4 mg/ml. The supernatant (200 μl) obtained was analyzed by gel filtration. Typically, Blue Dextran 2000 eluted in fractions 12 and 13 whereas free ^{125}I-GRP eluted between fractions 20 and 26. (C) Solubilization of ^{125}I-GRP-receptor complexes occurred when the ligand was prebound to the membrane receptor prior to detergent extraction. Swiss 3T3 membranes (1 mg) were incubated in the binding medium in the absence (triangles) or presence (circles) of ^{125}I-GRP (0.5 nM), for 10 min at 37°C. The membranes were immediately solubilized without centrifugation in 0.5% TDOC for 30 min at 4°C. Following removal of nonextractable material by centrifugation, the supernatant of the nonprelabeled membranes (triangles) was incubated with 1 nM ^{125}I-GRP at 37°C for 1 hr. The samples (200 μl) were then applied and eluted from Sephadex G-100 columns. In the presence of 10 μM bombesin, the profiles (omitted for clarity) were similar to the nonprelabeled membranes. (D) Dissociation of the ^{125}I-GRP-receptor complex at 4°C or 37°C. Swiss 3T3 membranes (1 mg) prelabeled with ^{125}I-GRP, were solubilized with 0.5% DOC (at 4 mg protein/ml) and applied to a Sephadex G-100 column. The fractions corresponding to the ^{125}I-GRP–receptor complex (12 and 13) were pooled (*insert*). Half this pool was maintained at 4°C (open circles) and half incubated at 37°C for 1 hr (closed circles). Then both samples were applied to identical Sephadex G-100 columns, and eluted as described in the section, Solubilization of Bombesin/Gastrin-Releasing Peptide Receptors.

Demonstration of Functional Association of the Bombesin/Gastrin-Releasing Peptide Receptor with a G Protein

Susceptibility of the solubilized ligand–receptor complex to regulation by guanine nucleotides provides a crucial test for functional association of the receptor with a G protein. The choice of detergent is especially important here. Unoccupied bombesin receptor solubilized using a mixture of CHAPS and cholesterol hemisuccinate (38) failed to exhibit regulation by guanine nucleotide (39). Functional association of bombesin/GRP receptors solubilized using TDOC with a G protein is examined in the following way. Fractions eluting in the void volume of a G-100 column and containing the ligand–receptor complex are pooled and then incubated in the absence or in the presence of increasing concentrations of the nonhydrolyzable GTP analog, GTPγS, for 30 min at 37°C. Bound ^{125}I-GRP is separated from dissociated ligand by spun-column chromatography as follows. Aliquots (50–100 μl) of solubilized receptors are applied to 1-ml syringes packed with Sephadex G-100 equilibrated in 30 mM HEPES, pH 7.4, 5 mM MgCl$_2$, 1% (w/v) BSA followed by centrifugation at 1000 g for 1 min. The columns are then washed by centrifugation (1000 g, 1 min) with 200 μl 30 mM HEPES, pH 7.4, 5 mM MgCl$_2$ and the radioactivity in the total elution volume determined. As shown in Fig. 5A, GTPγS causes a dose-dependent decrease in the level of ^{125}I-GRP–receptor complex. Half-maximal and maximal effects are achieved at 0.12 and 10 μM, respectively. The specificity of this effect is shown in Fig. 5B. Addition of either GMP, ATP, or ATPγS at 100 μ has no detectable effect on the stability of the solubilized ^{125}I-GRP–receptor complex whereas either GTPγS or GTP causes a 50% reduction in the level of bound ^{125}I-GRP in parallel samples. Similar results are obtained when the separation of bound from unbound ^{125}I-GRP is carried out by rechromatography on Sephadex G-100 columns instead of by spun-column chromatography.

Affinity Chromatography and Reconstitution into Phospholipid Vesicles

This section describes an affinity chromatographic procedure to isolate the bombesin receptor from Swiss 3T3 cell membranes using biotinylated [Lys^3]-bombesin (BLB) bound to the receptor prior to detergent solubilization (40).

Biotinylation of [Lys^3]Bombesin

Sulfosuccinimidyl 6-(biotinamido)hexanoate (NHS-LC-biotin; 60 μmol) is added to a solution of [Lys^3]bombesin (12 μmol) in 10 ml of 100 mM HEPES,

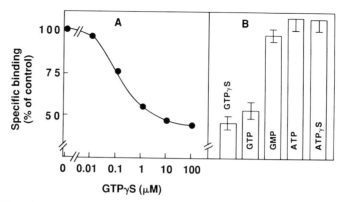

FIG. 5   GTPγS promotes dissociation of ^{125}I-GRP from solubilized ^{125}I-GRP-receptor complexes in a concentration-dependent (A) and specific (B) manner. Swiss 3T3 membranes (2×1.0 mg) were labeled with ^{125}I-GRP (0.5 nM) in binding medium at 37°C for 10 min, solubilized with 0.5% DOC, and chromatographed on two identical Sephadex G-100 columns. Fractions containing the solubilized ^{125}I-GRP receptor were then pooled. Aliquots (50–100 μl) were incubated at 37°C for 30 min either in the absence or presence of GTPγS at the indicated concentrations (A) or the specified nucleotides as indicated, all at 100 μM (B). Dissociated free ^{125}I-GRP was separated from the ^{125}I-GRP-receptor complex by spin-column chromatography. The results are expressed as the percentage of ^{125}I-GRP that remained bound to the receptor-complex with respect to the control. The data represent the means ± SEM; $n = 6$. Other experimental details are described in text.

pH 7.4. The solution is stirred for 1 hr, after which time the reaction is terminated with 20 μl ethanolamine. The products are chromatographed on a BioGel (Bio-Rad, Richmond, CA) P2 column (2.5×65 cm) equilibrated and eluted with 1% (v/v) acetic acid (0.16 M). Fractions of the main peak of ultraviolet (UV) absorption at 280 nm (fractions 33–37; 5 ml/fraction) are collected, lyophilized, and dissolved in distilled H$_2$O. Further purification of the [Lys^3]bombesin is achieved using fast protein liquid chromatography (FPLC) on a Pep RPC IIR5/5 column (Pharmacia). BLB is eluted by a gradient of 0.1% (v/v) trifluoroacetic acid in water (solvent · system A) and 0.1% trifluoracetic acid in 99.9% acetonitrile (solvent system B, 10–40%) for 33 min at a flow rate of 0.7 ml/min. The [Lys^3]bombesin and BLB elute at 28 and 31.5% of solvent B, respectively. BLB retains biological activity as judged by its ability to cause a dose-dependent increase in [Ca^{2+}] and stimulates DNA synthesis as effectively as [Lys^3]bombesin (39).

Affinity Chromatography of the Bombesin Receptor

Membranes (40–400 mg) are incubated in 8–80 ml of binding medium in the presence of either 100 nM BLB or 100 nM bombesin for 15 min at 37°C and then in the presence of 1% (v/v) TDOC. Solubilized material is then incubated with 10–100 mg of streptavidin-coated magnetic beads (Dynal beads) at 4°C for 1 hr. Following this incubation the beads are separated from the supernatant with a magnet (MPC-1, Dynal, U.K.) and washed five times with solubilization buffer containing 0.33% TDOC at 4°C. The bound proteins are eluted by one of the following methods: (1) Total bound proteins are eluted with 100 μl 2× sample buffer. (2) Acid-dissociable proteins are eluted by incubating the beads with 100 μl of 30 mM HEPES, pH 5.0, containing 0.1% TDOC, 5 mM MgCl$_2$, 1 mM leupeptin, and 50 μM PMSF, for 30 min at 4°C. (3) Dissociable proteins at an increased temperature are eluted by incubating the beads in 1 ml 30 mM HEPES containing 0.33% TDOC, 5 mM MgCl$_2$, 1 mM leupeptin, and 50 μM PMSF, pH 7.4, at 28°C for 30 min. The eluted proteins produced by methods 1 and 2 are analyzed by SDS-polyacrylamide gel electrophotoresis (PAGE) and the eluate from method 3 assayed for ^{125}I-GRP-binding activity after reconstitution into phospholipid vesicles as described below.

Reconstitution of Affinity-Chromatographed Bombesin Receptor into Phospholipid Vesicles

Phospholipid vesicles were prepared from α-lecithin (70 mg/ml) either by sonication for 30 min (41) or by freeze/thaw fracture and extrusion through 0.4-μm nylon filters (42). If the protein differentially extracted by BLB is in fact the bombesin receptor, it should be possible to demonstrate ^{125}I-GRP-binding activity to reconstituted phospholipid vesicles provided the receptor is not denatured during the elution. The rate of dissociation of ^{125}I-GRP from either membranes or receptor-solubilized preparations is strikingly enhanced by an increase in temperature (e.g., from 4 to 30°C) at neutral pH (32, 37). Consequently, solubilized BLB–receptor complexes bound to streptavidin-coated beads are incubated at 28°C for 30 min in the presence of 0.33% TDOC to dissociate bombesin receptors from the immobilized complexes (method 3 of the previous section). The soluble bombesin receptors are reconstituted into the phospholipid vesicles by mixing equal volumes (1 ml) of phospholipid vesicles and affinity eluate together with 50 μg/ml BSA as carrier, followed by removal of the TDOC using an Extracti-gel D (Pierce, U.K.) column (1 × 1 cm), equilibrated and eluted with 30 mM HEPES, 5 mM MgCl$_2$, pH 7.4.

The determination of ^{125}I-GRP binding to reconstituted bombesin receptor is performed as follows: aliquots (100 μl) of reconstituted eluate containing 0.2% BSA, 1 mg/ml bacitracin, and 10 μg/ml aprotonin are incubated with 1 nM ^{125}I-GRP at 22°C for 30 min. At the end of the incubation ^{125}I-GRP associated with macromolecular components is separated by spun-column chromatography (see above) and the radioactivity in the total elution volume is then determined.

Summary

The discovery that bombesin and other neuropeptides are potent cellular growth factors not only has important physiological and pathological implications (1–3), but has also provided a valuable approach to elucidating the molecular mechanisms leading to cell proliferation. In particular, it is now evident that proliferative responses can be initiated through G protein signal transduction pathways. Identification of the G protein(s) coupled to the bombesin/GRP receptor remains a major challenge. Indeed, while a growing number of receptors for neuropeptides have been cloned, the specificities of the G protein–receptor relationship are only beginning to be clarified. The present chapter has focused on some of the techniques that are most relevant to achieve this aim. Direct evidence for a functional association of the bombesin receptor with a G protein(s) has come from biochemical studies using permeabilized cells (25, 26), membrane preparations (see above), and ^{125}I-GRP–receptor complexes solubilized from cell membranes (see Solubilization of Bombesin/Gastrin-Releasing Peptide Receptors). These studies demonstrate that bombesin acts through signal transduction pathways in which effector stimulation is tightly coupled to activation of a G protein. Recently, Gq has been identified as the G protein that couples receptors to activation of phospholipase C (43–45). In view of the complex array of events stimulated by peptides of the bombesin family in Swiss 3T3 cells (see Introduction), it is unclear whether a single G protein is responsible for receptor coupling to multiple effector systems. Mutational analysis of the bombesin receptor will help to define whether the receptor activates multiple signaling pathways through one or more G proteins. However, the reconstitution of the purified receptor into phospholipid vesicles together with other purified components will be crucial to unambiguously elucidate the molecular nature of the G protein(s) that participate in the transduction of the mitogenic signal.

References

1. I. Zachary, P. Woll, and E. Rozengurt, *Dev. Biol.* **124,** 295 (1987).
2. P. J. Woll and E. Rozengurt, *Br. Med. Bull.* **45,** 492 (1989).
3. E. Rozengurt, *Eur. J. Clin. Invest.* **21,** 123 (1991).
4. I. Zachary and E. Rozengurt, *Proc. Natl. Acad. Sci. U.S.A.* **82,** 7616 (1985).
5. E. Rozengurt and J. Sinnett-Smith, *Philos. Trans. R. Soc. London, Ser. B* **327,** 209 (1990).
6. F. Cuttitta, D. N. Carney, J. Mulshine, T. W. Moody, J. Fedorko, A. Fischler, and J. D. Minna, *Nature (London)* **316,** 823 (1985).
7. T. Sethi and E. Rozengurt, *Cancer Res.* **51,** 3621 (1991).
8. T. Sethi, S. Langdon, J. Smyth, and E. Rozengurt, *Cancer Res.* **52,** 2737s (suppl.) (1992).
9. J. P. Heslop, D. M. Blakeley, K. D. Brown, R. F. Irvine, and M. J. Berridge, *Cell (Cambridge, Mass.)* **47,** 703 (1986).
10. N. Takuwa, Y. Takuwa, W. E. Bollag, and H. Rasmussen, *J. Biol. Chem.* **262,** 182 (1987).
11. E. Nånberg and E. Rozengurt, *EMBO J.* **7,** 2741 (1988).
12. S. A. Mendoza, J. A. Schneider, A. Lopez-Rivas, J. W. Sinnett-Smith, and E. Rozengurt, *J. Cell Biol.* **102,** 2223 (1986).
13. A. Lopez-Rivas, S. A. Mendoza, E. Nånberg, J. Sinnett-Smith, and E. Rozengurt, *Proc. Natl. Acad. Sci. U.S.A.* **84,** 5768 (1987).
14. E. Rozengurt and S. A. Mendoza, *Curr. Top. Memb. Transp. (L. Mandel and D. Benos, eds.)* **27,** 163 (1986).
15. I. Zachary, J. W. Sinnett-Smith, and E. Rozengurt, *J. Cell Biol.* **102,** 2211 (1986).
16. C. M. Isacke, J. Meisenhelder, K. D. Brown, K. L. Gould, S. J. Gould, and T. Hunter, *EMBO J.* **5,** 2889 (1986).
17. A. Rodriguez-Peña, I. Zachary, and E. Rozengurt, *Biochem. Biophys. Res. Commun.* **140,** 379 (1986).
18. E. Rozengurt and J. Sinnett-Smith, *J. Cell. Physiol.* **131,** 218 (1987).
19. E. Rozengurt and J. Sinnett-Smith, *Prog. Nucleic Acid Res. Mol. Biol.* **35,** 261 (1988).
20. H. Mehmet, J. B. A. Millar, W. Lehmann, T. Higgins, and E. Rozengurt, *Exp. Cell Res.* **190,** 265 (1990).
21. J. B. A. Millar and E. Rozengurt, *J. Biol. Chem.* **265,** 12052 (1990).
22. J. B. A. Millar and E. Rozengurt, *Proc. Natl. Acad. Sci. U.S.A.* **86,** 3204 (1989).
23. I. Zachary, J. Gil, W. Lehmann, J. Sinnett-Smith and E. Rozengurt, *Proc. Natl. Acad. Sci. U.S.A.* **88,** 4577 (1991).
24. I. Zachary, J. Sinnett-Smith, and E. Rozengurt, *J. Biol. Chem.* **266,** 24126 (1991).
25. J. D. Erusalimksy, I. Friedberg, and E. Rozengurt, *J. Biol. Chem.* **263,** 19188 (1988).
26. J. D. Erusalimsky and E. Rozengurt, *J. Cell. Physiol.* **141,** 253 (1989).
27. J. F. Battey, J. M. Way, M. H. Corjay, H. Shapira, K. Kusano, R. Harkins, J. M. Wu, T. Slattery, E. Mann, and R. I. Feldman, *Proc. Natl. Acad. Sci. U.S.A.* **88,** 395 (1991).

28. E. R. Spindel, E. Giladi, P. Brehm, R. H. Goodman, and T. P. Segerson, *Mol. Endocrinol.* **4,** 1956 (1990).
29. P. Dicker and E. Rozengurt, *Nature (London)* **287,** 607 (1980).
30. I. Zachary and E. Rozengurt, *J. Biol. Chem.* **262,** 3947 (1987).
31. I. Zachary and E. Rozengurt, *EMBO J.* **6,** 2233 (1987).
32. J. Sinnett-Smith, W. Lehmann, and E. Rozengurt, *Biochem. J.* **265,** 485 (1990).
33. M. Bradford, *Anal. Biochem.* **72,** 248 (1976).
34. A. Maelicke, W. Fulpius, R. P. Klett, and E. Reid, *J. Biol. Chem.* **252,** 4811 (1977).
35. J. Sinnett-Smith, I. Zachary, and E. Rozengurt, *J. Cell. Biochem.* **38,** 237 (1988).
36. R. M. Kris, R. Hazan, J. Villines, T. W. Moody, and J. Schlessinger, *J. Biol. Chem.* **262,** 11215 (1987).
37. A. Coffer, I. Fabregat, J. Sinnett-Smith, and E. Rozengurt, *FEBS Lett.* **263,** 80 (1990).
38. L. Naldini, D. Cirillo, T. W. Moody, P. M. Comoglio, J. Schlessinger, and R. Kris, *Biochemistry* **29,** 5133 (1990).
39. R. I. Feldman, J. M. Wu, J. C. Jenson, and E. Mann, *J. Biol. Chem.* **265,** 17364 (1990).
40. A. Coffer, J. Sinnett-Smith, and E. Rozengurt, *FEBS Lett.* **275,** 159 (1990).
41. B. F. Dickey, J. B. Fishman, R. E. Fines, and J. Navarro, *J. Biol. Chem.* **262,** 8738 (1987).
42. L. D. Mayer, M. J. Hope, and R. R. Cullis, *Biochim. Biophys. Acta* **858,** 161 (1986).
43. A. V. Smrcka, J. R. Hepler, K. O. Brown, and P. C. Sternweis, *Science* **251,** 804 (1991).
44. S. Taylor, H. Chae, S. G. Rhee, and J. Exton, *Nature (London)* **350,** 516 (1991).
45. D. Wu, C. H. Lee, S. G. Rhee, and M. I. Simon, *J. Biol. Chem.* **267,** 1811 (1992).

[17] Receptors for Bombesin-like Peptides in the Rat Central Nervous System

Ellen E. Ladenheim, Timothy H. Moran, and Robert T. Jensen

Introduction

Bombesin (BN), a tetradecapeptide originally isolated from anuran skin (1), belongs to a larger family of peptides consisting of both amphibian and mammalian representatives so designated because of their close structural homology with BN (2).

Since their discovery, bombesin-like peptides have been shown to exhibit diverse physiological and behavioral effects in mammals. Peripheral actions of BN include the stimulation of gastrin release and gastric acid secretion (3), smooth muscle contraction (4), pancreatic enzyme secretion (5, 6), release of several gastrointestinal hormones (7), and the inhibition of food intake (8). In the central nervous system, BN has been associated with thermoregulation (9), analgesia (10), glucose homeostasis (11), grooming and locomotor behavior (12, 13), and the control of food intake (14, 15).

The large family of bombesin-like peptides has been further divided into three subfamilies based on similarities in their amino acid structures and pharmacological activity (16) (Fig. 1). The bombesin subfamily is characterized by the amino acid leucine in position 2 from the carboxyl terminal and includes the mammalian representative, gastrin-releasing peptide (GRP). The litorin/ranatensin subfamily differs from bombesin by the substitution of a phenylalanine in place of leucine in position 2 from the carboxyl terminal. This subfamily contains the mammalian peptide neuromedin B (NMB). Last, the phyllolitorin subfamily is characterized by a serine in the third position from the carboxyl terminal. No counterparts with this amino acid sequence have yet been isolated from mammalian tissue.

Although members of this family of peptides display much structural homology, the differences in the carboxyl-terminal portion of the peptide account for differences in receptor interaction and biological activity. Evidence for functional differences has been provided by earlier work on structure–activity relationships with bombesin-like peptides on several *in situ* smooth muscle preparations (16). These studies demonstrated that bombesin-like peptides belonging to different subfamilies exhibited varying degrees of potency in their ability to elicit smooth muscle contraction in each preparation,

Peptide	Amino acid sequence
	Bombesin subfamily
Bombesin	pGlu-Gln-Arg-Leu-Gly-Asn-Gln-Trp-Ala-Val-Gly-His-Leu-Met-NH$_2$
GRP(27)	Ala-Pro-Val-Ser-Val-Gly-Gly-Thr-Val-Leu-Ala-Lys-Met-Tyr-Pro-
	Arg-Gly-Asn-His-Trp-Ala-Val-Gly-His-Leu-Met-NH$_2$
GRP(18-27) or Neuromedin C	Gly-Asn-His-Trp-Ala-Val-Gly-His-Leu-Met-NH$_2$
	Litorin/ranatensin subfamily
Litorin	pGlu-Gln-Trp-Ala-Val-Gly-His-Phe-Met-NH$_2$
Ranatensin	pGlu-Val-Pro-Gln-Trp-Ala-Val-Gly-His-Phe-Met-NH$_2$
Neuromedin B	Gly-Asn-Leu-Trp-Ala-Thr-Gly-His-Phe-Met-NH$_2$
	Phyllolitorin subfamily
Phyllolitorin	pGlu-Leu-Trp-Ala-Val-Gly-Ser-Phe-Met-NH$_2$

FIG. 1 Amino acid structures of bombesin-like peptides. Structural similarities in each subfamily are underlined.

suggesting the likelihood of multiple BN receptor subtypes. More recently, von Schrenck *et al.* (17) have provided convincing pharmacological and functional evidence for the existence of two classes of receptors for bombesin-like peptides. One class, identified in pancreatic tissue, displayed a high affinity for GRP and BN and a low affinity for NMB (GRP preferring). In contrast, a second class, found in esophageal smooth muscle tissue, had a higher affinity for NMB than for BN or GRP (NMB preferring), although the affinity for BN was similar to that found in pancreatic tissue. Thus, BN binds with equal and high affinity to both classes of receptors for BN-like peptides. An extension of this work, using recently developed potent and specific BN receptor antagonists targeted toward the GRP-preferring subtype, demonstrated that these two classes can be readily distinguished by the differential ability of the antagonists to inhibit both binding and biological activity at these two receptor subtypes (18).

As in peripheral tissues, two pharmacologically distinct populations of BN receptors have been identified in the rat central nervous system. Using receptor autoradiography, we found that specific brain regions containing BN-binding sites displayed different relative affinities for BN, NMB, and specific GRP-preferring receptor antagonists (19, 20). Recently, *in situ* hybridization studies have determined that brain regions differentially express mRNA for either the GRP- or NMB-preferring receptor subtype (21). The pattern of mRNA expression for each receptor subtype was in general agreement with our autoradiographic analysis, suggesting that a majority of binding we identified autoradiographically was localized to cell bodies.

Because BN binds with high affinity to receptors that are both GRP and NMB preferring, binding with radiolabeled BN shows the general distribution of binding sites for BN-like peptides but will not allow for the differentiation of BN receptor subtypes. In this chapter, the autoradiographic methods used to differentiate these two BN receptor subtypes using ^{125}I-labeled [Tyr^4]BN and competitive antagonism with unlabeled agonists will be compared to the utility of using ^{125}I-labeled [D-Tyr^0]NMB and ^{125}I-labeled GRP, which are more selective for the individual BN receptor subpopulations. The differentiation of these populations of receptors for BN-like peptides will be crucial for examining their function as separate and distinct neuropeptides in the rat central nervous system (CNS).

Methodology

Preparation of Radioligands

Preparation of ^{125}I-Labeled [Tyr^4]Bombesin and Gastrin-Releasing Peptide
^{125}I-Labeled [Tyr^4]BN (2000 Ci/mmol) is prepared using Iodogen (Pierce, Rockford, IL) and purified by high-performance liquid chromatography (HPLC) using a modification of the method described previously (22). ^{125}I-Labeled GRP is prepared by adding 0.4 μg Iodogen to 6.0 μg of GRP with 1 mCi Na^{125}I in 20 μl of 0.5 M KPO$_4$ buffer (pH 7.4). After incubation at 22°C for 6 min, 300 μl of 1.5 M dithiothreitol is added and the reaction mixture incubated at 80°C for 60 min. Free ^{125}I is separated by applying the reaction mixture to a Sep-Pak (Waters Associates, Milford, MA), which is prepared by washing with 5 ml of methanol, 5 ml of 0.1% (v/v) trifluoroacetic acid, and 5 ml of water. Free ^{125}I is eluted by 5 ml of 0.1% trifluoroacetic acid, and the radiolabeled peptide by ten 200-μl sequential elutions with 60% acetonitrile in 0.1% trifluoroacetic acid. Radiolabeled peptide is separated from unlabeled peptide by combining the three elutions (0.6 ml) with the highest radioactivity and applying them to a reversed-phase high-performance liquid chromatograph (model 204, with a Rheodyne injector; Waters) with a μBondapak column (0.46 × 25 cm). The column is eluted with a linear gradient of acetonitrile in 0.1% (v/v) trifluoroacetic acid from 24 to 72% acetonitrile in 60 min with a flow rate of 1.0 ml/min. ^{125}I-Labeled GRP is stored with 1% (w/v) bovine serum albumin (BSA) at −20°C and is stable for at least 6 weeks.

Preparation of ^{125}I-Labeled [D-Tyr^0]Neuromedin B

The preparation of this radioligand is a modification of the method used for preparing ^{125}I-labeled [Tyr^4]BN and ^{125}I-labeled GRP. Synthetic [D-Tyr^0]NMB was obtained from Dr. D. H. Coy, Peptide Research Laboratories, Tulane University Medical Center (New Orleans, LA). Twenty micrograms of Iodogen (1,3,4,6-tetrachloro-3α,6α-diphenylglycouril; Pierce) is dissolved in 1000 μl of chloroform (0.02 μg/μl). Twenty microliters of this solution (0.4 μg Iodogen) is then added to an iodination vial and dried under a gentle stream of nitrogen. Twenty microliters of 0.5 M KH$_2$PO$_4$ (pH 7.4), 8 μg of [D-Tyr^0]NMB in 4 μl of water, and 2 mCi of Na^{125}I is added to this vial. This reaction mixture is incubated for 6 min at room temperature, during which it is vortexed briefly every minute. After incubation, 300 μl of distilled water is added and the free iodine is removed using a Sep-Pak cartridge. The diluted iodination mixture is added to a Sep-Pak cartridge (C$_{18}$ cartridge; Waters) that has been pretreated with 5 ml of methanol, 5 ml of 0.1% trifluoroacetic acid (TFA), and 5 ml of water. The Sep-Pak cartridge is then eluted with 5 ml of water, 5 ml of 0.1% TFA, and 200-μl fractions of 60% acetonitrile in 0.1% TFA. One one-hundredth of the volume of each fraction is counted on a γ counter and the three acetonitrile/TFA tubes containing the maximal radioactivity are combined (usually tubes 4, 5, or 6). The solution is loaded on a high-performance liquid chromatograph containing a C$_{18}$ μBondapak column (0.46 $\times$ 25 cm; 5-μm particle size). ^{125}I-Labeled [D-Tyr^0]NMB is eluted using a linear gradient from 0 to 65% acetonitrile using 80% acetonitrile in 0.1% TFA at a flow rate of 1 ml/min. The biologically active ^{125}I-labeled [D-Tyr^0]NMB appears at 46 min.

Tissue Preparation

Male Sprague–Dawley rats are sacrificed by decapitation and the brains rapidly removed. To ensure even freezing, the brains are cut in the coronal plane into several sections (blocked) and then immediately submerged for 15–30 sec in isopentane (2-methylbutane) that has been cooled on dry ice to $-40°$C. The frozen brain tissue can then be stored in a freezer in a sealed plastic bag for later use or used immediately. The blocked brain tissue is sectioned on a cryostat at $-20°$C at a thickness of 20 μm and thaw-mounted at room temperature onto slides that have been thoroughly cleaned with ethanol, rinsed in distilled water, and coated with a chrome alum/gelatin solution (subbed). This solution is prepared by dissolving 2.5 g gelatin in 500 ml distilled water that has been heated to 55°C, cooled to 31°C, and to which 0.25 g chromium potassium sulfate (chrome alum) is then added. The slides are slowly dipped in this solution and allowed to dry overnight. This procedure is essential for preventing the mounted tissue sections from floating off the slide during incubation.

Tissue sections are mounted onto subbed slides in a sequential manner so that multiple sets are created for either independent processing or histological evaluation. We frequently do not use the entire slide for mounting in order to conserve radioligand. Following mounting, the sections are allowed to dry at room temperature in a desiccator under partial vacuum pressure for 30 min and stored in slide boxes in airtight plastic bags containing anhydrous calcium sulfate desiccant (Drierite) at $-70°C$ until used for binding studies. We have found that tissue can be stored for 6 months in this manner without adversely affecting binding.

Receptor Autoradiography

Differentiation of Receptor Subtypes Using ^{125}I-Labeled [Tyr^4]Bombesin

As mentioned previously, BN binds with equal affinity to both classes of BN receptors, those that are GRP preferring or NMB preferring. However, differentiation can be accomplished by using ^{125}I-labeled [Tyr^4]BN as a radioligand and inhibiting binding with unlabeled BN or NMB. In peripheral tissues it has been shown that while BN has equivalent affinity for both subtypes, NMB has a greater than 100-fold affinity for the NMB-preferring subtype than for the GRP-preferring subtype (17). Thus using this method of differentiation takes advantage of the different relative affinities of the receptor subtypes for these two peptides.

Tissue is prepared as described above. If using frozen slide-mounted tissue sections, they should be removed from the freezer and thawed briefly (1–2 min) at room temperature. The slides are then placed in a slide rack and immersed for 20 min in 50 mM morpholineethanesulfonic acid (MES) buffer containing 0.5% (w/v) bovine serum albumin (BSA) at pH 6.5. This initial preincubation step is necessary to eliminate any endogenous ligand remaining in the tissue. The slides are then transferred from the slide racks into plastic cytology mailers (Cyto Mailers; Lab Tek, Naperville, IL). It is advisable to use plastic for the incubation buffer as many peptides stick to glass surfaces and this reduces the amount of radioligand available for binding.

To determine total binding, tissue sections are incubated in 50 mM MES buffer containing 0.5% (w/v) BSA, 130 mM NaCl, 7.7 mM KCl, 5 mM MgCl$_2$, 1 mM ethylene glycol-bis(β-aminoethyl ether)-N,N,N',N'-tetraacetic acid (EGTA), 0.025% bacitracin, 4 μg/ml leupeptin, and 2 μg/ml chymostatin, and which contains 40–50 pM ^{125}I-labeled [Tyr^4]BN for 300 min at pH 6.5. In preliminary experiments, we conducted both a time course and pH determination of optimal binding conditions for ^{125}I-labeled [Tyr^4]BN in rat cerebral cortex. As shown in Fig. 2, binding of BN increased rapidly in the first 90 min, reaching equilibrium at approximately 300 min. As shown in Fig. 3, the pH that produces the maximum total binding is 6.5, decreasing dramatically

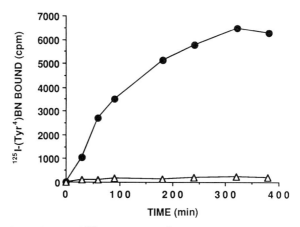

FIG. 2   Time dependence of ^{125}I-labeled [Tyr⁴]BN binding in the rat cortex. Cortical tissue sections were incubated at room temperature in medium containing 40 pM ^{125}I-labeled [Tyr⁴]BN alone (total, ●) or in the presence of 1 μM unlabeled BN (nonspecific, △) for 360 min. Total binding increased rapidly during the first 90 min and reached equilibrium by 300 min. Nonspecific binding remained constant throughout the incubation period.

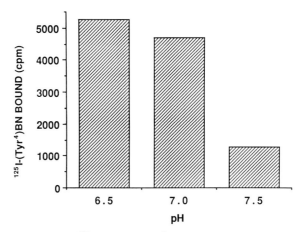

FIG. 3   pH dependence of ^{125}I-labeled [Tyr⁴]BN binding in the rat cortex. Cortical tissue sections were incubated for 300 min at pH 6.5, 7.0, and 7.5 with 40 pM ^{125}I-labeled [Tyr⁴]BN. The pH that yielded the highest total binding was 6.5. Binding was slightly decreased at pH 7.0 and substantially decreased at pH 7.5.

at pH 7.5. In the presence of 1 μM unlabeled BN nonspecific binding was less than 10% at all pH values. These conditions have previously been used for ^{125}I-labeled [Tyr⁴]BN binding in peripheral tissues (17) and have also provided good results with both the ^{125}I-labeled [Tyr⁰]NMB and ^{125}I-labeled GRP radioligands (20).

In our initial differentiation of BN receptor subtypes, we incubated sections in medium containing ^{125}I-labeled [Tyr⁴]BN as described above in the presence of either unlabeled 100 nM BN or 100 nM NMB. We found in a preliminary study that this concentration of NMB inhibits binding of ^{125}I-labeled [Tyr⁴]BN by approximately 80% at the NMB preferring receptor subtype whereas the same concentration inhibits binding by only 20% at the GRP preferring receptor subtype (19). Since this initial evaluation, we have determined that using unlabeled GRP as a competitive inhibitor is preferable to BN, as GRP has a lower affinity for the NMB preferring receptor subtype and is therefore more selective than BN (20).

Following incubation, slides are removed from the Cyto Mailers (Lab Tek), transferred into slide racks, and rinsed four times for 5 min each in ice-cold 50 mM MES buffer containing 0.5% BSA (pH 6.5). Rinsing is important to rid the tissue of nonspecifically bound radioligand while slowing the dissociation of specifically bound radioligand. This increases the ratio of specific to nonspecific binding and ultimately allows for improved visualization of binding sites. The slides are then dried with a stream of warm air using a handheld hairdryer and placed in a desiccator under partial vacuum overnight for complete dehydration. The slides are placed in an X-ray cassette and apposed to high-resolution film such as Hyperfilm-³H (Amersham, Arlington Heights, IL) for 3–5 days. For quantitation purposes a commercially prepared ^{125}I standard should be included in each cassette. After exposure, the film is developed for 5 min in Kodak (Rochester, NY) D-19 developer, rinsed briefly in water, placed in rapid fixer for 5 min, and rinsed in water for 20 min. All reagents are kept at room temperature.

To determine the anatomical localization of binding sites, the tissue sections used for autoradiography should be stained with Cresyl Violet and the stained section projected onto a plain piece of paper using a projection microscope. A detailed drawing of the section is then outlined on the paper, the corresponding autoradiogram is superimposed onto the drawing and the binding is filled in. Exact localization of binding sites can be determined with the aid of a rat brain atlas. Quantitation of binding density is performed using a computer-based microdensitometry system (LOATS). The optical density readings are compared with a standard curve generated using the ^{125}I standards. These standards contain known amounts of radioactivity and thus allow binding density to be converted to femtomoles of radioligand bound per milligram of protein.

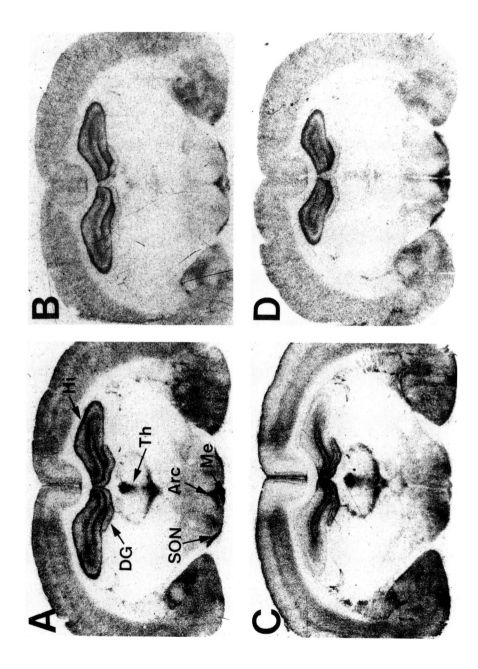

The two distinct binding patterns used for differentiation of BN receptor subtypes are shown in Fig. 4. For sites we classified as GRP preferring, binding of ^{125}I-labeled [Tyr^4]BN was inhibited by 100 nM BN, but not by the same concentration of NMB. For sites we classified as NMB preferring ^{125}I-labeled [Tyr^4]BN binding was inhibited by both 100 nM BN and 100 nM NMB. As shown in Fig. 4B the thalamus (Th) and dentate gyrus (DG) contained sites that were NMB preferring because total binding of ^{125}I-labeled [Tyr^4]BN (Fig. 4A) was inhibited by 100 nM NMB. In contrast, regions in the hippocampal formation were not inhibited by NMB (Fig. 4B) but were inhibited by BN, and thus were classified as GRP preferring.

Binding of ^{125}I-Labeled [D-Tyr^0]Neuromedin B and
Gastrin-Releasing Peptide

The methods used for binding with ^{125}I-labeled [D-Tyr^0]NMB and ^{125}I-labeled GRP are similar to those described for ^{125}I-labeled [Tyr^4]BN with the following exception. Nonspecific binding is determined by the addition to the incubation method of a 1 μM concentration of the appropriate unlabeled peptide. For quantitative purposes, the amount of nonspecific binding is subtracted from total binding to obtain specific binding of the radioligand.

As mentioned previously, in peripheral tissue NMB has a greater than 100-fold affinity for the NMB preferring subtype than for the GRP preferring subtype (17). Therefore, using either radiolabeled NMB or GRP provides greater selectivity and is a more efficient method for identification of individual receptor subtypes while providing results similar to those obtained using the method described above. The disadvantages, however, are that these

---

FIG. 4   Differentiation of BN-binding sites in the rat forebrain. (A) Total binding of ^{125}I-labeled [Tyr^4]BN. High densities of binding sites for BN-like peptides were observed in the thalamus (Th), hippocampus (Hi), dentate gyrus (DG), arcuate (Arc), supraoptic nucleus (SON), and median eminence (Me). (B) Binding of ^{125}I-labeled [Tyr^4]BN in a tissue section adjacent to that in (A) in the presence of 100 nM unlabeled NMB. Binding was inhibited in the Th and DG by this concentration of NMB, and therefore these sites were classified as NMB preferring. In contrast, ^{125}I-labeled [Tyr^4]BN binding in the Hi, SON, Arc, and Me was not inhibited by 100 nM NMB, and thus these sites were classified as GRP preferring. (C) Binding of ^{125}I-labeled [D-Tyr^0]NMB. Consistent with the binding pattern described for NMB preferring sites in (B), the Th and DG exhibited high densities of binding of ^{125}I-labeled [D-Tyr^0]NMB. The sites designated as GRP preferring, the Hi, SON, Arc, and Me, did not bind ^{125}I-labeled [D-Tyr^0]NMB. (D) Binding of ^{125}I-labeled GRP. The Hi, Arc, Me, and SON exhibited high densities of ^{125}I-labeled GRP binding whereas no binding was observed in the Th and DG, sites that were classified as NMB preferring.

radioligands are more costly and less commercially available than radiolabeled BN.

As mentioned above, the thalamus (Th) and dentate gyrus (DG) were identified as NMB-preferring sites because total binding of radiolabeled BN (Fig. 4A) was inhibited by 100 nM NMB (Fig. 4B). Consistent with this designation, the thalamus and dentate gyrus also bound ^{125}I-labeled [D-Tyr^0]NMB (Fig. 4C) but did not bind ^{125}I-labeled GRP (Fig. 4D). Likewise, the hippocampus (Hi), arcuate, (Arc), supraoptic nucleus (SON), and median eminence (Me) were sites identified as GRP preferring because binding of ^{125}I-labeled [Tyr^4]BN was not inhibited by unlabeled NMB. In agreement with this classification, these regions bound ^{125}I-labeled GRP (Fig. 4D) but did not bind ^{125}I-labeled [D-Tyr^0]NMB (Fig. 4C).

Using these methods, we have found that BN receptor subtypes can be reliably identified based on their relative affinities for either GRP or NMB and that these subtypes are distinct at all levels of the rat central nervous system.

References

1. A. Anastasi, V. Erspamer, and M. Bucci, *Experientia* **27,** 166–167 (1971).
2. E. Spindel, *Trends Neurol. Sci.* **9,** 130–133 (1986).
3. M. Impicciatore, H. Debas, J. H. Walsh, M. I. Grossman, and G. Bertaccini, *Rend. Gastroenterol.* **6,** 99–101 (1974).
4. M. Broccardo, G. Falconieri Erspamer, P. Melchiorri, L. Negri, and R. De Castiglione, *Br. J. Pharmacol.* **55,** 221–227 (1975).
5. M. Deschodt-Lanckman, P. Robberecht, P. DeNeef, M. Lammens, and J. Christophe, *J. Clin. Invest.* **58,** 891–898 (1976).
6. R. T. Jensen, T. Moody, C. Pert, J. E. Rivier, and J. D. Gardner, *Proc. Natl. Acad. Sci. U.S.A.* **75,** 6139–6143 (1978).
7. M. A. Ghatei, R. T. Jung, J. C. Stevenson, C. J. Hillyard, T. C. Adrian, Y. C. Lee, N. D. Christofides, D. L. Sarson, K. Mashiter, I. MacIntyre, and S. R. Bloom, *J. Clin. Endocrinol. Metab.* **54,** 980–985 (1982).
8. J. Gibbs, D. J. Fauser, E. A. Rowe, B. J. Rolls, E. T. Rolls, and S. P. Maddison, *Nature (London)* **282,** 208–210 (1979).
9. M. R. Brown, J. Rivier, and W. Vale, *Science* **196,** 998–1000 (1977).
10. A. Pert, T. W. Moody, C. B. Pert, L. A. Dewald, and J. Rivier, *Brain Res.* **193,** 209–220 (1980).
11. M. R. Brown, J. Rivier, and W. Vale, *Life Sci.* **21,** 1729–1734 (1978).
12. D. W. Schulz, P. W. Kalivas, C. B. Nemeroff, and A. J. Prange, *Brain Res.* **304,** 377–382 (1984).
13. S. A. Johnston and Z. Merali, *Peptides (N.Y.)* **9,** Suppl. 1, 245–256 (1988).
14. P. J. Kulkosky, J. Gibbs, and G. P. Smith, *Brain Res.* **242,** 194–196 (1982).
15. E. E. Ladenheim and R. C. Ritter, *Am. J. Physiol.* **24,** R988–R992 (1988).

16. G. Falconieri Erspamer, C. Severini, V. Erspamer, P. Melchiorri, G. Delle Fave, and T. Nakajima, *Regul. Pept.* **21,** 1–11 (1988).

17. T. von Schrenck, P. Heinz-Erian, T. H. Moran, S. A. Mantey, J. D. Gardner, and R. T. Jensen, *Am. J. Physiol.* **256,** G747–G758 (1989).

18. T. von Schrenck, L.-H. Wang, D. H. Coy, M. L. Villanueva, S. Mantey, and R. T. Jensen, *Am. J. Physiol.* **259,** G468–G473 (1990).

19. E. E. Ladenheim, R. T. Jensen, S. A. Mantey, P. R. McHugh, and T. H. Moran, *Brain Res.* **537,** 233–240 (1990).

20. E. E. Ladenheim, R. T. Jensen, D. H. Coy, S. A. Mantey, and T. H. Moran, *Soc. Neurosci. Abstr.* **17,** 800 (1991).

21. E. Wada, J. Way, H. Shapira, K. Kusano, A. M. Lebacq-Verheyden, D. Coy, R. Jensen, and J. Battey, *Neuron* **6,** 421–430 (1991).

22. R. T. Jensen, D. H. Coy, Z. A. Saeed, P. Heinz-Erian, S. Mantey, and J. D. Gardner, *Ann. N.Y. Acad. Sci.* **547,** 138–149 (1988).

[18]   Retinal Insulin Receptors

Steven A. Rosenzweig

Introduction

Insulin receptors have been shown to be widely distributed throughout the central nervous system (CNS) as in the case of the periphery; however, fewer details are known about the neuronal receptors. Included in the CNS is the retina, which represents a highly specialized and accessible portion of the brain and which expresses neuronal insulin receptors (1). The need for methods of high sensitivity, specificity, and reliability are in particular demand to ensure progress in this area of research. This chapter provides a methodological base with which to approach future studies on neuronal insulin receptors in the retina and other regions of the CNS. It is anticipated that it will also serve to demonstrate that the retina provides an attractive model system for the study of insulin receptor function in neural tissue.

Insulin Receptor Structure

Insulin receptors are synthesized as single-chain precursors that form a heterodimer of distinct α and β subunits (of 125 and 95 kDa, respectively) following posttranslational processing. These in turn form the fully active, disulfide-linked heterotetrameric receptor (Fig. 1). The α subunit is completely extracellular and contains within its structure the ligand-binding domain (2). The amino-terminal end of the β subunit is extracellular, followed by the single transmembrane domain of the heterodimer. The endodomain of the β subunit bears greater than 80% homology between the insulin and insulin-like growth factor type I (IGF-I) receptors; this region contains a tyrosine kinase domain and an ATP-binding site (3). Ligand binding to the α subunit results in the tyrosyl autophosphorylation of the β subunit (4). The molecular details of the subsequent cascade of events leading to a biological response for both the insulin and IGF-I receptor remain the subject of active investigation (5).

Methods in Neurosciences, Volume 11

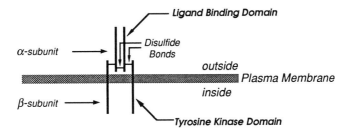

FIG. 1   Structure of the insulin receptor.

Neuronal Insulin Receptor Subtypes

Biochemical comparisons of insulin receptors from the CNS and periphery have shown that two subtypes of insulin receptor exist (6–13). These subtypes are distinguishable on the basis of the molecular weights of their α subunits, with the neuronal receptor α subunit having a molecular weight of ~115K (~10,000 less than the α subunit from peripheral tissues). The same situation holds true for neuronal insulin receptors in the retina (14). This difference in molecular weight is due to differential glycosylation of the neuronal receptor: the neuronal receptor is insensitive to neuraminidase digestion, as it lacks terminal sialic acid residues (1, 6, 9, 12, 13).

Retinal Insulin Receptor Structure and Function

The presence of the neuronal insulin receptor subtype has been demonstrated in the human, bovine, porcine, rabbit, rat, chick, and road retina (1, 14, 15). The mammalian retina (with human, bovine, pig, rabbit, and rat retinas having been studied thus far) contains both neuronal and peripheral subtypes of insulin receptor (1, 14, 16). Capillary endothelial cells (17–20) and vascular pericytes (21) express the peripheral subtype, with the neuronal insulin receptor subtype being present in the neural portion of the retina (1, 14, 16). Rod outer segment membranes have been reported to contain peripheral insulin receptors (22, 23). In contrast to the mammalian retina, chick and toad retinas exclusively express neuronal insulin receptors owing to their avascular morphology (14, 15).

Biochemical and Pharmacological Analysis of Retinal Insulin Receptors

As with other receptor–ligand systems, competition binding studies of retinal insulin receptors utilizing ^{125}I-labeled insulin, in conjunction with either crude membranes or synaptosomal preparations from whole retina or dispersed cell preparations, can provide important information with respect to receptor specificity, affinity, and density. An additional step to be considered in the preparation of retinal membranes is the removal of rod outer segments for separate analysis prior to membrane fractionation. To be sure that one is measuring insulin binding to its cognate receptor and not to the IGF-I receptor, binding assays employing each hormone and its radioiodinated counterpart are required. These analyses can provide important information regarding receptor affinity and specificity and may be complemented by affinity-labeling analysis, allowing the direct visualization of receptor α subunits on sodium dodecyl sulfate (SDS)-polyacrylamide gels. Finally, the application of receptor-specific antibodies to these studies can provide rapid and definitive identification of the receptor under investigation, showing whether it is the insulin or IGF-I receptor, and whether it is a neuronal or peripheral subtype.

Retinal Membrane Preparation

Crude Retinal Membranes

The methods described here have been applied to the preparation of human, bovine, porcine, rabbit, rat, chick, and toad retinal membranes. Prior to homogenization of the retina, an additional subfractionation of the tissue to remove rod outer segment (ROS) membranes can be accomplished as described by Caretta and Stein (24). To this end, retinas are shaken in 40% (w/w) sucrose containing 100 mM Tris-HCl, pH 7.7, 1 mM MgCl$_2$, and 5 mM dithiothreitol (DTT) at 4°C and centrifuged at 100,000 g for 60 min. Rod outer segment-depleted pellets are then homogenized in 10 vol of 0.25 M sucrose in 10 mM Tris, pH 7.4, containing 5 mM ethylenediaminetetraacetic acid (EDTA), 1 mM phenylmethylsulfonyl fluoride (PMSF), 1 mM bacitracin, 1 μg/ml aprotinin, and 5 μM leupeptin using six strokes of a motor-driven pestle [Brendler-type pestle (Kontes, Vineland, NJ), i.e., Teflon pestle with serrations] at 2200 rpm. The homogenate is then centrifuged at 3310 g for 15 min and the pellet discarded. The supernatant is pelleted by centrifugation at 35,000 g for 30 min in a Beckman-type 35 rotor (Beckman, Fullerton, CA). The final pellets are pooled, resuspended by gentle homogenization in 25 mM N-2-hydroxyethylpiperazine-N'-2-ethanesulfonic acid (HEPES), pH 7.4, containing 5 mM $MgCl_2$, 104 mM NaCl (HMS buffer), containing 0.2% (w/v) bovine serum albumin (BSA), 0.01% soybean trypsin inhibitor (STI), 1 mM bacitracin, and 1 mM PMSF and stored frozen in aliquots at $-80°C$ until use. For phosphorylation experiments, DTT should be omitted from the buffer to avoid cleavage of the heterotetrameric insulin receptor to heterodimers incapable of undergoing insulin-induced autophosphorylation (25).

Retinal Synaptosomes

To obtain a retinal membrane fraction free of peripheral insulin receptors present on vascular pericytes and endothelial cell membranes, retinal synaptosomes can be prepared from crude human, bovine, or rat retinal membranes using standard fractionation techniques originally described for the preparation of rat brain cortical synaptosomes (26). It should be pointed out, however, that electron microscopic analysis of these preparations reveals a heterogeneous mixture of membranous structures, unlike what one obtains with cortex. Crude retinal membranes are homogenized in 0.32 M sucrose containing 1 mM PMSF (1 g/10 ml) using six strokes of a motor-driven Teflon pestle (Brendler-type at 2200 rpm). The homogenate is then centrifuged at 1000 g for 8 min and the supernatant kept on ice. The pellet is rehomogenized and centrifuged and the supernatants combined and centrifuged at 17,000 g for 30 min. The pellet obtained is homogenized in 0.32 M sucrose as described above. The homogenate is then layered onto a discontinuous sucrose gradient to yield 12 ml of 1.2 M sucrose, 12 ml of 0.8 M sucrose, and 14 ml of homogenate (0.32 M). The gradients are then loaded into an SW 27 rotor (Beckman) and centrifuged at 62,000 g (21,500 rpm) for 2 hr. Membranes (synaptosomes) banding at the 0.8–1.2 M interface are then collected, diluted 2.5-fold with ice-cold distilled water containing 1 mM PMSF, and pelleted by centrifugation at 35,000 g for 15 min. The final pellet is resuspended in HMS as described above, aliquoted, and stored at $-80°C$ until used. When crude rat or bovine membranes are compared to synaptosomal membranes by affinity labeling or immunoblotting techniques (see below) only neuronal insulin receptors are detectable in these membrane preparations (Fig. 3; 14). An alternative method is to prepare retinal vascular capillaries free of neural tissue (17) to obtain an enriched fraction of neuronal receptors. This approach has been found to be much less efficient than the above-described method.

Competition Binding Analysis

Standard equilibrium binding assays can be carried out on the membrane preparations described using a variety of protocols as presented in other chapters in this series. We typically use an assay procedure employing centrifugation as a means of separating membrane-associated from free ligand. The assay is carried out in 0.4-ml microfuge tubes at 23°C for 20 to 120 min in a total volume of 0.2 ml of HMS buffer (defined above) containing 0.2% (w/v) BSA, 0.01% (w/v) STI, 1 mM bacitracin, 1 mM PMSF, 100,000 cpm of radioligand [^{125}I-labeled insulin (human insulin labeled on the A14 tyrosyl residue) or ^{125}I-labeled IGF-I (human, Thr^{59}; Amersham, Arlington Heights, IL)], and various concentrations of unlabeled ligand. The binding reaction is terminated by placing the tubes on ice and adding 0.2 ml of ice-cold binding buffer. The tubes are centrifuged for 3 min in a microcentrifuge (15,000 g), and the supernatants aspirated. The pellets are then rinsed with 0.2 ml of buffer, followed by centrifugation for 30 sec and removal of the supernatant. The tips of the tubes are then removed with a razor blade and the radioactivity in the pellets quantified in a γ spectrometer. As shown in Fig. 2, use of both radioligands allows one to demonstrate receptor affinity and specificity. In the example shown, toad retinal membranes showed dual specificity for insulin and IGF-I. This protocol can also be used for Scatchard analysis or modified for the analysis of dissociation rates.

Affinity-Labeling of Insulin Receptors

Direct identification of insulin receptor α subunits in retinal membranes can be accomplished using the technique of affinity labeling or chemical cross-linking. For these analyses one needs retinal membranes, ^{125}I-labeled insulin (human insulin labeled on the A14 tyrosyl residue; Amersham), ^{125}I-labeled IGF-I (human, Thr^{59}; Amersham), and the chemical cross-linking reagents disuccinimidyl suberate (DSS) or *m*-maleimidobenzoyl-*N*-hydroxysuccinimide ester (MBS), at a final concentration of 500 or 50 μM, respectively. DSS will cross-link to receptor via free NH$_2$ groups whereas MBS will cross-link a free NH$_2$ group to an SH group as present in the cysteine-rich region of the insulin and IGF-I receptors. Thawed membranes are centrifuged at 15,000 g for 2 min in the microcentrifuge. Pellets are resuspended in buffer [25 mM HEPES, pH 7.4, 104 mM NaCl, 5 mM MgCl$_2$, 0.2% (w/v) bovine serum albumin, 1 mM bacitracin, and 1 mM PMSF] and incubated at 23°C for 15–30 min with ^{125}I-labeled insulin or ^{125}I-labeled IGF-I (10^5–10^6 cpm/incubation) in a total reaction volume of 200 μl. To determine nonspecific binding, 2 μg of unlabeled ligand is added to control incubations. Membranes

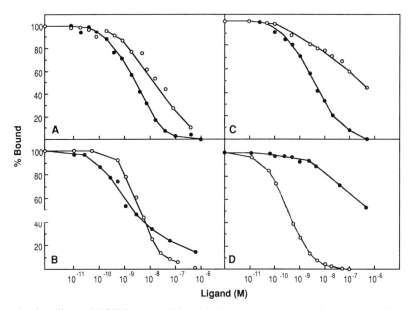

FIG. 2 Insulin and IGF-I competition binding to retinal membranes. Equilibrium binding of ^{125}I-labeled insulin (A and C) and ^{125}I-labeled IGF-I (B and D) was examined in crude membranes prepared from toad (A and B) and cow retinas (C and D). (●) Insulin; (○) IGF-I. Each point represents the mean of duplicate determinations obtained in at least two separate experiments. Identical results were obtained when using bovine retinal synaptosomes instead of crude retinal membranes. Note that the bovine retinal membranes display a greater specificity for each ligand than the toad membranes. [From Zetterström *et al.* (14), Fig. 1, with permission of Raven Press, New York.]

are then pelleted in the microcentrifuge, washed, repelleted, resuspended in protein-free HMS (98 μl), and then cross-linked with DSS or MBS [2 μl of a stock 25 mM or 2.5 mM solution, respectively, freshly dissolved in dimethylsulfoxide (DMSO) immediately prior to cross-linking] using a modification (27) of the method described by Pilch and Czech (28). Cross-linking is allowed to proceed for 5 min at 0°C in a total volume of 100 μl of 25 mM HEPES, pH 7.4, 104 mM NaCl, and 5 mM MgCl$_2$. Cross-linking is terminated by quenching any unreacted cross-linker present by the addition of 0.2 M Tris, pH 7.4 (10 μl). Membranes are then pelleted in the microcentrifuge and the cross-linked pellets solubilized in SDS sample buffer for analysis by SDS-polyacrylamide gel electrophoresis (PAGE) and autoradiography (Fig. 3) or in immunoprecipitation solubilization buffer (see below) in preparation for immunoprecipitation analysis.

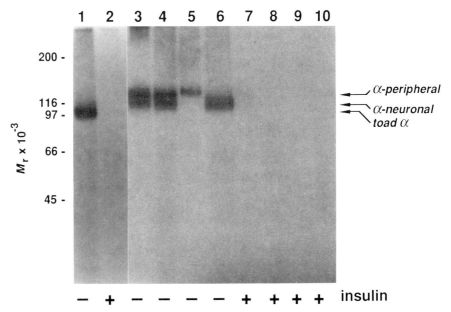

FIG. 3   Affinity labeling of insulin receptors in toad and bovine retinal membranes. Crude membranes from toad and bovine retina, bovine synaptosomes, and rat liver plasma membranes were affinity labeled with ^{125}I-labeled insulin using 500 μM DSS. Specific labeling was determined by inclusion of 2 μg of cold bovine insulin during ligand binding as indicated ($+$). Samples were resolved on a 10% (w/v) SDS-polyacrylamide gel. Shown is the autoradiograph of the dried gel. Toad retina, lanes 1 and 2; crude bovine retina, lanes 3 and 7; rat liver plasma membranes, lanes 5 and 9; bovine synaptosomes, lanes 6 and 10; mixture of rat liver plasma membranes and bovine synaptosomes, lanes 4 and 8. α-peripheral, peripheral subtype of α subunit; α-neuronal, neuronal subtype of α subunit; toad α, toad retinal insulin receptor α subunit. [Modified from Zetterström *et al.* (14), Fig. 2, with permission of Raven Press, New York.]

Sodium Dodecyl Sulfate Gel Electrophoresis and Autoradiography

Affinity-labeled membrane proteins are analyzed by SDS-PAGE according to the method of Laemmli (29) with the following modifications. Sample buffer consists of 0.125 M Tris, pH 6.95, containing 4% (w/v) SDS, 10 mM EDTA, 15% (w/v) sucrose, 0.01% (w/v) bromphenol blue, with or without 0.1 M DTT. The stacking gel [3.5% (w/v) acrylamide, pH 6.8] and the resolving gel [7.5% (w/v) acrylamide, pH 8.9] solutions contain 2 mM EDTA. The running buffer is adjusted to pH 8.75 immediately prior to electrophoresis and contains 2 mM EDTA and 0.43 M glycine. After electrophoresis, the gels are fixed and stained with Coomassie Brilliant Blue. The dried gels are exposed to Kodak (Rochester, NY) XAR-5 X-ray film for 1–7 days at $-80°C$ using a Du Pont (Wilmington, DE) Cronex Lightning Plus intensifying screen. Molecular weight markers are myosin (M_r 205,000), β-galactosidase (M_r 116,500), phosphorylase b (M_r 97,400), bovine serum albumin (M_r 66,000), and ovalbumin (M_r 45,000). Labeled α subunits are visualized on the autoradiographs and their molecular weights calculated. The relative amount of ^{125}I-labeled insulin incorporated may be determined by excising the band from the gel and quantifying its radioactive content in a γ counter. Alternatively, the autoradiographs can be quantified by scanning the exposed films on an XRS 3cx scanner (X-Ray Scanner Corp., Torrance, CA) using the transmitted light mode. The scanned image is imported into a Macintosh II computer and analyzed using Image 1.43 software [written and provided by Dr. Wayne Rasband, National Institute of Mental Health (NIMH)] which may be downloaded from the National Institute of Health (NIH).

Immunoblot Analysis

Extremely valuable information can be obtained from binding and affinity-labeling studies regarding receptor subtype, affinity, specificity, and α subunit molecular weight. However, a potential drawback of affinity labeling is the difficulty incurred in analyzing a large number of samples. In addition, the relative yield of covalently labeled receptor generally represents ~10% of the total receptor population binding ligand under the best of experimental conditions. There is also the problem of labeling the IGF-I receptor when using radiolabeled insulin in these studies (and vice versa). One way of circumventing these problems and which we have applied to our own studies of insulin receptors in the retina is to prepare site-specific anti-peptide antibodies to the insulin receptor for use in immunoblotting, immunoprecipitation, and immunohistochemical studies (1, 14–16).

Partial Purification of Insulin Receptors from Retinal Membranes

To enrich retinal membrane preparations for insulin receptors and thereby increase the sensitivity of immunoblot analysis, insulin receptors may be purified on columns of agarose-bound wheat germ agglutinin (WGA). In preparation for chromatography, membranes (1–2 mg) are solubilized in HMS containing 0.2% (w/v) BSA, 0.01% (w/v) STI, 1 mM bacitracin, 1 mM PMSF, and 2% (v/v) Nonidet P-40 (NP-40) by gentle agitation and incubation on ice for 10 min and then gently rocked for 5 min at 4°C. Insoluble material is removed by centrifugation at 15,000 g for 30 min. The soluble fraction is diluted to 0.2% (v/v) NP-40 by addition of 50 mM HEPES containing 0.1 M NaCl and added to the WGA-agarose beads (Vector Laboratories, Inc., Burlingame, CA) equilibrated in 50 mM HEPES, pH 7.5, containing 0.1 M NaCl and 0.1% (v/v) NP-40. The slurry is then incubated by end-over-end agitation for 2 hr at room temperature and packed into a Bio-Rad Econo column (Bio-Rad, Richmond, CA). The gel is then sequentially washed with 10 vol each of 0.1 M NaCl, 0.5 M NaCl, and finally 0.3 M N-acetylglucosamine (GlcNAc) in 0.5 M NaCl all in 50 mM HEPES, pH 7.4, containing 0.1% (v/v) NP-40. The purified proteins eluted by competing sugar are concentrated in a Centriprep 30 cartridge (Amicon, Danvers, MA) followed by a Centricon 10 microconcentrator (Amicon) and frozen as aliquots at −80°C until use. Alternative enrichment procedures to lectin chromatography include high-salt or high-salt/alkaline washes of the membranes to remove peripheral membrane proteins prior to solubilization of the samples in SDS sample buffer.

Identification of Insulin Receptor α Subunits

Preparation of Site-Specific Polyclonal Antibodies to the Insulin Receptor

Preparation of Immunogen

The application of receptor-specific antibodies to the analysis of insulin receptors in the retina has provided definitive identification of insulin receptor subtypes in this tissue. This approach has a number of advantages over the use of affinity labeling, such as not requiring receptor to bind ligand, not requiring the purchase or preparation of radioligand, and not relying on chemical coupling of ligand to receptor and thus suffering from signal loss due to low cross-linking efficiencies. For the preparation of anti-peptide sera, the sequences of the human insulin and IGF-I receptors were aligned and compared by eye to determine which region of their α subunits was the least homologous between the two proteins. This task can more easily be accomplished by using the HyperCard-based program, HyperBlast (Basic Local Alignment and Statistical Tool, written by Dr. Michael Cherry of Harvard University) and accessing the National Center for Biotechnology Information Server to search various databases and verify that the chosen sequences are indeed unique to the protein in question. For the insulin receptor, a pentadecapeptide corresponding to residues 657–670 of the car-

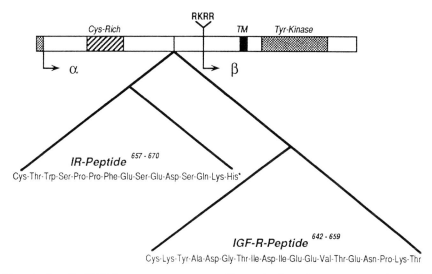

FIG. 4   Insulin/IGF-I receptor structure. Shown is the primary structural motif of the insulin and IGF-I receptors and the amino acid sequences of the peptides used in generating site-specific antibodies. Cys-Rich, cysteine-rich domain; TM, transmembrane domain; Tyr-Kinase, tyrosine kinase domain. After Ullrich *et al.* (3). [From Rosenzweig *et al.* (1), Fig. 1, with permission of the American Society for Biochemistry and Molecular Biology, Inc., Bethesda, MD.]

boxyl-terminal tail of the human insulin proreceptor α subunit (3) containing an additional amino-terminal cysteinyl residue was synthesized and purified by reversed-phase high-performance liquid chromatography (HPLC). The COOH-terminal histidine residue of this peptide was amidated to eliminate the charge that would be contributed by a carboxylic acid, and to allow the peptide to resemble more closely the intact receptor. For the IGF-I receptor, an octadecapeptide corresponding to residues 642–659 of the human IGF-I proreceptor α subunit was similarly prepared (Fig. 4).

The insulin and IGF-I receptor peptides were coupled to MBS-derivatized keyhole limpet hemocyanin (KLH) essentially as follows. Keyhole limpet hemocyanin (in 6 M NH$_2$SO$_4$; Calbiochem, La Jolla, CA) is first desalted and equilibrated to pH 8.0 in 50 mM sodium phosphate buffer. It is then brought to a concentration of 5 mg/0.25 ml for each peptide reaction. MBS (0.875 mg dissolved in DMSO and representing an ~40-fold molar excess over KLH) is then added dropwise under constant vortexing and is allowed to react with the KLH for 30–60 min at room temperature. The reaction is terminated by dilution of the sample with 50 mM sodium phosphate buffer, and unreacted MBS is removed by concentration–dialysis in a Centriprep 30 cartridge

(Amicon). The MBS–KLH is then reequilibrated to 50 mM sodium phosphate buffer, pH 7.5, and concentrated (~0.5-ml final volume). Peptide (5 mg dissolved in 50 mM sodium phosphate buffer, pH 7.5; 0.2- to 1.0-ml volume) is then added to the MBS–KLH and the mixture is constantly stirred at room temperature for 3 hr followed by overnight incubation at 4°C. The final product is then dialyzed and aliquoted or aliquoted directly and stored frozen (-20°C) until needed in the immunization protocol. It should be noted that the solubility of each peptide should be determined empirically and, if necessary, it can be dissolved in a small quantity of 0.5 M acetic acid followed by neutralization in phosphate buffer or it may be dissolved in sodium borate, pH 9.2. In the latter case, the spontaneous oxidation of cysteine residues under alkaline conditions to yield disulfide-bonded peptide dimers has not been a problem.

Immunization of Rabbits

New Zealand White rabbits (female; 5–6 lb) are immunized with peptide–KLH conjugates containing 100 or 200 μg of receptor peptide per aliquot (0.5 ml), first using multiple intradermal or subcutaneous sites of injection in Freund's complete adjuvant (1 : 1, v/v). Two weeks later the rabbits are boosted intradermally (or subcutaneously) with immunogen in incomplete Freund's adjuvant (1 : 1), followed by intraperitoneal boosts of immunogen in alum (or subcutaneous boosts of immunogen in incomplete Freund's adjuvant) with bleeding at 2 weeks after each boost. Up to 50 ml of blood can be obtained per rabbit per bleed based on the size of the rabbit at the time of bleed. Following clotting and centrifugation at 4°C, serum is aliquoted into 5-ml portions and stored at -80°C until purified. Because the intradermal route of injection causes significant distress to the animals, we have gone to subcutaneous injections of 0.25 ml of immunogen per site with excellent results. The intraperitoneal injections in alum are the least deleterious to the health of the animals, provided one takes care to avoid hitting an internal organ during the injection.

Solid-Phase Radioimmunoassay

Antiserum can easily be screened for reactivity toward peptide antigen using a solid-phase radioimmunoassay protocol. Polystyrene test tubes (Maxisorp tubes; Nunc, Roskilde, Denmark) are first coated with synthetic receptor peptide by incubation with a series of dilutions of peptide in 0.1 ml 0.2 M sodium borate, pH 9.2, for 10 min at room temperature. The tubes are then rinsed three times with 0.25 ml each of wash buffer containing 50 mM HEPES, pH 7.4, 0.15 M NaCl, and 0.05% (w/v) sodium azide. Anti-peptide antibody (0.1-ml final volume) at a 1 : 100 dilution is then added and incubated in the tubes for 30 min at room temperature, after which the solution is aspirated and the tubes washed three times with wash buffer. ^{125}I-labeled IgG (goat anti-rabbit) is then added to each tube and incubated for 30 min at room temperature. At the end of this incubation the tubes are washed as described above and their radioactive contents quantified in a γ spectrometer. Alternative assays may be performed to ensure early information concerning the generation of a specific antibody, such as dot-blot assay or enzyme-linked immunosorbent assay (ELISA) prior to employing the immune serum to analyze tissue or cell samples. We also screen our antibody preparations for their ability to block or enhance ligand binding and receptor autophosphorylation *in vitro* and *in vivo*. An additional check should also include screening for the production of anti-KLH antibodies.

Affinity Purification of Anti-Peptide IgG

We routinely affinity purify our sera by chromatography on columns of peptide-Sepharose as described below. Affinity supports are prepared using CH-Sepharose (Pharmacia-LKB, Piscataway, NJ) according to the instructions of the manufacturer. The active group on this support is N-hydroxysuccinimide ester, which will form a peptide bond with a free NH_2 group on the peptide, whether that is the NH_2-terminal cysteine residue or an ε-NH_2 group of a lysine residue in the peptide. To this end, 1.1 g of CH-Sepharose is suspended in and washed with 200 ml of 1 mM HCl over a 15-min period on a sintered glass funnel. The rehydrated beads are then rapidly washed three times (5 ml each wash) with 0.1 M NaHCO$_3$, pH 8.0, 0.5 M NaCl, transferred to a 15-ml conical tube, and centrifuged such that when the centrifuge reaches 500 rpm it is turned off. The supernatant is removed and the beads are resuspended in 3 ml of 0.1 M NaHCO$_3$, pH 8.0, 0.5 M NaCl. As the beads are washing, 4.5 mg of peptide is dissolved in 2 ml of 0.1 M NaHCO$_3$, pH 8.0, 0.5 M NaCl, which is then added to the equilibrated beads. The coupling reaction is allowed to proceed for several hours at room temperature, followed by overnight incubation at 4°C, all with continuous end-over-end agitation. The beads are then centrifuged as described and the supernatant is removed and replaced with 2 ml of 0.1 M Tris, pH 8.0, to quench any unreacted N-hydroxysuccinimide ester on the Sepharose. After 1 hr at 4°C, the beads are washed using three cycles of alternating pH. Each cycle consists of a wash at pH 4.0 (0.1 M sodium acetate, 0.5 M NaCl), followed by a wash at pH 8.0 (0.1 M Tris, 0.5 M NaCl) using ~200 ml buffer per wash. Finally, the beads are washed with storage buffer consisting of 50 mM HEPES, pH 7.4, 0.15 M NaCl, 0.05% (w/v) NaN$_3$. The efficiency of peptide coupling can be monitored by spiking the coupling reaction with

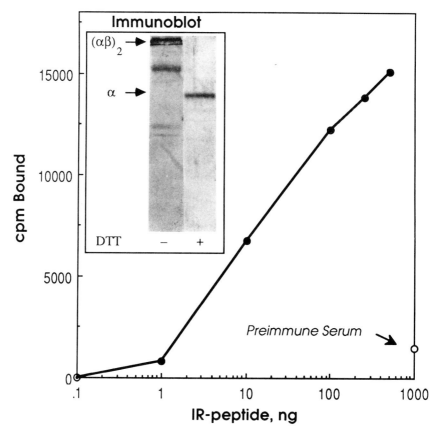

FIG. 5 Solid-phase radioimmunoassay of affinity-purified antibodies. Peptide antigen was coated onto polystyrene test tubes at the concentrations indicated. Affinity-purified or preimmune serum followed by ^{125}I-labeled goat anti-rabbit antibodies was added to each tube as described in Methods. Under the conditions utilized, from 1 ng to 1 μg of immobilized peptide could be detected. Data reflects mean of duplicate samples for each point assayed. [From Rosenzweig *et al.* (1), Fig. 2, with permission of the American Society for Biochemistry and Molecular Biology, Inc., Bethesda, MD.]

radiolabeled peptide (e.g., if the peptide contains a tyrosyl residue, one can add radioiodinated peptide) or simply by monitoring the optical density of the peptide solution before adding it to the Sepharose and after completing the reaction.

For affinity purification, 10 ml of serum is diluted with 20 ml of column buffer consisting of 0.05 M glycine, pH 7.5, containing 0.5 M NaCl (30) and added to a 1-ml slurry of receptor–peptide–Sepharose and incubated with constant stirring for 4 hr at room temperature or overnight at 4°C. The slurry is then packed into a column and washed with 60 column volumes of the above buffer and then the matrix-bound antibody is eluted with 10 ml of 0.2 M glycine, pH 2.5, containing 0.5 M NaCl (30). One-milliliter fractions are collected directly into tubes containing 50 μl of 2 M NH$_4$HCO$_3$ to enable rapid neutralization of IgG. Following chromatography, 10 ml of 50 mM HEPES, pH 7.4, containing 0.15 M NaCl and 0.5% (w/v) NaN$_3$ and 1 ml of 1 M HEPES, pH 7.4, are added to the column and the Sepharose is gently resuspended using a plastic transfer pipette. The pH of the column effluent can be monitored to assure neutralization. The protein content of each column fraction is determined by protein assay [31; Bradford reagent (Bio-Rad)] using 10 μl of each fraction in the assay and bovine IgG as standard. Fractions containing IgG are then pooled and an equal amount of BSA [fraction V, radioimmunoassay (RIA) grade; Sigma, St. Louis, MO] is then added to the pool. The IgG is then dialyzed, concentrated, aliquoted, and stored frozen at -20°C. Typically, 0.5–2.5 mg of purified IgG is obtained from 10 ml of serum. Next, the antibodies need to be characterized with respect to their abilities to identify receptors by immunoprecipitation and immunoblotting procedures.

Immunoblot Analysis of Insulin Receptor α Subunits

Insulin receptor α subunits in WGA-agarose-purified retinal membrane preparations can be analyzed by immunoblot analysis using site-specific antipeptide IgG as follows (1). Proteins resolved on SDS gels are transferred onto nitrocellulose with a TE 70 SemiPhor apparatus (Hoefer Scientific Instruments, San Francisco, CA) using a one-buffer system containing 48 mM Tris, 39 mM glycine, 0.0375% (w/v) SDS, and 20% (v/v) methanol. Transfers are routinely carried out at room temperature for 70 min using constant current. After transfer, the nitrocellulose is quenched for at least 60 min in Tris-buffered saline, containing 0.1% (w/v) Tween and 5% (v/v) nonfat dry milk (32). Although there is much discussion in the literature concerning the use of nonfat dry milk and its potential for high backgrounds due to nonspecific binding of IgG to nitrocellulose, we have experienced superior results over the use of 5% (w/v) BSA. Quenched filters can be stored in the freezer or incubated with affinity-purified antibody at 0.5 to 5 μg/ml in the same buffer for 18 hr at 4°C. The blots are then incubated with secondary antibody or reagent for 1 hr at room temperature. For this step the filters can be decorated with a variety of different secondary reagents, all having varying sensitivities. We have had excellent results using alkaline phosphatase-conjugated secondary followed by development with 5-bromo-4-chloro-3-indolyl-phosphate-toluidine salt (BCIP) and p-nitro blue tetrazolium chloride (NBT). The level of sensitivity obtained exceeded that observed with the use of ^{125}I-labeled protein A or goat anti-rabbit IgG. More recently we have been able to further increase the sensitivity of our procedures by ~10-fold by employing a chemiluminescence-based reagent and peroxidase-conjugated goat anti-rabbit antibody secondary. Blots so incubated are then reacted with the ECL (Enhanced Chemiluminescence) Western blotting detection system (Amersham) for 1 min, followed by exposure of the blots to Kodak XRP X-ray film for 15 sec to 2 min. The additional advantage of this method is that one obtains a "hard copy" of the data on X-ray film. It may also be possible to reprobe developed blots by stripping them free of primary and secondary antibodies. Amersham Corporation has described a method that involves incubating the blot in a solution of 2% (w/v) SDS, 0.1 M 2-mercaptoethanol in Tris buffer at 50°C for 30 min followed by washing, quenching in 5% (w/v) nonfat dry milk, and repeating the immunodetection protocol described above. This method works on blots that have not been allowed to dry and provides the investigator with a way to analyze extremely small quantities of sample numerous times.

Deglycosylation of Insulin Receptors

As discussed above, the principal difference between peripheral and neuronal forms of the retinal insulin receptor is the presence of sialic acid residues on the peripheral forms of the receptor. This can be demonstrated by digesting peripheral receptors with neuraminidase, which results in receptor α subunits with electrophoretic mobilities identical to those of their neuronal counterparts (1). Complete removal of N-linked oligosaccharides with the use of endoglycosidase F (Endo F) or commercially obtained N-glycanase (Genzyme Corp., Boston, MA) results in a protein core that cannot be distinguished on the basis of the receptor subtype from which it was prepared (14). One notable difference is the toad retinal insulin receptor α subunit, which has an unusually small molecular mass of ~105 kDa and whose N-linked free core is consequently smaller than has been found for other species (14). For N-glycanase digestion analysis of insulin receptor α subunits, affinity-labeled membranes or WGA-agarose-enriched membrane proteins can be analyzed (33). The samples are first brought to pH 6.1 in phosphate or citrate buffer containing 50 mM EDTA, 1% (w/v) Nonidet P-40, 0.1% (v/v) SDS, and 1% (v/v) 2-mercaptoethanol, heated at 95°C for 3 min (to denature the substrates and inactivate proteases), and allowed to cool to room temperature. N-Glycanase and/or sample buffer is then added to each aliquot and digestion is allowed to proceed for 18 hr at 37°C. The reaction is stopped by addition of an equal volume of SDS sample buffer and the samples are resolved on an SDS slab gel. The change in electrophoretic mobility/loss of mass contributed by N-linked glycans can then be determined following autoradiography of the dried gel for the affinity-labeled samples or following transfer to nitrocellulose and immunoblotting of the α subunits with anti-receptor IgG.

Analysis of Insulin Receptor β Subunits

Autophosphorylation of Insulin and Insulin-like Growth Factor I Receptors

For the *in vitro* analysis of insulin-induced insulin receptor autophosphorylation, 10–20 μg of WGA-agarose-purified membranes is incubated in 50 mM HEPES, pH 7.4, containing 0.1% (v/v) NP-40 and 2 mM MnCl$_2$ in the presence of different concentrations of insulin (or IGF-I) for 30 min at 23°C. The samples are then incubated for 30 min at 23°C after addition of [γ-^{32}P]ATP (2.5 μCi, 25 μM ATP). The reaction is then stopped by the addition of SDS sample buffer and the samples analyzed directly by SDS-PAGE and autoradiography. Alternatively, the reaction can be stopped by the addition of 150 μl of 50 mM HEPES, pH 7.4, containing 1% (w/v) NP-40, 10 mM sodium pyrophosphate, 100 mM sodium fluoride, 4 mM EDTA, 2 mM sodium orthovanadate, 2 mM PMSF, and 100 units/ml aprotinin. Insulin receptors may then be immunoprecipitated from the mixtures with anti-receptor IgG or with anti-phosphotyrosine (α-py) IgG (see below).

For analysis of insulin receptors by immunoprecipitation with anti-receptor IgG or with α-py IgG, we routinely utilize Pansorbin (heat-inactivated, formalin-fixed *Staphylococcus aureus;* Calbiochem) to absorb out the antibody-bound antigen. Alternatives to this method are the use of protein A-Sepharose, protein G-Sepharose, or a second antibody such as goat anti-rabbit IgG immobilized on a carrier. We have found the use of Pansorbin to be extremely efficient, reproducible, and relatively inexpensive, particularly in comparison to the above-mentioned alternatives. Before use, the commercially obtained preparation of Pansorbin is further treated using a modification of the method described by Hedo (34). The cells are pelleted by centrifugation at 1500 g for 30 min and resuspended in 20 mM Tris, pH 7.2, containing 0.1 M NaCl, 3% (w/v) SDS, and 1.5 M 2-mercaptoethanol. The suspension is then boiled for 30 min, pelleted, and fresh buffer is added and the cells boiled for an additional 30 min. The pellet so obtained is then washed six times by alternating centrifugation in 50 mM HEPES, pH 7.4, containing 0.15 M NaCl and 0.05% (w/v) NaN$_3$. The final pellet is then weighed and a 10% (w/v) solution of bacteria in 50 mM HEPES, pH 7.4, containing 0.15 M NaCl and 0.05% (w/v) NaN$_3$ is made and stored at 4°C.

The phosphorylated proteins are processed for immunoprecipitation as follows. The supernatants are first cleared of nonspecific binding activity by incubation with 50 μl of washed Pansorbin suspension for 1 hr at 4°C. Following centrifugation at 15,000 g for 2 min the supernatants are transferred to clean tubes and incubated with anti-receptor or α-py IgG (2 μg IgG/ml) for 18 hr at 4°C. Fifty microliters of Pansorbin suspension is added to each tube and the samples are gently rocked for 1 hr at 4°C. The samples are pelleted in the microfuge and the pellets are then alternately washed five times with 50 mM HEPES, pH 7.4, containing 1% (v/v) NP-40, 0.1% (w/v) SDS, 150 mM NaCl (containing 100 mM NaF and 2 mM Na$_2$VO$_4$ in the case of α-py IgG) and 50 mM HEPES, pH 7.4, containing 0.1 (v/v) NP-40 and 500 mM NaCl. The washed pellets are resuspended in SDS sample buffer and boiled for 3 min prior to electrophoresis on 7.5% (w/v) SDS polyacrylamide gels. The gels are fixed and stained with Coomassie Brilliant Blue following electrophoresis. The dried, destained gels are exposed to Kodak XRP X-ray film for up to 5 days at −80°C using a Du Pont Cronex Lightning Plus intensifying screen.

In some experiments the samples may be sequentially immunoprecipitated using a two-antibody procedure. First, all of the tyrosyl-phosphorylated proteins are immunoprecipitated with α-py IgG as described above. After the first washings, the Pansorbin-bound immune complexes are resuspended in 200 μl of 10 mM O-phospho-L-Tyrosine (Sigma) followed by a 2-hr incubation at 4°C. The eluted proteins are recovered by centrifugation at 15,000 g for 3 min, transferred to clean tubes, and subsequently incubated with anti-peptide antibody as described above. For some analyses the radioactive β-subunit bands may be cut from the gel and dissolved in 30% (v/v) hydrogen peroxide : 30% (v/v) ammonium hydroxide (99 : 1) for 16 hr in 60°C. Ecoscint (National Diagnostics, Manville, NJ) scintillation fluid is then added to each sample and the ^{32}P counts per minute are quantified in a liquid scintillation counter. Alternatively, receptors can be autophosphorylated in the presence of nonradioactive ATP and the phosphorylation of tyrosyl residues on the β subunit quantified by immunoblotting with anti-py IgG (see below).

Immunoblot Analysis of Phosphotyrosine-Containing Insulin Receptors

Preparation of Anti-Phosphotyrosine Polyclonal Antibodies

An alternative approach to the use of [γ-^{32}P]ATP in *in vitro* phosphorylation experiments is to substitute cold ATP and quantify the presence of phosphotyrosyl residues on receptor β subunits by immunoblot analysis with α-py IgG. A number of methods have been described for the preparation of polyclonal and monoclonal α-py antibodies. We have compared our α-py IgG to these preparations and have found them of equal if not superior utility.

To generate an antiserum that specifically and exclusively recognizes phosphotyrosyl residues in the presence of an abundant background of proteins phosphorylated on serine and threonine residues, various hapten-based immunogens have been applied. These include phosphotyrosine, phosphotyramine, p-aminobenzylphosphonic acid, arsenylic acid (35), and the autophosphorylated v-abl protein (36). All of these methods work well with varying degrees of nonspecific binding and antibody titers being obtained. At the time of this writing, several commercial firms offer polyclonal and monoclonal α-py antibodies, all of which have been used and cited in the literature. For our own α-py IgG we synthesize N-bromoacetyl-O-phosphotyramine and couple it to KLH (37). A synopsis of this method and its efficiency follow.

To a dry, three-necked flask with a reflux condenser and drying tube attached is added tyramine (1 g, 0.00729 mol; Aldrich, Milwaukee, WI), phosphorus pentaoxide (4.2 g, 0.0296 mol), and 85% (v/v) phosphoric acid (4.1 ml). The mixture is allowed to stir for 48 hr at 100°C in a well-ventilated hood. Water is then added to the cooled, brown reaction mixture, which is then applied to a column of Dowex 50 (20-ml bed volume) equilibrated in water. The column is eluted with water and the fractions monitored at 268 nm. The initial effluent absorbing at 268 nm is discarded. The following large volume (1–2 liters) of material absorbing at 268 nm (which often crystallizes and clogs the column outlet) is pooled and concentrated by lyophilization to yield fluffy, colorless crystals of phosphotyramine. The purity of this fraction can be verified by reversed-phase HPLC in 0.5% (v/v) trifluoroacetic acid under isocratic conditions. This material can be stored desiccated until needed in the next reaction. To synthesize N-bromoacetyl-O-phosphotyramine, phosphotyramine (1 g, 0.0046 mol) is dissolved in 100 mM sodium borate (20 ml) and the pH of the solution is adjusted to 8.5 with 0.5 M LiOH. Bromoacetyl bromide (8.8 g, 0.0436 mol, 3.8 ml; Aldrich) is slowly added dropwise while the reaction mixture is vigorously mixed and titrated with 0.5 M LiOH to maintain a pH of 8.5 following each addition. Once all of the bromoacetyl bromide is added the reaction mix is frozen and lyophilized to yield a pale yellow solid. The product is then washed three times with cold diethyl ether, three times with ethanol, and the resultant white solid is air dried and stored desiccated in brown glass.

Keyhole limpet hemocyanin is then derivatized with N-bromoacetyl-O-phosphotyramine by dissolving 30 mg of KLH in 0.1 M sodium borate, pH 9.25, and adding 350 mg of N-bromoacetyl-O-phosphotyramine in small portions (20–30 mg). The pH is monitored frequently and maintained at

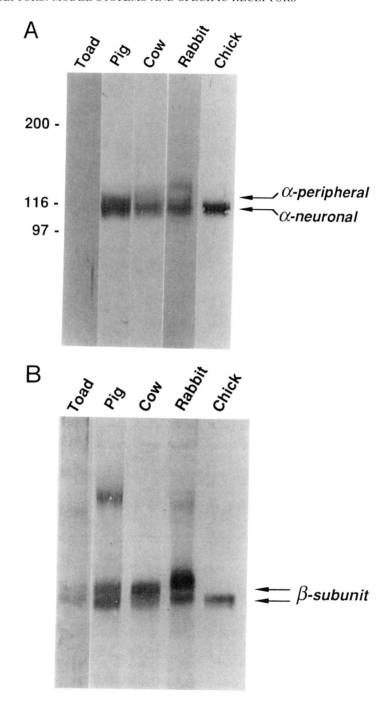

9.0–9.5 by the addition of 1 M LiOH. The reaction is allowed to proceed for 96 hr at room temperature with constant end-over-end mixing of a 15-ml polypropylene tube. The final product, which should appear flocculent, is dialyzed against sodium phosphate, pH 7.4, or equilibrated in a Centriprep (Amicon). Typically one obtains the coupling of 20–40 molecules of phosphotyramine per molecule of KLH (35). The dialyzed immunogen is then stored at $-20°C$ in 1-mg aliquots until immunization.

Rabbits are immunized with phosphotyramine–KLH in Freund's complete adjuvant using multiple intradermal or subcutaneous sites of injection as described for the production of anti-peptide antisera. Unlike the peptide schedule all subsequent boosts are in incomplete adjuvant instead of intraperitoneal boosts in alum. It has been our experience that the intraperitoneal route of immunization as performed with peptide immunogens results in a substantive diminution in the immune titer with this particular immunogen. A more relaxed schedule of monthly boosts and bleedings 2 weeks hence helps improve titers.

Immunoblot Analysis of Autophosphorylated Insulin Receptors

As indicated above, a convenient method of analyzing insulin receptor autophosphorylation is the use of α-py IgG in conjunction with insulin receptors autophosphorylated *in vitro* in the presence of cold ATP. Although this method is not as sensitive as the use of $[\gamma\text{-}^{32}P]ATP$, it avoids the use of radioactivity and can be coupled with more than one analysis of the immunoblot following stripping and reprobing with a different primary antibody. For these analyses, 20–100 μg of WGA-agarose-purified membranes is incu-

---

FIG. 6 Immunoblot analysis of insulin receptor α and β subunits. (A) WGA-purified membrane proteins (50 μg) were resolved on a 7.5% (w/v) acrylamide SDS gel. Proteins were transferred to nitrocellulose sheets and probed with a site-specific IgG to the human insulin receptor α subunit. (B) WGA-purified membrane proteins (50 μg) were incubated for 20 min on ice with 0.1 μM insulin, IGF-I, or EGF. ATP (10 μM) was then added to each sample followed by incubation at room temperature for an additional 10 min. The reaction was stopped by the addition of SDS sample buffer and the samples were resolved on a 7.5% (w/v) SDS polyacrylamide gel. Proteins were transferred to nitrocellulose sheets and probed with α-py IgG. In both (A) and (B), the immune complexes were identified using alkaline phosphatase-conjugated goat anti-rabbit IgG. [(A) From Zetterström *et al.* (14), Fig. 5, with permission of Raven Press, New York.]

bated with different doses of insulin at room temperature for 20–30 min. Cold ATP (100 μM) is then added and the mixture is incubated for 10 min. The reaction is terminated by the addition of sample buffer and the samples are boiled and treated as described above for immunoblot analysis of insulin receptor α subunits. The blots are then probed with α-py IgG and the tyrosyl-autophosphorylated β subunits visualized.

Summary

The demonstration of neuronal insulin receptors in the retina utilizing the techniques described in this chapter provides a sound basis for future analyses of the role these receptors play in the normal functioning of the retina. Additional insight into their active role in this tissue comes from studies of retinas of type I diabetics (1) and of animal models of this disease (16), in which the selective up regulation of neuronal insulin receptors has been clearly established with the use of a combined methodological approach.

Acknowledgments

The work described in this chapter was carried out while the author was in the Departments of Ophthalmology and Visual Science and Cell Biology, Yale University School of Medicine. Research in the author's laboratory was supported by NIH Grants EY06581 and DK34389, the Juvenile Diabetes Foundation International (Grant 186141), and a research award from the Ronald McDonald Children's Charities. I am indebted to the many talented individuals with whom I have been associated with over the last few years and whose input has become an integral part of these research efforts. In particular, I wish to thank Ann Benjamin and Gloria Tressler for excellent technical assistance, and Michelle Peterson, Sybil Lombillo, Carrie Fang, and Brad Miller for contributions during student rotations in my laboratory; some of their studies provided the groundwork in the earlier stages of this project. Finally, I wish to thank Drs. Charlotta Zetterström, Norman Law, Barry Oemar, Matthew Raymond, and Anne Swedlund for their many stimulating conversations and experimental contributions.

References

1. S. A. Rosenzweig, C. Zetterström, and A. Benjamin, *J. Biol. Chem.* **265**, 18030–18034 (1990).
2. A. Ullrich, J. R. Bell, E. Y. Chen, R. Herrera, L. M. Petruzelli, T. J. Dull, A. Gray, L. Coussens, Y.-C. Liao, M. Tsubokawa, A. Masom, P. H. Seeburg, C.

Grunfeld, O. M. Rosen, and J. Ramachandran, *Nature* (*London*) **313**, 756–761 (1985).

 3. A. Ullrich, A. Gray, A. W. Tam, T. Yang-Feng, M. Tsubokawa, C. Collins, W. Henzel, T. LeBon, S. Kathuria, E. Chen, S. Jacobs, U. Francke, J. Ramachandran, Y. Fujita-Yamaguchi, *EMBO J.* **5**, 2503–2512 (1986).

 4. A. Ullrich and J. Schlessinger, *Cell* (*Cambridge, Mass.*) **61**, 203–212 (1990).

 5. B. S. Oemar, N. M. Law, and S. A. Rosenzweig, *J. Biol. Chem.* **266**, 24241–24244 (1991).

 6. C. C. Yip, M. L. Moule, and C. W.-T. Yeung, *Biochem. Biophys. Res. Commun.* **96**, 1671–1678 (1980).

 7. J. F. Haskell, E. Meezan, and D. J. Pillion, *Am. J. Physiol.* **248**, E115–E125 (1985).

 8. K. A. Heidenreich, N. R. Zahniser, P. Berhanu, D. Brandenburg, and J. M. Olefsky, *J. Biol. Chem.* **258**, 8527–8530 (1983).

 9. K. A. Heidenreich and D. Brandenburg, *Endocrinology* **118**, 1835–1842 (1986).

10. S. A. Hendricks, C.-D. Agardh, S. I. Taylor, and J. Roth, *J. Neurochem.* **43**, 1302–1309 (1984).

11. S. Gammeltoft, A. Kowalski, M. Fehlmann, and E. van Obberghen, *FEBS Lett.* **172**, 87–90 (1984).

12. J. Simon and D. LeRoith, *Eur. J. Biochem.* **158**, 125–132 (1986).

13. W. Lowe, Jr. and D. LeRoith, *Endocrinology* (*Baltimore*) **118**, 1669–1677 (1986).

14. C. Zetterström, C. Fang, A. Benjamin, and S. A. Rosenzweig, *J. Neurochem.* **57**, 1332–1339 (1991).

15. C. Zetterström and S. A. Rosenzweig, *Invest. Ophthalmol. Visual Sci.* **32**, 924a (1991).

16. C. Zetterström, A. Benjamin, and S. A. Rosenzweig, *Diabetes* **41**, 818–825 (1992).

17. J. F. Haskell, E. Meezan, and D. J. Pillion, *Endocrinology* **115**, 698–704 (1984).

18. I. Jialal, G. L. King, S. Buchwald, C. R. Kahn, and M. Crettaz, *Diabetes* **33**, 794–800 (1984).

19. I. Jialal, M. Crettaz, H. L. Hachiya, C. R. Kahn, A. C. Moses, S. M. Buzney, and G. L. King, *Endocrinology* (*Baltimore*) **117**, 1222–1229 (1985).

20. G. L. King and S. M. Johnson, *Science* **227**, 1583–1586 (1985).

21. C. R. H. James and E. Cotlier, *Br. J. Ophthalmol.* **67**, 80–88 (1983).

22. R. J. Waldbillig, R. T. Fletcher, G. J. Chader, S. Rajagopalan, M. Rodrigues, and D. LeRoith, *Exp. Eye Res.* **45**, 823–835 (1987).

23. R. J. Waldbillig, R. T. Fletcher, G. J. Chader, S. Rajagopalan, M. Rodrigues, and D. LeRoith, *Exp. Eye Res.* **45**, 837–844 (1987).

24. A. Caretta and P. J. Stein, *Biochemistry* **24**, 5685–5692 (1985).

25. L. J. Sweet, B. D. Morrison, P. A. Wilden, and J. E. Pessin, *J. Biol. Chem.* **262**, 16730–16738 (1987).

26. E. G. Gray and V. P. Whittaker, *J. Anat.* **96**, 79–88 (1962).

27. L. D. Madison, S. A. Rosenzweig, and J. D. Jamieson, *J. Biol. Chem.* **259**, 14818–14823 (1984).

28. P. F. Pilch and M. P. Czech, *J. Biol. Chem.* **254**, 3375–3381 (1979).

29. U. K. Laemmli, *Nature* (*London*) **227**, 680–685 (1970).

30. P. Gierschik, G. Milligan, M. Pines, P. Goldsmith, J. Codina, W. Klee, and A. Spiegel, *Proc. Natl. Acad. Sci. U.S.A.* **83**, 2258–2262 (1986).

31. M. M. Bradford, *Anal. Biochem.* **72,** 248–254 (1976).
32. D. A. Johnson, J. W. Gautsch, J. R. Sportsman, and J. H. Elder, *Gene Anal. Technol.* **1,** 3–8 (1984).
33. S. A. Rosenzweig, L. D. Madison, and J. D. Jamieson, *J. Cell Biol.* **99,** 1110–1116 (1984).
34. J. A. Hedo, *in* ''Receptor Biochemistry and Methodology'' (C. R. Kahn and L. C. Harrison, eds.), pp. 83–89. Liss, New York, 1988.
35. M. P. Kamps and B. M. Sefton, *Oncogene* **2,** 305–315 (1988).
36. Y. J. Wang, *in* ''Methods in Enzymology'' (T. Hunter and B. Sefton, eds.), Vol. 201, pp. 53–65. Academic Press, San Diego, 1991.
37. D. T. Pang, B. R. Sharma, and J. A. Shafer, *Arch. Biochem. Biophys.* **242,** 176–186 (1985).

[19] Pancreatic Polypeptide Receptors in Rat Brain

David C. Whitcomb, Steven R. Vigna, and Ian L. Taylor

Introduction

Pancreatic polypeptide (PP), a 36-amino acid gut hormone, was originally isolated from the pancreas during purification of chicken insulin (1). Subsequently, highly conserved pancreatic polypeptides have been identified in fish, amphibians, reptiles, birds, and mammals, including rat and human [see review by Taylor (2)]. In all species studied, the highest concentration of PP is found in the ventral pancreas, with lower amounts in the dorsal pancreas (2, 3). Other structurally related peptides have been isolated from the brain (neuropeptide Y) and duodenal mucosa (peptide YY). Pancreatic polypeptide-like immunoreactivity (PP-IR) that is distinct from neuropeptide Y (NPY) and peptide YY (PYY) is also present in the colon and rectum of rats, but is undetectable in numerous other tissues, including the central nervous system (4). Thus, it appears that PP is strictly a peripheral hormone.

Pancreatic polypeptide and the other members of the PP hormone family have a variety of actions *in vivo,* including inhibition of pancreatic secretion, inhibition of gallbladder contraction, inhibition of gastric motility, and inhibition of acid secretion (2). However, the mechanism by which PP acts has remained obscure because no receptors for PP have been demonstrated on the presumed target organs. Because receptors are the link between peptide hormones and their action, the identification and characterization of receptors offer a potential approach by which the mechanism of action of a peptide can be delineated.

Early attempts to identify PP receptors in the rat brain may have failed in part because of the high nonspecific binding in homogenized brain tissue, the small number of receptors in whole-brain membrane preparations, the use of the relatively harsh chemistries for iodinating PP, and incomplete purification of the products of radioiodination (5). Furthermore, interest in central PP receptors in mammals appeared to decline after 1981 with the discovery of high concentrations of NPY in the brain (6).

A role for PP in modulating central nervous system (CNS) function may have appeared unlikely because PP is not found in the CNS and peripheral hormones are largely excluded from the central nervous system by the blood–brain barrier. However, several lines of evidence have suggested that

PP and its sister hormone PYY might both be acting centrally as endocrine neuromodulators. First, Pappas *et al.* (7) demonstrated that PYY specifically inhibited the cephalic phase of gastric acid secretion in dogs. Second, Putnam *et al.* (8) demonstrated that PP and PYY were both much more potent inhibitors of pancreatic secretion when stimulated by a central stimulant (2-deoxyglucose) compared to secretion stimulated either directly (by cholecystokinin or bethanechol) or by stimulation of the cut distal end of the vagus nerve. Based on these studies and preliminary *in vivo* studies (9–11), we hypothesized that PP was acting centrally and that it gained access to the brain in regions where there was an incomplete blood–brain barrier (BBB), that is, in one or more of the circumventricular organs (12–15). We therefore screened the known circumventricular organs for PP receptors using *in vitro* receptor autoradiography. We were aided in this goal by the development of improved techniques for preparing highly purified, selectively monoiodinated PP (16). In the final series of experiments we used an *in vivo* radioreceptor assay (10) to demonstrate that intravenously administered PP, circulating at physiological concentrations in the blood, could indeed gain access to receptors within the brain itself.

Using *in vitro* and *in vivo* radioreceptor autoradiography, we have identified receptors for PP in several important areas of the brain, including the dorsal vagal complex [i.e., area postrema (AP), nucleus of the tractus solitarius (NTS), and the dorsal motor nucleus of the vagus (DMV)] (17). The AP and NTS both have dense receptor populations for PP and are leaky areas of the BBB (13). We hypothesize that circulating PP crosses the BBB at the AP and parts of the NTS and binds to receptors on cells that inhibit vagal tone. In this chapter we will describe the techniques we employed to demonstrate PP receptors in the brain and to characterize this receptor population.

Labeling of Pancreatic Polypeptide and the Purification of Monoiodinated Ligands

The PP molecule has four tyrosine residues that are potential sites for oxidative radioiodination (Table I). Taylor and Kimmel (18) have shown that 19 distinct iodinated species of avian PP can be generated depending on the reaction pH. The relative reactivities of the four tyrosines at pH 7.5 are Tyr-36 ≫ Tyr-21 ≫ Tyr-27 > Tyr-7. When bovine PP (bPP) is labeled with radioiodine using the method of Frank *et al.* (16), the most readily labeled tyrosine residues appear to be Tyr-36 > Tyr-27. Other minor iodination products were also observed, at least some of which reflect PP species with oxidized methionine residues (19). We currently employ a modification of

TABLE I Amino Acid Sequences of Pancreatic Polypeptide, Peptide YY, and Neuropeptide Y from Several Species[a]

Peptide	Sequence
	1 10 20 30 36
Pancreatic polypeptide	
Human	Ala-Pro-Leu-Glu-Pro-Val-**Tyr**-Pro-Gly-Asp-Asn-Ala-Thr-Pro-Glu-Gln-Met-Ala-Gln-**Tyr**-Ala-Ala-Asp-Leu-Arg-Arg-**Tyr**-Ile-Asn-Met-Leu-Thr-Arg-Pro-Arg-**Tyr**-NH₂
Bovine	Ala-Pro-Leu-Glu-Pro-Glu-**Tyr**-Pro-Gly-Asp-Asn-Ala-Thr-Pro-Glu-Gln-Met-Ala-Gln-**Tyr**-Ala-Ala-Glu-Leu-Arg-Arg-**Tyr**-Ile-Asn-Met-Leu-Thr-Arg-Pro-Arg-**Tyr**-NH₂
Porcine	Ala-Pro-Leu-Glu-Pro-Val-**Tyr**-Pro-Gly-Asp-Asp-Ala-Thr-Pro-Glu-Gln-Met-Ala-Gln-**Tyr**-Ala-Ala-Glu-Leu-Arg-Arg-**Tyr**-Ile-Asn-Met-Leu-Thr-Arg-Pro-Arg-**Tyr**-NH₂
Rat	Ala-Pro-Leu-Glu-Pro-Met-**Tyr**-Pro-Gly-Asp-**Tyr**-Ala-Thr-His-Glu-Gln-Arg-Ala-Gln-**Tyr**-Glu-Thr-Gln-Leu-Arg-Arg-**Tyr**-Ile-Asn-Thr-Leu-Thr-Arg-Pro-Arg-**Tyr**-NH₂
Peptide YY	
Porcine	**Tyr**-Pro-Ala-Lys-Pro-Glu-Ala-Pro-Gly-Glu-Asp-Ala-Ser-Pro-Glu-Glu-Leu-Ser-Arg-**Tyr**-**Tyr**-Ala-Ser-Leu-Arg-His-**Tyr**-Leu-Asn-Leu-Val-Thr-Arg-Gln-Arg-**Tyr**-NH₂
Neuropeptide Y	
Human	**Tyr**-Pro-Ser-Lys-Pro-Asp-Asn-Pro-Gly-Glu-Asp-Ala-Pro-Ala-Glu-Asp-Met-Ala-Arg-**Tyr**-**Tyr**-Ser-Ala-Leu-Arg-His-**Tyr**-Ile-Asn-Leu-Ile-Thr-Arg-Gln-Arg-**Tyr**-NH₂

[a] Numbers indicate position of specific amino acids, counting from the amino terminus. Tyrosine residues (potential sites for iodination) are shown in bold letters.

the method described by Frank *et al.* (16) to label bovine PP that is relatively simple and highly reproducible.

Lactoperoxidase Iodination

1. Use a 12×75 mm borosilicate glass culture tube as the reaction vessel; add 40 μl of 200 mM phosphate buffer, pH 7.5 (PB); this starting buffer should *not* contain any protein carrier.

2. Add 500 μCi Na^{125}I (5 μl of 100-mCi/ml stock), 4 nmol of bPP (10 μg peptide in 20 μl PB), and 0.4 mIU bovine milk lactoperoxidase (20 μg/ml lyophilized lactoperoxidase at 100 IU/mg).

3. Add 10 μl of 0.006% (v/v) hydrogen peroxide in PB to start the oxidation reaction and allow the reaction to proceed for 10 min at room temperature with occasional shaking. Add another 10 μl of 0.006% hydrogen peroxide and allow the reaction to proceed for an additional 10 minutes.

4. Stop the reaction by the addition of 100 μl of 50% (v/v) acetic acid.

Reversed-Phase High-Performance Liquid Chromatography Purification

1. The reaction mixture is then loaded into the high-performance liquid chromatography (HPLC) injector together with three 100-μl acetic acid (50%, v/v) washings of the reaction tube.

2. The reaction mixture is injected onto a C$_{18}$ column (Rainin Instrument, Woburn, MA) equilibrated with 0.1% (v/v) trifluoroacetic acid, and eluted by running a linear gradient of 50% acetonitrile dissolved in 0.1% trifluoroacetic acid from 32.5 to 35% acetonitrile over 50 min (Fig. 1). If necessary, improved separation may be achieved by using a column with 3 μm packing and eluting the column isocratically. The column eluate is monitored by measuring the radioactivity in line with a γ detector and by ultraviolet (UV) absorbance at 220 nm.

3. Add 25 μl 0.1% (w/v) bovine serum albumin to the tubes containing the ^{125}I-labeled bPP to be used for receptor studies to protect the label from radiation decay damage and loss due to surface adsorption.

4. Cap the tubes and stored at -20°C until use.

The major labeled peaks of radioactivity seen in a typical HPLC elution profile (Fig. 1A) are (1) ^{125}I-labeled[Tyr^{36}, oxy-Met^{30}]bPP, (2) ^{125}I-labeled [Tyr^{27}, oxy-Met^{30}]bPP, (3) ^{125}I-labeled[Tyr^{36}]bPP, and (4) ^{125}I-labeled[Tyr^{27}] bPP [cf. Ref. (19); Fig. 1]. Subsequent peaks contain diiodinated PP and other

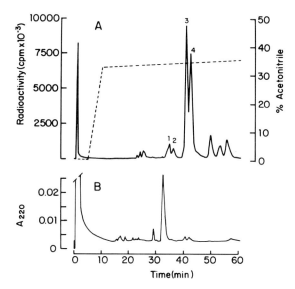

FIG. 1 Purification of ^{125}I-labeled pancreatic polypeptide by reversed-phase HPLC. (A) Fractionation of the initial oxidative iodination products. The solid line is the radioactivity measured in line with a radioisotope detector. The dashed line represents the gradient of acetonitrile in 0.1% (v/v) trifluoroacetic acid used to elute the column. Major radioactive peaks are (1) ^{125}I-labeled [Tyr[36], oxy-Met[30]]bPP, (2) ^{125}I-labeled [Tyr[27], oxy-Met[30]]bPP, (3) ^{125}I-labeled [Tyr[36]]bPP, and (4) ^{125}I-labeled [Tyr[27]]bPP. (B) UV absorbance at 280 nm of the column eluate depicted in (A).

derivatives. The efficiency of incorporation of radioiodine into the peptide is low because of the gentle iodination conditions (Fig. 1B). However, the specific activity of the HPLC-purified products approaches the theoretical maximum because the monoiodinated species are almost completely separated from unlabeled peptide and the other iodinated products. We have tested each of the peaks and although some receptor binding occurs with all of the peaks (e.g., ^{125}I-labeled[Tyr[27]]bPP), optimal binding is observed with peak 3 (i.e., ^{125}I-labeled[Tyr[36]]bPP). Therefore, this fraction has been used for all subsequent radioligand-binding studies; typically, we use tracers that are less than 3 weeks old.

In Vitro Receptor Autoradiography

The technique of *in vitro* receptor autoradiography has become a powerful tool with which to study receptor systems because it allows the investigator to both localize and characterize binding sites (20, 21). *In vitro* autoradiography, when combined with quantitative microdensitometry, allows characterization of the binding sites in terms of specificity, association, and dissociation time course, dissociation constant (K_D), and binding site number (B_{max}) (22–24).

Autoradiographic localization of receptors is possible using frozen tissue sections mounted on glass slides. To prevent detachment of the tissue from the slide during incubation and washings we have used gelatin-coated slides (25, 26). More recently, we have experimented with pretreated slides designed to maximize tissue adhesion without the need for gelatin-coating (Superfrost/Plus microscope slides; Fisher Scientific, Pittsburgh, PA). These slides not only save time but also avoid some of the problems encountered with gelatin coating (i.e., uneven coating and increased background staining).

Preparation of Tissue

Tissue sections for PP receptor autoradiography are made from freshly obtained whole rat brains that are embedded in Tissue-Tek OCT compound (Miles, Elkhart, IN) and frozen on dry ice. The brains are serially sectioned (10–30 μm) at -8 to -12°C, thaw-mounted onto microscope slides, and stored desiccated at -80°C until use. Tissues stored in this manner retain PP-binding activity for at least 1 year.

The incubation conditions used to demonstrate binding of ^{125}I-labeled [Tyr^{36}]bPP to the tissue receptors are a composite based on modifications of several previously described methods (19, 22, 27). Frozen slides are allowed to warm to room temperature while sealed in the storage boxes containing desiccant. If the tissues are removed from the storage boxes while still frozen the tissue no longer binds to the gelatin-coated slide and becomes detached during the incubation or washing steps.

Binding Protocol

1. Preincubate the slide-mounted tissue sections in 25 mM N-2-hydroxy-ethylpiperazine-N'-2-ethanesulfonic acid (HEPES), pH 7.4, 5 mM CaCl$_2$, 3 mM o-phenanthroline, and 1% (w/v) bovine serum albumin for 1 hr at room temperature.

2. Briefly drip-dry the slides, then place them on a flat surface with the tissue side up. Cover the tissue with 1 ml of the binding buffer containing 100 pM ^{125}I-labeled[Tyr^{36}]bPP. Varying concentrations of unlabeled bPP, NPY, or PYY can be added for specificity studies or to determine nonspecific

binding. Incubate for 1 hr at room temperature in a humid chamber to prevent evaporation that will alter the hormone concentration.

3. Pour the radioactive incubation buffer into radioactive waste. Rinse the slides twice in ice-cold incubation buffer for 15 min each, twice in ice-cold distilled water for 5 sec each, and then dry in a stream of cold air.

4. Place the dried slide-mounted tissue sections in a desiccant-filled storage box and allow them to dry overnight at room temperature.

5. Remove the slide-mounted tissue sections from the storage box and secure them in a film cassette. We typically use a 9 × 12 in. sheet of cardboard with two strips of double-sticky tape placed at 3 and 9 in. Thirty-five slides (plus a radioactive microscale standard; Amersham, Arlington Heights, IL) are then arranged in 4 rows with 1 edge of each slide secured on the bottom by the exposed side of the tape.

6. Place the slides in apposition to radiosensitive film, for example, Hyperfilm (Amersham) or Ultrofilm (Pharmacia, Piscataway, NJ) and expose for 7–10 days.

7. Develop the film in Kodak (Rochester, NY) D-19 and save the slide-mounted tissue sections for histochemical stains.

Autoradiographic Prints

Figure 2 illustrates autoradiographic binding of ^{125}I-labeled[Tyr^{36}]bPP to sections of rat brain. For this type of illustration we stain the slide-mounted tissue section with Cresyl Violet and make a high-quality photomicrograph. The autoradiographic film from the area overlying the tissue section that was incubated with 1 μM unlabeled PP (nonsaturable binding) is loaded in a photographic enlarger and focused on the photomicrograph so that all the prints will be exactly the same size. Autoradiograms are printed on Kodabromide SW F5 paper (Kodak). The exposure time is increased until the image from the nonsaturable binding autoradiogram is barely visible and a final print is made. The first autoradiographic film is then removed and the autoradiographic film that overlaid the tissue section incubated with labeled PP alone (total binding) is placed in the enlarger, focused, and another print is made with exactly the same exposure time as with the previous autoradiograph. Areas that appear white on the final print represent total binding.

Quantitative Microdensitometry

There are a number of companies that offer microdensitometry systems to quantitate density of the silver grains in autoradiographs. In our laboratory, we use the Bioquant Meg IV system (R&M Biometrics, Nashville, TN) with

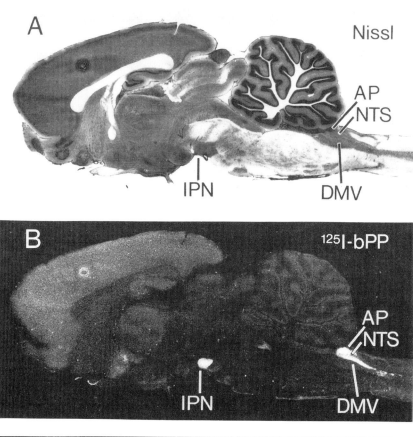

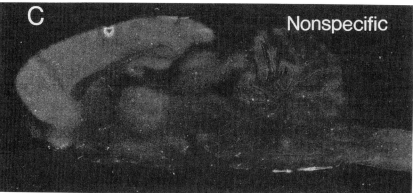

FIG. 2   Autoradiographic localization of pancreatic polypeptide (PP) receptors in rat brain. (A) Nissl stain of a sagittal section of rat brain from near midline. (B) Dark-field photomicrograph of the tritium-sensitive film that overlaid section from (A) for

a CCD-7 solid state video camera (Dage-MTI, Michigan City, IN) on a Wild M5A stereomicroscope with light-field base (E. Leitz, Rockleigh, NJ). In our studies images are digitized by a Targa M8 image capture board and data analyzed on a Northgate 286/16 computer (Plymouth, MN). Because of the nonlinear sensitivity of the film, radioactive ^{125}I standards (Amersham) are exposed to Hyperfilm together with the tissue sections and then used to correct the sample densities (23, 24, 28). Saturable binding is obtained by subtracting the density of nonspecific binding [binding in the presence of an excess (1 μM) unlabeled bPP] from the density measured in the total binding samples. Competitive inhibition curves are constructed by incubating serial sections with ^{125}I-labeled bPP (100 pM) together with increasing concentrations of nonradioactive bPP, NPY, or PYY. The results of quantitative densitometry of the binding of ^{125}I-labeled bPP in the AP, NTS, and DMV are shown in Fig. 3.

In Vivo Receptor Assay

While the *in vitro* studies demonstrate PP receptors in rat brains, they do not establish that a circulating hormone like PP gains access to this region and can bind to these receptors in physiological concentrations. We, therefore, used an *in vivo* receptor assay for PP to (1) demonstrate that circulating PP gained access to these binding sites and (2) demonstrate that physiological concentrations of PP can bind to these receptors in the brain. Complex *in vivo* methods requiring sophisticated computer modeling were not necessary because our objectives did not include the study of possible receptor-mediated transport mechanisms or the pharmacokinetics of infused peptides in the circulation (29). Although receptor characterization is possible with *in vivo* methods (10, 29), these experiments are by their nature more accurately performed using receptor autoradiography with microdensitometry as described above. We therefore used a simple *in vivo* assay that uses only four measured parameters and simple calculations (that are easily performed using a computer spreadsheet program) to measure saturable PP binding in the brain at physiological PP concentrations. A detailed discussion of the assumptions and theoretical basis for this assay has been published (10).

---

10 days (total binding). White areas, representing areas of high concentration of ^{125}I-labeled bPP binding, are observed in the area postrema (AP), nucleus tractus solitarius (NTS), dorsal motor nucleus of the vagus (DMV), and the interpedunclear nucleus (IPN). (C) Dark-field photomicrograph of a control section adjacent to the section shown in (B) that was incubated with 1 μM unlabeled bPP (nonspecific binding). [Reprinted with permission from Whitcomb *et al.* (17).]

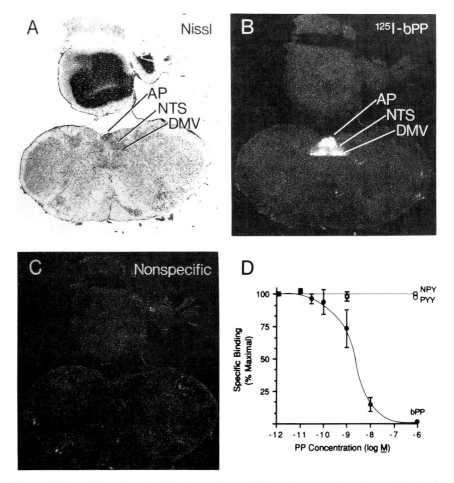

FIG. 3   Autoradiographic localization and specificity of pancreatic polypeptide-binding sites in the medulla oblongata. (A) Nissl stain of a transverse section of the rat brain at the level of the area postrema. (B) Dark-field photomicrograph of the film that overlaid the section from (A) for 10 days (total binding). High concentrations of ^{125}I-labeled bPP binding are present in the AP and DMV whereas the NTS exhibited a slightly lower concentration of binding sites. (C) Binding in the AP, NTS, and DMV was abolished by incubation with 1 μM unlabeled bPP (nonsaturable binding). (D) Competitive inhibition of ^{125}I-labeled bPP binding to the area postrema by increasing concentrations of nonradioactive bPP (●), NPY (○), and PYY (□). The data are shown as means ± SEM (n = 4). Increasing concentrations of bPP cause increasing displacement of saturable ^{125}I-labeled bPP binding with one-half maximal displacement occurring at a bPP concentration of 3 nM. Nonradioactive NPY and PYY at concentrations up to 1 μM did not significantly inhibit saturable ^{125}I-labeled bPP binding. The results in the NTS and DMV were identical to those in the AP (not shown). [Reprinted with permission from Whitcomb et al. (17).]

In brief, this approach takes advantage of the fact that specific tissues have characteristic cell volumes, interstitial volumes, and plasma volumes. Second, it makes use of volume markers, that is, molecules that are useful for estimating unknown volumes based on the total amount of the marker and its concentration. Radiolabeled molecules are often used *in vivo* because the amount present in an organ and the concentration in various fluids (e.g., plasma) can be readily measured. The distribution volume within a tissue is calculated by measuring the total amount of marker present and dividing by its concentration in plasma.

Peptide hormones, because of their size and chemical nature, are excluded from the cells, but freely distribute between the plasma and interstitial space. At steady state the amount of peptide in a tissue sample reflects the peptide in plasma and in the interstitial fluid. If one knows the amount of peptide in a sample tissue (measured by counting radiolabeled tracers) and the concentration of the peptide tracer in the tissue (calculated by measuring the radiolabeled tracer concentration in a peripheral plasma sample at steady state) the distribution volume for the tissue can be calculated. In this case the peptide distribution volume is called the plasma equivalent volume (PEV) because it is a volume calculated from the concentration of tracer found in plasma. If in a sample tissue, a peptide hormone is confined to the plasma and interstitial spaces, then the PEV in this tissue is the sum of these two anatomical spaces. However, if some of the peptide hormone is also bound to receptors, more hormone is present in the tissue sample than is predicted by the anatomical space. Thus, the overestimation of the two anatomical volumes by the PEV reflects hormone–receptor binding.

Biological receptors have at least two characteristics that allow binding to be identified *in vivo*: they have a high affinity for the ligand and the binding is saturable. If a sufficiently high concentration of unlabeled hormone is infused *in vivo,* almost all of the receptors will bind unlabeled hormone. If a radiolabeled hormone tracer is infused in addition to the excess unlabeled hormone, the tracer will largely be confined to the plasma and interstitial fluid spaces. In this case the PEV will reflect the volume of these spaces. If, however, tracer alone is given, then the amount of tracer in a tissue will reflect the sum of the amounts in the plasma, interstitial space, and bound to receptors. In the second case the calculated PEV will be greater than the anatomical plasma and interstitial spaces. Thus, the difference in the PEV calculated in the presence or absence of excess unlabeled hormone reflects saturable binding of the tracer to the receptor.

In practice we also measure the plasma volume using ^{131}I-labeled albumin because infusion of excess hormone may affect the plasma and/or interstitial volumes. Thus one can also account and make corrections for small changes in plasma and interstitial volumes caused by the infusion of a peptide with vasoactive properties (10). The following section describes the methods used to demonstrate saturable PP binding sites in the rat brain *in vivo* (17).

In Vivo Receptor Assay for Rat Brain

A number of factors had to be considered in designing an *in vivo* experiment to demonstrate ^{125}I-labeled bPP binding in specific regions of the rat brain using physiological concentrations of PP in the circulation. First, we estimated the distribution volume for PP in the rat to be 35–40 ml/100-g rat or 100 ml/250- to 300-g rat, that is, similar to the extracellular fluid volume. Therefore, to achieve a final PP concentration of 25 pM [i.e., physiological range (2)], a 250-g rat would require an infusion of 2.5–5 pmol labeled PP. If monoiodinated ^{125}I-labeled PP had a specific activity of 2000 μCi/nmol (or $2000 \times 2.22 \times 10^6$ dpm/nmol $= 4.44 \times 10^6$ dpm/pmol), then each rat would receive between 11 and 22×10^6 dpm labeled PP. We used 15×10^6 cpm/rat (75% counting efficiency).

To block the endogenous receptors with unlabeled PP we chose a dose that would result in a final PP concentration *at least* two orders of magnitude greater than the receptor K_D. To achieve a final concentration of unlabeled PP of at least 300 nM (100 times a K_D of 3 nM) in a distribution volume of 100 ml/250-g rat, each rat would receive 30 nmol unlabeled PP. Converting nanomoles to micrograms results in an approximate dose of 125 μg/rat. We chose to use twice this amount (250 μg PP/250-g rat or 1 μg PP/g body weight) with an estimated final concentration in plasma of over 0.5 μM to saturate endogenous binding sites.

To measure the plasma volume we chose to use 7×10^6 cpm ^{131}I-labeled bovine serum albumin (BSA) per rat because we have found that this amount is easily detectable in plasma and tissue levels without obscuring the ^{125}I counts. To obtain reproducible sections of the small areas of the brain that had high concentrations of PP receptors demonstrated by *in vitro* autoradiography experiments, we chose to freeze the brains rapidly at the end of each experiment and used a predetermined pattern for the dissection of specific brain regions (Fig. 4). A period of 10 min was allowed for the PP to equilibrate in the various tissues [see Whitcomb *et al.* (17) for rationale] before the animals were killed.

Experimental Procedure

Two groups of twelve 250- to 300-g male rats were fasted overnight in metabolic cages but were allowed free access to water. Each rat was anesthetized

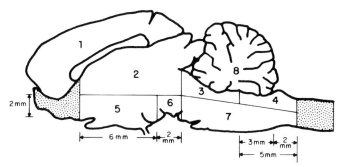

FIG. 4   Schematic diagram of the rat brain, the eight regions of which are dissected in the *in vivo* radioreceptor assay. The diagram is based on the autoradiographic localization of PP receptors shown in Fig. 2B. The brains were frozen and trimmed to within 1.5–2 mm of midline. The eight regions were then dissected according to the measurements indicated before being separated, weighed, and counted. [Reprinted with permission from Whitcomb *et al.* (17).]

with Nembutal [50 mg/kg intraperitoneal (i.p.)] and the femoral vein cannulated. The 12 control rats received 1 μg unlabeled bPP/g body weight to saturate endogenous PP receptors. All rats were injected with 1.5×10^7 cpm ^{125}I-labeled bPP to reproduce physiological plasma concentrations of bPP (see above) and 7×10^6 cpm ^{131}I-labeled BSA as a plasma volume marker. After 10 min 1-ml blood samples were taken by cardiac puncture for determination of the plasma concentrations of the ^{125}I and ^{131}I tracers. The anesthetized animals were killed by rapid intravenous injection of 0.5 ml of saturated KCl, which caused immediate cardiac arrest. The rapid circulation standstill prevents tracers from leaving the tissue even if the labeled PP is dislodged from the receptor or is degraded.

The blood samples were placed in 1.5-ml microcentrifuge tubes with 10 μl heparin (1000 U/ml) and centrifuged at 10,000 g for 1 min. One hundred-microliter aliquots of plasma were removed and counted for each radioisotope in a γ spectrometer with windows set at 5–35 keV for ^{125}I and 50–1000 keV for ^{131}I. Background counts and overlap of ^{131}I on the ^{125}I channel were calculated and appropriate corrections made (see below).

The brains were rapidly removed, rinsed in ice-cold saline, and any adherent structures (e.g., meninges) were carefully dissected. Because most of the PP-binding sites identified by *in vitro* autoradiography were within 1.5 mm of midline, the brains were cut approximately 2.5 mm on each side of midline and the lateral portions of the brain discarded. The central portion was frozen at -20°C and then trimmed with a scalpel to within 1.5–2 mm of midline. This central section of the brain was then divided into eight parts (Fig. 4), and each part was separately weighed and counted. Because some of the brain pieces were small and had relatively few counts we chose to count each section for 20 min to maximize counting accuracy.

Calculations of Plasma Equivalent Volumes and in Vivo Binding

The ^{131}I counts in plasma and tissue samples are used to calculate the tissue plasma volume (PV) and the ^{125}I counts in plasma and tissue samples are used to calculate the PP plasma equivalent volume (PEV). The PEV in each sample is standardized to microliters per gram and to the PV.

The data obtained were organized using a computer spreadsheet. The counts from the γ counter were entered and corrections made for the background counts and the overlap of ^{125}I and ^{131}I counts. The PV and PEV for each tissue section were calculated using the corrected plasma counts per minute per microliter for each isotope. These volumes were divided by the tissue weight and expressed in microliters per gram wet weight. The PVs and PEVs of labeled PP with and without an excess of cold PP were then compared using a nonparametric Mann–Whitney U test. There were no significant differences in plasma volumes in the various tissue sections. However, there was a significant decrease in the PEV of region 4 (Fig. 5) when an excess of unlabeled PP was infused. This finding suggests that a significant portion of the labeled PP in this section was in a saturable compartment (i.e., on receptors) because it was displaced with 0.5 μM unlabeled PP. Region 4 is the region of the brain containing the dorsal vagal complex, an area that had high concentrations of PP receptors based on the *in vitro* work. The AP and portions of the NTS, which have an incomplete BBB, lie immediately above the DMV and together constitute the dorsal vagal complex. Other areas in the brain did not show saturable binding of PP in our *in vivo* radioreceptor assay.

Other Considerations

In tissues with abundant receptors, excess unlabeled hormone will result in a marked and easily detectable reduction in the PEV of radiolabeled hormone, a reduction that reflects saturable binding [see above and Ref. (30)]. However, if the receptor is less abundant, changes in blood volume and radioactive degradation products *may* obscure saturable hormone binding (10). Corrections can be made for these variables if (a) degradation products distribute between the plasma and interstitial space in a way similar to unbound radioli-

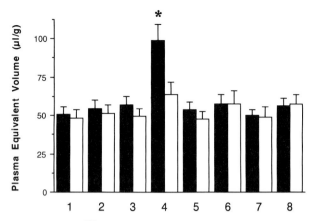

F IG. 5 *In vivo* binding of ^{125}I-bPP in the rat brain. Solid bars indicate the plasma equivalent volume of labeled PP in the absence of exogenous PP and includes plasma and interstitial compartments as well as PP bound to its receptor. The open bars represent the control plasma equivalent volume of labeled PP in the presence of excess unlabeled PP (1 mg/g) to displace binding of labeled PP from the receptor. The difference in plasma equivalent volumes between experimental and control animals reflects saturable binding. Saturable binding is present in region 4 (see Fig. 4), which contained the dorsal vagal complex ($p < 0.02$). No significant saturable binding was observed in the other brain areas, including region 6, which contained the IPN. The data are given as mean $\pm$ SEM ($N = 12$). [Reprinted with permission from Whitcomb *et al.* (17).]

gand (10), and (b) changes in tissue plasma volume are paralleled by changes in interstitial volume. Under these circumstances, saturable binding can still be demonstrated even in the presence of significant degradation or small changes in plasma volume. This is accomplished by standardizing the tissue samples to the average plasma volume and calculating a "corrected PEV" based on the ratio between the measured PEV and measured plasma volume. For a detailed discussion of the assumptions used and application see Whitcomb *et al.* (10, 30). These controls are essential if there is significant degradation of the labeled hormone or if the hormone causes changes in the plasma volume. These factors were not important in the study of PP because PP was minimally degraded after 10 min in the circulation (as assessed by trichloroacetic acid precipitation), the final concentrations of labeled PP in the two groups were similar, and the plasma volume did not significantly change with infusion of excess unlabeled PP (D. C. Whitcomb, S. R. Vigna, and I. L. Taylor, unpublished observations).

Conclusion

The development of new *in vitro* techniques for receptor identification and characterization, along with improved methods for preparing and purifying highly purified radioligands, has played a critical role in the identification and characterization of PP receptors in the rat brain. In addition, the development and application of new *in vivo* techniques has allowed demonstration of saturable binding of systemically infused PP circulating at physiological concentrations. These findings provide an anatomical explanation for the indirect effects of PP on its target organs, that is, in the intact animal PP can influence gut function by inhibiting vagal tone through receptors in the AP, NTS, and DMV. These studies also demonstrate the entry of a gut hormone into the brain through a leaky region of the blood–brain barrier. Furthermore, they provide evidence that PP functions as an endocrine neuromodulator that directly influences brain function.

Acknowledgment

Supported by a research grant from the Veterans Administration and project Grant #DK 44072 from the National Institutes of Health, Bethesda, Maryland.

References

1. J. R. Kimmel, H. G. Pollock, and R. L. Hazelwood, *Endocrinology* (*Baltimore*) **83**, 1323–1330 (1968).
2. I. L. Taylor, in "Handbook of Physiology" (S. G. Schultz, ed.), Sect. 6, Vol. 2, pp. 475–544. Am. Physiol. Soc., Bethesda, MD, 1989.
3. D. Baetens, F. Malaisse-Lagea, A. Perrelet, and L. Orci, *Science* **206**, 1323–1325 (1979).
4. K. Miyazaki and A. Funakoshi, *Regul. Pept.* **21**, 37–43 (1988).
5. J. R. Kimmel and H. G. Pollock, *Endocrinology* (*Baltimore*) **109**, 1693–1699 (1981).
6. K. Tatemoto and V. Mutt, *Nature* (*London*) **285**, 417–418 (1981).
7. T. N. Pappas, H. T. Debas, and I. L. Taylor, *J. Clin. Invest.* **77**, 49–53 (1986).
8. W. S. Putnam, R. A. Liddle, and J. A. Williams, *Am. J. Physiol.* **256**, G698–G703 (1989).
9. M. Shetzline, W. Zipf, D. Whitcomb, and M. Nishikawara, *Fed. Proc., Fed. Am. Soc. Exp. Biol.* **44**, 616 (1985).
10. D. C. Whitcomb, T. M. O'Dorisio, S. Cataland, and M. T. Nishikawara, *Am. J. Physiol.* **249**, E555–E560 (1985).

11. D. C. Whitcomb, S. R. Vigna, and I. L. Taylor, *Gastroenterology* **98**, 531A (1990).

12. J. Fenstermacher, P. Gross, N. Sposito, V. Acuff, and K. Gruber, *Ann. N.Y. Acad. Sci.* **529**, 21–30 (1988).

13. P. Gross, K. Wall, J. Pang, S. Shaver, and D. Wainvan, *Am. J. Physiol.* **259**, R1131–R1138 (1990).

14. W. M. Pardridge, *Annu. Rev. Physiol.* **45**, 73–82 (1983).

15. W. M. Pardridge, *Endocr. Rev.* **7**, 314–330 (1986).

16. B. H. Frank, M. J. Beckage, and K. A. Willey, *J. Chromatogr.* **266**, 239–248 (1983).

17. D. C. Whitcomb, I. L. Taylor, and S. R. Vigna, *Am. J. Physiol.* **259**, G687–G691 (1990).

18. T. C. Taylor and J. R. Kimmel, *Anal. Biochem.* **166**, 194–203 (1987).

19. W. R. Gilbert, J. L. Kramer, B. H. Frank, and R. L. Gingerich, *Endocrinology* (*Baltimore*) **118**, 2495–2499 (1986).

20. W. S. Young and M. J. Kuhar, *Brain Res.* **178**, 255–270 (1979).

21. M. J. Kuhar, E. B. DeSousa, and J. R. Unnerstall, *Annu. Rev. Neurosci.* **9**, 27–59 (1986).

22. M. J. Kuhar, *in* "Neurotransmitter Receptor Binding" (H. I. Yamamura *et al.,* eds.), pp. 153–175. Raven Press, New York, 1985.

23. T. C. Rainbow, W. V. Bleisch, A. Biegon, and B. S. McEwen, *J. Neurosci. Methods* **5**, 127–138 (1982).

24. M. D. Hall, A. P. Davenport, and C. R. Clark, *Nature (London)* **324**, 493–494 (1986).

25. A. Hendrickson and S. B. Edwards, *in* "Neuroanatomical Research Techniques" (R. T. Roberston, ed.), pp. 241–290. Academic Press, New York, 1978.

26. A. W. Rogers, "Techniques of Autoradiography." Elsevier/North-Holland, New York, 1979.

27. R. A. Leslie, T. J. McDonald, and H. A. Robertson, *Peptides (N.Y.)* **9**, 1071–1076 (1988).

28. D. G. Baskin, P. E. Filuk, and W. L. Stahl, *J. Histochem. Cytochem.* **37**, 1337–1344 (1989).

29. Y. Sugiyama and M. Hanano, *Pharm. Res.* **6**, 192–202 (1989).

30. D. C. Whitcomb, T. M. O'Dorisio, S. Cataland, M. A. Shetzline, and M. T. Nishikawara, *Am. J. Physiol.* **249**, E561–E567 (1985).

[20] Neurotensin Receptors in Primary Culture of Neurons

Jean Mazella, Joëlle Chabry, Frédéric Checler, Alain Beaudet, and Jean-Pierre Vincent

Introduction

The neuromodulatory role of neurotensin is supported by its actions through specific high-affinity binding sites in discrete regions of the mammalian central nervous system (1). These neurotensin receptors are localized along dopaminergic pathways (2) and have been extensively studied in terms of biochemical, anatomical, functional, and molecular properties. Several indications suggest the existence of at least two distinct neurotensin receptors. Indeed, two binding sites with different affinities have been described in murine and human brains (3–5), the lower affinity component being specifically and totally blocked by the antihistaminic H_1 drug levocabastine (6). Moreover, purified (7–9) and cloned (10) neurotensin receptors seem to be different molecular entities. The first part of this chapter concerns the description of a set of tools and methods to study neurotensin binding to dispersed neurons in primary culture, while the second part details some techniques that allow visualization of neurotensin receptors, both *in situ* and in denaturing conditions by radioautography. Finally, the regulatory mechanisms and the functional relevance of neurotensin receptors present in this neuronal cell system are examined.

Preliminary Comments

Studies dealing with the interaction of radiolabeled neurotensin with intact neurons at 37°C involve essentially two problems: (a) the presence of a variety of peptidases responsible for the degradation and inactivation of the peptide (11) and (b) the fact that neurotensin is internalized into cells following its interaction to its receptors (12).

The first problem can be easily resolved by incubating ^{125}I-labeled [Tyr^3]-neurotensin in the presence of 1 mM 1,10-phenanthroline and 0.1 μM Z-pro-prolinal, which totally prevent the degradation of the extracellular peptide (11).

Methods in Neurosciences, Volume 11

The second problem concerning the internalization of a part of the bound peptide is more complicated, not only because this process is hardly detectable in classical binding experiments (11), but also because the usual technical conditions described to inhibit this phenomenon (low temperature or chemical inhibitors) lead to alterations of binding parameters. Obviously, these parameters can be examined by experiments on membrane preparations (in a physiological buffer or not). However, when the major goal is to study the receptor regulation and the specificity of the peptide sequestration, it appears important to be able to characterize binding parameters directly on intact cells.

The following sections describe techniques to perform neurotensin-binding experiments on neurons or membrane preparations and precautions that must be taken to undertake neurotensin-binding, internalization, or degradation studies on plated neurons.

Materials and Methodologies

Radiolabeled Neurotensin

The neurotensin molecule contains tyrosine residues at positions 3 and 11 of the peptide sequence. The two residues can be radiolabeled by incorporation of iodine or by tritiation. However, only monoiodo-[Tyr^3]neurotensin conserves the whole biological and binding properties of the native peptide, whereas neurotensin can be tritiated on the two tyrosine residues without loss of activity.

Neurotensin (1 nmol), Na^{125}I (0.5 nmol, 1 mCi), and chloramine-T (1 nmol) are incubated at room temperature in a 10 mM NaH$_2$PO$_4$ buffer (pH 7.4). After 20 sec, the iodination reaction is terminated by addition of sodium metabisulfite (1 nmol) and bovine serum albumin (1 mg). The mixture is loaded on a sulfopropyl Sephadex C-25 column (5 ml; Pharmacia, Piscataway, NJ) equilibrated with 1 mM Tris-HCl (pH 8.6). The column is first eluted (2 ml/fraction) with 60 ml of the equilibration buffer, then with 40 ml of 25 mM Tris-HCl (pH 8.6). Monoiodo-[Tyr^3]neurotensin is separated from monoiodo-[Tyr^{11}]neurotensin at the end of the radioactive peak eluted with 50 mM Tris-HCl (pH 8.6). The purity of monoiodo-[Tyr^3]neurotensin (95%) is determined by trypsin cleavage at the Arg^8–Arg^9 bond and high-performance liquid chromatography (HPLC) analysis (13). This radioactive analog is used with respect to its high specific radioactivity (2000 Ci/mmol) in binding experiments. This ligand can also be obtained from New England Nuclear (Boston, MA).

Azidobenzoyl-neurotensin is prepared by incorporation of a photoreactive group on the Lys[6] of the neurotensin molecule. Neurotensin (0.5 μmol in 500 μl H_2O) and N-hydroxysuccinimidyl-4-azidobenzoate (10 μmol in 500 μl dimethylformamide; Pierce, Rockford, IL) are mixed overnight in the presence of 6 μl triethanolamine. The purification of the photoreactive neurotensin analog is performed by ion-exchange chromatography on a sulfopropyl Sephadex C-25 column (5 ml; Pharmacia) equilibrated with 10 mM ammonium acetate (pH 4), and followed by automatic recording of the absorbance at 280 nm. The column is washed (2 ml/fraction) with 20 ml of the equilibration buffer. Azidobenzoyl-[Lys[6]]neurotensin is eluted with 500 mM ammonium acetate (pH 4) and can be lyophilized and dissolved in water to determine its concentration by an ultraviolet (UV) spectrum between 230 and 340 nm, knowing that its molar extinction coefficient at 270 nm is 25 mM^{-1} cm^{-1}. Unmodified peptide is eluted with 1 M ammonium acetate (pH 4) (14).

Azidobenzoyl-neurotensin is iodinated as for neurotensin and the photoreactive monoiodo-[Tyr[3]]neurotensin derivative is purified on a 5-ml QAE Sephadex A-25 column (Pharmacia) equilibrated with 1 mM Tris-HCl (pH 8.6). After washing the column with the equilibration buffer (20 ml) and with 25 mM Tris-HCl (pH 8.6) (40 ml), monoiodo-[Tyr[3]]azidobenzoyl-neurotensin is collected at the beginning of the radioactive peak eluted with 100 mM Tris-HCl (pH 8.6) (14). Unlabeled neurotensin is eluted in the washing step and the diiodinated derivatives remain bound to the column in these conditions (13).

Tritiated neurotensin (40–60 Ci/mmol; New England Nuclear) appears particularly useful when radiolabeling of both tyrosyl residues is required, i.e., in degradation experiments (15) (see below).

Ligand Degradation

Primary cultures of nondifferentiated or differentiated neurons contain the necessary enzymatic equipment to inactivate neurotensin rapidly (11). By measuring the effects of specific peptidase inhibitors on neurotensin degradation products, the proteolytic activities involved in the catabolism have been identified and can be divided into two groups: (1) peptidases that are responsible for primary cleavages of the parent peptide, leading to degradation products totally devoid of biological activity (i.e., proline endopeptidase and endopeptidases 24-15 and 24-16), and (2) enzymes that are involved in the secondary processing of neurotensin degradation products, such as aminopeptidases.

By using a maximal concentration of 1 mM 1,10-phenanthroline (a higher concentration can be toxic to cells and inhibits neurotensin binding), which blocks the metalloendopeptidases 24-15 and 24-16, and 0.1 μM Z-pro-prolinal, which fully blocks proline endopeptidase, ^{125}I-labeled [Tyr[3]]neurotensin is totally protected during incubation with membranes of neurons or intact cells, whatever the temperature. These two inhibitors are now routinely added in binding and internalization experiments.

Evaluation of Binding Parameters

Equations for calculation of binding parameters (affinity and binding capacity) have been initially established for experiments carried out in a homogeneous medium in which all molecules can freely diffuse. This is not the case in experiments on culture dishes in which ligand is presented in solution, whereas the receptor is attached on a solid surface. However, analysis of data obtained on culture dishes gives results that appear consistent with a simple bimolecular interaction of a ligand with its receptors.

In primary cultures of neurons, the binding capacity is not expressed as a function of cell number. Indeed, the number of surviving cells is unknown at the time of experiments (between 4 and 8 days after plating). The binding capacity is therefore calculated, as for membrane preparations, in terms of femtomoles of ligand bound per milligram of proteins. The amount of protein corresponding to cells scraped in a well is evaluated by using the Bio-Rad (Richmond, CA) protein assay with ovalbumin as a standard.

Preparation and Culture of Neurons

Although by comparison with cell lines primary cultures of neurons cannot be passed and the important problem of cell heterogeneity is therefore raised, these cells have the advantage of being more closely related to neurons in their physiological setting than are other culture systems. Isolation of regions from brain embryos necessitates some experience in brain dissection. After extraction of the brain from 14-day-old mouse embryos, meninges are delicately removed, and olfactory bulbs, cerebral cortex, striatum, hypothalamus, and mesencephalic area can be relatively easily distinguished through a binocular microscope and aseptically cut off in phosphate-buffered saline (PBS; 136 mM NaCl, 9 mM Na$_2$HPO$_4$, 1.5 mM KH$_2$PO$_4$, 2.7 mM KCl, pH 7.5) containing 1% (w/v) glucose. The buffer is removed and tissues are mechanically disrupted by 10 passages through a Pasteur pipette in a 15-ml conical tube (Falcon 2097; Becton Dickinson, Oxnard, CA) with 2 ml of HAM-F12 medium (GIBCO-Bethesda Research Laboratories, Gaithersburg, MD) supplemented with 14 mM NaHCO$_3$, 0.6% (w/v) glucose, 10% (v/v) fetal calf serum (Boehringer Mannheim, Indianapolis, IN), 100 U/ml penicillin, and 100 μg/ml streptomycin (complete medium). After decantation for 20 min, the pellet is transferred to a new 15-ml conical tube containing 2 ml of fresh complete medium and dissociated again as described above through a flame-narrowed Pasteur pipette. Dissociated cells are centrifuged (10 min, 200 g) and resuspended with 5 or 10 ml of complete medium. When the medium is not completely homogeneous, cell suspension is filtered through a nylon mesh (80 μm) and the number of cells is evaluated by trypan blue exclusion with a Malassez counting cell.

Dissociated cells should be plated to a density of 3 $\times$ 10^6 cells/35-mm or 5 $\times$ 10^5 cells/12-mm (24-well Falcon multiwell; No. 3047) plastic tissue culture dish precoated for 2–4 hr with 10 μg/ml polylysine in water (M_r 70,000–150,000; Sigma, St. Louis, MO). Cells are incubated at 37°C, rinsed after 20 min with complete medium to remove nonattached and dead cells, and then grown in a humidified atmosphere of 5% CO_2, 95% air. Between days 3 and 4 of culture, cytosine arabinofuranoside (40 μM; Sigma), directly dissolved in the medium, is added to prevent background cell proliferation. Under these conditions, most of the cells (>95%) are neurons, and only rare dispersed glial cells are present. Neurons are used throughout the differentiation process from day 0 (plating) to days 4–8, at which time they are totally differentiated.

Neuronal Membrane Preparations

The following method is a simple technique to rapidly obtain a crude membrane preparation from neurons cultured in 100-mm dishes. Culture medium is removed and cells are scraped with a rubber policeman in ice-cold 25 mM Tris-HCl buffer, pH 7.5, containing 250 mM sucrose and 1 mM ethylenediaminetetraacetic acid (EDTA) (1 ml/100-mm dish), and transferred to Eppendorf centrifuge tubes. After centrifugation at 4°C for 15 min at 15,000 g, the cell pellet is resuspended and lysed for 30 min at 0°C in 1 ml of hypotonic buffer (Tris-HCl, 5 mM, EDTA, 5 mM, pH 7.5) containing 5 μg/ml DNase I (Boehringer Mannheim). The lysate is centrifuged at 4°C for 15 min at 15,000 g and the final pellet is either kept at -80°C or resuspended in 5 mM Tris-HCl to determine protein concentration before use in binding experiments.

^{125}I-Labeled [Tyr^3]Neurotensin Binding to Neuron Membranes

Binding experiments on neuron membranes are carried out at 25 or 0°C in a total volume of 250 μl/assay. The binding buffer is 50 mM Tris-HCl, pH 7.5, containing 0.02% (w/v) bovine serum albumin, 1 mM 1,10-phenanthroline, and 0.1 μM Z-pro-prolinal. Incubations are terminated by addition of 2 ml of ice-cold buffer followed by filtration under vacuum through 0.2-μm Sartorius filters (Sartorius-GmbH, Goettingen, Germany) presoaked for 1–2 hr at 4°C in the binding buffer. Tubes and filters are then washed twice with 2 ml of incubation buffer. The radioactivity retained on filters is counted with a γ counter. Saturation experiments are performed by incubation of 0.1-mg protein samples for 60 min at 0°C or 20 min at 25°C with increasing concentrations of ^{125}I-labeled [Tyr^3]neurotensin (from 25 to 200 pM) or with isotopic dilutions of 100 pM ^{125}I-labeled [Tyr^3]neurotensin with increasing concentrations of unlabeled neurotensin (0.1 to 100 nM). Nonspecific binding is determined in incubations carried out in the presence of an excess (1 μM) of unlabeled neurotensin. This binding technique applies to all membrane preparations containing neurotensin receptors.

[125]I-Labeled [Tyr^3]Neurotensin Binding to Neurons

Binding experiments can be easily performed on plated cells because ^{125}I-labeled [Tyr^3]neurotensin is a ligand that does not bind to plastic dishes, which allows the concentration of bovine serum albumin to be reduced. Monolayers of neurons are rinsed twice to remove any trace of complete medium and equilibrated with 500 μl of 25 mM N-2-hydroxyethylpiperazine-N'-2-ethanesulfonic acid (HEPES)-Tris buffer, pH 7.5, containing 140 mM NaCl, 5 mM KCl, 1.8 mM CaCl$_2$, 3.6 mM MgCl$_2$, 0.1% (w/v) bovine serum albumin, and 0.1% (w/v) glucose (binding buffer). The equilibration is carried out for 10 min either at 0–4°C or at 37°C in the presence of 10 μM phenylarsine oxide, which prevents internalization processes without affecting cell survival. The preincubation buffer is removed and saturation experiments are started (every 15 sec/well of a 24-well plate) in 300 μl of binding buffer, equilibrated at the appropriate temperature, and containing increasing concentrations of ^{125}I-labeled [Tyr^3]neurotensin (0.05, 0.1, or 0.2 nM; 2000 Ci/mmol) and mixtures of 0.2 nM ^{125}I-labeled [Tyr^3]neurotensin and unlabeled neurotensin to obtain specific radioactivities varying between 40 and 2000 Ci/mmol (concentration range from 0.4 to 12.8 nM). This saturation experiment technique avoids working with large amounts of radioactivity. However, it can be used only if the affinity of the radiolabeled analog is identical to that of the native peptide.

After 45 min of incubation, the medium is aspirated and cells are rapidly washed twice with 500 μl of binding buffer. The cells are scraped with 1 ml of 0.1 M NaOH and bound radioactivity is monitored with a γ counter. Nonspecific binding, which usually represents less than 2% of the total binding, is determined for each concentration of radiolabeled neurotensin in parallel incubations in the presence of excess (1 μM) unlabeled neurotensin and subtracted from total binding to determine the specific binding.

Photoaffinity Labeling

A general approach to determine the size of a protein subunit that specifically recognizes a given ligand is to covalently link the protein to a radiolabeled analog of the ligand and to analyze the covalent complex by sodium dodecyl sulfate–polyacrylamide gel electrophoresis (SDS–PAGE) and radioautography. A photoreactive and highly radioactive derivative of neurotensin is synthesized as previously described (14) and used to photoaffinity label neurotensin receptors in dissociated neurons primary cultured from mouse brain embryos.

The possibility of achieving specific labeling of a receptor on whole cells is interesting because problems concerning the degradation or inactivation of binding protein during the membrane preparation are eliminated. Equilibrated cells are incubated in the dark for 45 min at 37°C with 300 μl of binding buffer containing 0.2 nM ^{125}I-labeled azidobenzoyl-neurotensin (200,000 cpm, 2000 Ci/mmol). The incubation medium is then removed and cells are washed twice with the binding buffer without bovine serum albumin to eliminate any trace of this protein. Neurons are then either kept in the dark or directly exposed for 15 min at room temperature to a 4-W UV lamp (model UVSL-15, Ultra-violet Products, San Gabriel, CA) placed at a distance of 4 cm. Cells are scraped with ice-cold 5 mM Tris-HCl buffer, pH 7.5, collected in an Eppendorf centrifuge tube, and treated for 30 min at 0°C with 5 μg/ml of DNase I (Boehringer Mannheim) to destroy the viscous aggregate of chromosomal DNA. To eliminate the noncovalently bound peptide, crude neuron membranes are centrifuged at 10,000 g for 15 min at 4°C, the pellet is resuspended in 1 ml of 5 mM Tris-HCl buffer, and incubated for 45 min at 0°C. The washed pellet obtained after centrifugation is boiled for 3 min in 50 μl of 10 mM sodium phosphate buffer (pH 7.5) containing 2% (w/v) sodium dodecyl sulfate in the presence of 5% (v/v) 2-mercaptoethanol. Solubilized samples (50–100 μg of protein content from two wells) are analyzed by SDS–PAGE according to the method of Laemmli (16) with an 8 or 10% (w/v) acrylamide separating gel. After staining with Coomassie Brillant Blue and destaining, the gel is dried under vacuum on a sheet of Whatman (Clifton, NJ) 3MM prior to radioautography for 2 weeks on Kodak (Rochester, NY) X-AR-5 or 4 weeks on Kodak X-OMAT S with a Du Pont (Wilmington, DE) Cronex Lightning-Plus intensifying screen. Labeled protein bands are considered to be specific when they are undetectable in non-UV-irradiated samples and in experiments carried out in the presence of excess (1 μM) unlabeled peptide.

Chemical cross-linking reagents such as dissuccinimidyl suberate (DSS), which reacts with primary amines, can also be used to covalently cross-link a ligand to its receptors, but caution should be taken concerning the maximal concentration of DSS that can be used in order to avoid reticulation between two or several membrane proteins. Optimal pH activity of such reagents (between 8.5 to 9) and use of buffers that do not contain primary amines are other pitfalls that must be taken into account.

Ligand–Receptor Internalization

Biochemical Study

The difficulty of distinguishing surface-bound from sequestered radiolabeled peptide lies in the determination of conditions for efficient removing the membrane-bound ligand without destruction of neurons, which is a delicate cell culture system. In our experimental conditions, neurons are not affected by treatment for 2 min at 0–4°C or 37°C with 500 μl of binding buffer acidified to pH 4 with 1 M HCl, and containing a final concentration of 0.5 M NaCl (acid–NaCl buffer). Longer exposure to this buffer leads to a partial destruction of neurons (measured by the trypan blue exclusion technique). The washing conditions are validated by the fact that all the ^{125}I-labeled [Tyr^3]neurotensin bound to cells is eliminated by the acid–NaCl buffer in experiments in which internalization is inhibited (see above on neurotensin binding).

The amount of internalized neurotensin–receptor complexes is monitored at 37°C under the conditions of saturation experiments described above in the absence of phenylarsine oxide. To assess the total radioactivity trapped to neurons, corresponding to membrane-bound plus internalized ^{125}I-labeled [Tyr^3]neurotensin, incubations are terminated by washing cells rapidly twice with 500 μl of binding buffer, scraping with 1 ml of 0.1 M NaOH, and counting. In parallel assays, after the washing step with the binding buffer, cells are incubated for 2 min with 500 μl of acid–NaCl buffer. Detached radioactivity is removed, cells are washed again twice, and the remaining radioactivity, corresponding to sequestered ^{125}I-labeled [Tyr^3]neurotensin, is recovered with NaOH and counted.

Radioautographic Study

The purpose of this approach is to provide definitive evidence for the internalization of radiolabeled molecules. Radiolabeling is carried out at 37°C on cells grown in 35-mm dishes under experimental conditions similar to those of binding assays in the absence of phenylarsine oxide. At the end of incubations, the cells are washed out with ice-cold binding buffer and fixed by immersion in 3.5% (v/v) glutaraldehyde in phosphate buffer for 10 min at 4°C. This procedure ensures cross-linking of about 70% of ^{125}I-labeled [Tyr^3]-neurotensin bound to neurons. To investigate the presence of intracellular labeling, semithin (1 μm thick) cross-sections of cell monolayers are needed. To obtain such sections, the fixed cells are postfixed for 20 min at room temperature in a 2% (v/v) OsO$_4$ phosphate-buffered solution containing 7% (w/v) dextrose, dehydrated by successive 1-min baths in graded ethanol, and embedded in Epon. After polymerization for 16 hr at 60°C, the cells are detached from the bottom of the dish, and areas containing cell clusters are punched out and glued onto the tips of Epon blocks. Semithin sections (1 μm thick) are obtained from the surface of each block, deposited (or set down) on acid-washed glass slides, and dipped in NTB-2 emulsion (Kodak). Radio-autograms are exposed for 2–8 weeks and developed with D-19 (4 min at 17°C; Kodak). Cells are stained with toluidine blue and coverslipped with Permount.

Kinetics of Receptor Internalization

The rate of receptor internalization certainly depends on its degree of occupancy. This parameter can be monitored when equilibrium is achieved with a given concentration of ^{125}I-labeled [Tyr^3]neurotensin (0.4 nM) after 45 min at 0–4°C. Neurons are then rapidly transferred at 37°C and, at different times, washed twice with binding buffer and treated for 2 min with the acid–NaCl buffer. The radioactivity remaining attached to cells, corresponding to sequestered labeled ligand, is harvested with 1 ml of 0.1 M NaOH and counted.

Degradation of Internalized Ligand

Studies concerning the metabolism of neurotensin following the binding and internalization with its receptors are achieved by experiments carried out with tritiated neurotensin in the absence of peptidase inhibitors. Indeed, in the presence of 1,10-phenanthroline and Z-pro-prolinal, internalized neurotensin remains intact at 90% even after 60 min (12). As previously observed for 1,10-phenanthroline (17), this protection may be explained by the penetration of peptidase inhibitors through cell membranes. [^{3}H]Neurotensin (250,000 cpm, 40 Ci/mmol) is incubated for various times with neurons at 37°C. After washing of external and membrane-bound peptide as described above, the internal fraction of neurotensin degradation products is recovered by extraction with 2.5 M HCl and dried with a speed-vacuum concentrator. Degradation products are analyzed by HPLC performed on a Waters Associates (Milford, MA) apparatus equipped with an RP 18 Lichrosorb column (Merck, Rahway, NJ). Elutions are carried out by means of a linear gradient of 0.1% TFA (trifluoroacetic acid) and 0.05% TEA (triethylamine)/0.1% TFA, 0.05% TEA in acetonitrile from 90 : 10 (v/v) to 60 : 40 (v/v) over 42 min at a flow rate of 1 ml/min. Fractions of 500 μl are collected, mixed with 4 ml of scintillation liquid, and then counted for radioactivity. Radioactive degradation products are identified by their retention times in comparison with those of synthetic neurotensin partial sequences and can be compared with products resulting from the external degradation of neurotensin.

Double-Labeling Experiments

Among the peptidases involved in the inactivation of neurotensin, endopeptidase 24-16 (18) is the only enzyme that has been detected in all tissues where neurotensin receptors have been described (19). Therefore, this peptidase behaves as a putative candidate for a physiological inactivation of neurotensin. Endopeptidase 24-16 has been selected to examine its possible association with neuronal cells possessing neurotensin-binding sites that likely correspond to neurotensin target cells. This is achieved by using an immunohistochemical approach with specific polyclonal antibodies developed against the enzyme and by radiolabeling of receptors with ^{125}I-labeled [Tyr3]neurotensin on neurons from the cerebral cortex and other brain regions (20).

Neurotensin binding to attached neurons is carried out as described under Radioautographic Study (above). Covalent fixation of the radiolabeled ligand is achieved by immersion in 3.5% (v/v) glutaraldehyde in phosphate buffer for 10 min at 4°C. The fixation technique of both ligand and cells gives rise to a new problem. In our system, glutaraldehyde gives an efficient yield (70%) of cross-linked neurotensin and an excellent morphological preservation of neurons without inhibition of the interaction of anti-endopeptidase 24-16 antibodies with cells. In other immunoreactions, with neurotensin or dopamine antisera, for example, glutaraldehyde inhibits the binding of antibodies to their antigens on cells. To preserve the morphology of neuronal cells and to increase the reactivity of antibodies, glutaraldehyde can be replaced by paraformaldehyde (2 to 4%), but the latter reagent necessitates longer incubation times of 30–60 min. In this case, the radiolabeled ligand dissociates from its receptor and diffuses in the medium, leading to nonspecific uniform labeling of almost all cells. The best solution is to use a mixture of glutaraldehyde and paraformaldehyde to ensure both acceptable cross-linking, morphology, and antibody reactivity.

The glutaraldehyde-fixed cells are then cryoprotected by incubation for 30 min in a phosphate buffer (1 vol 0.2 M NaH_2PO_4, 5 vol 0.2 M K_2HPO_4) containing 30% (w/v) sucrose and frozen for 15 sec at $-40°C$ in methyl-2-butane. Neurons are rinsed with a 50 mM Tris-HCl buffer (pH 7.5) containing 140 mM NaCl (Tris-NaCl buffer), and nonspecific sites for IgG are blocked by incubation for 30 min in the Tris-NaCl buffer in the presence of 3% (w/v) skim milk and 0.2% (v/v) Triton X-100. Fixed cells are rinsed twice with 1% skim milk in Tris-NaCl buffer and exposed in the same buffer overnight at 4°C to a 1:300 dilution of the immune or preimmune IgG fractions (21). Finally, dishes are exposed for 90 min to a 1:200 dilution of goat anti-rabbit IgG coupled to peroxidase according to the recommendations of the manufacturer (Pharmacia). Cells are rinsed as above and the IgG–antigen complexes are revealed with diaminobenzidine (DAB), 10 mg in 100 ml H_2O containing 6 mM H_2O_2, for 6 min in the dark. To process for both peptidase and neurotensin receptor detection, neurons are dehydrated with graded ethanol and directly radioautographed, after cutting off the sides of the Petri dishes, by dipping in Kodak NTB-3 emulsion diluted 1:1. Radioautograms are developed with D-19 (2 min, 17°C) after 1–4 weeks of exposure. Cells are then counterstained with Cresyl Violet, coverslipped with glycerol, and examined with a Leitz Aristoplan microscope. Under these conditions, neurons positive for endopeptidase 24-16 are brown whereas cells that do not contain the enzyme appear blue. Neurotensin-binding sites are visualized by silver grains on cell bodies and neuronal processes. Statistical analyses are carried out according to the Student's t test.

Modulation of Second Messengers

All intracellular modifications appear rapidly after addition of the peptide and do not necessitate particular precautions in terms of degradation or internalization.

To measure the effect of neurotensin on cGMP level in neurons from cortex, cells are preincubated for 10 min at 37°C as described for binding experiments to neurons except that the binding buffer contains neither peptidase inhibitors nor phenylarsine oxide. Because this effect usually appears within 2 min, times of exposure to the effector must be chosen between 5 and 60 sec. Thus, almost all experimental points are started and stopped individually. Incubations are started by addition of 30 μl of thermostatted binding buffer containing either 1 μM neurotensin (final concentration, 0.1 μM) or no neurotensin (basal level). At given times, removing the medium by aspiration and washing with buffer must be carried out quickly (within 5 sec). The reaction is then terminated by addition of 500 μl of a mixture of

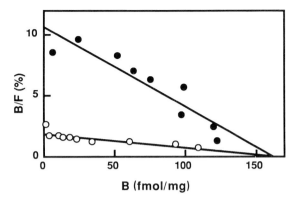

FIG. 1   Scatchard analysis of ^{125}I-labeled [Tyr³]neurotensin binding to intact neurons. Cells were incubated for 45 min at 37°C in the presence of 10 μM phenylarsine oxide (●) or at 0°C (○) with increasing concentrations of labeled peptide. The K_d values obtained are 0.48 nM at 37°C and 2.8 nM at 0°C for an identical B_{max} of 160 fmol/mg protein.

ethanol and 5 mM EDTA (2:1, v/v). Under these conditions, proteins and DNA of lysed cells remain precipitated and the cytoplasmic content is recovered in Eppendorf centrifuge tubes and lyophilized in a speed-vacuum concentrator before analysis with the Amersham (Arlington Heights, IL) radioimmunoassay (RIA) kit.

Results

Binding Properties on Intact Cells

Saturation binding experiments performed on differentiated neurons under conditions in which internalization is abolished lead to Scatchard representations (Fig. 1) that show a single family of neurotensin-binding sites with a maximal capacity of 160 fmol/mg of protein. A similar value is obtained for the membrane preparation of neuronal cells. These sites are insensitive to levocabastine and, as previously observed for high-affinity sites on membrane preparations (4), the affinity of ^{125}I-labeled [Tyr³]neurotensin for neurons is decreased by low temperature from 0.3 nM at 37°C to 1 nM at 0–4°C. Neurotensin receptors are undetectable on undifferentiated neurons. These receptors appear, in parallel with the morphological maturation of neuronal cells, to reach a maximal value after 4 days of culture, which is maintained for 8 days (11). The presence of neurotensin receptor can therefore be considered an *in vitro* neuronal differentiation marker.

The C-terminal hexapeptide neurotensin(8–13) displays all the activity of the native peptide. The general approach used to determine the binding specificity of a given neurotension receptor source is to perform competition experiments between ^{125}I-labeled [Tyr^3]neurotensin and increasing concentrations of a series of analogs modified on the C-terminal hexapeptide sequence. The order of decreasing affinity is neurotensin = acetylneurotensin(8–13) > neurotensin(9–13) > neurotensin(1–12), and corresponds to the common order of specificity observed in all radioreceptor assays for neurotensin (1).

Photoaffinity Labeling of Neurotensin Receptors on Intact Neurons

Using the photoaffinity-labeling method, which avoids the possibility of protein dimerization, radioautographs reveal that several polypeptides (49, 51, 60, and 100 kDa) are specifically labeled because the labeling is totally inhibited in the presence of 1 μM neurotensin. When an equivalent labeling experiment is carried out on membrane preparations from the same neuron culture, only proteins of 49 and 51 kDa remain specifically labeled. This discrepancy may be explained by molecular maturation or association of neurotensin receptors to regulatory proteins.

Internalization Properties

When experiments are carried out at 37°C in the absence of phenylarsine oxide, a discrepancy appears between the total amount of bound ^{125}I-labeled [Tyr^3]neurotensin (250 fmol/mg), and the number of receptors originally present on the cell surface (160 fmol/mg; Fig. 1). This finding suggests that the ligand-induced internalization leads to an appearance on neuron membranes of a new pool of neurotensin receptors. The origin of these binding sites is currently unknown. The amount of incorporated neurotensin as a function of the peptide concentration reveals a half-maximal effect at 0.3 nM (Fig. 2), a value that corresponds to a receptor-dependent sequestration of the effector.

Several studies also suggest that the interaction of neurotensin with its receptor is followed by a ligand-induced internalization of the peptide–receptor complex. High resolution and electron microscopic radioautographs demonstrate the pile-up and presence of intraperikaryal neurotensin-binding sites within the ligated vagus nerve and in neurons of the central nervous system,

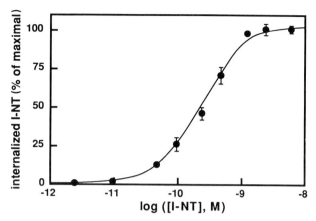

FIG. 2 Dependence of internalized neurotensin on free neurotensin concentration. Cells were incubated with increasing concentrations of ^{125}I-labeled [Tyr3]neurotensin for 45 min at 37°C. At the end of incubations, cells were treated for 2 min with the binding buffer containing 0.5 M NaCl, pH 4, and the radioactivity remaining bound (sequestered ^{125}I-labeled [Tyr3]neurotensin) was counted and plotted as a percentage of maximally internalized peptide. Values are means ± SEM from three independent experiments carried out in duplicate.

respectively (22, 23). A saturable retrograde transport of ^{125}I-labeled [Tyr3]-neurotensin is evidenced both biochemically and radioautographically within the rat nigrostriatal system (24). Using the murine neuroblastoma N1E-115 cell line (25) and the human HT29 cell line (26), biochemical studies indirectly indicate that desensitization of neurotensin-induced activation of second messenger systems results in part from a reduction in receptor number, which is attributed to intracellular sequestration of neurotensin receptors.

The internalization process is rapid ($t_{1/2} < 10$ min) and reaches a plateau value after 20 min (27). The rapidity of the phenomenon is consistent with a specific ligand-induced membrane transport of neurotensin receptors rather than a simple turnover of membrane proteins, which is generally observed within 6 to 12 hr.

Light microscopic examination of radioautographs clearly reveals the presence of intracellular silver grains associated with the cytoplasm in addition to the grains observed at the level of membranes. The corresponding radioactivity is considered to be internal, taking into account that neurons visualized on a 1-μm thin section are cut off through their cell bodies.

When the degradation of internalized neurotensin is assessed and compared with external catabolism, some different proteolytic activities are detected. For example, a carboxypeptidasic activity that leads to the formation of neurotensin(1–12) does not contribute to the external catabolism of neurotensin. Further experiments will be necessary to characterize these internal enzymatic activities on subcellular preparations from plated neurons by using specific peptidase inhibitors.

Colocalization of Neurotensin Receptors with Endopeptidase 24-16 and Tyrosine Hydroxylase

Endopeptidase 24-16 is detected in 80–85% of nondifferentiated neurons in which neurotensin receptors are not yet expressed. This proportion decreases during *in vitro* maturation to reach 35–40% after 4–8 days in culture, suggesting a possible involvement of this and other peptidases in the differentiation program or maturation processes. By contrast, neurotensin receptors appear during differentiation to attain a maximal value after 4 days of culture and are located on about 10% of neurons. Double-labeling experiments show that about 90% of cortical, hypothalamic, and striatal neurons bearing neurotensin receptors also contained endopeptidase 24-16, supporting the hypothesis that one of the putative functions of this enzyme could be the physiological inactivation of neurotensin. However, the presence of endopeptidase 24-16 on a set of neurons that do not exhibit neurotensin receptors also suggests that the enzyme could be involved in the degradation and/or maturation of other peptides (20).

Neurotensin receptors have also been indirectly localized on dopamine neurons from rat substantia nigra because they are depleted following injection of 6-hydroxydopamine (28). By combining ^{125}I-labeled [Tyr³]neurotensin radioautography and tyrosine hydroxylase immunohistochemistry on adjacent midbrain sections, correspondence between localizations of neurotensin receptors and of dopaminergic neurons has been observed in the rat substantia nigra and ventral tegmental area (29). In the second study, the problem concerning the difficulty of visualizing double labeling by using immunohistochemical and radioautographic techniques on the same section is discussed in terms of postfixation procedures.

Neurotensin-Induced Elevation of Intracellular cGMP Level

Numerous studies on cell lines have been performed to assess intracellular modifications following the interaction of neurotensin with its target cells. Effectively, intracellular levels of cGMP (30, 31), cAMP (32), inositol phosphates (33, 34), and Ca^{2+} (35) have been described to be specifically modulated by neurotensin. Incubation of cortical neurons with 0.1 μM neurotensin

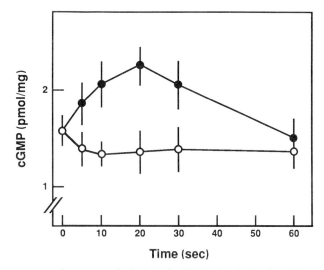

FIG. 3   Time course of neurotensin-induced cGMP stimulation in differentiated neurons. Cells (5×10^5 cells/well) were incubated at 37°C in the presence (●) or in the absence (○) of 0.1 μM neurotensin. After indicated incubation times, the cGMP cell content was measured with the Amersham RIA kit. Values are means ± SEM from three independent experiments carried out in duplicate.

produces a rapid and transient increase of less than twofold over the basal level of the intracellular cGMP concentration (Fig. 3). The response is maximal after 20 sec, then decreases progressively to reach the basal level after 60 sec. As previously observed on neuroblastoma N1E115 (31), this effect is abolished in the absence of Ca^{2+}. The slight amplitude of the effect, by comparison with neuroblastoma, is certainly due to cell heterogeneity because only about 10 to 15% of cortical neurons bear neurotensin receptors (20). In consequence, precise concentration–response curves for the effect of neurotensin are difficult to obtain. By using the calcium-sensitive dye, Fura-2, on cortical neurons and by measuring the formation of inositol phosphates (IPs) in the presence of LiCl on striatal neurons, neurotensin has been shown to increase the level of intracellular Ca^{2+} (36) by activation of phospholipase C (37).

Conclusion

We have described the main biochemical techniques available for neurotensin receptor characterization, localization, and regulation on primary cultures of neurons. These methods can be applied to other cell culture systems if cautions concerning degradation and internalization of the ligand are taken. Indeed, affinity-labeling experiments carried out on cells deriving from other species and tissues and comparison between data obtained on cells of different origin should give definitive answers concerning the existence of multiple forms of neurotensin receptors.

References

1. P. Kitabgi, F. Checler, J. Mazella, and J. P. Vincent, *Rev. Basic Clin. Pharmacol.* **5,** 397–484 (1985).
2. J. Kasckow and C. B. Nemeroff, *Regul. Pept.* **36,** 153–164 (1991).
3. J. Mazella, C. Poustis, C. Labbé, F. Checler, P. Kitabgi, C. Granier, J. Van Rietschoten, and J. P. Vincent, *J. Biol. Chem.* **258,** 3476–3481 (1983).
4. J. Mazella, J. Chabry, P. Kitabgi, and J. P. Vincent, *J. Biol. Chem.* **263,** 144–149 (1988).
5. J. L. Sadoul, F. Checler, F. Kitabgi, W. Rostène, F. Javoy-Agid, and J. P. Vincent, *Biochem. Biophys. Res. Commun.* **125,** 395–404 (1984).
6. A. Schotte and P. M. Laduron, *Brain Res.* **408,** 326–328 (1987).
7. A. Mills, C. D. Demoliou-Mason, and E. A. Barnard, *J. Biol. Chem.* **263,** 13–16 (1988).
8. J. Mazella, J. Chabry, N. Zsürger, and J. P. Vincent, *J. Biol. Chem.* **264,** 5559–5563 (1989).
9. Y. Miyamoto-Lee, S. Shiosaka, and M. Tohyama, *Peptides* (*N.Y.*) **12,** 1001–1006 (1991).
10. K. Tanaka, M. Masu, and S. Nakanishi, *Neuron* **4,** 847–854 (1990).
11. F. Checler, J. Mazella, P. Kitabgi, and J. P. Vincent, *J. Neurochem.* **47,** 1742–1748 (1986).
12. J. Mazella, K. Léonard, J. Chabry, P. Kitabgi, J. P. Vincent, and A. Beaudet, *Brain Res.* **564,** 249–255 (1991).
13. J. L. Sadoul, J. Mazella, S. Amar, P. Kitabgi, and J. P. Vincent, *Biochem. Biophys. Res. Commun.* **120,** 812–819 (1984).
14. J. Mazella, P. Kitabgi, and J. P. Vincent, *J. Biol. Chem.* **260,** 508–514 (1985).
15. F. Checler, J. P. Vincent, and P. Kitabgi, *J. Neurochem.* **41,** 375–384 (1983).
16. U. K. Laemmli, *Nature* (*London*) **227,** 680–685 (1970).
17. R. Hammerschlag, F. A. Bolen, and G. C. Stone, *J. Neurochem.* **52,** 268–273 (1989).
18. F. Checler, J. P. Vincent, and P. Kitabgi, *J. Biol. Chem.* **261,** 11274–11281 (1986).
19. F. Checler, H. Barelli, P. Kitabgi, and J. P. Vincent, *Biochimie* **70,** 75–82 (1988).
20. J. Chabry, F. Checler, J. P. Vincent, and J. Mazella, *J. Neurosci.* **10,** 3916–3921 (1990).
21. F. Checler, H. Barelli, and J. P. Vincent, *Biochem. J.* **257,** 549–554 (1989).
22. J. P. Kessler and A. Beaudet, *J. Neurosci.* **9,** 466–472 (1989).
23. C. Dana, M. Vial, K. Léonard, A. Beauregard, P. Kitabgi, J. P. Vincent, W. Rostène, and A. Beaudet, *J. Neurosci.* **9,** 2247–2257 (1989).

24. M. N. Castel, C. Malgouris, J. C. Polanchard, and P. M. Laduron, *Neuroscience* **36,** 425–430 (1990).
25. J. A. Gilbert, T. R. Strobel, and E. Richelson, *Biochem. Pharmacol.* **37,** 2833–2838 (1988).
26. J. T. Turner, M. R. James-Kracke, and J. M. Camden, *J. Pharmacol. Exp. Ther.* **253,** 1049–1056 (1990).
27. J. Chabry, J. P. Vincent, and J. Mazella, submitted for publication.
28. J. M. Palacios and M. J. Kuhar, *Nature* (*London*) **294,** 587–589 (1981).
29. E. Szigethy and A. Beaudet, *J. Comp. Neurol.* **279,** 128–137 (1989).
30. J. A. Gilbert, M. McKinney, and F. Richelson, *Soc. Neurosci. Abstr.* **10,** 378 (1984).
31. S. Amar, J. Mazella, F. Checler, P. Kitabgi, and J. P. Vincent, *Biochem. Biophys. Res. Commun.* **129,** 117–125 (1985).
32. J. C. Bozou, S. Amar, J. P. Vincent, and P. Kitabgi, *Mol. Pharmacol.* **29,** 489–496 (1986).
33. S. Amar, P. Kitabgi, and J. P. Vincent, *FEBS Lett.* **201,** 31–36 (1986).
34. S. Amar, P. Kitabgi, and J. P. Vincent, *J. Neurochem.* **49,** 999–1006 (1987).
35. J. C. Bozou, N. Rochet, I. Magnaldo, J. P. Vincent, and P. Kitabgi, *Biochem. J.* **264,** 871–878 (1989).
36. M. Sato, S. Shiosaka, and M. Tohyama, *Dev. Brain Res.* **58,** 97–103 (1991).
37. S. Weiss, B. H. Schmidt, M. Sebben, D. E. Kemp, J. Bockaert, and F. Sladeczek, *J. Neurochem.* **50,** 1425–1433 (1988).

[21] Analysis of the Structure and Function of the Fast Nerve Growth Factor Receptor

Andrew A. Welcher

Introduction

A central issue in cell biology is how a signal on the outside of a cell is communicated to the inside of the cell. Research has focused on the role of proteins, particularly receptors and channels, which are primarily responsible for transducing the signal across the cell membrane. Two general strategies have been used to analyze the structure and function of these proteins. The first consists of direct modification of the protein, before or after purification, and analyzing the effects of the modification. More recently, recombinant DNA technology has produced an alternative approach consisting of the isolation of DNA sequences that encode receptors. After isolation of the receptor-encoding sequence, it is possible to produce the normal protein as well as mutant forms of the protein in large amounts in various *in vitro* systems, which facilitates the analysis. Unfortunately, it is still not possible to simply look at the primary amino acid sequence of a protein and determine its exact three-dimensional structure. Ultimate determination of the structure can be accomplished by X-ray crystallography; however, this is a time-consuming process, and limited to laboratories that have access to the equipment. Even if the structure is known, the analysis of mutant forms of the protein can shed light on how the amino acid residues contribute to the function of the protein. This chapter describes some fundamental experiments that can be performed in virtually any laboratory with a minimum of equipment, to try to understand the structure and function of a particular receptor. Although this chapter deals with our studies on the rat fast nerve growth factor receptor, it must be emphasized that similar strategies have been used to look at a number of different receptors and channels (1–3).

We are interested in the role of neurotrophic factors in the nervous system (4, 5). Specifically, we would like to determine how the interaction between nerve growth factor (NGF) and its receptors leads to signal transduction. As an initial step in this process, we are interested in determining which amino acid residues in the NGF receptors are involved in the binding of NGF.

Numerous studies have uncovered the role of NGF in the development of sensory and sympathetic neurons, and have suggested a role for NGF in the maintenance of the cholinergic neurons of the basal forebrain (6–8). More

Methods in Neurosciences, Volume 11

recently it has been shown that NGF is a member of a family of neurotrophic factors that also include brain-derived neurotrophic factor (9), neurotrophin 3 (10), neurotrophin 4 (11), and neurotrophin 5 (12). Interestingly, these neurotrophic factors are able to bind to overlapping sets of receptors (13, 14), although it is known that these factors work on different neuronal populations *in vivo*. Therefore it is of general interest to determine how the receptors for these neurotrophic factors are able to discriminate between the various factors. Clearly, the manner in which a neurotrophic factor binds to a receptor will determine whether a signal is generated and transduced to the inside of the cell.

Work from a number of laboratories has started to identify the receptors for NGF. The first NGF receptor isolated, referred to in this chapter as the fast nerve growth factor receptor (fNGFR), has been cloned from rat (15), human (16), and chicken (17). More recently, another type of receptor for NGF has been identified in rats (18), and humans (19). This receptor differs from the fNGFR in a number of characteristics; significantly, this receptor is a member of the family of tyrosine kinase receptors, which has implications for how signal transduction is generated by NGF. By studying the interaction of NGF with these receptors, it may be possible to determine how NGF causes phenotypic changes in the nervous system. In addition, because both types of NGF receptors identified to date are part of larger families of receptors, the study of the interaction of NGF with its receptors will shed light on the binding of ligands to these other related receptors. This chapter will describe how a mutational analysis of the fNGFR was used to start to identify the amino acid residues that play important roles in the structure and function of the fNGFR.

Methodology

Computational Analysis

The strategy outlined here assumes that the DNA sequence encoding a particular receptor has been cloned. There are a number of strategies for doing this; these are outside the scope of this chapter, and can be found in a number of general laboratory manuals (20). Usually, the first experiments with a DNA sequence encoding a receptor are done on the computer. Ultimately, it will be possible to enter an amino acid sequence into the computer, and have the computer generate a picture of the three-dimensional structure of that protein, as well as highlight regions that may be involved in particular functions. Although the existing technology is not at this level, a computer analysis will make predictions about structure and function, and serves as a starting point for experiments to test those predictions. Several commercial programs are available for sequence analysis; the guiding factors in choosing the appropriate software are the price and the hardware available. Our own studies have used the Genetics Computer Group, Inc. (Madison, WI) software (GCG package; 21) Adaptations of this program, which will run on personal computers (IBM or Apple), are available from Intelligenetics (Mountain View, CA). The following programs, indicated in italics, were used. More detailed descriptions of these programs, and how to use them, can be found in the user's guide that comes with the programs. First, the DNA sequence was converted to the amino acid sequence using *Translate*. Once the protein sequence is determined, the protein sequence can be compared to other known proteins, using the *FASTA* program. This program allows the user to search for related sequences in the database that may reveal homology to other proteins of known structure and function. In addition the program can be used to identify repeating patterns within the same protein. This type of analysis was used to identify the repeating cysteine-rich sequences in the extracellular region of the fNGFR. More sophisticated versions of the *FASTA* program have been used to show that there is a family of proteins that appear to share this repeating cysteine structure (22). As structural and functional analysis is done on these other proteins, the information should be relevant to studies of the fNGFR and vice versa. A comparison of the rat, human, and chicken fNGFR sequences indicates that different regions of the protein show different extents of homology (17). Usually, the conservation of sequence between species indicates that those amino acid residues are important for structures or functions that have been conserved among the species. Studies on mouse NGF have shown that it can bind to the NGF receptors from all three species, thus the NGF-binding domains should be highly conserved. Unfortunately, in this case the three receptors are highly conserved in numerous portions of the receptor protein, so it is difficult to make predictions from this type of analysis. However, in other situations interspecies comparisons have been useful for localizing specific functions (23).

Next, the amino acid sequence was analyzed using the programs *Peptide-Structure* and *PlotStructure*. These two programs make predictions about potential secondary structures that may exist in the receptor. With receptors, the two most apparent structures that will appear from this analysis are the existence of any potential glycosylation sites, and also any regions of the protein that are likely to be associated with or cross the membrane. Analysis of the fNGFR revealed two potential N-linked glycosylation sites in one stretch of the protein, followed by a number of potential sites for O-linked glycosylation. This region was followed by an extremely hydrophobic region, which at 22 amino acid residues in length was long enough to transverse the

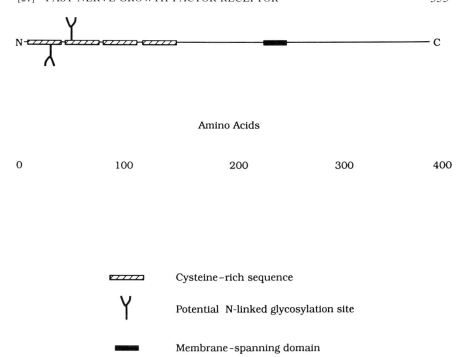

FIG. 1   Schematic representation of the fNGFR based on computational analysis of the primary amino acid sequence.

membrane. Additional functional domains can be identified through the use of the program *Motif*. This program compares the protein sequence to a database of several hundred patterns and functional sites identified for other proteins, and can often give clues as to how the receptor might function. In the case of the fNGFR, this program does not identify a consensus ATP-binding site in the intracellular domain of the receptor, thus indicating that the fNGFR is not a tyrosine kinase receptor.

The predictions from this combination of computer programs were used to generate a schematic structure of the fNGFR (Fig. 1). The N at the left refers to the amino terminus of the protein, while the C on the right side indicates the carboxy terminus. The receptor appeared to have three regions, an extracellular domain, a transmembrane domain (open box), and an intracellular domain. The extracellular domain was further subdivided into the cysteine-rich sequences (four hatched boxes), and the rest of the extracellular domain. In addition the two N-linked glycosylation sites are indicated in the cysteine-rich sequences. Although Fig. 1 provides a relatively crude structural diagram, it can be used to devise experiments. For example, is the hydrophobic region truly a membrane-spanning domain? Is there a functional difference between the two regions of the extracellular domain? What role do the N- and O-linked glycosylations have in the structure of the protein and do they influence NGF binding?

It should be stressed that there are much more sophisticated protein analysis programs that are better suited for the determination of local secondary structure, such as α helix or β sheets, based on the primary amino acid sequence (24, 25). The programs described here as well as commercial variations of these programs have been developed to the point that the novice should be capable of using them, and the information gathered will be helpful in the mutational analysis of receptors or ion channels.

Construction of Mutants

After using the computer to generate some structural information, the next step is to test directly the predictions made by the computer. This section describes two mutagenesis strategies to localize a particular structure or function to a limited number of amino acid residues. The first involves the deletion of amino acid residues from the protein. The removal of a large number of amino acid residues helps to limit the number of amino acid residues that must be studied. Once a structure or function is localized, the second strategy, site-directed mutagenesis, is used to study the role of individual amino acid residues. An alternate strategy that has been used is linker scanning mutagenesis (26), in which the spacing between particular amino acid residues is changed by the insertion of random amino acids. This approach will not be discussed here, as this approach has been more successfully applied to the study of promoter regions (27) rather than proteins.

In the case of the fNGFR our primary interest was in identifying the NGF-binding domain of the receptor. Work on a number of transmembrane receptors indicated that the ligands bind to the extracellular region. The mutational approach then seeks to narrow down the region responsible for ligand binding. In the case of the fNGFR, this region comprised 222 amino acid residues. Our initial approach (24) was to take advantage of two unique restriction enzymes, identified by the computer, that each cut at one place in the fNGFR cDNA sequence, to make two large deletions in the protein. These mutants are shown in Fig. 2. The first mutant, NGFRt256, was constructed by digestion with the restriction enzyme *Nar* I, which cleaved the cDNA sequence in the region encoding the protein just after the transmembrane region. NGFRt256 was constructed to test whether the intracellular domain had any role in the binding of NGF to the extracellular domain. The second mutant, NGFRt168, was constructed by digestion with the restriction

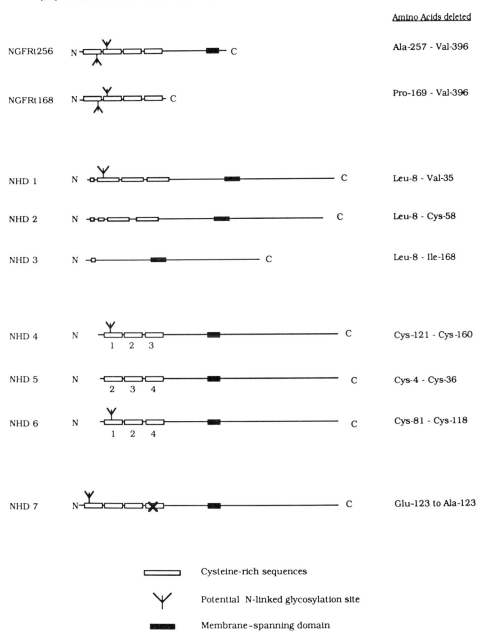

Fig. 2 Schematic representation of the fNGFR mutants. The left-hand column refers to the mutant name as discussed in text. The middle column is a graphical representation of the altered fNGFR protein. The right column lists the specific amino acid residues affected in each mutant.

enzyme *Bam*HI, which generated a truncated cDNA encoding the first 168 amino acid residues of the receptor. NGFRt168 was constructed to attempt to identify a smaller region of the extracellular domain that was needed for NGF binding. The *Bam*HI site also split the extracellular domain into two separate regions identified by the computer, the cysteine-rich sequences and the O-linked glycosylation-rich sequence. In both cases the truncated DNA fragments were generated or isolated and subcloned into expression vectors. A brief description of the expression vectors will be included in the next section. The two truncated sequences were artificially removed from the natural stop codon in the protein, which occurs after amino acid residue 396, so it was necessary to attach a synthetic DNA linker sequence encoding stop codons in all three frames (universal translation terminator, Pharmacia, Piscataway, NJ) to the 3' end of the cDNA sequences. In these two cases, the attachment of the synthetic linker resulted in the addition of some additional amino acid residues to the carboxy terminus of the truncated proteins (four amino acid residues to NGFRt256, two amino acid residues to NGFRt168). Because of the properties and location of the added amino acid residues it was unlikely that these additional amino acids would cause a problem. In general, one wants to minimize the number of extra amino acid residues added to the receptor of interest. These constructs were analyzed for their ability to bind NGF, as described in the following section. The results are summarized in Table I. The construct NGFRt256 bound NGF with an affinity comparable to wild type. Using a slightly different binding assay (24) it was shown that the mutant NGFRt168 also bound NGF with an affinity

TABLE I   Nerve Growth Factor-Binding
Ability Compared to Binding to
the Wild-Type Receptor in
Comparable Binding Assays[a]

NGFR mutant	NGF-binding ability
NGFRt256	+ + + + +
NGFRt168	+ + + + +
NHD 1	+
NHD 2	+
NHD 3	−
NHD 4	±
NHD 5	±
NHD 6	±
NHD 7	+ + + + +

[a] + + + + +, Identical NGF-binding ability between the wild-type and mutant NGF receptors. + or ±, Very low NGF binding.

comparable to a soluble form of the wild-type receptor. It should be noted that NGFRt168 was a non-membrane-bound form of the NGFR and thus we were unable to directly compare the affinity of NGF for this form to the wild-type, membrane-bound form of the receptor. These results indicated that the extracellular domain of the NGFR contained the NGF-binding site and, further, that the cysteine-rich region, consisting of 168 amino acid residues, could bind NGF. It should be mentioned that it was possible that other regions of the extracellular domain might also bind NGF. This was ruled out when Baldwin and co-workers took advantage of another unique restriction site (*Sac*II), and the noncysteine-rich region of the fNGFR was deleted (25). This protein was able to bind NGF comparable to wild type, indicating that the cysteine-rich region was necessary and sufficient for NGF binding.

Confronted with a group of 168 amino acid residues that appeared to bind NGF, we next tried to narrow down this region. Our approach was to make progressively larger deletions within this portion of the protein. Initially we decided to remove amino acids progressively from the amino terminus. We could have made internal deletions but we were concerned that this would juxtapose amino acid residues not normally together, which might destroy any remaining structure. One complication was that the N terminus contained the amino acid sequence for the signal sequence, which is necessary for proper protein processing (28). For this reason we had to reattach the signal sequence to our constructs after we had made deletions in the portion encoding the mature protein. An outline of the procedure is shown in Fig. 3. The left-hand side of the figure describes the isolation of the vector and the signal sequence of the fNGFR. We took advantage of a unique *Stu*I site that cleaved the DNA after the region that encoded the signal peptide sequence. In addition, the vector was digested with *Hin*dIII, which removed the remainder of the fNGFR cDNA. The right-hand side of Fig. 3 describes the preparation of the truncated sequences. The original vector was digested with *Eco*RI, and then treated with exonuclease III for varying lengths of time. A commercially available kit (Erase-A-Base; Promega, Madison, WI) was used to construct the internal deletions by following the instructions of the manufacturer. The only variability we noticed with this kit was that it was useful to do a time course of nuclease treatment, as there seemed to be some variability in the nuclease activity depending on the individual doing the titration. Once an individual had determined the time course, it was quite straightforward to produce a nested set of deletions. The truncated DNA was treated with Klenow fragment (Bethesda Research Laboratories, Gaithersburg, MD) to create a blunt end at the 5' end of the fNGFR cDNA, and the DNA was digested with *Hin*dIII, which released the truncated fNGFR sequences from the vector. The fNGFR DNA fragments were separated from the vector DNA by Tris–borate–ethylenediaminetetraacetic acid (EDTA)–agarose gel

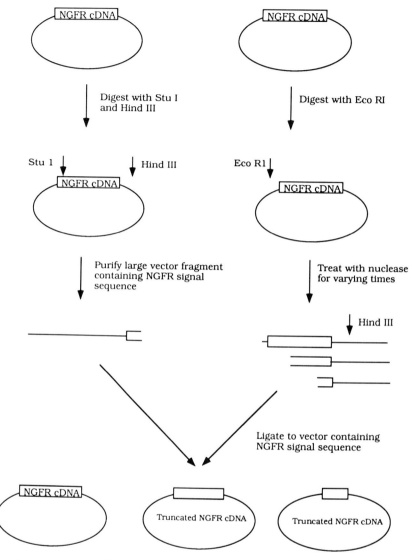

FIG. 3   Schematic outline of the construction of amino-terminus deletions of the fNGFR. The left side describes the construction of the vector containing the wild-type fNGFR signal sequence. The right side describes the construction of the truncated fNGFR sequences.

electrophoresis (20), and the DNA was purified from the gel (NA45 paper; Schleicher & Schuell; Keene, NH), following the instructions of the manufacturer. More recently the GeneClean kit (Bio 101; San Diego, CA) has been used for DNA isolation. This kit contains the instructions and reagents necessary for the isolation of DNA from agarose gels. This kit is somewhat easier to use than the NA45 paper, and is more efficient if the DNA pieces are several kilobases in length. The truncated fragments were then subcloned into the vector fragment containing the signal peptide sequence. The blunt-ended 5' cDNA was attached to the blunt-ended site generated by *Stu*I, while the two *Hin*dIII sites were ligated to each other. This created a series of fNGFR cDNA sequences that had the wild-type signal sequence but contained internal deletions of varying length within the mature protein-coding region. The constructs were sequenced by dideoxy sequencing (29), using primers from the vector sequence and the Sequenase kit (United States Biochemical, Cleveland, OH). The deletions stopped after different nucleotides, so it was necessary to determine which of the ligated fragments generated an NGFR open reading frame that started with the wild type signal sequence and continued with the partially deleted mature coding region. Three truncated sequences were chosen for further studies; they are shown in Fig. 2 as NHD 1, NHD 2, and NHD 3. NHD 1 had a small deletion in the first cysteine-rich sequence. NHD 2 had a small deletion in the first cysteine-rich sequence and lacked the second cysteine-rich sequence. NHD 3 contained only a small portion of the first cysteine-rich sequence but lacked the second, third, and fourth cysteine-rich sequences.

The reconstructed sequences were then excised from the original vector, subcloned into an expression vector (24), and expressed in COS cells. The ability of these three truncated proteins to bind NGF is shown in Table I. NHD 1 and NHD 2 were able to bind NGF but at greatly reduced levels relative to wild type. NHD 3 was unable to bind NGF at all. These results suggested that perhaps there were small regions that could partially bind NGF, but it appeared that a larger tertiary structure was needed for wild-type binding. The progressive deletions were useful in that large regions of the protein were removed at once; however, because they were of increasing length it was not possible to look at the role of individual cysteine-rich sequences in NGF binding. The extent of the deletions was determined by the exonuclease, and this made it difficult to delete a prescribed number of nucleotides specifically unless we screened a large number of deletions. In addition, approximately two of three of the truncated sequences resulted in a stop codon once the wild-type signal sequence was fused to the truncated sequences, therefore it was necessary to sequence a large number of truncated DNA sequences.

To circumvent these problems we switched to a procedure termed polymerase chain reaction (PCR) overlap extension (25, 30). This technique allows one to use oligonucleotides of a specific sequence, in conjunction with the polymerase chain reaction to construct either deletions or site-specific mutations. By choosing the correct oligonucleotide primers it is possible to tailor the mutations to specific nucleotides determined before the mutagenesis is performed. This procedure was used to remove each of the four cysteine-rich sequences individually, to try to determine if there were differences between the abilities of these regions to bind NGF. This procedure is outlined in Fig. 4. This example shows the deletion of the second cysteine-rich sequence; however, the same procedure, with different oligonucleotides, was used to specifically remove each of the cysteine-rich sequences (25). Oligonucleotides A and D contain the sequences at the 5' and 3' ends of the fNGFR cDNA, respectively. Oligonucleotide B contains the sequence for the 3' end of the first cysteine-rich sequence and the 5' end of the third cysteine-rich sequence. Oligonucleotide C is the complement of oligonucleotide B. Two PCR reactions are performed, one with oligonucleotides A and B, the other with C and D. The two amplified DNA pieces are purified as described earlier. The two fragments are then combined with oligonucleotides A and D, and a third PCR reaction is performed. Because of the sequences of oligonucleotides B and C, the fragments AB and CD have a region of overlap and thus will anneal. Significantly, the overlap between oligonucleotides B and C has deleted the sequence contained in the second cysteine-rich sequence, so the final amplification generates the product shown at the bottom of Fig. 4, which contains cysteine-rich sequences 1, 3, and 4, but not sequence 2. To simplify subcloning, restriction site recognition sequences were added to the ends of oligonucleotides A and D, so that the final amplification product could be subcloned into the vector of choice. The main considerations in the PCR reactions have been described in detail elsewhere (31). In general one should limit the length of the DNA that is being amplified, as the *Taq* polymerase does make errors at a frequency that can cause problems. In general, try to limit the amplification to less than 1 kilobase (kb). If the region being examined is larger, it should be possible to amplify only the region containing the deletion and then to place that back into the original construct, by taking advantage of unique restriction sites.

Reactions 1 and 2 consisted of 100 ng of starting wild-type template: 500 ng each of oligonucleotides A and B or oligonucleotides C and D; 1.25 mM dATP, dCTP, dGTP, and dTTP; 100 mM Tris-HCl, pH 8.3; 500 mM KCl; 1 mM MgCl$_2$; and 2.5 units of *Taq* polymerase (Perkin-Elmer, Norwalk, CT) in a total reaction volume of 100 μl. The amplification consisted of a total of 25 cycles, each cycle consisting of 1 min of denaturation at 94°C, 2 min of annealing at 55°C, and 3 min of extension at 72°C. At the end of 25 cycles, there was a final extension for 5 min at 72°C. The DNA samples were directly

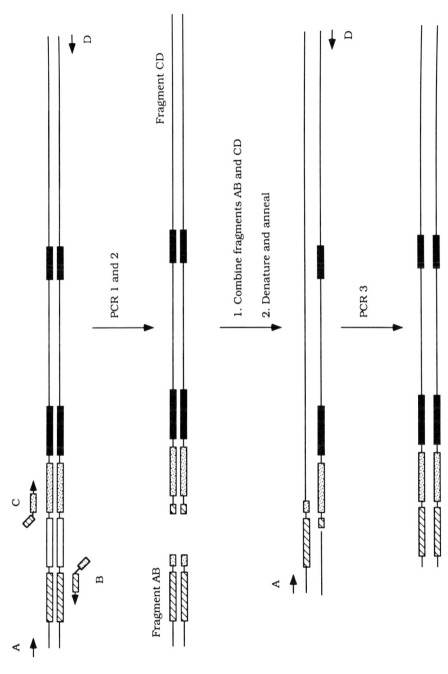

FIG. 4 Schematic outline of the method of mutagenesis by PCR overlap extension. Diagram shows the specific deletion of the second cysteine-rich sequence.

loaded onto a 1.2% (w/v) Tris–borate–EDTA (TBE)–agarose gel (20), fragments of the correct size were gel purified using GeneClean as described previously, and the DNA was eluted into 20 μl of distilled water. An aliquot of the purified DNA was electrophoresed on a TBE–agarose gel to determine the DNA concentration, by comparison to known amounts of DNA loaded on the same gel.

Reaction 3 was similar to reactions 1 and 2, except that the template consisted of 300–500 ng of purified DNA from the first two reactions, and oligonucleotides A and D were used. This PCR reaction was performed as before. A small aliquot from the completed reaction was then analyzed by TBE–agarose electrophoresis to determine that the overlap reaction had been successful. The reaction volume was then increased to 400 μl with distilled water, extracted one time with chloroform to remove mineral oil, extracted another time with a phenol–chloroform mixture (24:1, v/v) to completely remove any protein, and extracted one final time with an equal volume of chloroform. Forty microliters of 2.5 M sodium acetate, pH 5.2, was added, the sample mixed, and then 1 ml of 100% ethanol was added, and the tube incubated at $-20°C$ for at least 1 hr. The DNA was pelleted by centrifugation in a microfuge at 12,000 rpm for 10 min at 4°C, the pellet was washed by addition of 500 μl of 70% ethanol, and the tube was vortexed until the pellet was floating free. The DNA was immediately repelleted as before, the ethanol was removed, and the pellet was dried by vacuum centrifugation for 5 min at room temperature (Speed Vac; Savant Instruments, Hicksville, NY). The DNA was then digested with the appropriate restriction enzymes (based on the sites in oligonucleotides A and D) in a reaction volume of 20 to 50 μl for 2 hr at 37°C. The sample was directly loaded onto a 1.2% (w/v) TBE–agarose gel, and the correct-sized piece was gel purified as before. The purified DNA was ligated into the original construct, lacking the cysteine-rich sequence. For the fNGFR, the original construct was digested with *Eco*RI and *Bam*HI, and the vector–cDNA fragment isolated from the fragment containing the cysteine-rich encoding sequence. The amplified region of the constructs was sequenced using the double-stranded plasmids. Because of the potential artifacts generated by PCR it is important to sequence all amplified constructs. Finally, the constructs were excised from the prokaryotic vector with the restriction enzyme *Hinc*II, the truncated fragment was gel purified as before, and then ligated into the eukaryotic expression vector and used to transfect cells (24). Ideally, the PCR-amplified pieces would have been directly subcloned into the eukaryotic expression vector. Because of the available restriction sites in the fNGFR cDNA as well as the various vectors, it was necessary to use the two-step process outlined here.

Three of the constructed mutants are shown in schematic form in Fig. 2 (NHD 4, NHD 5, and NHD 6). The binding of NGF to these various mutants is outlined in Table I (25). The three mutants were able to bind NGF at only greatly reduced levels relative to the wild-type receptor. One of the mutants (not shown), which lacked repeat 2, failed to be expressed in the COS cells, so we were unable to determine NGF binding to this mutant.

These results suggested that at least three of the four repeats were necessary to form a structure that would bind NGF with wild-type affinity. It therefore seemed likely that there are either components in each of the repeats that directly contribute to NGF binding or, alternatively, the cysteine-rich sequences form a general structure that is needed for NGF binding.

Because removal of the individual cysteine-rich sequences had such a drastic effect on NGF binding, our next approach has been to make site-specific mutations of individual amino acid residues within the cysteine-rich sequences, and to analyze their effect on NGF binding. The site-specific mutants were generated by a modification of the PCR overlap extension protocol described earlier. In this variation, oligonucleotides B and C, shown in Fig. 4, span the mutation site, and each contains a single nucleotide change that results in an altered amino acid residue. An alternate procedure is well established for the development of site-specific mutants (32). Although this procedure has been used successfully a number of times, in our hands this approach involved more work than the PCR approach. The main differences are that the PCR approach uses two oligonucleotides instead of one, so price might be a concern; and the PCR may introduce errors, so it should be limited to small regions of DNA (less than 1 kb). By taking advantage of existing restriction sites, it should be possible to amplify a small piece containing the mutation, and then incorporate it into the larger construct, as described previously. Our initial approach has been to concentrate on the fourth cysteine-rich sequence. It is apparent that NGF is a basic protein with a pI of 9.3 (33). Computer analysis of the fNGFR indicated that the cysteine-rich sequences were of varying charge, but that the fourth cysteine-rich sequence was extremely acidic. This analysis suggests that there is an electrostatic interaction between the positively charged NGF and the negatively charged, fourth cysteine-rich sequence of the fNGFR. To directly test this hypothesis, four acidic amino acid residues were altered in the fourth repeat, changing those amino acids to alanine, a neutral amino acid residue often chosen in mutagenesis studies because it tends to have minimal impact on tertiary structure. Construction and analysis of the mutants were done as before. One of these mutants is shown as NHD 7 in Fig. 2, and binding analysis indicated that NHD 7 bound NGF to the same extent as the wild-type receptor (Table I). Analysis of the other individual mutants is in progress. It may be necessary to change all of the negatively charged residues collectively, to affect NGF binding measurably.

This section has described several procedures for mutating a particular stretch of protein to determine the role of that region in the structure or function of the protein. The general approach is to successively narrow down the functional domain to as few amino acid residues as possible. By limiting the number of amino acid residues involved, it is possible to make and test predictions of how those amino acid residues contribute to the structure and function of the protein.

Analysis of Mutations

After construction of different types of mutants, the mutants must be tested for the effect of the mutation on the structure or function of the protein. This section describes the production and analysis of the mutant proteins. Typically, one type of mutation would be constructed and tested, and based on the effects of that mutation, further mutations would then be constructed.

The basic goal of this step is to produce large enough amounts of the protein so that functional analysis can be done. There are a large number of systems currently being used to express recombinant proteins. These include bacteria, yeast, baculovirus, *Xenopus* oocytes, transient expression in mammalian cells, and stable expression in mammalian cells (34). Space limitations make it impossible to describe the pros and cons of every system, but the following points should be made. The bacterial systems are probably the fastest and easiest to use, but are not useful for membrane proteins and other proteins with large numbers of cysteine residues that will not fold correctly. The *Xenopus* system has been extensively used for the cloning and analysis of ion- and ligand-gated channels, and it is an excellent system when single-cell analysis can be performed; however, it is not technically possible to inject large numbers of oocytes to generate a large amount of recombinant protein. Baculovirus and stable transfected cell lines take the longest to generate, but result in the long-term expression of recombinant proteins, which may facilitate the analysis. This section will describe our work with a transient expression system using COS cells. This system is relatively fast and is capable of producing virtually any mammalian protein, soluble or membrane bound. Large numbers of cells, each containing large amounts of the recombinant protein, can be produced. The reason COS cells are so useful is that they were engineered (35) to produce the large T antigen of the simian virus 40 (SV40) virus. When the appropriate plasmids are introduced into these cells the large T antigen interacts with specific DNA sequences on the plasmid to increase the copy number greatly, as well as the amount of RNA produced from the cloned gene. This in turns generates large amounts of protein in the cells. The main drawback to transient expression is that not all the cells will take up DNA, and so not all the cells will express the protein. In our hands, 10 to 30% of the cells will express the recombinant protein, but those cells will express greater than 10^6 copies of the protein per cell. The efficiency of transfection is only a concern if for some reason the nonexpressing cells generate too high a background. In our hands, this has not been a problem. In general, using the COS cell system for the initial analysis and screening of receptor mutants is to be recommended, and the stable expression systems for long-term studies of a few interesting mutant proteins.

Transfection Procedure

The initial step in transient expression is to introduce the DNA into the cells. There are a number of procedures for getting the cells to take up DNA; currently it is not understood mechanistically how these work. We have tried several different transfection procedures, including DEAE-dextran, calcium phosphate, lipofectin, and electroporation (20). In our hands a modification of the DEAE-dextran method gives the most consistent results.

COS cells were grown in Dulbecco's modified Eagle's medium (DMEM), supplemented with 5% (v/v) horse serum (Hyclone, Logan, UT) and 5% (v/v) supplemented calf serum (Hyclone), at a temperature of 37°C, with 5% CO_2. The cells were grown on 100-mm dishes (Falcon; Becton Dickinson Labware, Oxnard, CA) until the cells were confluent. The night before the cells were to be transfected, they were removed from the plate with a solution of 171 mM NaCl, 3 mM KCl, 2 mM KH_2PO_4, and 5 mM Na_2HPO_4 [phosphate-buffered saline (PBS)] containing 0.05% (w/v) trypsin (GIBCO, Grand Island, NY), counted using a hemacytometer, and pelleted by centrifugation at 2000 rpm for 3 min in an IEC clinical centrifuge. The cells were resuspended in DMEM supplemented with serum, and plated out on 100-mm dishes at a concentration of 1×10^6 cells/plate. The next day the cells were transfected. The following mixture was prepared in a polypropylene tube, one tube per plate. To 2 ml of DMEM without serum were added 5 μg of DNA (volume, 1–100 μl), and 50 μl of a 20-mg/ml solution of DEAE-dextran (M_r 500,000; Pharmacia), and the tube was mixed gently. The cells were washed on the plate three times with 10 ml of DMEM without serum, the DNA mixture was added, and the cells were placed in the incubator for 30 min at 37°C. A 100× chloroquine mixture was prepared, consisting of 8 mM chloroquine (Sigma, St. Louis, MO) dissolved in autoclaved, distilled water. For each plate, 40 μl of this solution was added to 4 ml of DMEM without serum, and added to the cells after the 30-min incubation. The DNA mixture was not removed before addition of the chloroquine. The cells were placed back in the incubator for 2.5 hr at 37°C. The solution was then aspirated off the cells, and to each plate was added 4 ml of DMEM without serum containing 10% (v/v) dimethylsulfoxide (DMSO) (Aldrich, Milwaukee, WI). This was left on the cells for 2.5 min at 37°C, aspirated off, and 10 ml of DMEM with serum was added to the cells. The cells were then put into the incubator until they were harvested 48 to 72 hr after the transfection.

Cross-Linking Assay

Routinely, the cells are transfected in the afternoon, and harvested in the morning 3 days later (66 hr). Between 48 to 72 hr there is no significant change in the level of expression. When expressing secreted forms of the receptor, the cells and the conditioned medium were harvested 72 hr after the transfection, as the amount of soluble receptor in the medium increased with time.

To determine if the mutant receptors were able to bind NGF, usually a cross-linking analysis was done. Alternatively, the cells were used for soluble receptor-binding studies (24), or Scatchard analysis (36) was used to determine the equilibrium binding constants. Usually, one-half of a transfected plate was harvested for the binding study, and the other half of the plate was used for protein isolation, followed by Western blotting using anti-receptor antibodies to determine that the mutant receptors were being expressed.

Cells were removed from the plates with a solution of PBS containing 1 mM EDTA (do not use trypsin, as the receptors on the cell surface will be degraded), and pelleted by centrifugation as before. The cells from each 100-mm plate were resuspended in 2 ml of 137 mM NaCl, 5 mM KCl, 2.5 mM CaCl$_2$, 1 mM KH$_2$PO$_4$, 1 mM MgSO$_4$, 10 mM N-2-hydroxyethylpiperazine-N'-2-ethanesulfonic acid (HEPES), 1 mg/ml bovine serum albumin (BSA) (Sigma), 1 mg/ml glucose (NGF-binding buffer, pH 7.4) supplemented with 1 mM phenylmethylsulfonyl fluoride (PMSF; Sigma), triturated vigorously several times to generate a single-cell suspension, and an aliquot of cells was counted using a hemacytometer. Equivalent numbers of cells from the various transfections were removed for cross-linking and the remaining cells were stored on ice. The cells for cross-linking were placed into a polypropylene tube and pelleted by centrifugation as before. The cells were resuspended in 1 ml of NGF-binding buffer, and triturated with a P-1000 pipetman (Rainin, Woburn, MA) to dissociate the cells. ^{125}I-Labeled NGF (37) was added to the tube to a final NGF concentration of 1 nM, and the mixture was incubated at 0°C for 60 min with mixing every 10 min to resuspend settled cells. Next, 1-ethyl-3-(3-dimethylaminopropyl)carbodiimide (EDC; Sigma), dissolved in distilled water, was added to a final concentration of 2 mM, and the cells incubated for 30 min at room temperature, with mixing every 10 min. After this incubation, 1 ml of PBS containing 10 mM Tris-HCl, pH 7.5, was added to each tube, and the cells were pelleted by centrifugation at 4000 rpm for 3 min at 4°C. The cells were washed and pelleted three times with the PBS–Tris solution to inactivate residual EDC (after the final centrifugation), the supernatant was discarded, and the cells were stored on ice. Parallel tubes containing equivalent numbers of pelleted, uncross-linked cells were then prepared from the original aliquots of cells. All the sets of tubes were treated to isolate membrane proteins from the cells. The pelleted cells were resuspended in 200 μl of PBS, 1 mM EDTA, 0.5% (v/v) Nonidet P-40 (NP-40) (Sigma), 10 μM benzamidine, 1 mM PMSF, and 10 μg/ml 1,10-phenanthroline (Sigma), and transferred to microfuge tubes. The protease inhibitors were prepared as stock solutions beforehand, and were stored at -20°C for up to 1 year. The benzamidine and 1,10-phenanthroline were stored as 10,000× and 100× stocks, respectively; both were dissolved in ethanol. The PMSF was prepared as a 100× stock in 2-propanol. After being resuspended with a P-1000 pipetman, the cells were incubated on ice for 10 min, with mixing after 5 min. The cell debris was pelleted by centrifugation for 5 min at 5000 rpm at 4°C in a microfuge, and the supernatant was removed to a fresh microfuge tube to which was added 200 μl of 2× sample buffer [20% (v/v) glycerol, 0.13 M Tris, pH 6.8, 4% (w/v) sodium dodecyl sulfate (SDS), and the dye pyronin Y]. The samples were then stored at -20°C until electrophoresis.

Electrophoresis

Five microliters of 2-mercaptoethanol (Sigma) was added to 95 μl of the cross-linking samples, the samples were heated for 5 min at 65°C, and subjected to electrophoresis through 7.5% (w/v) SDS-polyacrylamide gels (18). The gel was dried under vacuum, and autoradiographed at -70°C with an intensifying screen (Kodak, Rochester, NY).

To test for expression of the mutant proteins, the uncross-linked cell samples were electrophoresed as above, then transferred to nitrocellulose (BA83; Schleicher & Schuell). When samples were examined with the MC192 anti-fNGFR antibody (38), 2-mercaptoethanol was left out of the samples before electrophoresis as this destroyed the MC192 epitope. After transfer, the nitrocellulose was incubated with PBS–0.05% (v/v) Tween, containing 5% (w/v) nonfat milk (Blotto), for at least 30 min at room temperature with agitation. The nitrocellulose was incubated with primary antibody diluted in Blotto for 1 hr at room temperature with agitation, washed three times with Blotto, then incubated with the secondary antibody for 1 hr at room temperature with agitation. The development reaction depended on the choice of secondary antibody. Because the COS cells produce large amounts of the recombinant protein, we used a horseradish peroxidase-conjugated secondary antibody (Cappel, Cochranville, PA), and bound antibody was visualized by development with diaminobenzamidine.

Electrophoresis Results

Typical cross-linking results can be seen in Fig. 5. The wild-type receptor bound the ^{125}I-labeled NGF and formed a complex of ~90 kDa (lane 2). NHD 1 and NHD 2 bound NGF at reduced amounts (lanes 3 and 4) and the complexes were of lower molecular weight, consistent with the internal deletions in these receptor mutants. NHD 3 and an antisense construct failed to show any NGF binding (lanes 5 and 6, respectively). Binding of the mutants was always compared to the wild-type receptor. The mutants were considered to bind NGF as long as the signal was greater than that seen from the antisense construct. It should be mentioned that this type of analysis (Table I) is qualitative. The deletion of amino acid residues might remove specific amino acid residues on the receptor that were necessary for cross-linking to the NGF, thus lowering the overall efficiency of cross-linking. However, because the cross-linker used is very short, cross-linking of NGF to the receptor by a particular amino acid residue implies that NGF must be in close proximity to that amino acid residue, and suggests a local binding pocket. A more quantitative analysis can be performed by incubating the mutants with varying concentrations of ^{125}I-labeled NGF and Scatchard analysis of the binding will generate the specific equilibrium constant of binding for each mutant and this can be compared to wild type. For initial results, the cross-linking assay is an easy way to determine which regions of the protein are involved in ligand binding. Once the binding site is localized, it becomes more important to perform quantitative measurements to determine the exact amount that each amino acid residue on the receptor contributes to ligand binding.

It should be stressed that in the mutational analysis one is looking for mutants that still bind the ligand. These mutants are the most informative. Mutants that fail to bind the ligand may have gross structural changes that disrupt the tertiary structure and, indirectly, the ligand-binding domain of the receptor. The use of several antibodies can greatly facilitate these experiments, as they show that mutant proteins are expressed even if they fail to bind ligand. An example of this analysis is shown in Fig. 6. Western blot analysis, using an antibody that recognizes the intracellular domain of the fNGFR (39), indicated that all three of the mutants were being expressed (lanes 2–4) although only two of the mutants were able to bind NGF. In addition the antibodies can determine that some areas of tertiary structure are maintained in the mutants that show reduced ligand binding. This analysis was used (25) to show that the mutants NHD 4, NHD 5, and NHD 6 (Fig. 2) were able to bind some anti-fNGFR antibodies. This suggests that some regions of the cysteine-rich sequence are able to form

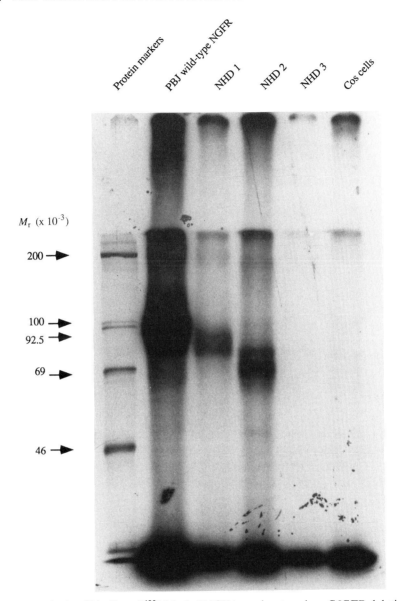

M_r (x 10^{-3})

200 →

100 →
92.5 →

69 →

46 →

FIG. 5   Analysis of binding of ^{125}I-labeled NGF to amino-terminus fNGFR deletions. COS cells were transfected with the various DNA constructs (indicated above the lanes), and then ^{125}I-labeled NGF was cross-linked to the cell surfaces. Proteins were prepared from the cells and separated by SDS-polyacrylamide electrophoresis. Visible bands consist of a complex between the ^{125}I-labeled NGF and the various fNGFRs. The far left lane contains radiolabeled protein molecular weight markers (Amersham, Arlington Heights, IL). [Reproduced from Welcher *et al.* (24).]

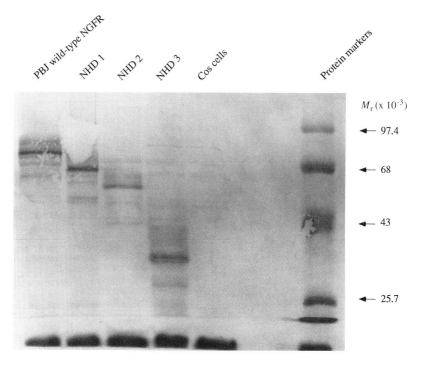

FIG. 6   Analysis of the expression of amino-terminus fNGFR deletions in COS cells. After transfection with the various DNA constructs (indicated above the lanes), proteins were prepared from the cells, separated by SDS-polyacrylamide electrophoresis, and transferred to nitrocellulose. The nitrocellulose was incubated with an anti-fNGFR antibody (39), and bound antibody detected by incubation with a horseradish peroxidase-conjugated secondary antibody (Cappel), followed by development with diaminobenzidine. The far right-hand lane contains protein molecular weight markers (Amersham). [Reproduced from Welcher *et al.* (24).]

a proper three-dimensional structure, and that the lack of NGF binding may reflect actual disruption of structures involved in NGF binding as opposed to the complete destruction of tertiary structure in the cysteine-rich sequences, which would indirectly prevent NGF binding.

Conclusions

This chapter describes the analysis of a cDNA sequence encoding a protein (receptor) of possibly unknown structure and function. Through the use of a computer, it may be possible to ascribe structure and function based on the previous analysis of other proteins. A reiterative mutational analysis is useful in narrowing down the number of amino acid residues that appear to be involved in the particular function. The expression of the wild-type and mutant receptors in large quantities allows their biochemical characterization. Ultimately, these type of studies used in conjunction with more sophisticated physical measurements such as X-ray crystallography, or nuclear magnetic resonance (NMR), can determine the molecular basis of structure and function for any protein.

Acknowledgments

The experiments reviewed in this chapter were done while I was a member of the laboratory of Dr. Eric M. Shooter at Stanford University. I thank my colleagues Anne Baldwin, Cathy Bitler, Monte Radeke, and Eric Shooter, who collaborated on some of the experiments reviewed here. I also thank Karen Allendoerfer for helpful criticism of the manuscript.

References

1. R. I. Hume, R. Dingledine, and S. F. Heinemann, *Science* **253,** 1028–1031 (1991).
2. A. M. Williams and C. A. Enns, *J. Biol. Chem.* **266,** 17648–17654 (1991).
3. J. M. Smith, *Biochem. Soc. Trans.* **19,** 2218 (1991).
4. A. A. Welcher, C. M. Bitler, M. J. Radeke, and E. M. Shooter, *Proc. Natl. Acad. Sci. U.S.A.* **88,** 159–163 (1988).
5. A. Baldwin, C. M. Bitler, A. A. Welcher, and E. M. Shooter, *J. Biol. Chem.* **267,** 8352–8359 (1992).
6. R. Levi-Montalcini, *Science* **237,** 1154–1162 (1987).
7. B. Will, and F. Hefti, *Behav. Brain Res.* **17,** 17–24 (1985).
8. L. R. Williams, S. Varon, G. M. Peterson, K. Wictorin, W. Fischer, A. Bjorklund, and F. H. Gage, *Proc. Natl. Acad. Sci. U.S.A.* **83,** 9231–9235 (1986).
9. J. Leibrock, F. Lottspeich, A. Hohn, M. Hofer, B. Hengerer, P. Masiakowski, H. Thoenen, and Y. Barde, *Nature* (*London*) **341,** 149–152 (1989).
10. P. C. Maisonpierre, L. Belluscio, S. Squinto, N. Y. Ip, M. E. Furth, R. M. Lindsay, and G. D. Yancopoulos, *Science* **247,** 1446–1451 (1990).
11. F. Halbook, C. F. Ibañez, and H. Persson, *Neuron* **6,** 845–848 (1991).
12. L. R. Berkemeier, J. W. Winslow, D. R. Kaplan, K. Nikolics, D. V. Goeddel, and A. Rosenthal, *Neuron* **7,** 857–866 (1991).
13. A. Rodriguez-Tebar, G. Dechant, and Y. A. Barde, *Neuron* **4,** 487–492 (1990).
14. R. Klein, V. Nanduri, S. Jing, F. Lamballe, P. Tapley, S. Bryant, C. Cordon-Cardo, K. R. Jones, L. F. Reichardt, and M. Barbacid, *Cell* (*Cambridge, Mass.*) **66,** 395–403 (1991).

15. M. J. Radeke, T. P. Misko, C. Hsu, L. A. Herzenberg, and E. M. Shooter, *Nature (London)* **325,** 593–597 (1987).
16. D. Johnson, A. Lanahan, C. R. Buck, A. Sehgal, C. Morgan, E. Mercer, M. Bothwell, and M. Chao, *Cell (Cambridge, Mass.)* **47,** 545–554 (1986).
17. T. H. Large, G. Weskamp, J. C. Helder, M. J. Radeke, T. P. Misko, E. M. Shooter, and L. F. Reichardt, *Neuron* **2,** 1123–1134 (1989).
18. D. R. Kaplan, B. L. Hempstead, D. Martin-Zanca, M. V. Chao, and L. F. Parada, *Science* **252,** 554–558 (1991).
19. R. Klein, S. Jing, V. Nanduri, E. O'Rourke, and M. Barbacid, *Cell (Cambridge, Mass.)* **65,** 189–197 (1991).
20. T. Maniatis, E. F. Fritsch, and J. Sambrook, "Molecular Cloning: A Lab Manual," 2nd ed., Cold Spring Harbor Lab., Cold Spring Harbor, New York, 1989.
21. J. Devereux, P. Haeberli, and O. Smithies, *Nucleic Acids Res.* **12,** 387–395 (1984).
22. H. Loetscher, Y. E. Pan, H. Lahm, R. Gentz, M. Brockhaus, H. Tabuchi, and W. Lesslauer, *Cell (Cambridge, Mass.)* **61,** 351–359 (1990).
23. C. W. Heizmann and W. Hunziker, *Trends Biochem. Sci.* **16,** 98–103 (1991).
24. M. J. Sternberg and M. J. Zvelebil, *Eur. J. Cancer* **26,** 1163–1166 (1990).
25. G. M. Maggiora, B. Mao, K. C. Chou, and S. L. Narasimhan, *Methods Biochem. Anal.* **35,** 1–86 (1991).
26. H. Yan and M. V. Chao, *J. Biol. Chem.* **266,** 12099–12104 (1991).
27. S. N. Seal, D. L. Davis, and J. B. Burch, *Mol. Cell. Biol.* **11,** 2704–2717 (1991).
28. H. Wiech, P. Klappa, and R. Zimmerman, *FEBS Lett.* **285,** 182–188 (1991).
29. F. Sanger, S. Nicklen, and A. R. Coulson, *Proc. Natl. Acad. Sci. U.S.A.* **74,** 5463–5467 (1977).
30. S. N. Ho, H. D. Hunt, R. M. Horton, J. K. Pullen, and L. R. Pease, *Gene* **77,** 51–59 (1989).
31. M. A. Innis, D. H. Gelfand, J. J. Sninsky, and T. J. White, "PCR Protocols: A Guide to Methods and Applications." Academic Press, San Diego, 1990.
32. R. Wu and L. Grossman, *in* "Methods in Enzymology" (R. Wu and L. Grossman, eds.), Vol. 154, pp. 329–429. Academic Press, Orlando, FL, 1987.
33. V. Bocchini, *Eur. J. Biochem.* **15,** 127 (1970).
34. D. V. Goeddel, ed., "Methods in Enzymology," Vol. 185. Academic Press, San Diego, 1990.
35. Y. Gluzman, *Cell (Cambridge, Mass.)* **23,** 175–182 (1981).
36. G. Scatchard, *Ann. N. Y. Acad. Sci.* **51,** 660–672 (1949).
37. R. D. Vale and E. M. Shooter, *in* "Methods in Enzymology" (L. Birnbaumer and B. O'Malley, eds.), Vol. 109, pp. 21–39. Academic Press, Orlando, FL, 1985.
38. C. E. Chandler, L. M. Parsons, M. Hosang, and E. M. Shooter, *J. Biol. Chem.* **259,** 6882–6889 (1984).
39. K. L. Allendoerfer, D. L. Shelton, E. M. Shooter, and C. J. Shatz, *Proc. Natl. Acad. Sci. U.S.A.* **87,** 187–190 (1990).

[22] Solubilization and Physicochemical Characterization of 5-HT$_3$ Receptor-Binding Sites

M.-C. Miquel, M. B. Emerit, J. A. Gingrich, H. Gozlan, and M. Hamon

Introduction

Mammalian 5-hydroxytryptamine (serotonin, 5-HT) receptors have generally been divided into three main classes termed 5-HT$_1$, 5-HT$_2$, and 5-HT$_3$, according to their different pharmacological properties, regional distributions, and functions in the central nervous system (CNS) (Bradley *et al.*,1986; Peroutka, 1988; Sanders-Bush, 1988; Hamon *et al.*, 1990). An additional class, designated 5-HT$_4$ (Dumuis *et al.*, 1988), has been identified more recently on brain neurons but very little is known yet about its pharmacological and functional properties.

Depending on their mechanism of action, the 5-HT receptors, like the receptors for acetylcholine, γ-aminobutyric acid (GABA), and glutamate, can be divided into two main superfamilies of membrane-bound receptors, the G protein-coupled receptors and the ligand-gated ion channels. The 5-HT$_1$, 5-HT$_2$, and 5-HT$_4$ receptor classes belong to the G protein-coupled receptor family, resembling in this respect the muscarinic, GABA$_B$, and metabotropic glutamate receptors.

In contrast, 5-HT$_3$ receptors belong to the second family of membrane-bound receptors, the ligand-gated ion channels (for a review, see Julius, 1991), that includes, among many others, the nicotinic cholinergic, GABA$_A$, and glutamate (NMDA, kainate, etc.) receptors. Although the cloning of one member of the 5-HT$_3$ class (Maricq *et al.*, 1991) has provided a wealth of structural information, little is still known about their biochemical and functional properties when compared with other, better characterized ion channels, such as the nicotinic and GABA$_A$ receptors. To date, most studies on 5-HT$_3$ receptors are restricted to *in vitro* binding investigations using high-affinity radioligands such as [^{3}H]GR 65630 (Kilpatrick *et al.*, 1987), [^{3}H]ICS 205-930 (tropisetron) (Hoyer and Neijt, 1987), its quaternized derivative [^{3}H]Q ICS 205-930 (Watling *et al.*, 1988), [^{3}H]zacopride (Barnes *et al.,* 1988), [³H]quipazine (Milburn and Peroutka, 1989), and [³H]granise-tron (Nelson and Thomas, 1989). Thus, radioligand-binding studies have demonstrated the presence of 5-HT₃ receptor sites not only in the periphery (Gordon *et al.,* 1989), where they were first identified, but also in the CNS, notably in the limbic areas and the spinal cord (Kilpatrick *et al.,* 1988; Hamon *et al.,* 1989; Radja *et al.,* 1991), confirming the results of different studies on the central functions of 5-HT₃ receptor antagonists, showing anxiolytic, promnesic, as well as antiemetic properties. Competition studies with a large series of agonists and antagonists have provided an extensive pharmacological characterization of central 5-HT₃ receptors (Barnes *et al.,* 1988; Bolaños *et al.,* 1990; Hoyer *et al.,* 1989; Hoyer and Neijt, 1988; Neijt *et al.,* 1988; Milburn and Peroutka, 1989; Sharif *et al.,* 1991). Electrophysiological investigations on central neurons in primary culture (Yakel and Jackson, 1988; Yakel *et al.,* 1990), clonal cell lines (Lambert *et al.,* 1989; Neijt *et al.,* 1989), and peripheral neurons (Derkach *et al.,* 1989) have confirmed 5-HT₃ receptors to be ligand-gated cation channels which mediate a 5-HT-induced depolarization via a cation influx. Finally, these receptors have been shown to be relatively abundant in several cell lines, including NCB20, N1E-115, and NG108-15 cells. Moreover, there is good pharmacological evidence that the receptors present in the NG108-15 (Bolaños *et al.,* 1990) and NCB20 (Shariff *et al.,* 1991) cell lines are similar to those expressed in brain. The relatively high abundance of the 5-HT₃ receptor in these cells has permitted several biochemical and molecular studies on solubilized receptor sites (McKernan *et al.,* 1990a,b; Lummis and Martin, 1990, 1991, 1992; Bolaños *et al.,* 1990; Gozlan *et al.,* 1989; Miquel *et al.,* 1990) as well as the purification of the receptor protein(s) (McKernan *et al.,* 1990c; Boess *et al.,* 1992). Indeed, solubilization of the 5-HT₃ receptor protein(s) from an appropriate source is the first step toward its purification, and is also a prerequisite for most studies of the physicochemical properties of the receptor.

In this chapter, we will first present the Materials and Methods section, which will describe in detail the different techniques that were used. Then we will discuss the problems of the choice of detergent and membrane source that must be resolved to solubilize the membrane-bound receptor protein. In the second part the results obtained by several different groups that fulfilled all the criteria for successful solubilization will be reviewed. Then the physicochemical characteristics of the 5-HT₃ receptor will be described and, finally, the different methods used to purify the 5-HT₃ receptor and the characteristics of the purified forms obtained from different sources will be reported.

Materials and Methods

NG108-15 Cell Culture

Mouse neuroblastoma-glioma cells of the clone NG108-15 were obtained as a generous gift from Dr. B. Zalc (INSERM U. 134, Paris), and grown in Dulbecco's modified Eagle's medium (DMEM) supplemented with 40 mM sodium bicarbonate, 1.8 mM L-glutamine, 10% (v/v) inactivated fetal calf serum (GIBCO, Grand Island, NY), and HAT (100 μM hypoxanthine, 1 μM aminopterin, 16 μM thymine) (GIBCO). Cells are cultured at 37°C, in a CO$_2$: air (7% : 93%, v/v) atmosphere in costar tissue culture flasks (152 cm^2; Becton Dickinson, Oxnard, CA) and subcultured every 2 days. The cells are harvested by vigorous shaking when they reach confluency.

Preparation of Membranes

NG108-15 cells are collected between passage numbers 35 and 55, pelleted by centrifugation at 900 g for 10 min, and resuspended in 25 mM Tris-HCl, pH 7.4, containing 1 mM phenylmethylsulfonyl fluoride (PMSF). They are subsequently stored at -80°C. No loss of [^{3}H]zacopride-binding capacity (see below) is noted under such storage conditions for at least 3 months. For each membrane preparation, cells are thawed, pooled, homogenized with a Polytron PT 10 OD disrupter (Kinematic GmbH, Luzern, Switzerland), and centrifuged at 40,000 g for 20 min at 4°C. The resulting pellet is resuspended in 10 vol (v/v) of the same Tris buffer and incubated at 37°C for 10 min to remove any endogenous 5-HT (originally present in the serum added to the culture medium). The membranes are then centrifuged (40,000 g) and washed twice by resuspension in 10 vol of Tris buffer followed by centrifugation. The final pellet is resuspended in 10 vol of 25 mM Tris-HCl, pH 7.4, containing 1 mM PMSF, and stored at -80°C until use.

Solubilization Procedure

Nine volumes of thawed membrane suspension ($\sim$2.0 mg of protein/ml) is gently mixed with 1 vol of a concentrated 3-[(3-cholamidopropyl)dimethylam-monio]-1-propane sulfonate (CHAPS) solution [15% (w/v) in water] and left at 4°C for 30 min (CHAPS final concentration: 1.5%, corresponding to 24 mM). The suspension is then centrifuged at 100,000 g for 60 min at 4°C. The resulting supernatant (~0.60 mg of protein/ml) is filtered through a 0.22-μm Millex GV membrane (Millipore, Bedford, MA) and used within a few hours as a source of solubilized binding sites (the number of sites decreases by about 20% when the solubilisate is kept at 4°C for 72 hr).

[^{3}H]Zacopride-Binding Assays

Crude Membranes

Aliquots of membrane suspension (50 μl, corresponding to ~0.10 mg of protein) are mixed with 25 mM Tris-HCl, pH 7.4, containing various concentrations of [^{3}H]zacopride and drugs in a total volume of 0.5 ml. Samples are incubated at 15°C for 60 min and then filtered under vacuum through Whatman (Clifton, NJ) GF/B filters which have been presoaked in 0.5% (v/v) polyethylenimine (PEI) (for 30 min at room temperature). Filters are washed three times with 3 ml of ice-cold 50 mM Tris-HCl buffer, dried, and immersed in 5 ml of Aquasol (New England Nuclear, Boston MA) for radioactivity counting. Nonspecific binding is determined from similar samples supplemented with an excess (10 μM) of unlabeled ICS 205-930. Triplicate determinations are made for each tested condition.

Soluble Preparations

Aliquots (50–450 μl, corresponding to ~0.006–0.10 mg of protein) of the 100,000 g supernatant or of various soluble extracts are mixed with 25 mM Tris-HCl, pH 7.4, containing various concentrations of [^{3}H]zacopride and drugs in a total volume of 0.5 ml. Samples are then incubated as described for the crude membranes, and the soluble binding site–[^{3}H]zacopride complex is separated from free [^{3}H]zacopride by filtration through Whatman GF/B filters presoaked in 0.5% (v/v) PEI (Bruns et al., 1983).

The concentration of CHAPS due to the addition of variable aliquots of soluble extracts ranges from 0.05 to 1.3% (w/v) in the assay mixture, but control experiments indicate that [^{3}H]zacopride-specific binding to the CHAPs extract (100,000 g supernatant) remains essentially unchanged when the assay mixture is supplemented with up to 1.5% of the detergent (not shown).

Sucrose Gradient Centrifugation

Linear sucrose gradients (12.5 ml) are prepared using 5 and 30% (w/v) sucrose solutions (in 25 mM Tris-HCl, pH 7.4), supplemented with 0.1% (w/v) CHAPS and prefiltered through a Nalgene (Rochester, NY) filter. The

100,000 g supernatant from CHAPS-treated NG108-15 cell membranes is filtered through a Millex GV 0.22-μm membrane (Millipore) and concentrated 30-fold using a MicroProDiCon dialysis apparatus (model MPDC-310; Bio-Molecular Dynamics, Beaverton, OR). The concentrated extract is saved, and the dialysis cell is rinsed twice with an equal volume of 25 mM Tris-HCl, pH 7.4, containing 1.5% (w/v) CHAPS. The extract and rinses are mixed, and 300 μl of the resulting mixture (concentrated 10-fold as compared to the starting 100,000 g supernatant) is layered on top of the gradients. The loaded gradients are spun at 200,000 g for 14 hr at 4°C in a Beckman (Gagny, France) SW 41 Ti rotor, and fractions of 0.25 ml are then collected at the bottom of each tube. [^{3}H]Zacopride-binding assays are carried out on 100-μl aliquots for each collected fraction, according to the procedure described above. Calibration of the gradients is achieved with thyroglobulin (18.4S), catalase (11.4S), β-amylase (8.7S), alcohol dehydrogenase (7.4S) and bovine serum albumin (BSA) (4.2S) from Sigma (St. Louis, MO).

Sephacryl S-400 Gel Filtration (at 4°C)

Five milliliters of filtered soluble extract is applied to a Sephacryl S-400 column (34 cm high; 2.5 cm in diameter) equilibrated with 0.05 M Tris-HCl supplemented with 0.5 M NaCl and 1.5% (w/v) CHAPS, pH 7.4. Elution is carried out using the same buffer at a flow rate of 20 ml/hr, and 5-ml fractions are collected. Binding assays are performed on 0.45-ml aliquots of each collected fraction as described above. Calibration of the Sephacryl S-400 column is achieved with the following proteins [from Sigma and Boehringer Mannheim (Indianapolis, IN): chymotrypsinogen A (25 kDa), carbonic anhydrase (29 kDa), alcohol dehydrogenase (150 kDa), β-amylase (200 kDa), catalase (240 kDa), apoferritin (443 kDa), thyroglobulin (669 kDa), and blue dextran (~2000 kDa).

Wheat Germ Agglutinin-Agarose Chromatography (at 4°C)

The filtered 100,000 g supernatant (2–5 ml) from CHAPS-treated NG108-15 cell membranes is incubated overnight at 4°C with an equal volume of wheat germ agglutinin (WGA)-agarose and the mixture is then poured into a column (1.5 cm in diameter). The column is washed with 25 mM Tris-HCl, pH 7.4, containing 0.1% (w/v) CHAPS, and elution is achieved with the same buffer supplemented with 0.25 M N-acetylglucosamine. The flow rate is maintained at 20 ml/hr for the entire procedure, and 4-ml fractions are collected. [^{3}H]Zacopride-binding assays are carried out on 0.45-ml aliquots of each collected fraction (see above).

Radiation Inactivation

NG108-15 cells are harvested as described, frozen at $-20°C$, and exposed to highly accelerated (10 MeV) electrons from a linear accelerator (Roskilde, Denmark). The samples are kept frozen ($-15°C$) during irradiation, which is delivered in doses of 1–2 Mrad. The total dose of radiation (1–20 Mrad) is determined using a thermodensitometer (see Gozlan *et al.*, 1986). Calibration of the radiation-induced inactivation procedure is made with seven different proteins of known molecular weights, as described in detail elsewhere (Gozlan *et al.*, 1986). Crude membranes from the irradiated samples are then prepared as above and aliquots are used for binding experiments according to the standard procedure.

Protein Determination

Proteins are estimated using the bicinchoninic acid (BCA) protein assay reagent (Pierce-Europe, BV, Oud-Beijerland, The Netherlands) with BSA as a standard.

Chemicals

[^{3}H]Zacopride (83 Ci/mmol) was generously provided by Delalande laboratories (Rueil-Malmaison, France). Other compounds used are 2-methyl-5-HT and 8-OH-DPAT (Research Biochemicals, Inc., Natick, MA), phenylbiguanide (Aldrich, Strasbourg, France), 5-HT creatinine sulfate (E. Merck, AG, Darmstadt, Germany), MDL 72222 (Merrell-Dow, Strasbourg, France), GR 38032 F (Ondansetron, Glaxo, Ware, England), quipazine (Miles, Elkhart, IN), ICS 205-930 (Sandoz, Basel, Switzerland), zacopride {4-amino-*N*-[1-azabicyclo(2.2.2)oct-3yl]-5-chloro-2-methoxybenzamide(*E*)-2-butenedioate; Delalande Laboratories}, phencyclidine [generously given by Dr. M. Ponchant, Commissariat à l'Energie Atomique (CEA), Gif-sur-Yvette, France], CHAPS (Serva, Heidelberg, Germany), GTP and Gpp(NH)p (Boehringer Mannheim), phenylmethylsulfonylfluoride (PMSF) (Sigma). Sephacryl S-400 and WGA-agarose are from Pharmacia. All other compounds are the purest commercially available (Merck, Prolabo).

Calculations

Data from saturation studies are analyzed by nonlinear computer-assisted curve fitting (Barlow, 1983) for the calculation of respective K_d and B_{max} values. Displacement curves are analyzed using the Graphpad program for the calculation of IC$_{50}$ and apparent Hill coefficient (nH) values.

Solubilization of 5-HT$_3$ Receptor-Binding Sites

Choice of Receptor Source

Successful solubilization of membrane-bound receptor proteins requires an abundant source of receptors. The density of 5-HT$_3$ receptor-binding sites in the mammalian CNS is relatively low (Kilpatrick *et al.*, 1987; Bolaños *et al.*, 1990), but receptor-binding sites with essentially identical radioligand-binding properties are highly expressed in a number of immortal cell lines (Hoyer and Neijt, 1987, 1988; Bolaños *et al.*, 1990; McKernan *et al.*, 1990a; Sharif *et al.*, 1991). Different receptor sources have been used for the solubilization of 5-HT$_3$ receptor-binding sites, including rabbit bowel (Gordon *et al.*, 1990), rat brain (McKernan *et al.*, 1990a), and the already mentioned cell lines, N1E-115 (Lummis and Martin, 1990, 1992), NCB20 (McKernan *et al.*, 1990b), and NG108-15 (Miquel *et al.*, 1990; Boess *et al.*, 1992).

Because of the postulated existence of 5-HT$_3$ receptor subtypes (Richardson and Engel, 1986), a prerequisite for the solubilization of 5-HT$_3$ receptors from the NG108-15 cell line was the demonstration that these sites were identical with those identified in the CNS. Thus, Bolaños *et al.* (1990) compared the physicochemical and pharmacological properties of specific binding sites for the potent 5-HT$_3$ antagonist, [^{3}H]zacopride, using membranes from rat posterior cortex or NG108-15 clonal cells. In both membrane preparations, [^{3}H]zacopride bound to a single class of specific sites with a K_d close to 0.5 nM. However, the B_{max} value in NG108-15 cell membranes (970 $\pm$ 194 fmol/mg of protein) was approximately 50 times higher than that in cortical membranes (19 $\pm$ 2 fmol/mg of protein). In each tissue, the specific binding of [^{3}H]zacopride was equally affected by the temperature, pH, and molarity of the assay medium, and equally insensitive to thiol and disulfide reagents and GTP. Finally, a highly significant, positive correlation ($r = 0.979$) was found between the respective pK_i values of 34 different drugs for their inhibition of [^{3}H]zacopride binding to cortical or NG108-15 cell membranes. Among these, the most potent was $S(-)$zacopride (pK_i = 9.55), followed by granisetron (BRL 43964), tropisetron (ICS 205-930), quipazine, $R(+)$zacopride, ondansetron (GR 38032F), and MDL 72222. The nearly identical physicochemical and pharmacological properties of the 5-HT$_3$ receptor-binding sites in cortical and NG108-15 cell membranes justify the use of these cells to characterize further the biochemical properties of the 5-HT$_3$ receptor in this system.

Choice of Detergent

In the solubilization procedure the choice of detergent is important, because the soluble protein must retain at least some of its native properties, most importantly its native ligand-binding properties, as currently there is no other way to "follow" a soluble receptor protein throughout the successive steps of purification or physicochemical analysis. Two additional considerations contribute to the choice of detergent. The first is the efficacy of the detergent in dissolving the artifactual aggregation of proteins, and the second is its electrical charge. However, if an ideal detergent cannot be found, one detergent may be used for the actual solubilization step, as we will see later in this chapter, and then be replaced by another one that does not interfere with the ligand-binding assays.

The following brief review summarizes the properties of the most common biological detergents and highlights their respective advantages and disadvantages. The bile salts, like sodium cholate, are nondenaturing as well as effective in disaggregating proteins, but they lack the charge neutrality necessary for compatibility with charge fractionation techniques. In contrast, Triton X-100, Lubrol PX, and other polyethoxy-type nonionic detergents are electrically neutral and nondenaturing but appear to be less efficient at breaking protein–protein interactions. N-Alkyl sulfobetaines are neutral and efficient at disaggregating proteins but unfortunately are strongly denaturing (Hjelmeland, 1980). The nondenaturing, zwitterionic detergent CHAPS was synthesized by Hjelmeland (1980) with the purpose of combining the useful properties of both the sulfobetaine-type detergents and the bile salt anions such as sodium cholate.

Thus CHAPS appeared to be theoretically the most appropriate detergent for the solubilization of receptor-binding sites. Moreover, it has been found to be particularly efficient in the solubilization of numerous functional neurotransmitter receptors such as the 5-HT$_{1A}$ (El Mestikawy et al., 1988), the 5-HT$_{1C}$ (Yagaloff and Hartig, 1986), and the 5-HT$_2$ (Wouters et al., 1985) receptors, and some members of the ionophoric receptor family, including GABA receptors (Mamalaki et al., 1989). For these reasons, we chose to use CHAPS to solubilize the 5-HT$_3$ receptors from NG108-15 cell membranes (Miquel et al., 1990).

However, several experiments have shown that other detergents are also efficient in solubilizing these receptors, probably because other imperatives must be taken into account when describing the properties of a detergent, for instance the lipid composition of the membrane, the tertiary and quaternary structure of the receptor, and the interactions between receptor and membrane. The different detergents which have been used by other groups to solubilize 5-HT₃ receptors include sodium cholate (Gordon *et al.*, 1990), sodium deoxycholate (McKernan *et al.*, 1990a), octylglucoside (Lummis and Martin, 1990), and Triton X-100 (Boess *et al.*, 1992).

Solubilization of 5-HT₃ Receptor-Binding Sites

The general solubilization procedures reported for the 5-HT₃ receptors are quite similar, involving the treatment of membranes with the selected detergent in a buffered solution which may contain protease inhibitors and salts, a brief sonication or simple agitation step followed by incubation for 10 to 60 min at 4°C, and then centrifugation at 100,000 g. In some cases, the supernatant is also passed through a 0.22 μm filter before use.

For the solubilization step, the protein concentration is normally in the range of 0.5 to 5 mg protein/ml, and the duration of incubation of the membrane–detergent mixture varies from 10 to 60 min. In our hands, systematic investigations indicated that 30 min at 4°C produced the best results for the solubilization of [³H]zacopride-binding sites from NG108-15 cell membranes.

For the various reported procedures, the solubilization yield (estimated by the binding capacity of the solubilized extract compared to the starting membrane preparation) ranges from 30 to 70% in the best cases, but much lower values have also been reported. In some instances, it was necessary to reduce the detergent concentration to measure ligand binding, and this was achieved by dialysis, gel filtration, or polystyrene bead adsorption. In addition, since solubilized receptors will not be retained by normal glass fiber filters, the receptors are either precipitated with polyethyleneglycol (PEG) or the filters are coated with a basic polymer such as polyethylenimine (PEI) prior to terminating the binding assays.

The solubilization yield ranged between 30 and 70%. The highest yield for 5-HT₃ receptor sites was obtained using rabbit small bowel muscularis membranes as a source (Gordon *et al.*, 1990). A mixture of 0.5% (w/v) sodium cholate and 0.4 M (NH₄)₂SO₄ gave a 70% recovery, and 1% (w/v) CHAPS supplemented with the same salt resulted in a 60% yield (Gordon *et al.*, 1990). Other groups have also succeeded in solubilizing high quantities of binding sites, and reported values of 50–55% using either 0.5% (w/v) sodium deoxycholate (McKernan *et al.*, 1990a,b) or CHAPS (Miller and Teitler, 1991), and 68% with 0.1% (w/v) Triton supplemented with 2 M NaCl (Boess *et al.*, 1992).

These conditions, however, were unsuitable for further physicochemical characterization of the receptor because the soluble form was either unstable (McKernan *et al.*, 1990b) or highly diluted (Boess *et al.*, 1992).

In our hands, the addition of 24 mM (1.5%, w/v) CHAPS to the membrane suspension (~2.0 mg protein/ml) in 25 mM Tris-HCl, pH 7.4, allowed a recovery as high as 35% of the initial [^{3}H]zacopride-binding capacity in the 100,000 g supernatant. A better yield (~50%) could be achieved by adding 0.5 M NaCl together with 24 mM CHAPS to the membrane suspension. However, the latter procedure also resulted in a markedly increased concentration of protein in the 100,000 g supernatant, leading to lower specific [^{3}H]zacopride binding. For this reason, 24 mM CHAPS alone was used for subsequent experiments.

Several lines of evidence demonstrated that 5-HT$_3$ receptor-binding sites were actually solubilized from NG108-15 cell membranes by CHAPS alone or by CHAPS–NaCl. First, soluble [^{3}H]zacopride-specific binding sites did not sediment after a 1-hr centrifugation in a low-density medium (25 mM Tris-HCl, pH 7.4, 24 mM CHAPS) at 100,000 g, and also remained in the middle of a 5–30% sucrose gradient after a 14-hr centrifugation at 200,000 g. Second, these soluble sites were not retained by a Millex GV filter of 0.22-μm pore size. Finally, soluble 5-HT$_3$ receptor-binding sites were retained on GF/B filters only when the latter had been presoaked in 0.5% PEI.

Pharmacological Characterization of Soluble 5-HT$_3$ Receptor-Binding Sites

To ascertain that the soluble ligand-binding sites actually correspond to 5-HT$_3$ receptor-binding sites, it was necessary to characterize them pharmacologically.

[^{3}H]Zacopride binding to CHAPS-soluble extracts was highest when assays were performed at 15°C for 60 min, as has been observed for membranes. Under such conditions (in 25 mM Tris-HCl, pH 7.4), specific binding represented 85–90% of total binding, using 1–10 μM ICS 205-930, quipazine, ondansetron (GR 38032F), (±)zacopride, or MDL 72222 for the determination of the nonspecific binding.

Scatchard transformation of [^{3}H]zacopride binding to the soluble extract under steady state conditions (see Materials and Methods) gave only one slope. The K_d value derived from this slope ($K_d = 0.19 \pm 0.02$ nM, mean $\pm$ SEM, $n = 6$) was close to that calculated from the kinetic analysis ($K_d = 0.12$ nM). Similar experiments with NG108-15 cell membranes indicated that both the K_d and B_{max} values were greater for membrane-bound sites than for their soluble extracts.

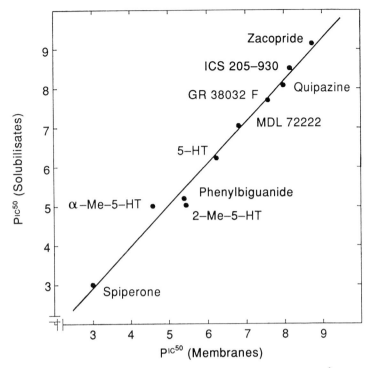

FIG. 1   Respective pK_i values of 10 different drugs for the inhibition of [³H]zacopride-specific binding to NG108-15 cell membranes (abscissa) and to their CHAPS-solubilized membranes (ordinate). Each inhibition curve was obtained from assays using 0.6 nM [³H]zacopride and eight different concentrations of each drug. Respective pK_i values were calculated using the Graphpad program. Each value is the mean of three independent determinations (with less than 25% variation between them). The correlation coefficient between pK_i values (r) was calculated to be 0.99 for the two membrane preparations.

The pharmacological properties of soluble [³H]zacopride-binding sites closely resembled those of 5-HT₃ receptors in membranes because a significant positive correlation ($r = 0.99$) was found between the respective potencies of a series of 10 drugs, both agonists and antagonists, to inhibit [³H]zacopride binding to the soluble fraction and to membranes (Fig. 1). In all cases, the inhibition curves for soluble extracts as well as for membranes were monophasic, with Hill coefficients not significantly different from unity. When reported, the Hill coefficients of other groups in comparable studies using different radioligands were within the same range. In addition, neither the IC₅₀ values nor the Hill coefficients within the present series of 10 drugs were significantly altered when binding assays were carried out in the presence of 10 mM GTP or Gpp(NH)p.

As mentioned above, absolute IC_{50} values of (most) 5-HT$_3$ antagonists, and the K_d value of zacopride, were lower in the CHAPS extract than in membranes, suggesting that solubilization was associated with an increase in the affinity of 5-HT$_3$ recognition sites for these drugs. However, higher IC_{50} values were generally found for agonist compounds such as 2-methyl-5-HT and phenylbiguanide. Although the molecular mechanisms responsible for such differential changes in the binding of agonists and antagonists are presently unknown, these observations further support previous data suggesting marked differences in the binding of agonists and antagonists to 5-HT$_3$ receptors in membranes (Kilpatrick *et al.*, 1987) and other findings on the soluble and membrane-bound forms of 5-HT$_3$ receptors from pooled rat cortical and hippocampal membranes (McKernan *et al.*, 1990a). At any rate, in all studies, in spite of the small changes found, the rank order of the affinity of receptor agonists and antagonists is essentially maintained in soluble preparations, indicating the preservation of the 5-HT$_3$ receptor-binding site in an intact form.

Physicochemical Characterization of the Soluble 5-HT$_3$ Receptor-Binding Sites

Interestingly, the 5-HT$_3$ receptor-binding site in the solubilized form was stable for several days at 4°C. This property allowed biochemical characterizations which require extended times, such as sucrose gradient centrifugation and chromatography.

One of the first characterization procedures that can be performed on solubilized receptors is the determination of the relative size of the complex by sucrose gradient sedimentation and molecular sieving. In our hands, the soluble [^{3}H]zacopride-binding sites sedimented in the sucrose gradient as a single broad peak with a Svedberg coefficient of 12S, corresponding to a molecular weight of ~300,000 for a globular protein. However, by molecular sieving on Sephacryl S-400, [^{3}H]zacopride-binding sites were resolved into three distinct peaks. The first peak came out in the void volume of the gel and probably corresponded to protein aggregates, as has been shown to occur with other solubilized receptors (Gorissen *et al.*, 1981; Yagaloff and Hartig, 1986; El Mestikawy *et al.*, 1988). The second and third peaks for [^{3}H]zacopride-specific binding sites corresponded to proteins that had penetrated into the Sephacryl beads, the larger one corresponding to ~600,000 and the smaller one to ~36,000. Interestingly, the 36,000 ± 2000 peak correlated well with results from target size analysis (using the irradiation inactivation method), which indicated an apparent molecular weight of 34,900 ± 1200 for the [³H]zacopride-binding subunit in NG108-15 cells and 35,400 ± 2200 in rat cerebral cortex (Gozlan *et al.*, 1989).

The apparent molecular weight calculated from the sucrose gradient sedimentation analysis, ~300,000, did not correspond to that found for the main peak eluted from the Sephacryl S-400 column, ~600,000. This discrepancy is most likely explained by an artifactual aggregation of the soluble sites leading to a high molecular weight form. This hypothesis is supported by the work of other groups, which found a similar result and were able to eliminate this artifact by exchanging detergents for both sucrose gradient sedimentation and gel-filtration experiments (Table I). After replacing the solubilization buffer containing 0.1% (w/v) Triton X-100 and 0.25 M NaCl by another one containing 0.6% (w/v) CHAPS and 0.1 M NaCl, Boess *et al.* (1992) reported a Svedberg coefficient of 11S for the soluble 5-HT₃ receptor-binding site after sucrose gradient sedimentation and an apparent molecular weight of 540,000 after gel-filtration experiments. However, when they used 0.1% dodecylmaltoside with 0.5 M NaCl in the exchange buffer instead of CHAPS, gel-filtration experiments resulted in an apparent molecular weight of 370,000 for the soluble 5-HT₃ receptor-binding site, suggesting that the receptor-binding proteins remained aggregated in the CHAPS buffer. When substituting the 0.5% sodium deoxycholate solubilization buffer for a buffer containing 0.2% (w/v) Lubrol, 0.5 M NaCl, and 10% (v/v) glycerol, McKernan *et al.*, (1990b,c) reported a Svedberg coefficient of 12.8S after sucrose gradient experiments and obtained an apparent molecular weight of 340,000 with molecular sieving experiments. Considering the respective physicochemical properties of these detergents (as mentioned in the section on Choice of Detergent), these findings are rather unexpected, because CHAPS is supposed to be more efficient at breaking protein–protein aggregation than Triton X-100, Lubrol PX, or dodecylmaltoside, and there is no straightforward explanation for this phenomenon.

The most reliable value is probably that obtained from the sucrose gradient experiments, which were carried out in both ¹H₂O and ²H₂O. This method allows correction for detergent binding to the receptor and gives a corrected molecular weight of 249,000 for the 5-HT₃ receptor (McKernan *et al.*, 1990b). This size is typical of the members of the ligand-gated ion channel family, such as the nicotinic receptor, the GABA_A receptor, and the strychnine-sensitive glycine receptor, which all have molecular weights within the range of 230,000–300,000 (Mamalaki *et al.*, 1989; Strange, 1988).

Purification of the 5-HT₃ Receptor-Binding Site

Different methods can be used to purify neurotransmitter receptors: lectin chromatography, ion-exchange chromatography, and ligand-affinity chroma-

TABLE I   Comparison of the Physicochemical Properties of the 5-HT$_3$ Receptor-Binding Sites Described by Several Groups[a]

| Detergent and salt conditions used | | Solubilization efficiency (%) | Detergent CMC (mM) | Average detergent micelle (M_r) | Method | Apparent 5-HT$_3$ receptor (M_r) | Svedberg coefficient (svedberg) | Membrane source | Ref. |
For solubilization	For measuring molecular weight and Svedberg coefficient								
0.5% deoxycholate, 0.1% Triton	0.2% Lubrol (≈ 3.4 mM, 0.5 M NaCl, 10% glycerol	50	0.1	64,000	Sucrose gradient/ gel filtration	340,000; after correction, 249,000	12.8S	NCB20	McKernan et al. (1990c)
0.1% Triton, 0.25 M NaCl	0.6% CHAPS (≈10 mM), 0.. M NaCl	≈45	3–5	6,000	Gel filtration/ sucrose gradient	540,000	11S	NG108-15	Boess et al. (1992)
0.1% Triton, 0.25 M NaCl	0.1% dodecylma-toside (≈2.8 mM), 0.5 M NaCl	≈45	0.16	nd	Gel filtration	370,000			
1.5% CHAPS	1.5% CHAPS ≈24 mM), 0.5 M NaCl	35	6–10	6,000	Gel filtration	600,000	12S	NG108-15	Miquel et al. (1990)
1.5% CHAPS	0.1% CHAPS (≈ 1.6 mM)	35	3–5	6,000	Sucrose gradient	300,000 (estimated)			

[a] The different data are presented with the respective membrane sources and solubilization conditions used. CMC, critical micellar concentration; nd, Not determined.

tography. To date only ligand-affinity chromatography has proved useful for the purification of the 5-HT$_3$ receptor. The other methods, however, give some information about the nature of the receptor protein.

Lectin chromatography exploits the specific interaction of lectins with certain carbohydrate structures and can be used to purify glycosylated proteins. Membrane-bound neurotransmitter receptors have been shown to be glycosylated in every case studied so far (Niznik *et al.*, 1986; Rauh *et al.*, 1986; Severne *et al.*, 1986; El Mestikawy *et al.*, 1988), and indeed, as expected, the 5-HT$_3$ receptor is adsorbed to lectin affinity gels. We have shown that wheat germ agglutinin (WGA)-agarose efficiently retains [^{3}H]zacopride-specific binding sites from a CHAPS-soluble extract (95%). Furthermore, these sites could be eluted by *N*-acetylglucosamine from the gel, suggesting that the interaction is specific and that the carbohydrate moieties associated with the receptor protein are probably *N*-acetylglucosamine and/or sialic acid. Often, a modest enrichment of receptor proteins can be achieved by lectin chromatography. Indeed, compared to that in the starting soluble extract, a ~10-fold enrichment in [^{3}H]zacopride-specific binding activity per milligram of protein was found in the peak fraction eluted from the WGA-agarose column. Using a lentil-lectin column, McKernan *et al.* (1990b) obtained a sevenfold purification, indicating the presence of high mannose moieties. These findings are consistent with the protein sequence deduced from the cloned 5-HT$_3$ receptor cDNA (Maricq *et al.*, 1991), which contains three consensus sequences for N-linked glycosylation in the predicted extracellular domain. Although it is certain that some of these sites are used, their exact location and the extent of their glycosylation are not known.

McKernan (1992) tested ion-exchange chromatography (QAE-Sepharose) and found it suitable for a modest purification of the 5-HT$_3$ receptor-binding site. Similar results were also obtained with hydroxyapatite and a phosphate gradient elution (McKernan, 1992).

In spite of these other methods, ligand affinity chromatography remains so far the most effective way to purify the 5-HT$_3$ receptor-binding sites. This method involves the specific interaction of the receptor-binding sites with a relatively high-affinity ligand immobilized on a solid support (such as agarose beads). Competition with a higher affinity ligand for the adsorbed sites then leads to the specific elution of the soluble sites. Three different high-affinity 5-HT$_3$ antagonists have been used to synthesize derivatives that retain a high affinity for the soluble binding sites when coupled to a resin. However, in only two cases were they successfully eluted: with L680,652 (which resembles Q-ICS 205-930) and GR65630 (McKernan *et al.*, 1990c; Lummis and Martin, 1991). We coupled aminopropylzacopride, a derivative of the highest affinity 5-HT$_3$ antagonist zacopride, to agarose. The resulting affinity resin was capable of almost completely depleting the CHAPS-soluble extract of [^{3}H]zacopride-binding sites. However, the interaction between the affinity resin and these soluble sites was such that only a small recovery of 5-HT$_3$-binding sites was reached, regardless of the competing zacopride concentration used (Miquel *et al.*, unpublished data).

McKernan *et al.*, (1990c) used a derivative of L680,652, L-685,603, coupled to agarose, and achieved an extensive purification (1700-fold) of the 5-HT$_3$ receptor-binding sites from NCB20 cells. The 5-HT$_3$ receptor-binding site was solubilized according to their usual procedure [0.5% (w/v) deoxycholate and 0.05% (w/v) Lubrol], and then exchanged to a Triton X-100/KCl buffer [respectively, 0.5% (w/v) and 0.3 *M* for loading, and 0.25% (w/v) and 0.15 *M* for biospecific elution]. Their preparation, close to theoretical purity, exhibited a size of 250,000 by gel filtration and appeared in sodium dodecyl sulfate-polyacrylamide gel electrophoresis (SDS-PAGE) to be composed of two major components of 54,000 and 38,000.

Lummis and Martin (1991) used an affinity column constructed with an analog of GR67330 to purify the 5-HT$_3$ receptor from N1E-115 cells. Analysis of their preparation with SDS-PAGE revealed only one species with a molecular weight of 54,700. In the same group, Boess *et al.* (1992) used an affinity gel bearing a derivative of GR65630, GR119566X, to purify the 5-HT$_3$ receptor from NG108-15 cells. Their soluble preparation was obtained according to their described protocol and loaded on the affinity column in a buffer containing 0.1% (w/v) Triton X-100 and 0.25 *M* NaCl, and biospecific elution was carried out after an exchange to a buffer containing 0.6% (w/v) CHAPS and 0.1 *M* NaCl. Their purified preparation was subjected to sucrose gradient sedimentation and gel-filtration experiments that confirmed the results previously obtained by other groups, that is, an 11S Svedberg coefficient and a molecular weight of 370,000 for the 5-HT$_3$ receptor (Table I). However, SDS-PAGE analysis of this purified preparation revealed the presence of several proteins with molecular weights of 36,000, 40,000, 50,000, and 76,000.

Molecular Size of the 5-HT$_3$ Receptor

In this section, we review the various values reported for the size of the 5-HT$_3$ receptor which have been derived from a variety of different studies (sucrose density sedimentation, gel filtration, radiation inactivation, purification, and molecular cloning) and discuss the discrepancies in light of what is known about other ligand-gated ion channels, in order to understand better the structure of the 5-HT$_3$ receptor.

Many neurotransmitter receptors have now been cloned and sequenced, which has enabled them to be classified based on their structure and homology into two categories, G protein-linked receptors and ligand-gated ion channels.

In all cases, G protein-linked receptors have been found to contain a single subunit which spans the membrane seven times, whereas members of the superfamily of ligand-gated ion channels are generally composed of multiple subunits which possess four transmembrane domains. More detailed sequence comparisons between the known ionotropic receptors suggest that this latter superfamily can be further subdivided into two classes. Homology with the nicotinic acetylcholine (nACh) receptor determines one class that groups the glycine and $GABA_A$ receptors, while the second class is defined by the ionotropic glutamate receptors (AMPA, NMDA, etc.).

The sequence of the cloned 5-HT₃ receptor subunit (Maricq *et al.,* 1991) places it firmly with the nACh receptor group and, by analogy, the receptor is likely to be composed of several subunits. The molecular size of the native 5-HT₃ receptor macromolecule is now proved to be in the range of 250,000–300,000 (for all the receptor sources studied so far; Table I), but the situation is less clear with regard to its subunit(s) size(s) and composition. Indeed, the different techniques used so far by several groups have led to various 5-HT₃ receptor subunit molecular weights. The results summarized in Table II were obtained from different receptor sources either after purification of binding subunits and SDS-PAGE or with the radiation inactivation technique. Among them two values appear to be conserved, one around 52 kDa (55.9, 54, 55, 50, and 49 kDa) and another around 36 kDa (38, 36, 34.9, and 35.4 kDa), but these values must be discussed with regard to the methods used to obtain them.

According to the cDNA sequence of the 5-HT₃ receptor subunit cloned by

TABLE II   Molecular Size of the 5-HT₃ Receptor-Binding Subunit(s)[a]

Method	Subunit size (kDa)	Source	Ref.
Deduced amino acid sequence of cloned protein	55.9	NCB20	Maricq *et al.* (1991)
Purification and SDS-PAGE	54, 38	NCB20	McKernan *et al.* (1990c)
Radiation inactivation	99	N1E-115	Lummis *et al.* (1990)
Purification and SDS-PAGE	55	N1E-115	Lummis and Martin (1992)
Purification and SDS-PAGE	36, 40, 50, 76	NG108-15	Boess *et al.* (1992)
Radiation inactivation	34.9	NG108-15	Bolaños *et al.* (1990)
Gel filtration	36	NG108-15	Miquel *et al.* (1990)
Radiation inactivation	49	Rat cortex	Lummis *et al.* (1990)
Radiation inactivation	35.4	Rat cortex	Bolaños *et al.* (1990); Gozlan *et al.* (1989)

[a] According to the technique of measurement and the membrane sources used by different authors.

Maricq *et al.* (1991) from NCB20 cells, the molecular weight calculated from the deduced amino acid sequence is 55,900. It is possible to assume that the ~52,000 band seen after SDS-PAGE analysis of 5-HT$_3$ receptor purified from different sources (Boess *et al.,* 1992; Lummis and Martin, 1992; McKernan *et al.,* 1990c) corresponds to this cloned 487-amino acid subunit. But two points must be noted which limit the apparent precision of this value. The first is the existence of a domain (~20 amino acids) in the N-terminal sequence of the receptor protein, which corresponds to a signal peptide and which is possibly excised from the mature protein, resulting in a modified total length. The second is the presence of glycosylated residues (see Purification of the 5-HT$_3$ Receptor Binding Site), which will more than likely add weight to the protein. This is the case for other glycosylated neurotransmitter receptors, such as the rat 5-HT$_{1A}$ receptor, the molecular weight of which calculated from the deduced amino acid sequence is 46,427 (Albert *et al.,* 1990) and which also contains some asparagine residues forming putative glycosylation sites. Indeed, methods identical to those applied to the 5-HT$_3$ receptor (i.e., radiation inactivation, purification, and SDS-PAGE) have been used to determine its apparent molecular weight and, in this case, all have agreed to give a value close to 60,000 (for a review, see Gozlan *et al.,* 1990). However, for the 5-HT$_3$ receptor the situation is different because it is more than likely a heterooligomeric protein. Furthermore, not only were the results reported by various groups inconsistent, but even those obtained with the same methods were different.

The overall discrepancies could be explained by the presence of various subtypes of 5-HT$_3$ receptors in the different tissues or clonal cell lines. These cell lines are certainly different, and probably contain different receptors, although they have all been derived from the same mouse neuroblastoma cell line, C1300. N1E-115 is the only cell resulting from direct cloning; the NG108-15 and NCB20 cells are hybrid cells obtained by fusing a 6-thioguanine-resistant mutant of the original clone N18 with a rat glioma C6BU-1 and Chinese hamster fetal brain cells, respectively (Hamprecht, 1977). Electrophysiological studies in undifferentiated NG108-15 cells, reported a single-channel conductance of 12 pS (Shao *et al.,* 1991), while studies with N1E-115 and N18 mouse neuroblastoma cells found subpicosiemens conductances (Lambert *et al.,* 1989; Yang, 1990).

However, species differences cannot explain the discrepancies observed with the same techniques, for example, radiation inactivation, because the same tissue, that is, rat cortex, was shown to contain ligand-binding targets of different sizes, 49,000 (Lummis *et al.,* 1990) and 35,400 (Gozlan *et al.,* 1989), although both groups were using the same facilities for the irradiation (Nielsen, Roskilde, Denmark). There is no straightforward explanation for this situation. Nevertheless, depending on the three-dimensional organization of the 5-HT$_3$ receptor within the various membranes, it is reasonable to assume that the binding site will respond differently to radiation inactivation. One explanation for the small molecular weight protein (reported from various membrane sources) would then be that the binding site is located on an external domain, protruding out of the receptor protein, and would therefore behave as a separate, small subunit. This domain will also be easily accessible to proteases, and form a protein migrating around 36,000 on SDS-PAGE (Boess *et al.*, 1992; McKernan *et al.*, 1990c).

As we will see below, the situation is not clear with regard to the composition of the other members of the ligand-gated receptor family, particularly the recently cloned NMDA receptor. In the "nACh receptor class," the molecular weights of the receptor subunits range from 40,000 to 65,000, ignoring the 93,000 cytoplasmic protein associated with the glycine receptor (Changeux, 1990; Couturier *et al.*, 1990; Langosch *et al.*, 1988; Strange, 1988). In the "glutamate receptor class," all the cloned non-NMDA receptors have a calculated size of around 100,000, but a kainate-binding protein with a molecular weight around 48,000 has been identified and is presumably responsible for the different characteristics of these receptor subtypes (Barnard and Henley, 1990). Due to electrophysiological and biochemical data, the glutamate NMDA receptor was first thought to be different from the non-NMDA receptors but cloning data seem to group these two forms into the same family. Indeed, the rat NMDA receptor encoded by the cloned cDNA is a single protein with a calculated relative molecular mass of 105,500, which shares significant sequence homology with the other glutamate receptors (Moriyoshi *et al.*, 1991). Biochemical studies, however, have reported contradictory results because the complex purified by affinity chromatography has been shown to contain four subunits with molecular weights of about 67,000, 57,000, 46,000, and 33,000, while both radiation inactivation analysis and photoaffinity labeling reported binding target sizes of about 120,000 (Moriyoshi *et al.*, 1991).

Comparison between the 5-HT$_3$ receptor and the other ionophoric receptors does not give clearcut answers. Sequencing data have confirmed the homologies already described between the 5-HT$_3$ receptor subunit and the nicotinic receptor family ligand-binding subunit, but some biochemical and electrophysiological data have shown that the 5-HT$_3$ receptor is more similar to the glutamate non-NMDA receptor group than to the nACh receptors group or to the NMDA receptor (Miquel *et al.*, 1991; Yakel *et al.*, 1991).

Indeed, the cloned 5-HT$_3$ receptor subunit shares significant similarities with the α subunit of the nicotinic acetylcholine receptor and with the 48K subunit of the glycine receptor (Maricq *et al.*, 1991), particularly in the conserved motifs present in the members of this family (for example, the Cys–Cys loop in the extracellular domain, which is 50% homologous to the above subunits, and the four putative transmembrane domains). However, the 5-HT$_3$ receptor subunit lacks some of the characteristic features of the nicotinic ligand-binding subunit, in particular with regard to the role of cysteine residues (Bolaños *et al.,* 1990; Miquel *et al.,* 1991).

Considering all these results, further studies, using both biochemical and molecular techniques, are needed to answer fully the question of the subunit composition of the 5-HT$_3$ receptor.

Conclusion

In summary, we have shown in this chapter that successful solubilization of 5-HT$_3$ receptor-binding sites can be achieved from an abundant source using a large spectrum of detergents and salt conditions. However, physicochemical studies require more restrictive conditions (as a general rule, this should be taken into account when choosing a biological detergent suitable for receptor solubilization).

The solubilization of the 5-HT$_3$ receptor-binding sites, achieved by different groups, allowed the determination of several of its physical properties and led to the purification of the ligand-binding protein(s). In addition, cloning techniques (through expression in oocytes of a clonal cell line library) were successful in unraveling the cDNA sequence of one 5-HT$_3$ receptor subunit. The physicochemical properties and the deduced amino acid sequence of the 5-HT$_3$ receptor-binding subunit are altogether consistent with it being a member of the superfamily of ionophoric receptors.

However, the data obtained so far will be easier to explain after the identification of additional homologous subunits. Studies with antibodies (immunoprecipitation and immunohistochemistry) and photoaffinity labeling of the receptor, which are presently being carried out in several laboratories, will give a more complete picture of the biochemistry of the 5-HT$_3$ receptor in the near future and should help to classify the 5-HT$_3$ receptor among the best known ligand-gated ion channels.

Acknowledgments

We would like to thank Dr. E. Kidd for critical reading of this manuscript. Unpublished data reported herein were obtained thanks to financial support from INSERM and DRET (Contract No. 90/085).

References

Albert, P. R., Zhou, Q. Y., Van Tol, H. H. M., Bunzow, J. R., and Civelli, O. (1990). *J. Biol. Chem.* **265,** 5825–5832.

Barlow, R. B. (1983). "Biodata Handling with Microcomputer." Elsevier Biosoft, Cambridge, UK.

Barnard, E. A., and Henley, J. M. (1990). *Trends Pharmacol. Sci.* **11,** 500–507.

Barnes, N. M., Costall, B., and Naylor, R. J. (1988). *J. Pharm. Pharmacol.* **40,** 548–551.

Boess, F. G., Lummis, S. C. R., and Martin, I. L. (1992). *J. Neurochem.* **59,** 1692–1701.

Bolaños, F. J., Schechter, L. E., Miquel, M.-C., Emerit, M. B., Rumigny, J. F., Hamon, M., and Gozlan, H. (1990). *Biochem. Pharmacol.* **40,** 1541–1550.

Bradley, P. B., Engel, G., Feniuk, W., Fozard, J. R., Humphrey, P. P. A., Middlemiss, D. N., Mylecharane, E. J., Richardson, B. P., and Saxena, P. R. (1986). *Neuropharmacology* **25,** 563–577.

Bruns, R. F., Lawson-Wendling, K., and Pugsley, T. A. (1983). *Anal. Biochem.* **132,** 74–81.

Changeux, J.-P. (1990). *Trends Pharmacol. Sci.* **11,** 485–492.

Couturier, S., Bertrand, D., Matter, J.-M., Hernandez, M.-C., Bertrand, S., Millar, N., Valera, S., Barkas, T., and Balivet, M. (1990). *Neuron,* **5,** 847–856.

Derkach, V., Surprenant, A., and North, R. A. (1989). *Nature (London)* **339,** 706–709.

Dumuis, A., Bouhelal, R., Sebben, M., Cory, R., and Bockaert, J. (1988). *Mol. Pharmacol.* **34,** 880–887.

El Mestikawy, S., Cognard, C., Gozlan, H., and Hamon, M. (1988). *J. Neurochem.* **51,** 1031–1040.

Gordon, J. C., Barefoot, D. S., Sarbin, N. S., and Pinkus, L. M. (1989). *J. Pharmacol. Exp. Ther.* **251,** 962–968.

Gordon, J. C., Sarbin, N. S., Barefoot, D. S., and Pinkus, L. M. (1990). *Eur. J. Pharmacol.—Mol. Pharmacol. Sect.* **188,** 313–319.

Gorissen, H., Aerts, G., Ilien, B., and Laduron, P. (1981). *Anal. Biochem.* **111,** 33–41.

Gozlan, H., Emerit, M. B., Hall, M. D., Nielsen, M., and Hamon, M. (1986). *Biochem. Pharmacol.* **35,** 1891–1897.

Gozlan, H., Schechter, L. E., Bolaños, F., Emerit, M. B., Miquel, M. C., Nielsen, M., and Hamon, M. (1989). *Eur. J. Pharmacol.—Mol. Pharmacol. Sect.* **172,** 497–500.

Gozlan, H., El Mestikawy, S., and Hamon, M. (1990). *In* "Receptor Purification" (G. Litwack, ed.), pp. 23–43. Humana Press, Clifton, NJ.

Hamon, M., Gallissot, M.-C., Ménard, F., Gozlan, H., Bourgoin, S., and Vergé, D. (1989). *Eur. J. Pharmacol.* **164,** 315–321.

Hamon, M., Lanfumey, L., El Mestikawy, S., Boni, C., Miquel, M.-C., Bolaños, F. J., Schechter, L. E., and Gozlan, H. (1990). *Neuropsychopharmacology* **3,** 349–360.

Hamprecht, B. (1977). *Int. Rev. Cytol.* **49,** 99–170.

Hjelmeland, L. M. (1980). *Proc. Natl. Acad. Sci. U.S.A.* **77,** 6368–6370.

Hoyer, D., and Neijt, H. C. (1987). *Eur. J. Pharmacol.* **143,** 291–292.

Hoyer, D., and Neijt, H. C. (1988). *Mol. Pharmacol.* **33,** 303–309.

Hoyer, D., Gozlan, H., Bolaños, F. J., Schechter, L. E., and Hamon, M. (1989). *Eur. J. Pharmacol.* **171,** 137–139.

Julius, D. (1991). *Annu. Rev. Neurosci.* **14,** 335–360.

Kilpatrick, G. J., Jones, B. J., and Tyers, M. B. (1987). *Nature (London)* **330,** 746–748.

Kilpatrick, G. J., Jones, B. J., and Tyers, M. B. (1988). *Neurosci. Lett.* **94,** 156–160.

Lambert, J. L., Peters, J. A., Hales, T. G., and Dempster, J. (1989). *Br. J. Pharmacol.* **97,** 27–40.

Langosch, D., Thomas, L., and Betz, H. (1988). *Proc. Natl. Acad. Sci. U.S.A.* **85,** 7394–7398.

Lummis, S. C. R., and Martin, I. L. (1990). *Biochem. Soc. Trans.* **18,** 1027–1028.

Lummis, S. C. R., and Martin, I. L. (1991). *J. Neurochem.* **57,** Suppl., S136.

Lummis, S. C. R., and Martin, I. L. (1992). *Mol. Pharmacol.* **41,** 18–23.

Lummis, S. C. R., Nielsen, M., Kilpatrick, G. J., and Martin, I. L. (1990). *Eur. J. Pharmacol.—Mol. Pharmacol. Sect.* **189,** 229–232.

Mamalaki, C., Barnard, E. A., and Stephenson, F. A. (1989). *J. Neurochem.* **52,** 124–134.

Maricq, A. V., Peterson, A. S., Brake, A. J., Myers, R. M., and Julius, D. (1991). *Science* **254,** 432–437.

McKernan, R. M. (1992). *In* ''Central and Peripheral 5-HT₃ Receptors'' (M. Hamon, ed.), pp. 89–102. Academic Press, London.

McKernan, R. M., Biggs, C. S., Gillard, N. P., Quirk, K., and Ragan, C. I. (1990a). *Biochem. J.* **269,** 623–628.

McKernan, R. M., Gillard, N. P., Quirk, K., Kneen, C. O., Stevenson, G. I., Swain, C. J., and Ragan, C. I. (1990b). *J. Biol. Chem.* **265,** 13572–13577.

McKernan, R. M., Quirk, K., Jackson, R. G., and Ragan, C. I. (1990c). *J. Neurochem.* **54,** 924–930.

Milburn, C. M., and Peroutka, S. J. (1989). *J. Neurochem.* **52,** 1787–1792.

Miller, K. J., and Teitler, M. (1991). *Soc. Neurosci. Abstr.* **17,** 599.

Miquel, M.-C., Emerit, M. B., Bolaños, F. J., Schechter, L. E., Gozlan, H., and Hamon, M. (1990). *J. Neurochem.* **55,** 1526–1536.

Miquel, M.-C., Emerit, M. B., Gozlan, H., and Hamon, M. (1991). *Biochem. Pharmacol.* **42,** 1453–1461.

Moriyoshi, K., Masayuki, M., Takahiro, I., Shigemoto, R., Mizuno, N., and Nakanishi, S. (1991). *Nature (London)* **354,** 31–37.

Neijt, H. C., Karpf, A., Schoeffter, P., Engel, G., and Hoyer, D. (1988). *Naunyn-Schmiedeberg's Arch. Pharmacol.* **337,** 493–499.

Neijt, H. C., Plomp, J. J., and Vijverberg, H. P. M. (1989). *J. Physiol. (London)* **411,** 257–269.

Nelson, D. R., and Thomas, D. R. (1989). *Biochem. Pharmacol.* **38,** 1693–1695.

Niznik, H. B., Grigoriadis, D. E., Otsuka, N. Y., Dumbrille-Ross, A., and Seeman, P. (1986). *Biochem. Pharmacol.* **35,** 2974–2977.

Peroutka, S. J. (1988). *Trends Neurosci.* **11**, 496–500.

Radja, F., Laporte, A.-M., Daval, G., Vergé, D., Gozlan, H., and Hamon, M. (1991). *Neurochem. Int.* **18**, 1–15.

Rauh, J. J., Lambert, M. P., Cho, N. J., Chin, H., and Klein, W. L. (1986). *J. Neurochem.* **46**, 23–32.

Richardson, B. P., and Engel, G. (1986). *Trends Neurosci.* **9**, 424–428.

Sanders-Bush, E., ed. (1988). "The Serotonin Receptors." Humana Press, Clifton, NJ.

Severne, Y., Jurss, R., and Vauquelin, G. (1986). *Biochem. Pharmacol.* **35**, 4375–4380.

Shao, M. X., Yakel, J. L., and Jackson, M. B. (1991). *J. Neurophysiol.* **65**, 630–638.

Sharif, N. A., Wong, E. H. F., Loury, D. N., Stefanich, E., Michel, A. D., Eglen, R. M., and Whiting, R. L. (1991). *Br. J. Pharmacol.* **102**, 919–925.

Strange, P. G. (1988). *Biochem. J.* **249**, 309–318.

Watling, K. J., Aspley, S., Swain, C. J., and Saunders, J. (1988). *Eur. J. Pharmacol.* **149**, 397–398.

Wouters, W., Van Dun, J., Leysen, J. E., and Laduron, P. M. (1985). *Eur. J. Pharmacol.* **115**, 1–9.

Yagaloff, K. A., and Hartig, P. R. (1986). *Mol. Pharmacol.* **29**, 120–125.

Yakel, J. L., and Jackson, M. B. (1988). *Neuron* **1**, 615–621.

Yakel, J. L., Shao, X. M., and Jackson, M. B. (1990). *Brain Res.* **533**, 46–52.

Yakel, J. L., Shao, X. M., and Jackson, M. B. (1991). *J. Physiol.* (*London*) **436**, 293–308.

Yang, J. (1990). *J. Gen. Physiol.* **96**, 1177–1198.

[23] Solubilization and Characterization of the Receptor for Gastrin-Releasing Peptide

Richard Kris, Daniela Cirillo, Terry W. Moody, and Luigi Naldini

Introduction

Gastrin-releasing peptide (GRP), the mammalian counterpart of bombesin (an amphibian hormone), is a neurohormone that exerts a number of different effects *in vivo* and *in vitro* (1). It has been postulated that an autocrine loop involving GRP and its receptor play a role in proliferation of small cell carcinoma of the lung (2). The GRP receptor is a G protein-coupled receptor that exerts its effects through stimulation of phospholipase C (3–5). Fischer and Schonbrunn (5a) have demonstrated the involvement of a G protein in the GRp receptor signaling pathway and the molecular cloning of the GRP receptor confirms that the GRP receptor has seven putative transmembrane regions and is a member of the G protein-coupled receptor superfamily (6, 7).

Purification of the GRP receptor necessitates the solubilization of the receptor from the membrane to purify it away from other protein and lipids in the membrane environment. The first step toward purification or analysis of a membrane receptor is the successful solubilization of the receptor in an active form. The choice of detergent for effective solubilization is empirical. A number of nonionic detergents are available for solubilization of membrane proteins. They feature both low denaturing potential and a high critical micellar concentration (useful for easier detergent removal at a later date if desired). Some receptors are easily solubilized in an active form. Other receptors, such as the receptor for the neuropeptide GRP, can be solubilized with detergents alone but no longer bind GRP (R. Kris, D. Cirillo, T. W. Moody, and L. Naldini, unpublished data). Here we describe the solubilization and characterization of GRP receptor in an active form by employing a combination of the detergent 3-[(3-cholamidopropyl)dimethyl-ammonio]-1-propanesulfonic acid (CHAPS) and the ester cholesteryl hemisuccinate (CHS) in a glycerol-containing buffer. Solubilization of a functional GRP receptor using CHAPS/CHS has been reported by our group and a group led by Feldman (8, 9).

Methods in Neurosciences, Volume 11

Characteristics of Bombesin Binding to the Gastrin-Releasing Peptide Receptor

Radioiodination of [Tyr⁴]Bombesin

Reagents

[Tyr⁴]Bombesin (1.5 μg) (Peninsula Laboratories, Belmont, CA)
Na^{125}I (Amersham, Arlington Heights, IL)
Chloramine T$_1$ 0.9 μg in 0.1 M phosphate buffer (pH 7.4)
Sodium metabisulfite, 1.4 μg
Sephadex LH-20 (Pharmacia-LKB, Rockville, MD)
Methanol/acetic acid/H$_2$O (10 : 2 : 1, v/v/v)
Dithiothreitol, 1 M (Sigma, St. Louis, MO)
C$_{18}$ Sep-Pak cartridge (Waters Associates, Milford, MA)
Acetonitrile [35% (v/v) in H$_2$O], with 0.1% (v/v) trifluoroacetic acid (TFA), 0.25% (w/v) bovine serum albumin (fraction V, protease free; Calbiochem, La Jolla, CA), 20 mM dithiothreitol, and 100 μg/ml aprotinin

The first step in determining optimal solubilization conditions is the development of a sensitive binding assay. Radiolabeled bombesin with high specific activity is necessary for detection of solubilized receptor. [Tyr⁴]Bombesin (1.5 μg, 0.9 nmol) is labeled with Na^{125}I (Amersham) according to the following procedure: 2 mCi of Na^{125}I is incubated at room temperature with 0.9 μg of chloramine T in 0.1 M phosphate buffer, pH 7.4, for 1 min (8). The oxidation reaction is stopped by the addition of 1.4 μg of sodium metabisulfite. Separation of labeled bombesin from unlabeled bombesin is accomplished by molecular seiving with Sephadex LH-20 (Pharmacia-LKB) equilibrated in methanol/acetic acid/H$_2$O (10 : 2 : 1, v/v/v). The labeled peptide is dried down in a Savant (Hicksville, NY) concentrator and reduced in the presence of 1 M dithiothreitol (DTT) (Sigma) at 80°C for 2 hr to allow reduction of the C-terminal methionine sulfoxide generated by chloramine T oxidation, which abolishes receptor binding and biological activity. Dithiothreitol and any remaining free ^{125}I is removed by filtration with C-18 Sep-Pak cartridge chromatography (Waters Associates). The free iodine and DTT are washed through with water and the labeled peptide eluted with 35% (v/v) acetonitrile in H$_2$O with 0.1% (v/v) TFA. The labeled peptide is dried to 30 μl in a Savant concentrator and diluted 25-fold or more with 0.25% (w/v) bovine serum albumin (fraction V, protease free; Calbiochem), 20 mM DTT, and 100 μg/ml aprotinin in 20 mM N-2-hydroxyethylpiperazine-N'-2-ethanesulfonic acid (HEPES), pH 7.4, to prevent reoxidation and radiolysis, aliquoted, and frozen at −20°C. Siliconized tubes are used to prevent sticking of the hydrophobic peptide to the walls of the tubes. The radiolabeled bombesin is stable for 3–4 weeks. High-performance liquid chromatography (HPLC) analysis of the purified labeled bombesin shows mostly monoiodinated (70%) and diiododinated (30%) bombesin and no free [125]I. The specific activity is usually between 1000 and 1500 Ci/mmol. The specific activity is measured by competition experiments with unlabeled [Tyr[4]]bombesin and Swiss 3T3 cell membranes.

Binding Parameters of Bombesin to Its Receptor in Membrane Preparations

Reagents

[125]I-Labeled [Tyr[4]]bombesin
[Tyr[4]]bombesin
Swiss 3T3 cells
GF/C glass fiber filters (Whatman, Clifton, NJ)
Poly(ethylenimine), 0.3% (v/v) in H_2O (Eastman Kodak, Rochester, NY)
Ice-cold lysis buffer: 50 mM Tris-HCl, pH 8.0, 1 mM ethylene glycol-bis(β-aminoethyl ether)-N,N,N',N'-tetraacetic acid (EGTA), 5 mM $MgCl_2$, 50 μg/ml leupeptin, 5 μg/ml pepstatin, 10 μg/ml aprotinin, 200 μg/ml bacitracin, 1 mM phenylmethylsulfonyl fluoride (PMSF)
HEMI buffer: 20 mM HEPES-KOH, pH 6.8, 1 mM EGTA, 5 mM $MgCl_2$, with protease inhibitors (leupeptin, 50 μg/ml; aprotinin, 10 μg/ml; pepstatin, 5 μg/ml; bacitracin, 200 μg/ml; 1 mM PMSF)

To determine conditions for bombesin binding to its receptor in a solubilized preparation, optimal parameters are first determined for binding to the bombesin receptor in membrane preparations. Crude membranes are prepared from Swiss 3T3 cells, which express 100,000 receptors per cell with a K_d of 1 nM for bombesin when measurements are made on whole cells (10). Briefly, confluent 15-cm plates of Swiss 3T3 cells are scraped in ice-cold phosphate-buffered saline (PBS) with 1 mM PMSF, centrifuged (800 g, 4°C, 5 min), and the pellet washed once in ice-cold lysis buffer. A homogenate is prepared using a Dounce (Wheaton, Millville, NJ) homogenizer (B-type glass pestle) (8). The rest of the procedure is done at 4°C or on ice. Following a 5-min (800 g) centrifugation step to remove debris and nuclei, the supernatant is centrifuged for 30 min at high speed (20,000 g), the pellet is resuspended in HEMI buffer, and protein content measured. The membranes are frozen quickly at −80°C in 30% (v/v) glycerol until needed (8).

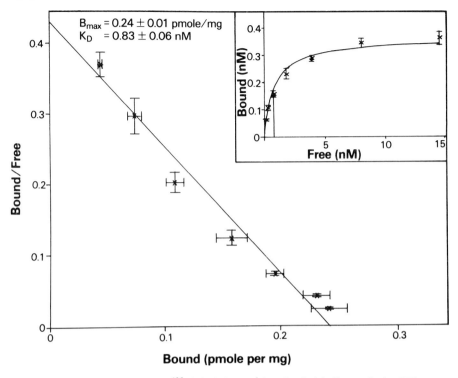

FIG. 1   Scatchard analysis of ^{125}I-labeled [Tyr[4]]bombesin binding to Swiss 3T3 membranes. Samples (150 μg) from a crude membrane preparation of Swiss 3T3 cells were incubated with increasing concentrations of ^{125}I-labeled [Tyr[4]]bombesin. Analysis of the binding data according to the method of Scatchard and the binding curve from a representative experiment (inset) are shown here.

The membranes are incubated with 0.5 nM ^{125}I-labeled [Tyr[4]]bombesin, in the presence or absence of unlabeled [Tyr[4]]bombesin, for indicated periods of time and filtered through Whatman GF/C glass fiber filters precoated with 0.3% (v/v) poly(ethylenimine) (Eastman Kodak) in H_2O for at least 2 hr (8). This effects the separation of receptor-bound ligand from free ligand. The filters are washed with 8–10 ml of 20 mM HEPES-KOH, pH 7.6. The background retention of the filters is approximately 1% of the counts per minute added. The filters are counted in a γ counter. Scatchard analysis of ^{125}I-labeled [Tyr[4]]bombesin to its receptor in crude membrane preparations at equilibrium shows a single class of sites (240 fmol receptor/mg of protein) with an affinity of 0.83 nM at 4°C (Fig. 1). This is in agreement with published values of bombesin binding to whole cells.

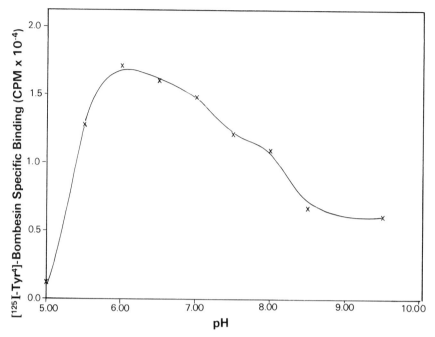

FIG. 2   The effect of pH on the binding of bombesin to its receptor in Swiss 3T3 membranes.

Association kinetics demonstrates that specific binding is maximal at 37°C for 15 min and at approximately 2 hr at 4°C (8). Proteins are more stable at 4°C, so all subsequent binding assays are done at 4°C for 2 hr.

Optimization of buffer constituents is necessary for optimal binding. The effects of monovalent cations on bombesin binding need to be analyzed. The binding of ^{125}I-labeled [Tyr^4]bombesin to its receptor in membrane preparations is drastically inhibited by NaCl, with an IC_{50} of 46 mM, and by KCl, with an IC_{50} of 166 mM (8). This suggests that Na$^+$ is more potent than K$^+$ in exerting this inhibition. Divalent cations also inhibit the binding, with CaCl$_2$ having an IC_{50} of 36 mM and MgCl$_2$ having an IC_{50} of 67 mM (R. Kris, D. Cirillo, T. W. Moody, and L. Naldini, unpublished data). Although cations at high concentrations inhibit GRP binding, a low concentration of divalent cations is necessary for binding. The pH optimal for binding to GRP receptor in Swiss 3T3 cell membrane preparations is between 6.4 and 6.8 (Fig. 2). Therefore, the binding buffer (HEMI) is made with 20 mM HEPES-KOH, pH 6.8, 1 mM EGTA, and 5 mM MgCl$_2$, with protease inhibitors (leupeptin, 50 μg/ml; aprotinin, 10 μg/ml; pepstatin, 5 μg/ml; bacitracin, 200 μg/ml; and 1 mM PMSF).

Solubilization of Gastrin-Releasing Peptide Receptor

Reagents

> ^{125}I-Labeled [Tyr^4]bombesin
> [Tyr^4]Bombesin
> Swiss 3T3 cell membranes
> GF/F glass fiber filters (Whatman)
> Poly(ethylenimine), 0.3% (v/v) in H$_2$O (Eastman Kodak)
> HEMI buffer (see above)
> CHAPS
> CHS
> Solubilization buffer: 0.75% (w/v) CHAPS and 0.15% (w/v) CHS in HEMGI buffer
> HEMGI buffer: 20 mM HEPES-KOH, pH 6.8, 1 mM EGTA, 5 mM MgCl$_2$, 10% (v/v) glycerol, protease inhibitors (aprotinin, 10 μg/ml; leupeptin, 50 μg/ml; pepstatin, 5 μg/ml; bacitracin, 200 μg/ml; 1 mM PMSF)

A filtration assay (similar to the membrane-binding assay) is used to analyze the binding of ^{125}I-labeled [Tyr^4]bombesin to its solubilized receptor. No specific binding is detected with detergent alone (CHAPS, Triton X-100, or n-octyl glucoside). A specific solubilization of the neurotensin receptor, the γ-aminobutyric acid/benzodiazepine receptor, and interleukin 1 receptor is effected by the use of the ester cholesteryl hemisuccinate in conjunction with the detergent CHAPS (11–13). This is also successful for the GRP receptor.

The preparation of the solubilization buffer is critical to efficient solubilization. First, a stock solution of CHAPS/CHS (5 : 1, w/w) must be prepared. The CHAPS solution (1.25%, w/v) is prepared in 20 mM HEPES, pH 6.8, and 10% (v/v) glycerol, and CHS (0.25%, w/v) is added and mixed overnight at 4°C (8). Membrane preparations of Swiss 3T3 cells are prepared as discussed above and solubilized at a concentration of 15 mg/ml (8). An optimal concentration for efficient solubilization is 15 mg/ml (8). The solubilization is accomplished by mixing the membranes with solubilization buffer at 4°C for 1 hr with gentle stirring. The glycerol improves the stability of the receptor. In the above solubilization buffer the receptor is stable at −80°C for several weeks with no detectable loss of activity and at 4°C with a half-life of 60 hr. The solubilized extract is centrifuged at 100,000 g for 1 hr to ensure that the receptor is completely soluble and used immediately or frozen at −80°C.

The receptor-binding assay for solubilized receptor is similar to that described above for membrane-bound receptor (8, 14). The solubilized receptor is diluted to 0.1% (w/v) CHAPS with HEMGI buffer and incubated with

0.5 nM ^{125}I-labeled [Tyr^4]bombesin for 3 hr at 4°C. Nonspecific binding is measured in the presence of a 1000-fold excess of unlabeled bombesin. Nonspecific binding is 10–30% of the total bound. Receptor-bound ligand is separated from free ligand by filtration through 0.3% (v/v) poly(ethylenimine)-coated Whatman GF/F glass fiber filters as described above.

The detergent-solubilized receptor can still bind its ligand although the assay needs to be done in 0.1% (w/v) CHAPS (8). The specific binding is between 65 and 80% of the total bound and optimal solubilization is accomplished by 1 hr of extraction with 0.75% (w/v) CHAPS at 4°C with 90% of the binding sites in the membrane preparation recovered. The pH optimum of bombesin binding to its detergent-solubilized receptor is pH 6.8–7.0 (R. Kris, D. Cirillo, T. W. Moody, and L. Naldini, unpublished data). This pH optimum is similar to that found for GRP binding to membrane-bound receptors (Fig. 2).

The association kinetics of the binding at 4°C is similar to that obtained from membrane preparations (8). Scatchard analysis of the binding indicates a single class of sites (120 fmol/mg protein) with an affinity of 0.8 nM (Fig. 3). This indicates that the affinity of the receptor for bombesin binding is not significantly affected by the solubilization procedures described here. A functional receptor can be solubilized only from tissues or cells that had previously been shown to express the GRP receptor (8). This demonstrates the specificity of the binding assay for solubilized GRP receptor.

Dissociation Kinetics of ^{125}I-Labeled [Tyr^4]Bombesin from Its Solubilized Receptor

The dissociation of ^{125}I-labeled [Tyr^4]bombesin from its solubilized receptor is very slow at 4°C in the presence of unlabeled bombesin (Fig. 4). The addition of 0.5 M NaCl causes a dissociation of the radiolabeled ligand with a half time of 4 min. In addition, chelation of Mg^{2+} causes dissociation of ^{125}I-labeled [Tyr^4]bombesin from its receptor with a half time of 12 min. These conditions can be used for purification of the receptor from an affinity matrix.

Affinity Chromatography

Affinity chromatography is an important step in the purification of receptors that are present in small amounts in cells and tissues. Several analogs of bombesin can be synthesized to produce a compound that can be bound to a matrix and still be able to bind its receptor. Analogs of bombesin were

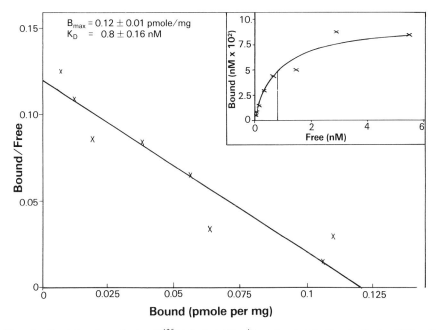

FIG. 3   Scatchard analysis of ^{125}I-labeled [Tyr[4]]bombesin binding to Swiss 3T3 cell extracts. Protein (40.5 μg) solubilized from crude membrane preparations of Swiss 3T3 cells was incubated with increasing concentrations of ^{125}I-labeled [Tyr[4]]bombesin. Analysis of the binding data according to the method of Scatchard and the binding curve from a representative experiment are shown here.

synthesized with N-terminal polyglycine extensions and a lysine residue at the N terminus. The compounds were purified by reversed-phase HPLC. An inhibition assay utilizing ^{125}I-labeled [Tyr[4]]bombesin, the unlabeled bombesin analogs, and Swiss 3T3 cell membranes shows that their potency is indistinguishable from that of bombesin. Radioiodination of an analog ([KG[4]]BN) showed direct binding to its receptor as confirmed by covalent nonlinking with the heterobifunctional cross-linking agent disuccinimidyl suberate (DSS) (R. Kris, D. Cirillo, T. W. Moody, and L. Naldini, unpublished results). These analogs are coupled to matrices. The apparent concentration of ligand in the matrices was estimated using a radiolabeled antibody specific for the C terminus of bombesin and titering the concentration of free bombesin that displaced half of the antibody specifically bound to the resin. These so-calculated concentrations of "available" ligand are always at least 10 times lower than those of a peptide actually incorporated into the resin.

To produce an affinity matrix, CNBr Sepharose 6B is activated with 1 mM

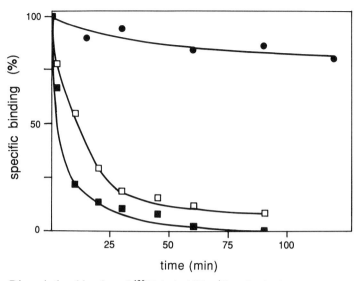

FIG. 4   Dissociation kinetics of ^{125}I-labeled [Tyr[4]]bombesin from soluble Swiss 3T3 receptor. Protein samples (50 μg) solubilized from Swiss 3T3 cells were incubated with 0.1 nM ^{125}I-labeled [Tyr[4]]bombesin for 3 hr. Samples were then diluted 15-fold with the following buffers containing 100 nM unlabeled [Tyr[4]]bombesin and further incubated for the indicated times. (●) Control HEMI buffer; (□) 10 mM EDTA in HEMI buffer without $MgCl_2$; (■) 500 mM NaCl in HEMI buffer. [Reprinted from Naldini *et al.* (8) with permission. Copyright 1990 American Chemical Society.]

HCl for 15 min. CNBr-activated Sepharose 6B (1 g) is treated with coupling buffer (0.1 M sodium bicarbonate, 0.5 M NaCl, pH 8.3). Five milligrams of peptide (KG[4])BN is added and the solution shaken for 60 min at 25°C. The resin is centrifuged at 1000 g for 5 min, the supernatant removed, and the resin washed in 0.1 M acetic acid (pH 4), 0.5. M NaCl, followed by 0.1 M Tris-HCl (pH 8), 0.5 M NaCl. This cycle of washing is repeated two additional times. The affinity resin is centrifuged, and resuspended in 10 mM HEPES-NaOH (pH 7.4), 1 mM EGTA, and 5 mM $MgCl_2$ containing 0.02% (w/v) azide at 4°C until use. The Swiss 3T3 extract is diluted 7.5-fold so that the final CHAPS/CHS concentration is 0.1/0.2% (w/v). Affinity resin is added to the dilute extract and the sample shaken at 4°C for 16 hr. The mixture is applied to a column (5 ml) and after the affinity resin settles it is washed extensively with buffer (50 ml). Then the GRP receptor is slowly eluted from the affinity resin with a 0.5 M NaCl gradient. Fractions (1 ml) are collected and concentrated using a Centricon (Amicon, Lexington, MA). The concentrated fractions are rinsed twice with 1 ml of buffer that is NaCl free. The

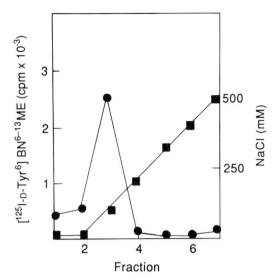

F$_{\text{IG}}$. 5   Affinity purification of bombesin/GRP receptor. Swiss 3T3 cell extract was loaded onto a [KG^4]BN affinity resin column and eluted with an NaCl gradient (■). The samples were then concentrated on a Centricon and assayed for specific ^{125}I-labeled [D-Tyr^6]BN$^{6-13}$Methylester binding (●).

concentrated fractions are then assayed for ^{125}I-labeled [D-Tyr^6]BN$^{6-13}$Methylester (a GRP receptor antagonist) or ^{125}I-labeled [Tyr^4]BN (a GRP receptor agonist) binding activity using the GRP soluble receptor assay.

Figure 5 shows that ^{125}I-labeled [D-Tyr^6]BN$^{6-13}$Methylester binding activity is detected in fraction 3, corresponding to approximately 100 mM NaCl. Similar binding data are obtained using ^{125}I-labeled [Tyr^4]BN as a receptor ligand although the counts per minute bound are approximately fivefold lower. Because the partially purified Swiss 3T3 extract bound ^{125}I-labeled [D-Tyr^6]BN$^{6-13}$ME better than ^{125}I-labeled [Tyr^4]BN, the partially purified GRP receptor may have impaired ability to bind agonists. In contrast, the crude Swiss 3T3 extract bound ^{125}I-labeled [D-Tyr^6]BN$^{6-13}$ME and ^{125}I-labeled [Tyr^4]BN with similar affinity. Also, binding of ^{125}I-labeled GRP to the Swiss 3T3 BN/GRP receptor purified on a [Nle^{14,27}et al.]GRP$^{13-27}$ affinity resin is insensitive to guanine nucleotide (15), suggesting that the guanine nucleotide-binding subunit had dissociated from the receptor. In the crude Swiss 3T3 extract, however, GTP enhanced dissociation of ^{125}I-labeled GRP from the GRP receptor (16). These data suggest that a guanine nucleotide-binding protein may be associated with the crude but not partially purified soluble

A

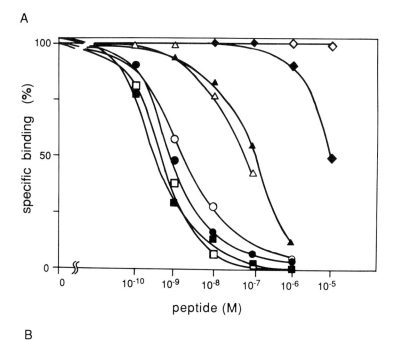

B

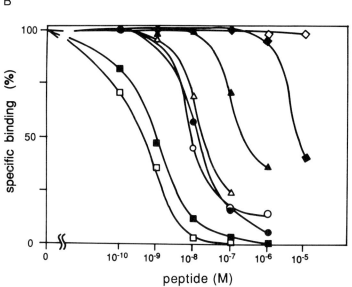

Fig. 6   Inhibition of ^{125}I-labeled [Tyr[4]]bombesin binding to membrane-bound and soluble receptor from Swiss 3T3 cells by a spectrum of bombesin analogs. Samples containing either 100 μg of a crude membrane preparation of Swiss 3T3 cells (A) or

GRP receptor. Alternatively, the difference may be due to the different detergents used for solubilization (discussed under Characterization of the Solubilized Receptor for Gastrin-Releasing Peptide).

Preliminary data indicate that the GRP receptor is purified approximately 200-fold using the [KG^4]BN affinity resin. The GRP receptor could be purified another 200-fold by passing the partially purified Swiss 3T3 extract over an additional affinity resin containing KG^2[D-Tyr^6]BN^{6-13}Propylamine (a GRP receptor antagonist). By sodium dodecyl sulfate-polyacrylamide gel electrophoresis (SDS-PAGE) analysis, the purified Swiss 3T3 extract had major proteins of 65 and 115 kDa (data not shown). Similarly, Feldman et al. (15) purified the GRP receptor from Swiss 3T3 extract using an [$Nle^{14,27}$]GRP^{13-27} agarose resin and obtained a major 75- to 100-kDa protein (15). Partial amino acid sequences were obtained, which facilitated GRP receptor cloning (7). The cloned GRP receptor contains 384 amino acid residues and 7 hydrophobic domains (6, 7).

Pharmacology of Bombesin Analogs with Membrane-Bound and Solubilized Receptor

The ability of various bombesin analogs to inhibit the binding of ^{125}I-labeled [Tyr^4]bombesin to its membrane-bound or solubilized receptor needs to be evaluated to determine that the solubilized receptor has the same binding characteristics as the membrane-bound form. Several concentrations of the analogs are incubated with 0.5 nM ^{125}I-labeled [Tyr^4]bombesin for 30 min at 37°C (crude membranes) or for 3 hr at 4°C (solubilized cells). Bound ligand is separated from free ligand as described earlier. The agonists used are [Tyr^4]bombesin, gastrin-releasing peptide (GRP), GRP^{14-27} (14 C-terminal amino acids of GRP), GRP^{18-27} (10 C-terminal amino acids of GRP), neuromedin B, and bombesin$^{8-14}$ (C-terminal bombesin heptapeptide). An antagonist is also tested: [D-Arg^1,D-Pro^2,D-$Trp^{7,9}$,Leu^{11}] substance P and the inactive GRP^{1-16} (16 N-terminal amino acids of GRP). The results of inhibition of the various analogs is shown for both membrane-bound (Fig. 6A) and solubilized receptor (Fig. 6B). There is a good correlation between the pharmacology of binding of the analogs to the receptor in membrane-bound and solubilized forms.

40 μg of proteins solubilized from it with CHAPS and CHS (B). The peptides tested were as follow: □, GRP; ■, [Tyr^4]bombesin; ●, GRP^{14-27}; ○, GRP^{10}; △, bombesin$^{8-14}$; ▲, neuromedin B; ◆, [D-Arg^1,D-Pro^2,D-$Trp^{7,9}$, Leu^{11}]substance P; ◇, GRP^{1-16}). [Reprinted from Naldini et al. (8) with permission. Copyright 1990 American Chemical Society.]

Characterization of the Solubilized Receptor for Gastrin-Releasing Peptide

Reagents

Ethyleneglycol-bis(succinimidylsuccinate) (EGS) (Pierce, Rockford, IL)
[125]I-Labeled GRP (Amersham)
GRP (Peninsula Laboratories)
HMG buffer: 20 mM HEPES, pH 6.8, 5 mM MgCl$_2$, 0.1% (w/v) CHAPS, 0.02% (w/v) CHS, 10% (v/v) glycerol

Once the receptor is solubilized, it can be analyzed to determine its size in detergent, to determine if it is interacting with other proteins, and the receptor may be purified by chromatographic methods. Previous work using ^{125}I-labeled GRP, covalent cross-linking, and SDS–PAGE had demonstrated that the size of the GRP receptor from Swiss 3T3 cells is 65–85 kDa (17, 18). The cross-linked receptor can also be analyzed by molecular seiving chromatography to determine if it retains the same size under detergent-solubilized conditions.

To study the size of the detergent-solubilized receptor, the receptor is first cross-linked with ^{125}I-labeled GRP. This is accomplished by covalently cross-linking ^{125}I-labeled GRP to its receptor after equilibrium binding using EGS. A Swiss 3T3 crude membrane preparation (500 μg) is incubated with 1.5 nM ^{125}I-labeled GRP in the presence or absence of 1 μM unlabeled GRP for 30 min at 37°C in HEMI buffer. The membranes are centrifuged (15 min at 18,000 g at 4°C) and washed once with HEMI buffer to remove the unbound radiolabeled ligand. The washed membranes are suspended with 5 mM EGS in ice-cold phosphate buffer, pH 7.0, and incubated for 20 min on ice. Tris, pH 7.6 (final concentration, 20 mM), is used to stop the cross-linking reaction.

The radiolabeled cross-linked material is solubilized as described above and analyzed by HPLC molecular sieving chromatography on a TSK 4000 (Pharmacia Biotechnology, Inc., Piscataway, NJ) column (the column is equilibrated with HMG buffer). The protein-bound radioactivity elutes in two peaks: a more prominent peak 1 of apparent M_r 220,000 and a smaller peak 2 of apparent M_r 80,000. The column is calibrated with CHAPS-solubilized ^{32}P-labeled EGF receptor (170 kDa) and a truncated EGF receptor mutant (80 kDa) (Fig. 7). SDS-PAGE is used to analyze concentrated material from peak fractions. The major covalently labeled species in both peaks is the 75-kDa species described as the GRP receptor in Swiss 3T3 cells (Fig. 7, inset). The molecular length of the cross-linker or the solubility properties of the cross-linker used does not affect the elution profile (14).

Apparent molecular weights of 220,000 and 80,000 can be estimated for

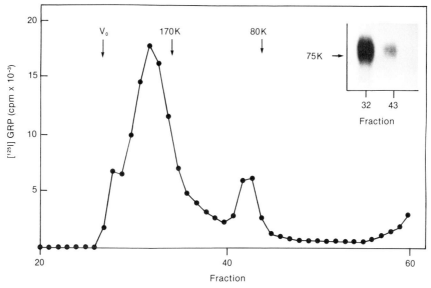

FIG. 7   Molecular sieving chromatography of CHAPS extract of ^{125}I-labeled GRP covalently labeled Swiss 3T3 membranes. ^{125}I-Labeled GRP covalently labeled Swiss 3T3 membranes were analyzed by molecular sieving chromatography on a TSK preparative column after solubilization under nondenaturing conditions. Void volume (V_0) is the elution volume of blue dextran. Arrows show the elution volume of the epidermal growth factor (EGF) receptor (170K) and truncated EGF receptor mutant (80K) used as markers. *Inset:* SDS-PAGE analysis of the peaks. The number of the original fraction of the chromatography profile is indicated. [Reproduced from Cirillo *et al.* (14) with permission.]

the two peaks using the labeled membrane proteins as molecular weight standards. A similar amount of the protein–detergent complex is assumed for both markers and cross-linked receptor (14). Their relative positions are preserved in sucrose density sedimentation (14). Other G protein-coupled receptors show larger sizes when solubilized with nonionic detergents (in comparison with expected sizes derived from cross-linking studies) (19–21). Because both peak 1 and peak 2 contain the 75-kDa species, the GRP receptor in peak 1 may be associating noncovalently with another molecule. In fact, SDS treatment of peak 1 converts it into peak 2 (75-kDa species) and a smaller peak (14). The large molecular size of the receptor could instead represent an oligomeric structure held together by noncovalent interaction. Other G protein-coupled receptors, such as the β-adrenergic receptor and adenosine receptor, still have an associated G protein after solubilization with detergent (22, 23). The effect of GTPγS on the high molecular weight component of ^{125}I-labeled GRP-cross-linked receptor is analyzed to determine if an associated G protein could account for the larger size. Detergent (CHAPS/CHS)-solubilized GRP receptor does not seem to be associated with a G protein after detergent solubilization (14). However, more recent reports using a different detergent (taurodeoxycholate) indicate that a G protein might be associated with the GRP receptor solubilized using taurodeoxycholate (16). In these studies, Coffer *et al.* incubated cell membranes with ^{125}I-labeled GRP before solubilization. It is possible that a G protein remains associated with the GRP receptor after solubilization with detergent if the receptor–G protein interaction is stabilized by ligand binding. It is also possible that taurodeoxycholate is more effective in preserving G protein association with the GRP receptor than CHAPS/CHS.

In conclusion, solubilization of the GRP receptor in an active form is the first step toward purification of the receptor. The purified receptor can be used in reconstitution studies to investigate its interaction with other purified proteins such as kinases and G proteins.

Acknowledgments

This research is supported in part by NCI Grant CA-53477 (T.W.M.), NSF Grant BNS-88-15133 (T.W.M.) and an Irma T. Hirschl Charitable Trust/Monique Weill-Caulier Charitable Trust Career Scientist award (R.K.)

References

1. M. E. Sunday, L. M. Kaplan, E. Moroyama, W. W. Chin, and E. R. Spindel, *Lab. Invest.* **59,** 5 (1988).
2. F. Cuttitta, D. N. Carney, J. Mulshine, T. W. Moody, J. Fedorko, A. Fischler, and J. D. Minna, *Nature (London)* **316,** 823 (1985).
3. H. Hasegawa, H. Saaki, F. Lutz, and T. Sasaki, *J. Biol. Chem.* **263,** 12970 (1988).
4. J. P. Heslop, D. M. Blekley, K. D. Brown, R. F. Irvine, and M. J. Berridge, *Cell (Cambridge, Mass.)* **47,** 703 (1986).
5. N. Takuwa, Y. Takuwa, W. E. Bollag, and H. Rasmussen, *J. Biol. Chem.* **262,** 182 (1987).
5a. J. B. Fischer and A. Schonbrunn, *J. Biol. Chem.* **263,** 2808–2816 (1988).
6. E. R. Spindel, E. Giladi, P. Brehm, R. H. Goodman, and T. P. Segerson, *Mol. Endocrinol.* **4,** 1956 (1990).
7. J. F. Battey, J. M. Way, M. H. Corjay, H. Shapira, K. Kusano, R. Harkins, J. M. Wu, T. Slattery, E. Mann, and R. I. Feldman, *Proc. Natl. Acad. Sci. U.S.A.* **88,** 395 (1991).
8. L. Naldini, D. Cirillo, T. W. Moody, P. M. Comoglio, J. Schlessinger, and R. Kris, *Biochemistry* **29,** 5153 (1990).

 9. R. I. Feldman, J. M. Wu, J. C. Jenson, and E. Mann, *J. Biol. Chem.* **265,** 17364 (1990).

10. I. Zachary and E. Rozengurt, *Proc. Natl. Acad. Sci. U.S.A.* **82,** 7616 (1985).

11. J. Mazella, J. Chabry, P. Kirabgi, and J. P. Vincent, *J. Biol. Chem.* **263,** 144 (1988).

12. D. R. Bristow and I. L. Martin, *J. Neurochem.* **49,** 1386 (1987).

13. K. A. Paganelli, A. S. Stern, and P. L. Kilian, *J. Immunol.* **138,** 2249 (1987).

14. D. Cirillo, L. Naldini, T. W. Moody, P. Comoglio, J. Schlessinger, and R. Kris, *Peptides* (*N.Y.*) **11,** 737 (1990).

15. R. I. Feldman, J. M. Wu, J. C. Jensen, and E. Mann, *J. Biol. Chem.* **265,** 17364 (1990).

16. A. Coffer, I. Fabregat, J. Sinnett-Smith, and E. Rozengurt, *FEBS Lett.* **263,** 80 (1990).

17. R. T. Jensen, T. W. Moody, C. Pert, J. E. Rivier, and J. D. Gardner, *Proc. Natl. Acad. Sci. U.S.A.* **75,** 6139 (1978).

18. R. M. Kris, R. Hazan, J. Villines, T. W. Moody, and J. Schlessinger, *J. Biol. Chem.* **262,** 11215 (1987).

19. M. Tohkin, T. Yagami, T. Katada, and T. Matsubara, *Eur. J. Biochem.* **194,** 81 (1990).

20. J. Hu and E. E. El-Fakahany, *Mol. Pharmacol.* **38,** 895 (1990).

21. D. J. Stewart, D. Langleben, P. Cernacek, and K. Cianflone, *Am. J. Physiol.* **259,** H1928 (1990).

22. A. Levitzki, *J. Recept. Res.* **4,** 399 (1984).

23. G. L. Stiles, *J. Biol. Chem.* **260,** 6728 (1985).

[24] Assays for Pituitary Adenylate Cyclase-Activating Peptide Receptors Coupled to Adenylate Cyclase: Comparison between Rat Brain and Human Neuroblastoma Cells

Jean Christophe, André Vandermeers,
Marie-Claire Vandermeers-Piret, Annick Cauvin,
and Patrick Robberecht

Introduction

PACAP(1–38)-NH$_2$ [pituitary adenylate cyclase-activating polypeptide, (PACAP-38)] is an amidated 38-amino acid neuropeptide isolated from ovine hypothalamus in 1989 (1). The molecular cloning of a single hybridizing cDNA for PACAP-38 from cDNA libraries of ovine hypothalamus, rat brain, and human testicles indicates a phylogenetically similar precursor sequence in the three animal species and suggests that the peptide may be synthesized in several tissues (2). The shorter amidated PACAP(1–27)-NH$_2$ form (PACAP-27) is also present in ovine hypothalamus (1). PACAP-27 exhibits 68% homology to vasoactive intestinal peptide (VIP), this being especially evident in the N-terminal areas (residues 1–3 and 6–8) and in the central region (residues 14–23). By contrast, the C-terminal end (residues 29–38) of PACAP-38, with 6 cationic amino acid residues, shows no homology with any known parent peptide of similar length (Table I). Based on their immuno-reactivity, PACAP 38 and PACAP-27 are widely distributed in brain and most notably in the cortex, cerebellum, and hypothalamus, at the picomole per gram wet weight level (3–7). A physiological role for their receptors is suggested by the fact that PACAP-38 activates adenylate cyclase to a much greater extent than VIP in rat neurons and rat astrocyte cultures (8, 9). PACAP probably also favors neuronal survival.

A high density of specific PACAP receptors, positively coupled to adenylate cyclase, has been documented in membranes from several rat brain areas (10–15). PACAP receptors coupled to adenylate cyclase are likewise present in the human neuroblastoma cell line NB-OK-1 (16), in cultured rat astrocytes (8), and in a rat adrenal pheochromocytoma cell line (17). On the whole, specific PACAP receptors recognize PACAP-38 and PACAP-27 equally well

Methods in Neurosciences, Volume 11

and with high affinity (K_d 0.5–1.0 nM) and their poor affinity for VIP allows a clear distinction with the high-affinity VIP receptors from rat liver (18), pancreas (19), and lung (12), which interact with VIP and PACAP with similar affinity.

The methods we use to characterize PACAP receptors pharmacologically, based on radioligand binding and adenylate cyclase coupling, and to initiate a molecular identification of PACAP receptors, are discussed in this chapter.

Materials and Methods

Crude Membrane Preparation from Rat Brain and Spinal Cord

Wistar adult male albino rats weighing 200–250 g are killed by decapitation. The olfactory bulb, hypothalamus, temporal cortex, hippocampus, striatum, pons, cerebellum, and cervicodorsal spinal cord are rapidly dissected out on ice and homogenized in an ice-cold 0.25 M sucrose solution (0.1 g wet weight/ 5 ml) with a glass–Teflon homogenizer. Each homogenate is centrifuged at 4°C at 200 g for 10 min. The supernatant is centrifuged at 4°C at 26,000 g for 15 min. The pellets are rehomogenized in 1 mM $NaHCO_3$ to obtain a protein concentration of approximately 200 μg/ml. These crude membrane suspensions are used immediately for binding and adenylate cyclase assays.

Culture of the Human Neuroblastoma Cell Line NB-OK-1 and Crude Membrane Preparation

The human neuroblastoma cell line NB-OK-1 was kindly donated by Dr. N. Yanaihara (Laboratory of Bioorganic Chemistry, University of Shizuoka School of Pharmaceutical Sciences, Shizuoka 422, Japan) in 1983. Cells are grown at 37°C in RPMI medium supplemented with 10% (by volume) fetal calf serum (from GIBCO, Grand Island, NY), 20 mM glutamine, and antibiotics (100 IU/ml penicillin plus 100 μg/ml streptomycin). Stock cultures are diluted every 3 days with 4 vol of fresh medium.

For crude membrane preparations the cells at confluence are detached with a rubber policeman, centrifuged at 100 g for 5 min at 20°C, washed in standard culture medium (without supplement), and lysed in hypotonic 1 mM $NaHCO_3$ (pH 7.0), then quickly frozen in liquid nitrogen. The lysate is defrosted and centrifuged at 200 g for 10 min at 4°C. The resulting supernatant is centrifuged at 20,000 g for 10 min at 4°C. The final pellet is rehomogenized in 1 mM $NaHCO_3$ and immediately used for binding assays and adenylate cyclase assays.

TABLE I Comparison of the Amino Acid Sequence of PACAP(1–38)-NH$_2$ and PACAP(1–27)-NH$_2$ with Six Related Peptides[a]

Species[b]	Peptide	Amino acid sequence (positions 1–45)
o	PACAP-38	H-S-D-G-I-F-T-D-S-Y-S-R-Y-R-K-Q-M-A-V-K-K-Y-L-A-A-V-L-G-K-R-Y-K-Q-R-V-K-N-K-*
o	PACAP-27	H-S-D-G-I-F-T-D-S-Y-S-R-Y-R-K-Q-M-A-V-K-K-Y-L-A-A-V-L-*
b/do/h/p/r	VIP	H-S-D-A-V-F-T-D-N-Y-T-R-L-R-K-Q-M-A-V-K-K-Y-L-N-S-I-L-N-*
b	PHI	H-A-D-G-V-F-T-S-D-Y-S-R-L-L-G-Q-L-S-A-K-K-Y-L-E-S-L-I-*
r	PHI	H-A-D-G-V-F-T-S-D-Y-S-R-L-L-G-Q-I-S-A-K-K-Y-L-E-S-L-I-*
r	PHV(1–42)	H-A-D-G-V-F-T-S-D-Y-S-R-L-L-G-Q-I-S-A-K-K-Y-L-E-S-L-I-G-K-R-I-S-S-I-S-E-D-P-V-P-V
r	Secretin	H-S-D-G-T-F-T-S-E-L-S-R-L-Q-E-G-A-R-L-Q-R-L-L-Q-G-L-V-*-
p	GRF(1–44)	Y-A-D-A-I-F-T-N-S-Y-R-K-V-L-G-Q-L-S-A-R-K-L-L-Q-D-I-M-S-R-Q-Q-G-E-R-N-Q-E-Q-G-A-R-V-R-L-*

[a] Differences with PACAP(1–38)-NH$_2$ are underlined; *, NH$_2$.
[b] b, Bovine; d, dog; h, human; o, ovine; p, porcine; r, rat.

Radioiodination of PACAP-27, [AC-His¹]PACAP-27, and PACAP-38

Radioiodination of PACAP-27, [AC-His¹]PACAP-27, and PACAP-38

PACAP-27 is radioiodinated by the Iodogen (Pierce, Rockford, IL) method
(20). Synthetic porcine PACAP-27 (5 μg) in 10 μl of 0.1 M acetic acid is
added to 35 μl of 0.4 M potassium phosphate (pH 8.5), 20 μl of distilled
water, and 80 MBq of Na^{125}I (20 MBq/μl). The reaction is initiated on ice by
transfer of the mixture into a 1-ml Iodogen-coated glass tube (prepared by
evaporating 10 μl of a 0.2-mg/ml Iodogen solution in dichloromethane under
a stream of N$_2$). This reaction is stopped by transfer into a polypropylene
tube and addition of 100 μl 0.1% (v/v) trifluoroacetic acid (TFA). The percentage of ^{125}I incorporated is estimated by 5% (w/v) trichloroacetic acid
precipitability of a 1-μl aliquot (typically 70–90% of the radioactivity offered).

At present, in our laboratory, ^{125}I-labeled [AC-His¹]PACAP-27 (the
N-acetyl-His¹ derivative of PACAP-27) is used as tracer, in preference to ^{125}I-
labeled PACAP-27, as it shows a higher ratio of total binding over nonspecific
binding (see below). [AC-His¹]PACAP-27 and also PACAP-38 are radioiodinated by the Iodogen method as described above.

Tracer Purification

Tracer Purification

^{125}I-Labeled PACAP-27 is separated from unreacted iodine through a Sep-
Pak C$_{18}$ cartridge (Waters Associates, Milford, MA). The radioactivity elu-
ated with 3 ml 50% acetonitrile–0.1% TFA (v/v) is precipitable at more than
98% by 5% (w/v) trichloroacetic acid. After evaporation of acetonitrile under
a stream of N$_2$, this material is diluted in 10 mM sodium phosphate buffer
(pH 7.4), 150 mM NaCl enriched with 0.1% (w/v) sodium azide and with
0.2% (w/v) bovine serum albumin (BSA) and 0.05% (v/v) Tween 20 (to avoid
peptide adsorption to the polypropylene tubes). The tracer is divided into 74-
kBq portions, freeze-dried, and kept at $-20°C$. It can be used over a 2-month
period. The specific radioactivity of this unpurified tracer is typically 28
MBq/nmol, based on iodine incorporation.

Alternatively, ^{125}I-labeled PACAP-27 can be purified by radio-high per-
formance liquid chromatography (HPLC), in order to discard unlabeled
PACAP-27. In this case the Iodogen reaction is stopped by dilution to a final
volume of 1 ml with 5% acetonitrile–0.1% TFA (v/v), and the sample is
immediately injected into a reversed-phase μBondapak C$_{18}$ column (3.9 $\times$
300 mm) equipped with a guard column (Waters Associates) preequilibrated
with 5% acetonitrile–0.1% TFA (v/v). After 15 min, a linear gradient of 80%
acetonitrile–0.1% TFA (v/v) (30–35% over 60 min) is applied with a flow rate
of 1 ml/min. Fractions of 0.5 ml are collected, and the radioactivity in each
fraction is determined by counting 2-μl portions in a γ-radiation spectrometer.

^{125}I-Labeled PACAP-27 appears as a symmetrical peak (retention time 50 min) after unlabeled PACAP-27 (at 47 min). The three or four radioactive fractions showing the best affinity for human NB-OK neuroblastoma membranes (see below) are located at the top and along the descending part of the radioactive peak, then pooled, and the acetonitrile is evaporated off under a stream of N_2. Aliquots are kept as described above. The specific radioactivity is typically 35 MBq/nmol.

For ^{125}I-labeled [AC-His^1]PACAP-27, elution from the μBondapak C$_{18}$ column is performed at a flow rate of 1 ml/min with a 0–35% linear gradient of 80% acetonitrile–0.1% TFA (v/v) over 5 min, followed by a 35–75% linear gradient of the same solvent over 40 min. Free ^{125}I and unlabeled [AC-His^1] PACAP-27 are separated from three or four peaks of trichloroacetic acid-precipitable ^{125}I. The first and major radioactive peak, eluting with 54% of solvent, shows the highest capacity to bind to neuroblastoma cell membranes after acetonitrile evaporation. The phosphate buffer used to dilute ^{125}I-labeled PACAP-27 (see above) is also used in this case. The specific radioactivity is typically 80 MBq/nmol.

^{125}I-Labeled PACAP-38 is purified similarly, using a 0–37% linear gradient of 80% acetonitrile–0.1% TFA (v/v) over 5 min, followed by a 37–70% linear gradient of the same solvent over 66 min at a flow rate of 1 ml/min. ^{125}I-Labeled PACAP-38 appears as a single symmetrical peak (retention time, 27 min). The three or four radioactive fractions offering the best affinity for rat brain membranes (see below) are located on the top and the descending part of the radioactive peak. They are conditioned as described above.

Binding Assays with ^{125}I-Labeled PACAP-27, [AC-His^1]PACAP-27, and PACAP-38

Tracer binding to NB-OK-1 membranes and rat brain membranes is carried out in a 50 mM Tris-maleate buffer (pH 7.4) containing 5 mM MgCl$_2$, 0.5 mg/ml bacitracin, 100 kallikrein inhibitor units/ml Trasylol, 1% (w/v) bovine serum albumin (BSA), ^{125}I-labeled PACAP-27, ^{125}I-labeled [AC-His^1] PACAP-27, or ^{125}I-labeled PACAP-38 (either in an 8000–200,000 cpm/assay range in saturation experiments or with a fixed amount of 20,000–50,000 cpm/assay under standard binding conditions that correspond to 60 pM–0.16 nM tracer), with or without increasing concentrations of unlabeled peptide, and (approximately) 4 μg rat brain membrane protein or 5 μg NB-OK-1 membrane protein in a total volume of 120 μl. Binding assay with ^{125}I-labeled PACAP-38 is conducted in the absence of BSA, but in the added presence of 0.3 M NaCl, in order to reduce nonspecific binding. Incubations are conducted at 37°C and terminated after 30 min (to allow binding equilibrium;

see below) by dilution with 2 ml ice-cold 50 mM sodium phosphate buffer (pH 7.4) enriched with 1% BSA. Membrane-bound and free labeled peptides are separated by rapid filtration through glass fiber filters [GF/C; Whatman, Clifton, NJ], presoaked for at least 24 hr in 0.1% (v/v) polyethyleneimine to reduce nonspecific binding. The filters are rinsed three times with 2 ml of the same phosphate buffer, and their radioactivity is measured. Nonspecific binding is determined in the presence of 1 μM unlabeled PACAP-27 for ^{125}I-labeled PACAP-27 and [AC-His[1]]PACAP-27-binding experiments or in the presence of 0.1 μM PACAP-38 in the case of ^{125}I-labeled PACAP-38-binding experiments. It accounts for approximately 30, 20, and 40%, respectively, of total binding for the three tracers [we observe that the nonspecific binding of the latter tracer spuriously decreases when using a high (above 1 μM) unlabeled PACAP-38 concentration; this is due to the release of tracer unspecifically bound to the glass fiber filter]. Specific binding is defined as total binding minus nonspecific binding and always represents less than 25% of the total radioactivity offered.

For pharmacological characterization by competition curves, care must be taken to reach a steady state reflecting equilibrium between binding, dissociation, and degradation rates of tracer after binding equilibrium. Non-equilibrium data are indeed especially prone to generating artifactual receptor selectivity, for example, if binding equilibrium is attained more rapidly for PACAP-38 than for PACAP-27 (21). This is why, in control experiments, we repeat our dose–effect curves of binding (and adenylate cyclase activation) using various incubation periods (2, 15, and 30 min, for example).

The apparent selectivity of PACAP receptors might also be artifactual if nonspecific binding of PACAP-38 to test tubes shifts the dose–effect curve of adenylate cyclase activation to the right. We observed that the data are, however, not modified when adding 1% (w/v) human serum albumin to the enzyme assay medium.

Dissociation of ^{125}I-labeled tracer from membranes, after the binding step, can be induced by adding 0.1 μM unlabeled ligand, either alone or combined with 10 μM GTP.

Cross-Linking of ^{125}I-Labeled PACAP-27, Electrophoresis, and Autoradiography

Membranes are incubated for 20 min at 37°C with 0.3 nM ^{125}I-labeled PACAP-27 in the medium used for binding assay but with 1% (w/v) ovalbumin instead of 1% (w/v) BSA. Membranes are washed twice with ice-cold 10 mM phosphate buffer (pH 7.4) containing 150 mM NaCl (PBS) and resuspended in the same buffer. One volume of 100 mM disuccinimidyl suberate (dissolved immediately before use in dry dimethyl sulfoxide) is added to 99 vol of the membrane suspension. After a 30-min incubation at 4°C, the membranes are washed twice in ice-cold PBS and solubilized in an electrophoresis sample buffer made of 125 mM Tris-HCl (pH 6.8) containing 5% (w/v) sodium dodecyl sulfate (SDS), 1% (w/v) dithiothreitol, 4% (v/v) 2-mercaptoethanol, 10% (w/v) sucrose, and 0.02% (w/v) bromphenol blue. Each sample is heated at 100°C for 5 min, then submitted to SDS-polyacrylamide gel electrophoresis (PAGE).

SDS-PAGE is performed under reducing conditions, using a discontinuous system (22) buffer with an electrophoresis buffer concentration twice that mentioned in the original method. Samples are applied to a 4% (w/v) poly-acrylamide stacking gel over a 12% (w/v) polyacrylamide separating gel. The dimensions of the gel are 180 × 200 × 1.5 mm. Electrophoresis is performed in the Pharmacia (Piscataway, NJ) GE 2/4 LS apparatus for 16 hr at 90 V. After electrophoresis, the gels are fixed and stained with Coomassie blue, 0.1% (w/v) in 50% ethanol–10% acetic acid (v/v), destained with 25% (v/v) ethanol and 7% (v/v) acetic acid, dried, and autoradiographed with high-sensitivity Kodak (Rochester, NY) XAR films in Kodak X-Omatic cassettes equipped with Cronex intensifying screens. Exposures are conducted for 2 weeks at −80°C. Cassettes are protected from environmental rays by a 3-mm lead sheet.

Gel calibration is performed with standard protein kits from Pharmacia and Bio-Rad (Richmond, CA). Molecular weight standards used in a parallel run are myosin (M_r 200,000), β-galactosidase (M_r 116,000), phosphorylase b (M_r 94,000), bovine serum albumin (M_r 67,000), ovalbumin (M_r 45,000), carbonate dehydratase (M_r 30,000), trypsin inhibitor (M_r 20,000), and α-lactalbumin (M_r 14,000).

Adenylate Cyclase Assay

Adenylate cyclase activity is determined according to the procedure of Salomon *et al.* (23). Membrane protein (20–30 μg) is incubated in a total volume of 60 μl containing 0.5 mM [α-^{32}P]ATP, 10 μM GTP, 5 mM MgCl$_2$, 0.5 mM ethylene glycol-bis(β-aminoethyl ether)-N,N,N',N'-tetraacetic acid (EGTA), 1 mM cyclic AMP, 0.5 mM theophylline, 10 mM phosphoenolpyruvate, 30 μg/ml pyruvate kinase, and 30 mM Tris-HCl at a final pH of 7.5. The reaction is initiated by addition of membranes and is terminated after a 15-min incubation at 37°C by adding 0.5 ml of a 0.5% (w/v) SDS solution containing 0.5 mM ATP, 0.5 mM cyclic AMP, and 20,000 cpm cyclic [8-^{3}H]AMP (to determine cyclic AMP recovery). Cyclic AMP is separated from ATP by two successive chromatographies on Dowex 50W-X8 and neutral alumina. Under all conditions tested, cyclic AMP production is linear during the incubation period and proportional to the amount of protein added.

Protein Determination

Protein determination is performed according to the method of Lowry *et al.* (24), using bovine serum albumin as a standard.

Analysis of Data

Competition curves are analyzed to determine the potency of all peptides, assuming that the ligand recognizes one or two subclasses of receptors, using the Ligand microcomputer program developed by Richardson and Humrich (25). With the low tracer concentration used, the concentration of unlabeled peptide required for half-maximal binding inhibition (the IC_{50} value) is considered as close to the K_D of the peptide (concentration required for half-maximal occupancy of binding sites with tracer).

All peptides are also tested for their ability to stimulate adenylate cyclase. The EC_{50} value, which equals the K_{act} value (the concentration exerting half-maximal stimulation), of adenylate cyclase is calculated from the complete dose–effect curve or by extrapolation (considering that all peptides act through interaction with a single class of receptor). When a PACAP analog is inactive [IA (efficacy) = 0] or very poorly active (i.e., an agonist with low intrinsic activity: IA < 1, considering the maximal effect of PACAP-27 as 1), its antagonist potential is tested in combination with the full agonist (either PACAP-27 or PACAP-38) to examine the specificity and potency (the K_i value, which is the concentration required for half-maximal inhibition of adenylate cyclase stimulation) of its inhibitory action on adenylate cyclase activation. To determine the K_i of an antagonist or partial agonist, the complete dose–effect curves of PACAP-27 or PACAP-38 on adenylate cyclase are obtained in the absence or presence of at least two concentrations of antagonist. The K_i value is then derived from

$$\frac{[A']}{[A]} - 1 = \frac{[I]}{[K_i]}$$

where A' and A are the two PACAP-27 (or PACAP-38) concentrations giving the same stimulation in, respectively, the presence and absence of concentration $[I]$ of antagonist.

Chemicals

Synthesis and Purification of PACAP-27, PACAP-38, and PACAP Analogs

Synthetic PACAP-38 is a gift from Dr. J. P. Durieux (Novabiochem, Laüfelfingen, Switzerland). PACAP-27 and all PACAP analogs and fragments are synthesized in our laboratory with solid-phase methodology with an automated 431 A Applied Biosystems (Foster City, CA) apparatus, using the FMOC strategy with a 4-(2′,4′-dimethoxyphenyl-fluoren-9-yl-methoxycarbonylaminomethyl)phenoxy resin and fluoren-9-yl-methoxycarbonyl-labeled amino acids activated with *N*-hydroxybenzotriazole and *O*-benzotriazol-1-*N,N,N′,N′*-tetramethyluronium hexafluorophosphate (26). Acetic anhydride is used for capping after each coupling and for N-terminal acetylation (whenever indicated). The peptides are purified by preparative reversed-phase HPLC using a Nucleosil (Machecey-Nagel, Düren, Germany) 300-5 C_{18} column (25 × 1 cm) eluted with 0.1% (v/v) trifluoroacetic acid (TFA) and a 20–60% (v/v) acetonitrile gradient over 40 min. The flow rate is 2.0 ml/min, and the typical load is 10–20 mg of peptide. Eluate is monitored by ultraviolet (UV) detection at 226 nm and fractionated on the basis of UV reading. Peptide-containing fractions are collected, lyophilized, and further purified by analytical HPLC using a Vydac (Hesperia, CA) 218 TP 104 column (25 × 0.46 cm) with 0.1% (v/v) TFA and a 25–50% (v/v) acetonitrile gradient over 50 min. The conformity of the peptides is established by global amino acid composition of the hydrolysate and by at least 10 cycles of Edman degradation in an Applied Biosystems 477 A sequencer coupled to a 120 A PTH-amino acid analyzer.

Porcine VIP, porcine PHI (peptide histidine-isoleucinamide), and human GRF(1–29)-NH_2 (growth hormone-releasing factor) are synthesized by Dr. D. H. Coy (Section of Endocrinology, Department of Medicine, Tulane University School of Medicine, New Orleans, LA).

Other Reagents

Carrier-free Na^{125}I (IMS 300, 13–22 GBq/ml) and [8-^{3}H]cAMP (0.7–1.1 TBq/mmol) are purchased from Amersham International (Amersham, Buckinghamshire, England) and [α-^{32}P]ATP (0.4–1.8 TBq/mmol) from New England Nuclear (Boston, MA). Iodogen is from Pierce Chemical Company (Rockford, IL). Phosphoenolpyruvate, pyruvate kinase, cyclic AMP, GTP, and ATP are purchased from Sigma Chemical Company (St. Louis, MO). Bovine serum albumin (fraction V) and bacitracin are from Sigma. Kallikrein inhibitor (Trasylol) is from Bayer (Leverküsen, Germany). Fetal calf serum and medium for cell cultures are from GIBCO (Grand Island, NY). All reagents for peptide synthesis are purchased from Novabiochem (Laüfelfingen, Switzerland). All other reagents are of the highest grade available.

One Type of PACAP Receptor in the Human Neuroblastoma Cell Line NB-OK-1 (16)

With both ^{125}I-labeled PACAP-27 and ^{125}I-labeled [AC-His[1]]PACAP-27, specific binding reaches a steady state after 30 min at 37°C, being maintained for at least 60 min. Dissociation of bound tracer as evaluated by addition of 0.1 μM unlabeled PACAP-27, after a 20-min preincubation, does not correspond to a first-order mechanism. The addition of 10 μM GTP accelerates the dissociation moderately. Using increasing ^{125}I-labeled [AC-His[1]]PACAP-27 concentrations (from 30 to 1200 pM), the Scatchard transformation of saturation curves is compatible with the existence of one high-affinity class of receptors exhibiting a K_D of 0.5 nM.

[125]I-Labeled PACAP-27 binding is inhibited dose dependently by PACAP-27 and PACAP-38 (IC$_{50}$ 0.2–0.4 nM). The curves for binding inhibition are compatible with the existence of one homogeneous class of PACAP-27 receptors. Vasoactive intestinal peptide inhibits ^{125}I-labeled PACAP-27 binding 300- to 1000-fold less potently than PACAP-27 and PACAP-38.

Adenylate cyclase shows, in the presence of 10 μM GTP, a four- to fivefold higher activity at maximal PACAP-27 concentration as compared to basal activity. PACAP-27 and PACAP-38 stimulate the enzyme dose dependently with similar efficacy and potency (K_{act} 0.2–0.3 nM), indicating that the C-terminal extension (residues 28–38) in natural PACAP-38 is not important for enzyme activation (Table II). Considering the good correlation between K_D (IC$_{50}$) and K_{act} (EC$_{50}$ for adenylate cyclase activation, which is the concentration exerting half-maximal stimulation of adenylate cyclase) values, PACAP-preferring receptors in the human NB-OK-1 cells are likely to be functional receptors coupled to adenylate cyclase. Vasoactive intestinal peptide is markedly less potent and less efficient than PACAP on this enzyme. It can, thus, be concluded that if VIP-preferring receptors coexist with PACAP-preferring receptors in this cell line, they are much less abundant, so that this neuroblastoma cell line provides a source of PACAP receptors reasonably free of VIP receptors.

Two Types of PACAP Receptors in Rat Brain and Medulla (10)

[125]I-Labeled PACAP-27 and PACAP-38 bind rapidly and specifically on rat brain membranes. The binding of both tracers reaches an apparent steady state after 30 min at 37°C and is reversible. Half of the bound tracer dissociates within 5–9 min after addition of 0.1 μM unlabeled ligand, this process being of a complex order and moderately accelerated by 10 μM GTP.

Scatchard analysis of ^{125}I-labeled PACAP-27 as compared to ^{125}I-labeled

TABLE II Binding of PACAP-27 and PACAP-38 Analogs and Fragments and Adenylate Cyclase Activation in Human Neuroblastoma Cell Membranes[a]

	IC_{50}	K_{act}	K_i	IA
PACAP(1–27)	0.4	0.3		1.00
PACAP(2–27)	20	30		0.90
PACAP(3–27)	600		200	0
PACAP(5–27)	200		150	0
PACAP(6–27)	80		60	0
PACAP(7–27)	600		200	0
PACAP(9–27)	1500			0
[AC-His1]PACAP-27	0.2	0.3		0.80
[Phe1]PACAP-27	10	20		0.60
[Ala2]PACAP-27	0.2	0.2		0.65
[Des-His1,Ala2]PACAP-27	50	50		0.30
[AC-His1,Ala2]PACAP-27	0.5	0.5		0.60
[D-Ala2]PACAP-27	0.1	1.0		0.80
[AC-His1,D-Ala2]PACAP-27	1.2	3		0.80
[Arg2]PACAP-27	400	1000		0.20
[AC-His1,Arg2]PACAP-27	400	2000		0.30
[D-Arg2]PACAP-27	300	400		0.50
[AC-His1,D-Arg2]PACAP-27	500	1000		0.60
[Phe2]PACAP-27	100		200	0.10
[AC-His1,Phe2]PACAP-27	20		100	0.15
[D-Phe2]PACAP-27	100		300	0.20
[AC-His1,D-Phe2]PACAP-27	350		1000	0.18
[Glu3]PACAP-27	5	10		0.70
[Des-His1,Glu3]PACAP-27	1000		300	0
[Asn3]PACAP-27	200	200		0.40
[Des-His1,Asn3]PACAP-27	300		150	0
[Gly21]PACAP-27	2	1		0.65
[Gly20,Gly21]PACAP-27	200	30		0.50

	IC_{50}	K_{act}	K_i	IA
PACAP(1–38)	0.2	0.2		1.00
PACAP(2–38)	2.0	2.0		0.90
PACAP(4–38)	10		5.0	0
PACAP(5–38)	5		5.0	0
PACAP(6–38)	2		1.5	0
PACAP(7–38)	10		8.0	0
—				
—				
[Ala2]PACAP-38	1.5	0.8		0.90
—				
[AC-His1,Ala2]PACAP-38	0.5	1.5		0.90
[D-Ala2]PACAP-38	0.3	1		0.90
[AC-His1,D-Ala2]PACAP-38	0.3	1		0.90
[Arg2]PACAP-38	20	50		0.30
[AC-His1,Arg2]PACAP-38	10	50		0.30
[D-Arg2]PACAP-38	1.5	15		0.45
[AC-His1,D-Arg2]PACAP-38	3	15		0.30
[Phe2]PACAP-38	2		10	0.13
[AC-His1,Phe2]PACAP-38	3		10	0.06
[D-Phe2]PACAP-38	2		10	0.12
[AC-His1,D-Phe2]PACAP-38	2		10	0.08
—				
[Ala3]PACAP-38	3	4		0.17
—				
[Des-His1,Glu3]PACAP-38	10		15	0
—				

[a] Values (nM) are means of at least three determinations. IC_{50}, Concentration inhibiting 50% of ^{125}I-labeled [AC-His1]PACAP-27 binding; K_{act}, concentration provoking half-maximal adenylate cyclase activation; K_i, concentration inhibiting 50% of adenylate cyclase stimulation by PACAP-27; IA, intrinsic activity (expressed as a fraction, using 1.0 as the maximal effect of PACAP-27. The SEM of each value was below 5%; nd, Not determined.

PACAP-38 saturation curves indicates a twofold higher number of receptors labeled with the second radioligand. Binding competition curves reveal that VIP inhibits only partially ^{125}I-labeled PACAP-27 binding at 1 μM, and PHI, GRF(1–29)-NH$_2$, and secretin are ineffective. However, the inhibition curve of ^{125}I-labeled PACAP-27 binding by PACAP-27 is flatter than that obtained with PACAP-38 and the inhibition curve of ^{125}I-labeled PACAP-38 binding by PACAP-38 is flatter than that obtained with PACAP-27. These competition curves are compatible with the labeling of two classes of PACAP receptors in that curve fitting is of higher quality when considering a two-sites model rather than a one-site model.

Basal, 0.1 μM PACAP-27-, and 0.1 μM PACAP-38-stimulated adenylate cyclase activities amount to, respectively, 135 ± 10, 353 ± 36 and 364 ± 10 pmol cyclic AMP/min/mg protein in membranes from rat olfactory bulb, taken as an example. This notable adenylate cyclase activation by PACAP-27 and PACAP-38 shows similar dose–response curves that extend over more than 3 logarithms and can be resolved in two components.

We conclude from all our data (10) that PACAP receptors are efficiently coupled to adenylate cyclase, considering the good correlation between K_D and K_{act} values, and because tracer dissociation is accelerated by GTP. In addition, two types of PACAP receptors coexist in high density (B_{max} in the 1- to 2-pmol/mg protein range) in eight areas from the rat central nervous system (the cortex, olfactory bulb, hypothalamus, hippocampus, striatum, cerebellum, pons, and cervicodorsal spinal cord). The first class (PACAP-A receptors) recognizes PACAP-27 with a somewhat higher affinity than PACAP-38 whereas the second class (PACAP-B receptors) recognizes only PACAP-38 with high affinity and PACAP-27 with low affinity.

Specificity of PACAP Receptors Coupled to Adenylate Cyclase in the Human Neuroblastoma Cell Line NB-OK-1 (3)

Structural predictions indicate that PACAP-27 and PACAP-38 may have a first β-bend structure in the region containing residues 2–4, a second β-bend in the region containing residues 8–11, and an α-helical conformation in the region containing residues 14–27. The carboxyl-terminal prolongation of PACAP-27 by the large, hydrophilic 11-amino acid carboxy terminus present in PACAP-38 is also important (see below). We used the human neuroblastoma cell line for a pharmacological characterization of PACAP receptors, as this cell line is much less heterogeneous than the central nervous system, is of neuronal origin, and shows only one type of PACAP receptor (see above).

A free α-amino group is unimportant for optimal IA, as indicated by the good IA and K_{act} values of [AC-His[1]]PACAP-27 (Table II). By contrast, the integrity of the imidazole ring of His[1] is more important. Changes in position 2 are relatively specific for receptor–effector coupling: L- and D-Ala[2] derivatives are agonists, whereas L- and D-Arg[2] or L- and D-Phe[2] derivatives are either poor activators or antagonists. More precisely, replacement of Ser[2] in PACAP(1–27) by alanine improves slightly the potency of PACAP-27. By contrast, increasing the bulkiness in position 2 plays a highly unfavorable role, with the hydrophobicity of Phe[2] being even more disadvantageous than the basicity of Arg[2]. Apparently, position 2 in PACAP-27 can tolerate only isosteric substitutions. The same holds true for PACAP-38. The presence of the acidic Asp[3] residue in PACAP-27 is critical. After its replacement, [Glu[3]]PACAP-27 and [Asn[3]]PACAP-27 present, respectively, only 70 and 40% of the IA of PACAP-27. The two highly hydrophilic residues (Lys[20] and Lys[21]) located in the central portion of a hydrophobic domain in PACAP-27 (Table II) are also important for PACAP receptor recognition: the helix-breaking Gly[20] and Gly[21] substitutions in PACAP-27 reduce the affinity of the resulting peptide 500-fold.

After minimal N-terminal deletion, PACAP(2–27) and PACAP(2–38) are still full agonists (on the basis of their IA values) but PACAP(2–27) is already 100-fold less potent than PACAP(1–27) whereas PACAP(2–38) is only 10-fold less potent than PACAP(1–38), indicating that the amino acid extension in PACAP-38 provides additional binding stability in the absence of His[1] (Table II). With deletions increasing further away from the N-terminal extremity in the PACAP-27 series, the IC_{50} of C-terminal fragments of PACAP increases, decreases, then increases again: PACAP(2–27) < PACAP(6–27) < PACAP(5–27) < PACAP(3–27) = PACAP(7–27) < PACAP(9–27). PACAP(2–27) is still biologically active, PACAP(3–27) is inactive, and PACAP(7–27) acts as an antagonist (K_i 200 nM).

In the N-shortened PACAP-38 series, the trend in IC_{50} values is also irregular, so that the IC_{50} of PACAP(7–38) is similar to that of PACAP(4–38) (10 nM) and the fragments PACAP(2–38) and PACAP(6–38) show the same relatively high binding potency (IC_{50} 2 nM). However, PACAP(2–38) stimulates adenylate cyclase whereas PACAP(6–38) does not. PACAP(4–38), PACAP(5–38), and PACAP(7–38) are without detectable efficacy and are capable of inhibiting competitively the PACAP-27-stimulated enzyme with K_i values in the 5–8 nM range. PACAP(6–38) has an even lower K_i (1.5 nM) and may thus serve as a potent antagonist (K_i 1.5 nM).

The inhibition exerted by PACAP(6–38) on PACAP-38 stimulation of adenylate cyclase is weaker (K_i 30 nM) than that exerted on PACAP-27 and [D-Arg[2]]PACAP-38 stimulations (K_i values of 1.5 and 2.0 nM, respectively) (Table II). This apparently paradoxical situation may reflect high spareness among the numerous PACAP receptors and be revealed by good receptor coupling to adenylate cyclase with PACAP-38 but not with PACAP-27, the reason lying probably in a distinct secondary structure of PACAP-38 that promotes the conformational preference of receptors. Theoretically indeed, if a fraction only of receptors needs to be occupied by PACAP-38 to provoke full activation, inhibition would occur only after full receptor occupancy by PACAP-38 and/or antagonist. With PACAP-27 and with the partial agonist [D-Arg^2]PACAP-38, ''spareness'' could not operate because of poor coupling, so that the PACAP(6–38) antagonist could then reveal its high potency (K_i 1.5–3 nM).

Chemical Cross-Linking of ^{125}I-Labeled PACAP

Specific chemical cross-linking of ^{125}I-labeled PACAP-27 followed by SDS-PAGE and autoradiography reveals a single 64- to 68-kDa protein (including 3 kDa for one PACAP-27 molecule) in NB-OK-1 cell membranes (16) and rat brain membranes (10). This labeling is fully inhibited when the radioligand is incubated in the presence of 1 μM PACAP and unaffected after incubation in the presence of 1 μM VIP.

Acknowledgments

Aided by Grant 3.4525.91 from the Fund for Medical Scientific Research (Belgium), Grant BEO2 PUJU 1 from the European Economic Community, and the ''Concerted Research Action'' 87/92-108 from the Ministry of Scientific Policy (Belgium). We thank N. Peuchot and M. Stiévenart for their secretarial help.

References

1. A. Miyata, A. Arimura, R. R. Dahl, N. Minamino, A. Uehara, L. Jiang, M. D. Culler, and D. H. Coy, *Biochem. Biophys. Res. Commun.* **164,** 567 (1989).
2. A. Miyata, L. Jiang, R. D. Dahl, C. Kitada, K. Kubo, M. Fujino, N. Minamino, and A. Arimura, *Biochem. Biophys. Res. Commun.* **170,** 643 (1990).
3. Abstracts of the Fifth International Symposium on VIP and Related Peptides, *Biomed. Res. Suppl.* **1** (1991).
4. A. Arimura, A. Somogyvári-Vigh, A. Miyata, K. Mizuno, D. H. Coy, and C. Kitada, *Endocrinology (Baltimore)* **129,** 2787 (1991).
5. K. Köves, A. Arimura, A. Somogyvári-Vigh, S. Vigh, and J. Miller, *Endocrinology (Baltimore)* **127,** 264 (1990).

6. K. Köves, A. Arimura, T. G. Görcs, and A. Somogyvári-Vigh, *Neuroendocrinology* **54,** 159 (1991).

7. S. Vigh, A. Arimura, K. Köves, A. Somogyvári-Vigh, J. Sitton, and C. D. Fermin, *Peptides (N.Y.)* **12,** 313 (1991).

8. I. Tatsuno, P. E. Gottschall, K. Köves, and A. Arimura, *Biochem. Biophys. Res. Commun.* **168,** 1027 (1990).

9. I. Tatsuno, P. E. Gottschall, and A. Arimura, *Peptides (N.Y.)* **12,** 617 (1991).

10. A. Cauvin, P. Robberecht, P. De Neef, P. Gourlet, A. Vandermeers, M.-C. Vandermeers-Piret, and J. Christophe, *Regul. Pept.* **35,** 161 (1991).

11. P. E. Gottschall, I. Tatsuno, A. Miyata, and A. Arimura, *Endocrinology (Baltimore)* **127,** 272 (1990).

12. H.-C. Lam, K. Takahashi, M. A. Ghatei, S. M. Kanse, J. M. Polak, and S. R. Bloom, *Eur. J. Biochem.* **193,** 725 (1990).

13. Y. Masuo, T. Ohtaki, Y. Masuda, Y. Nagai, M. Suno, M. Tsuda, and M. Fujino, *Neurosci. Lett.* **126,** 103 (1991).

14. T. Ohtaki, T. Watanabe, Y. Ishibashi, C. Kitada, M. Tsuda, P. E. Gottschall, A. Arimura, and M. Fujino, *Biochem. Biophys. Res. Commun.* **171,** 838 (1990).

15. B. D. Shivers, T. J. Görcs, P. E. Gottschall, and A. Arimura, *Endocrinology (Baltimore)* **128,** 3055 (1991).

16. A. Cauvin, L. Buscail, P. Gourlet, P. De Neef, D. Gossen, A. Arimura, A. Miyata, D. H. Coy, P. Robberecht, and J. Christophe, *Peptides (N.Y.)* **11,** 773 (1990).

17. T. Watanabe, T. Ohtaki, C. Kitada, M. Tsuda, and M. Fujino, *Biochem. Biophys. Res. Commun.* **173,** 252 (1990).

18. P. Robberecht, P. Gourlet, A. Cauvin, L. Buscail, P. De Neef, A. Arimura, and J. Christophe, *Am. J. Physiol.* **260,** G97 (1991).

19. P. Gourlet, M.-C. Woussen-Colle, P. Robberecht, P. De Neef, A. Cauvin, M.-C. Vandermeers-Piret, A. Vandermeers, and J. Christophe, *Eur. J. Biochem.* **195,** 535 (1991).

20. P. J. Fraker and J. C. Speck, Jr., *Biochem. Biophys. Res. Commun.* **80,** 849 (1978).

21. P. Robberecht, A. Cauvin, P. Gourlet, and J. Christophe, *Arch. Int. Pharmacodyn. Ther.* **303,** 51–66 (1990).

22. U. K. Laemmli, *Nature (London)* **227,** 680 (1970).

23. Y. Salomon, C. Londos, and M. Rodbell, *Anal. Biochem.* **58,** 541 (1974).

24. O. H. Lowry, N. J. Rosebrough, A. L. Farr, and R. J. Randall, *J. Biol. Chem.* **193,** 265 (1951).

25. A. Richardson and A. Humrich, *Trends Pharmacol. Sci.* **5,** 47 (1984).

26. D. Ambrosius, M. Casaretto, R. Gerardy-Schahn, D. Saunders, D. Brandenburg, and H. Zahn, *Biol. Chem. Hoppe-Seyler* **370,** 217 (1989).

Index